SYMBOLS AND UNITS OF PHYSICAL QUANTITI

QUANTITY	SYMBOL*	UNITS	QUANTITY	SYMBOL*	UNITS
Acceleration	$\mathbf{a}$	m/s^2	Entropy		
Angle	θ, ϕ	rad	Force		
Angular acceleration	α	$rad/s^2, s^{-2}$	Frequency	f	Hz
Angular frequency, angular			Heat	Q	J
speed, angular velocity	$\omega, \boldsymbol{\omega}$	$rad/s, s^{-1}$	Heat flow	H	J/s
Angular momentum	$\mathbf{L}$	$kg \cdot m^2/s$	Inductance	L	H
Atomic number	Z		Intensity	$I, S, \mathbf{S}$	W/m^2
Capacitance	C	F	Magnetic field	$\mathbf{B}$	T
Charge	q, Q, e	C	Magnetic flux	ϕ_B	$T \cdot m^2$
Charge density			Mass	m, M	kg
Line	λ	C/m	Mass number	A	
Surface	σ	C/m^2	Molar specific heat	C_V, C_P	$J/mol \cdot K$
Volume	ρ	C/m^3	Momentum	$\mathbf{p}$	$kg \cdot m/s$
Conductivity	σ	$\Omega^{-1} \cdot m^{-1}$	Period	T	s
Current	I	A	Power	P	W
Current density	$\mathbf{J}$	A/m^2	Pressure	P	Pa
Density	ρ	kg/m^3	Resistance	R	Ω
Dielectric constant	κ		Resistivity	ρ	$\Omega \cdot m$
Dipole moment, electric	$\mathbf{p}$	$C \cdot m$	Rotational inertia	I	$kg \cdot m^2$
Dipole moment, magnetic	$\boldsymbol{\mu}$	$A \cdot m^2$	Temperature	T	K
Distance, displacement,	$x, y, z, s, d,$		Time	t	s
length, position	$\ell, w, h, \mathbf{r}$	m	Torque	τ	$N \cdot m$
Electric field	$\mathbf{E}$	N/C, V/m	Specific heat	c	$J/kg \cdot k$
Electric flux	ϕ, ϕ_E	$N \cdot m^2/C$	Speed, velocity	$v, \mathbf{v}$	m/s
Electric potential	V	V	Volume	V	m^3
Electromotive force	$\mathscr{E}$	V	Wavelength	λ	m
Energy	E, U, K	J	Wavenumber	k	m^{-1}
			Work	W	J

*Boldface indicates vector quantities.

TRIGONOMETRY

Definition of angle (in radians): $\theta = \dfrac{s}{r}$

2π radians in complete circle
1 radian $\simeq 57.3° = 2.06$ arc sec

TRIGONOMETRIC FUNCTIONS

$\sin\theta = \dfrac{y}{r}$

$\cos\theta = \dfrac{x}{r}$

$\tan\theta = \dfrac{\sin\theta}{\cos\theta} = \dfrac{y}{x}$

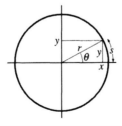

THE GREEK ALPHABET

	UPPERCASE	LOWERCASE
Alpha	A	α
Beta	B	β
Gamma	Γ	γ
Delta	Δ	δ
Epsilon	E	ε
Zeta	Z	ζ
Eta	H	η
Theta	Θ	θ
Iota	I	ι
Kappa	K	κ
Lambda	Λ	λ
Mu	M	μ
Nu	N	ν
Xi	Ξ	ξ
Omicron	O	o
Pi	Π	π
Rho	P	ρ
Sigma	Σ	σ
Tau	T	τ
Upsilon	Υ	υ
Phi	Φ	ϕ
Chi	X	χ
Psi	Ψ	ψ
Omega	Ω	ω

PHYSICS FOR SCIENTISTS AND ENGINEERS

VOLUME II

RICHARD WOLFSON | JAY M. PASACHOFF

Taken from:

Physics for Scientists and Engineers, Third Edition
by Richard Wolfson and Jay M. Pasachoff

Second Custom Edition for University of California, San Diego

Custom Publishing

New York   Boston   San Francisco
London   Toronto   Sydney   Tokyo   Singapore   Madrid
Mexico City   Munich   Paris   Cape Town   Hong Kong   Montreal

Cover Art: *Electr1* by Barry Cronin

Taken from:

Physics For Scientists and Engineers, Third Edition
by Richard Wolfson and Jay M. Pasachoff
Copyright © 1999 by Addison Wesley Longman, Inc.
A Pearson Education Company
Boston, Massachusetts 02116

This special edition published in cooperation with Pearson Custom Publishing.

Printed in the United States of America

5 6 7 8 9 10 0BRV 14 13 12 11 10

2008460109

JL

**Pearson
Custom Publishing**
is a division of

www.pearsonhighered.com

ISBN 10: 0-558-02208-1
ISBN 13: 978-0-558-02208-2

Brief Contents

Contents

Preface

PHYSICS: CHALLENGE AND SIMPLICITY

Physics is fundamental. To understand physics is to understand how the world works, both at the everyday level and on scales of time and space so small and large that they defy intuition.

To the student, physics can be at once fascinating, challenging, subtle, and yet simple. Physics fascinates with its applications throughout science and engineering and in its revelation of unexpected phenomena like superconductivity, black holes, and chaos. It challenges with the need for precise thinking and skillful application of mathematics. Physics can be subtle, especially in describing phenomena at odds with everyday intuition. Most importantly, physics is simple. Its few fundamental laws are succinct, yet they encompass a universe of natural phenomena and technological devices.

GOALS OF THIS BOOK

This text is for science and engineering students. Its main goals are:

- to help students develop an understanding of the physical universe at its most fundamental level
- to explore a wide range of physics applications in science, technology, and everyday life
- to develop students' analytical and quantitative skills as applied to problems in science and engineering

The standard version of this text covers the full sequence of calculus-based university physics, and the extended version adds seven chapters on modern physics.

ORGANIZATION

The book is organized into six parts. Part 1 (Chapters 2 through 14) develops the basics of mechanics. Part 2 (Chapters 15 through 18) applies mechanics to the study of oscillations, waves, and fluids. Part 3 (Chapters 19 through 22) covers thermodynamics. Part 4 (Chapters 23–34) deals with electricity and magnetism. Part 5 (Chapters 35 through 37) treats optics. Part 6 (Chapters 38 and 39) briefly introduces relativity and quantum physics. Part 6 of the extended version (Chapters 38 through 45) expands the coverage of modern physics and its applications to atoms, molecules, and the solid state; nuclear physics and its applications; and particle physics and cosmology. Each part ends with a set of Cumulative Problems that synthesize concepts from the chapters in that part.

Distinguishing Features of the Third Edition

This third edition continues to hone the text and illustrations for clarity and precision, and to ensure that physics is tied closely with the latest in applications that are scientifically exciting and relevant to the student's everyday experience or future professional activities. Below we detail the many changes we've made, as well as describing new and continuing features designed to help students learn.

Improvements in Content This revision includes many substantial changes and improvements, most of which were suggested by instructors who have used the text or reviewed the manuscript. We've also added new pedagogical features to help develop both conceptual and quantitative understanding, and to test students' understanding of subtle concepts. Here are some of the more significant changes we've implemented in this edition.

- We extensively rewrote Chapters 5 (Force and Motion) and 6 (Using Newton's Laws) to account for the results of new research in physics education, especially the Force Concept Inventory.
- We substantially reorganized a number of other chapters to enhance the clarity and logical structure. For example, readers will find the presentations of magnetism and of physical optics much clearer due to chapter reorganization in this new edition. In all chapters, significant rewriting and art revisions improve clarity and provide tie-ins with preceding material.
- We revised the problem sets to include more "real-world" problems and a better balance of easy, multi-step, and challenging problems. In each chapter, up to 20 percent of the problems are new.
- A new category of "annotated figures" links text and art, using captions within the figure to guide students through complex concepts.
- A new feature, **Got It!** boxes, provide conceptual and largely non-quantitative reinforcement of students' understanding.
- The new **Math Toolbox** feature presents important mathematical tools separately from the main text.
- We have integrated *ActivPhysics*—the comprehensive simulation and visualization software—throughout the book, to provide a valuable option for both instructors and students. *ActivPhysics* helps students explore the major concepts from all parts of physics. Students can make predictions and test assumptions by changing variables and running the simulations. *ActivPhysics* references in the text, and icons in the margin, are strategically placed at common student trouble spots. Used in the classroom, lab, or for self-study, *ActivPhysics* will help the student develop imagery and intuition, and will reinforce the student's understanding of basic physics.
- We've updated for new scientific discoveries and technological developments, including the finding that neutrinos have mass, advances in superconductivity, and fiber optic technology, and many others.

Other features carry over from the second edition with significant revisions and improvements. These include

Applications and Examples A rich array of practical and up-to-date applications illustrates the use of physics principles in both technology and in natural phenomena. Applications range from the life sciences through the frontiers of technology, and include biomedical technology, antilock brakes, global warming, microelectronics, lasers, and much more. Some new applications and examples in this third edition include hybrid cars with flywheel energy storage; the digital video disc; kayaking; electrical models for the cell membrane; gel electrophoresis for protein separation; capacitive transducers; medical defibrillators, and many others. As in previous editions, we integrate many applications with the text and problem sets, rather than presenting just a few applications as guest essays.

Questions These follow the chapter synopsis and can be used for class discussion, in peer-based learning strategies, or to get students thinking about concepts before they begin work on quantitative problems.

Problems Science and engineering students learn physics best by working physics problems. This third edition contains nearly 3,000 end-of-chapter problems, with significant revision of the problem sets, especially in the early chapters. Problems range from simple confidence builders, to more complex and realistic multi-problems, to difficult **Supplementary Problems** that will challenge the best students. A section of unique **Paired Problems** for each chapter lets students practice problem-solving techniques on a pair of problems whose solutions involve closely related physical concepts or mathematical approaches. **Cumulative Problems** integrate material from the chapters of each major part of the text. Frequent text references to specific problems link text and problems in the common purpose of enhancing the student's understanding of physics.

Worked Examples These reinforce basic concepts, illustrate problem-solving strategies, and often serve to introduce "real-world" applications of physics. Most examples are followed by an exercise that further reinforces concepts and strategies. A **Similar Problems** line after each example points out related end-of-chapter problems.

Tip Boxes Tip boxes appear throughout the text and warn against common pitfalls or give helpful problem-solving hints.

Pedagogical Use of Color The book's design is an essential pedagogical feature. The carefully planned use of color in figures and in highlighting important equations and definitions, as well as the selection of photographs, all reinforce the text and enhance communication of concepts to the student. Specific colors are used consistently for different physical elements in the figures; for example, velocity vectors and graphs of velocity use the same color, while force vectors and graphs consistently use a different color. A list of elements and their colors follows this preface.

Chapter Synopses Chapter summaries emphasize key concepts and remind students of new terms and mathematical symbols. Each summary ends with a reminder of limitations and approximations used in the theories, models, and equations developed in the chapter.

Appendices and Endpapers The book's appendices and endpapers contain a mathematical review and a wealth of up-to-date physical data, conversion factors, and information on measurements systems.

PHYSICS AND MATHEMATICS

For many students, the university physics course is their first contact with practical applications of calculus. We recognize that students have a range of mathematical abilities, from those taking their first calculus course concurrently with physics to those fluent in both differential and integral calculus. The former will find our new Math Toolboxes, along with many of the Tip boxes and figures, helpful in building confidence in their mathematical skills; the latter will find a selection of challenging calculus-based problems.

In this book mathematics is a tool, not an end in itself. Therefore we always relate mathematical solutions and derivations back to the underlying physics. After deriving an equation or solving a sample problem, we frequently ask: "Does this result make sense?" We show that it does by examining easily understood special cases, thus building physical intuition along with mathematical confidence. We explore the meaning of equations verbally and through figures, ensuring that concepts are clear before students begin to use the material quantitatively.

SUPPLEMENTS

Professors and students alike find it useful to have supplements designed to complement their text. For the third edition, we offer a new expanded supplements package.

For the Instructor

Instructor's Solutions Manual (0-321-03578-X), prepared by Edw. S. Ginsberg, University of Massachusetts-Boston, includes worked solutions to all problems in the text. The solutions manual is now available on CD-ROM in TEX, techexplorer, and Microsoft Word, for easy editing and posting of homework solutions in documents or on the web (0-321-05149-1).

TestGen-EQ Computerized Test Bank is an expanded testbank that allows instructors to edit and change the order of questions, add entirely new questions in six different formats and print different versions of a test. The testbank is available for Windows (0-321-03579-8) and Macintosh (0-321-03580-1). A print version is also available (0-321-03590-9).

Transparency Acetates (0-321-03577-1) contain over 150 color acetates of figures from the text, useful in lectures and classroom discussions.

For the Student

Student Solutions Manual (0-321-03575-5), by Edw. S. Ginsberg, University of Massachusetts-Boston, includes detailed solutions to all the odd-numbered problems in the text.

Study Guide with ActivPhysics, is a book and CD package. The study guide, by Jeffrey J. Braun, University of Evansville, provides an overview of each chapter of *Physics for Scientists and Engineers* and summarizes definitions and key equations. The *ActivPhysics* worksheets and CD-ROM by Alan Van Heuvelen, The Ohio State University, and Paul D'Alessandris help students develop imagery and intuition by changing variables and running the simulations. *ActivPhysics* prompts students with questions that help develop a more thorough understanding, step by step. The *ActivPhysics* CD-ROM is dual platform, for both Macintosh and Windows. *Study Guide with ActivPhysics* is available in two volumes.

- *Volume 1 (covering Wolfson/Pasachoff—Physics for Scientists and Engineers Chapters 1–22)* 0-321-05148-3
- *Volume 2 (covering Wolfson/Pasachoff—Physics for Scientists and Engineers Chapters 23–45)* 0-321-05147-5.

Preparing for General Physics: Math Skill Drills and Other Useful Help, by Arnold D. Pickar of Portland State University, is a self-study workbook that reviews algebra and trigonometry topics for university physics (0-201-53802-4).

ACKNOWLEDGMENTS

A project of this magnitude is not the work of its author alone. Here we acknowledge the many people whose contributions made the book possible. Colleagues using the second edition at universities and colleges throughout the world have volunteered suggestions, and will find most of those incorporated here. Students in Middlebury's Physics 109–110 courses have made significant contributions to the book's accuracy and readability. RW's Middlebury colleagues Ann Broughton, Cris Butler, Jeff Dunham, Bob Prigo, Steve Ratcliff, Susan Watson, and Frank Winkler all provided substantial suggestions or help on this project. We are especially grateful to a group of "on call" reviewers who provided instant feedback to questions from author and editors during the revision: Jerry Hosken, *City College of San Francisco;* Andy Odel, *Northern Arizona University;* James Rohlf, *Boston University;* Gurbax Singh, *University of Maryland;* Robert Weidman, *Michigan Technological University.*

It is frustrating to find numerical errors in a textbook, especially in answers to problems. We have gone to great lengths to make this book as free from error as possible, and we credit the people who helped achieved this goal. Edw. S. Ginsberg, *University of Massachusetts-Boston,* meticulously checked all numerical results in examples, exercises, and end-of-chapter problems. Mark Coffey of the *University of Colorado at Boulder,* and John Bartelt of the *Stanford Linear Accelerator Center* provided valuable accuracy checks.

Prior to this revision, every chapter of the book was thoroughly reviewed by users of both this and competing texts. Reviewers made general as well as more detailed suggestions, nearly all of which we have been able to incorporate in the third edition. We are grateful to these reviewers, and to reviewers of the second edition:

Edward Adelson, *Ohio State University*
Vijendra Agarwal, *Moorhead State University*
William Anderson, *Phoenix College*
Gordon J. Aubrecht, *Ohio State University—Marion*
Paul Avery, *University of Florida*
Douglas Bennett, *University of California, Los Angeles*
Marvin Blecher, *Virginia Polytechnic Institute and State University*
Gary Bowman, *Northern Arizona University*
John Brient, *University of Texas at El Paso*
James H. Burgess, *Washington University*
Bernard Chasan, *Boston University*
Roger Clapp, *University of South Florida*
Claire D. Dewberry, *Florida Community College at Jacksonville*
Jeffrey Dunne, *Purdue University*
Robert J. Endorf, *University of Cincinnati*
Heidi Fearn, *California State University—Fullerton*
Shechao Feng, *University of California, Los Angeles*
Albert L. Ford, *Texas A & M University*
Ian Gatland, *Georgia Institute of Technology*
Edw. S. Ginsberg, *University of Massachusetts—Boston*
James Goff, *Pima Community College*
Alan I. Goldman, *Iowa State University*
Philip Goode, *New Jersey Institute of Technology*
Denise S. Graves, *Clark Atlanta University*
Donald Greenberg, *University of Alaska*
Phillip Gutierrez, *University of Oklahoma*
Stephen Hanzely, *Youngstown State University*
Kenneth Hardy, *Florida International University*
Gerald Harmon, *University of Maine at Orono*
Randy Harris, *University of California, Davis*
Warren Hein, *American Association of Physics Teachers*
Roger Herman, *The Pennsylvania State University*
P. G. Hjorth, *Technical University of Denmark*
Francis L. Howell, *University of North Dakota*
J. N. Huffaker, *University of Oklahoma*
Quinton Hurst, *Arizona State University*
Javed Iqbal, *University of British Columbia*
Wayne James, *University of South Dakota*
Karen Johnston, *North Carolina State University*
Evan Jones, *Sierra College*
Randy Knight, *California Polytechnic State University*
Dean Langely, *St. John's University*
Chew-Lean Lee, *Florida Community College*
Brian Logan, *University of Ottawa*

Peter Loly, *University of Manitoba*
Hilliard K. Macomber, *University of Northern Iowa*
David Markowitz, *University of Connecticut*
Daniel Marlow, *Princeton University*
Nolan Massey, *University of Texas at Arlington*
Ralph McGrew, *Broome Community College*
Victor Michalk, *Southwest Texas State University*
Allen Mincer, *New York University*
P. James Moser, *Bloomsburg University*
Vinod Nangia, *University of Minnesota*
Andrew Odell, *Northern Arizona University*
Robert Osborne, *Yakima Valley Community College*
Michael O'Shea, *Kansas State University*
George Parker, *North Carolina State University*
Graham Pearson, *Novia Scotia Agricultural College*
R. J. Peterson, *University of Colorado*
Slawomir Piatek, *New Jersey Institute of Technology*
Gerald Pogatshnik, *Southern Illinois University*
Joseph F. Polen, *Shasta College*
Talat Rahman, *Kansas State University*
Dennis Roark, *The King's College*
James Rohlf, *Boston University*
Alfons Schulte, *University of Central Florida*
Neil Shafer-Ray, *University of Oklahoma*
Gurbax Singh, *University of Maryland*
Roger F. Sipson, *Moorhead State University*
John Sperry, *Sierra College*
Lon D. Spight, *University of Nevada at Las Vegas*

Robert Sprague, *Foothill College*
Julien. C. Sprott, *University of Wisconsin-Madison*
Konrad M. Stein, *Golden West College*
Bryan H. Suits, *Michigan Technological University*
Leo Takahashi, *The Pennsylvania State University—Beaver Campus*
Frank Tanherlini, *College of the Holy Cross*
Karl Trappe, *University of Texas*
Michael Trinkala, *Hudson Valley Community College*
Loren Vian, *Centralia College*
Clarence Wagener, *Creighton University*
Robert Weidman, *Michigan Technological University*
George Williams, *University of Utah*
Robert J. Wilson, *Colorado State University*
Arthur Winston, *Gordon Institute*
David Yee, *City College of San Francisco*
John Yelton, *University of Florida*
Dale Yoder-Short, *Michigan Technological University*

We also thank editors Catherine Flack, Sami Iwata, Joan Marsh, and publisher Robin Heyden at Addison Wesley for their vigorous support of and collaboration on this project, and Ingrid Mount of Elm Street Publishing Services for her skillful efforts in bringing it to fruition. Finally, RW thanks his family, colleagues, and students for their patience during the intense process of revising this book.

Richard Wolfson
Jay M. Pasachoff

A Visual Guide to the Book

Tip

How Does the Battery Know? How does the battery in Fig. 28-5 "know" how much current to supply? How does it even "know" there are two resistors, and what their values are? For the brief instant when the circuit is first connected, the battery doesn't "know," and some rather complicated action occurs as charge moves from the battery, encounters resistance, and accumulates to establish the potential differences across the resistors. During that brief time the current is not the same everywhere. But very soon the circuit reaches a steady state, with the same current throughout. Later in this chapter, when we consider circuits with capacitors, we'll look in more detail at the approach to the steady state; for now, our analyses assume that circuits have already reached that state.

Tip boxes appear throughout the text to help a student with difficult concepts, warn against common pitfalls, and give problem-solving hints.

EXAMPLE 28-1 | *Designing a Voltage Divider*

A light bulb with a resistance (when on) of 5.0 Ω is designed to operate at a current of 600 mA. To operate this lamp from a 12-V battery, what resistance should you place in series with it?

Solution

Let R_2 be the lamp and R_1 the unknown series resistor. Since resistors in series add, the current through both resistors is $I = \mathcal{E}/(R_1 + R_2)$, which is supposed to be 600 mA or 0.60 A. Solving for R_1 gives

$$R_1 = \frac{\mathcal{E} - IR_2}{I} = \frac{12\text{ V} - (0.60\text{ A})(5.0\text{ }\Omega)}{0.60\text{ A}} = 15\text{ }\Omega.$$

You can also get this result by noting that the light bulb's proper operating voltage is $V = IR_2 = (0.60\text{ A})(5.0\text{ }\Omega) = 3.0$ V. This is one-fourth of the battery voltage, so the light bulb's 5-Ω resistance should be one-fourth of the total. That makes the total 20 Ω, leaving 15 Ω for R_1.

EXERCISE Suppose that in Fig. 28-5 $R_1 = 470$ Ω. If the voltage across R_2 is 59% of the battery voltage, find R_2.

Answer: 676 Ω

Some problems similar to Example 28-1: 23–25

Got It!

What is the voltage across the resistor R at the top of each circuit shown in Fig. 28-7? In (a) the second resistor has the same resistance R, and in (b) the ga[...] is an open circuit (infinite resistance). Think about it first, then verify y[...] answers using Equations 28-2.

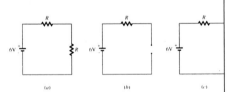

FIGURE 28-7 What's the voltage across the upper resistor in each circuit?

(a)   (b)   (c)

Got It! boxes provide conceptual reinforcement of a student's understanding.

Here the student is asked to stop and think about three simple circuits, to probe their understanding before moving on to the next topic. They are asked to apply what they have learned in a qualitative way, and then asked to verify using the equations.

If I is the current in the circuit of Fig. 28-5, then there must be a voltage $V_1 = IR_1$ across R_1 to drive the current through this resistor. Similarly, the voltage across R_2 is $V_2 = IR_2$. Thus, the voltage across the two resistors together is $V_1 + V_2 = IR_1 + IR_2$. But the battery is connected directly across this series combination, so we have

$$IR_1 + IR_2 = \mathcal{E}.$$

or

$$I = \frac{\mathcal{E}}{R_1 + R_2}.$$

Comparison with Ohm's law in the form $I = V/R$ shows that the two resistors in series behave like an equivalent resistance equal to the sum of their resistances. In an obvious generalization to more resistors in series, we have

$$R_{\text{series}} = R_1 + R_2 + R_3 + \cdots \quad (28\text{-}1)$$

In other words, resistors in series add.

Given the current, we can use Ohm's law in the form $V = IR$ to solve for the voltage across each resistor:

$$V_1 = \frac{R_1}{R_1 + R_2}\mathcal{E} \quad (28\text{-}2a)$$

and

$$V_2 = \frac{R_2}{R_1 + R_2}\mathcal{E}. \quad (28\text{-}2b)$$

These expressions show that the battery voltage divides between the two resistors in proportion to their resistance. For this reason a series combination of resistors is called a **voltage divider**. Figure 28-6 depicts the voltages throughout the circuit of Fig. 28-5, and shows explicitly that the resistors divide the battery voltage.

Annotated figures guide a student through complex concepts.

Here we see potential difference in a simple circuit explained step-by-step. Leading the student through the graphical representation of this important, but tricky, concept can lead to a more thorough understanding of the phenomena of voltage.

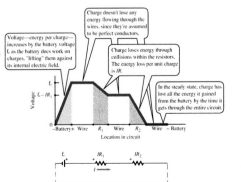

FIGURE 28-6 Voltages in the circuit of Fig. 28-5, with $V = 0$ at the negative battery terminal. Note that there is no potential difference across the wires, since they have negligible resistance, and that potential increases across the battery and decreases across the resistors. Can you tell from the graph which resistance is greater? (Here we've "unrolled" the circuit so we can clearly show the voltage as a function of position around the circuit. But remember that the circuit is a closed loop, so the left and right ends of the graph represent the same physical point, namely the negative battery terminal.)

Charge doesn't lose any energy flowing through the wires, since they're assumed to be perfect conductors.

Voltage—energy per charge—increases by the battery voltage $\mathcal{E}$ as the battery does work on charges, "lifting" them against its internal electric field.

Charge loses energy through collisions within the resistors. The energy loss per unit charge is IR.

In the steady state, charge has lost all the energy it gained from the battery by the time it gets through the entire circuit.

A rich array of **applications** reinforces understanding of underlying physics in both technology and natural phenomena. Applications range from the life sciences through the latest technology. They bring the subject alive by providing relevance of the theory to a student's everyday world.

Here DVDs are compared to CDs to give the student knowledge of this topical development.

Throughout the book, icons in the margins and references in the text link to the powerful simulation package *ActivPhysics.* The simulations in *ActivPhysics* provide an opportunity for students to make predictions and test those predictions. The student becomes an active participant through manipulation and visualization of hard-to-grasp concepts.

---

998 Chapter 37 Interference and Diffraction

EXAMPLE 37-8	Asteroid Alert!

An asteroid appears on a collision course with Earth, at a distance of 20×10^6 km. What is the minimum size asteroid that the 2.4-m-diameter diffraction-limited Hubble Space Telescope could resolve at this distance, using 550-nm reflected sunlight?

Solution

Resolving the asteroid means being able to distinguish its opposite edges in the telescope image and therefore to assess its size. Suppose the asteroid's long dimension (it might not be spherical) is ℓ. Then at a distance $L \gg \ell$ it subtends an angle given very nearly by $\theta = \ell/L$. Using this result in Equation 37-13b with the mirror diameter and wavelength given, we have

$$\frac{\ell}{L} = \frac{1.22\lambda}{D}.$$

or

$$\ell = \frac{1.22\lambda L}{D} = \frac{(1.22)(550\times10^{-9}\text{ m})(20\times10^6\text{ m})}{2.4\text{ m}} = 5.6\text{ km}.$$

This is a potentially dangerous object, comparable in size to the asteroid that scientists believe caused the extinction of the dinosaurs, and somewhat larger than the comet fragments that slammed into Jupiter in 1994, causing Earth-sized disturbances on the giant planet.

EXERCISE Two ants stand 1 cm apart. Assuming diffraction limited vision, at what distance could a human eye, with an iris aperture of 4 mm, tell that two are indeed separate creatures? Assume a wavelength of 550 nm, near the middle of the visible spectrum. (Other limitations of the human eye prevent its realizing this diffraction limit.)

Answer: 60 m

Some problems similar to Example 37-8: 55–59

APPLICATION	Movies on Disc: From CD to DVD

Standard audio CDs have a maximum playing time of 74 minutes–a value that's set by the optical diffraction limit. In the Application "CD Music, Continued" earlier in this chapter, we showed how a CD encodes information in "pits" 1.6 μm apart and as short as 0.83 μm in length. Standard CDs are read with 780-nm infrared laser light and the pit size and separation are chosen to ensure that diffraction effects at this wavelength don't cause the CD player's optical system to confuse adjacent pits. Ultimately, therefore, the 74-minute playing time is limited by the laser wavelength.

When CDs were first developed, inexpensive semiconductor lasers were available only in the infrared. But today's semiconductor lasers produce light well into the visible–with significantly shorter wavelengths than the infrared light used in CD players and CD-ROM drives. The new DVDs introduced in the late 1990s (read either "digital video disc" or "digital versatile disc") exploit these shorter-wavelength lasers.

Using laser wavelengths of 635 and 650 nm, DVDs can function with significantly lower pit sizes and spacings because of the lower diffraction limit at these shorter wavelengths (Fig. 37-39). Coupled with a two-layer structure (as opposed to the standard CD's single information layer) and more sophisticated data-compression schemes, the smaller pits and pit spacing give DVDs more than 12 times the information-storage capacity of standard CDs. That translates into more than two hours of high quality video and audio, as opposed to the CD's 74 minutes of audio alone. In computer use, it means a DVD can hold some 8.5 gigabytes of information as opposed to a CD's 680 megabytes (by comparison, a 3.5″ floppy disc holds only 1.44 MB). And DVDs can be made in two-sided versions, providing another doubling in capacity. Despite their high capacity, DVDs are physically the same size as CDs, and DVD players are compatible with standard CDs as well.

FIGURE 37-39 A comparison of a standard CD and a DVD. The smaller pit size and closer pit spacing of the DVD result in a much higher information storage capacity, and are made possible by the lower diffraction limit associated with the DVD player's shorter wavelength laser light. Both images are microphotographs of the same size region, about 8 μm on a side. The pits lie on a single spiral track that covers most of the disc.

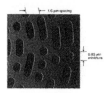

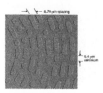

(a)　　　(b)

---

946 Chapter 36 Image Formation and Optical Instruments

last step in this equality follows from Equation for ℓ' and using the result in the equati

$$f = \frac{R}{2}$$

Thus the focal length of a spherical mirro We emphasize that the results derived based on the assumption that the spherical parabola. Equivalent ways of describing curvature radius is large compared wit Fig. 36-12c and (2) that all rays reflecti nearly parallel to the mirror axis (the para ings can't accurately reflect these conditi clearly the ray paths.

15.7 *ActivPhysics* — Spherical Mirror Problems

EXAMPLE 36-2	Sizing Up Hubble: A Concave Mirror

During assembly of the Hubble Space Telescope, a technician stood 3.85 m in front of the telescope's concave mirror and viewed his image (Fig. 36-13). Given the telescope's focal length of 5.52 m, find (a) the location and (b) the magnification of the technician's image. (c) Repeat for the case when the technician stands 15.0 m from the mirror.

Solution

Since the mirror is *concave,* the focal length f is *positive.* (a) We can solve the mirror equation (Equation 36-2) to get

$$\frac{1}{\ell'} = \frac{1}{f} - \frac{1}{\ell} = \frac{\ell - f}{f\ell}.$$

or

$$\ell' = \frac{f\ell}{\ell - f} = \frac{(5.52\text{ m})(3.85\text{ m})}{3.85\text{ m} - 5.52\text{ m}} = -12.7\text{ m}.$$

Why the *negative* answer? Because the technician is closer to the mirror than the focal point, so this is a *virtual* image located *behind* the mirror.
(b) Equation 36-1 gives the magnification:

$$M = -\frac{\ell'}{\ell} = -\frac{(-12.7\text{ m})}{3.85\text{ m}} = 3.30.$$

This *positive* answer indicates an *upright* image, enlarged about three times as shown in Fig. 36-13.
(c) If the technician stands 15.0 m from the mirror, similar calculations give

$$\ell' = \frac{f\ell}{\ell - f} = \frac{(5.52\text{ m})(15.0\text{ m})}{15.0\text{ m} - 5.52\text{ m}} = 8.73\text{ m}$$

and

$$M = -\frac{\ell'}{\ell} = -\frac{8.73\text{ m}}{15.0\text{ m}} = -0.582.$$

FIGURE 36-13 A technician standing in front of the Hubble Space Telescope mirror. Where and how big is the technician's image?

Now ℓ' is positive, so the image is *real* and in *front* of the mirror; the *negative* magnification shows that it's *inverted,* and it's reduced in size.

EXERCISE You're scrutinizing your nose using a handheld concave mirror with curvature radius 2.2 m. How far from your face should you hold the mirror to see your nose doubled in size?

Answer: 55 cm

Some problems similar to Example 36-2: 3–9, 11–14

Worked examples are an integral part of the text and reinforce basic concepts. Real world applications are interwoven to give relevance to a student's experience. Many worked examples are followed by **Exercises. Similar Problems** from the end-of-chapter problems are indicated for students who want to work more problems on the topic.

In principle, we could imagine making the interval Δt as close to zero as we like, and getting ever better approximations to the instantaneous velocity. In practice, given a graph of position versus time, an easy approach is to "eyeball" the tangent line to the graph at the point we're interested in; the slope of the tangent line is the slope of the graph at that point, and is therefore the instantaneous velocity. Figure 2-5 shows this approach. Note that the slope of the tangent line, and therefore the velocity, varies from place to place on the graph. That's the whole point of the instantaneous velocity–it's a quantity that can vary continually.

FIGURE 2-5 The instantaneous velocity at a given time is the slope of the tangent line at the point on the position-versus-time graph corresponding to that time. If the position-versus-time graph is not a straight line, then the instantaneous velocity varies with time.

Got It!

Figure 2-6 shows position-versus-time graphs for several objects. Which object is moving with constant speed? Which reverses direction? Which starts slowly and then speeds up?

Often, we're given the position as a mathematical function of time. We could draw a graph and measure the slopes of tangent lines to find the velocity at different points. But calculus provides a quicker way. In calculus, the result of the limiting process described in Equation 2-2a is called the **derivative** of x with respect to t, and is given the special symbol dx/dt:

$$\frac{dx}{dt} = \lim_{\Delta t \to 0} \frac{\Delta x}{\Delta t}.$$

The quantities dx and dt are called **infinitesimals**; they represent vanishingly small quantities that result from the limiting process. We can then write Equation 2-2a as

$$v = \frac{dx}{dt}. \qquad (2\text{-}2b)$$

(a)

(b)

When we're given the position x as a function of time t, calculus provi[des a] simple way to calculate the velocity $v = dx/dt$. Consult the Math Toolbox i[f you] haven't yet seen derivatives in your calculus class, or if you need a refre[sher.]

Math Toolbox

Derivatives Do we need to go through an elaborate limiting process every [time] we want an instantaneous velocity? No! In calculus you either have or will [learn] formulas for the derivatives of common functions. For example, any functi[on of] the form

$$x = bt^n.$$

where b and n are constants, has the derivative

$$\frac{dx}{dt} = bnt^{n-1}.$$

Derivatives of other common functions, including trig functions, exponen[tials,] and logarithms, are listed in Appendix A. If a function is made up of a su[m of] terms, its derivative is just the sum of the derivatives of the individual te[rms.]

Chapter Synopses emphasize key concepts and remind students of new terms and mathematical symbols. **Limitations to Keep in Mind** remind students of approximations, idealizations, and limited applications of physical concepts and equations. The **Problems You Should Be Able To Solve** section allows a student to evaluate their comprehension of the material in the chapter.

Math Toolboxes help a student through the math necessary for a full understanding of the physics. They emphasize math as a tool, in context with the physics.

CHAPTER SYNOPSIS

Summary

1. Newton's **first law of motion** states that a body continues in uniform motion unless acted on by a nonzero net force. Uniform motion is a natural state; the study of motion then emphasizes not the cause of motion itself, but the cause of *changes* in motion.

2. Newton's **second law of motion** quantifies the change in motion brought about by a force. The law states that the rate of change of a body's momentum (product of mass and velocity; symbol **p**) is equal to the net force on the body:

$$\mathbf{F}_{net} = \frac{d\mathbf{p}}{dt}$$

As long as the mass of the body does not change, Newton's second law can also be written in the form

$$\mathbf{F}_{net} = m\mathbf{a}.$$

Here $\mathbf{F}_{net}$ is the **net force** on a body—that is, the vector sum of all the individual interaction forces acting on the body. The SI unit of force is the **newton**, defined as the force that gives a 1-kg mass an acceleration of 1 m/s².

3. **Weight** is the force of gravity on an object: $\mathbf{W} = m\mathbf{g}$. In an accelerated frame of reference, the **apparent weight** differs from the gravitational force; in particular, the apparent weight of an object in free fall is zero.

4. Newton's **third law of motion** states that forces always come in pairs. When one object exerts a force on another, the second object exerts an oppositely directed force of equal magnitude back on the first. Newton's second and third laws together permit a consistent description of the motions of interacting objects.

5. Elastic objects such as springs provide a practical way of measuring forces. When the force exerted by a spring is directly proportional to the amount of stretch or compression, the spring is said to obey **Hooke's law**; the force is then given by

$$F = -kx. \quad \text{(Hooke's law)}$$

where k is the **spring constant**, with SI units of N/m.

Terms You Should Understand

(Pairs are closely related terms whose distinction is important; number in parentheses is chapter section where term first appears.)

dynamics (introduction)
Aristotle, Galileo, Newton (5-1)
force, net force, interaction force (5-2)
momentum (5-2)
Newton's laws of motion (5-2, 5-7)
inertia (5-2)
gravitational, electroweak, color forces (5-3)
mass, weight (5-5)
apparent weight (5-5, 5-8), weightlessness (5-5)
third-law pair (5-7)
normal force (5-7)
tension force, compression force (5-8)
Hooke's law (5-8)
spring constant (5-8)

Symbols You Should Recognize

F (5-2)
p (5-2)
N (5-4)
g (5-5)
W (5-5)
k (5-8)

Problems You Should Be Able to Solve

calculating force, mass, or acceleration from the other two quantities (5-4)
calculating weight or mass given the other (5-5)
solving for forces or accelerations in one-dimensional situations (5-6)
applying Newton's second and third laws together in one-dimensional situations (5-7)
determining spring force, extension/compression, or spring constant given the other two quantities (5-8)
determining apparent weight (5-8)

Limitations to Keep in Mind

Newton's laws apply only when relative velocities are much less than the speed of light; aside from that restriction, the basic material of this chapter is universally applicable.
Newton's laws are valid in inertial reference frames.
Newton's second law in the form $\mathbf{F} = m\mathbf{a}$ is valid only when mass remains constant; the form $\mathbf{F} = d\mathbf{p}/dt$ is more general.
Real springs deviate from ideal Hooke's law behavior when stretched or compressed substantially.

Questions will prompt a student to think about concepts in a chapter before they start on the problems.

Paired Problems let a student practice problem-solving on a pair of problems whose solutions involve closely related physical concepts or mathematical approaches.

Almost 3000 **end-of-chapter problems,** ranging from confidence builders to realistic multi-problems, will help a student understand concepts and develop problem-solving skills. The problems are thought provoking and encourage critical thinking, and are relevant to a student's everyday life.

Most of the problems are **referenced by section** to allow a student to refer easily to the relevant text.

Supplementary Problems drawn from throughout the chapter are more difficult problems that will challenge the best students.

The student is asked to integrate knowledge from previous chapters to solve the **Cumulative Problems.** They test a student's understanding of a range of topics, and accumulation of knowledge.

---

652   Chapter 25 Electric Potential

QUESTIONS

1. Why can a bird perch on a high-voltage power line without getting electrocuted?
2. One proton is accelerated from rest by a uniform electric field, the other by a nonuniform electric field. If they move through the same potential difference. how do their final speeds compare?
3. Would a free electron move toward higher or lower potential?
4. The potential difference from A to B in Fig. 25-33 is zero since the two points are equidistant from the charge Q. How can this be, when a charge moving along the path shown clearly experiences an electric force not perpendicular to the path?

DANGER
ELECTROCUTION HAZARD
KEEP CLEAR
DEATH OR SERIOUS INJURY CAN RESULT FROM CONTACT WITH LOAD, MACHINE OR VEHICLE IF THEY BECOME ELECTRICALLY CHARGED

FIGURE 25-34 Question 12.

how this hazard a...
to someone on th...

Section 25-5 Potentials of Charged Conductors

52. (a) What is the maximum potential (measured from infinity) for the sphere of Example 25-3 before dielectric breakdown of air occurs at the sphere's surface? (Breakdown of air occurs at a field strength of 3 MVm.) (b) What is the charge on the sphere when it's at this potential?
53. The spark plug in an automobile engine has a center electrode made from wire 2.0 mm in diameter. The electrode is worn to a hemispherical shape, so it behaves approximately like a charged sphere. What is the minimum potential on this electrode that will ensure the plug sparks in air? Neglect the presence of the second electrode.
54. A large metal sphere has three times the diameter of a smaller sphere and carries three times as much charge. Both spheres are isolated, so their surface charge densities ...form. Com... d (b) the electric

...re far apart. One ...other −10 nC. ...the spheres are ...potential on each ...ach charge must ...eve equilibrium? ...r the isolated.

...in diameter and ...part. Determine ...ld strength at the ...midway between ...ce between the

Paired Problems

(Both problems in a pair involve the same principles and techniques. If you can get the first problem, you should be able to solve the second one.)

59. Three 50-pC charges sit at the vertices of an equilateral triangle 1.5 mm on a side. How much work would it take to bring a proton from very far away to the midpoint of one of the triangle's sides?
60. Repeat the preceding problem for the case when one of the charges is −50 pC and the proton is brought to the midpoint of the side between the two positive charges.
61. A pair of equal charges q lies on the x axis at $x = \pm a$. (a) Find expressions for the potential at points on the x axis for which $x > a$ and (b) show that your result reduces to a point-charge potential for $x \gg a$.
62. (a) For the charge distribution of the preceding problem, find an expression for the potential at *all* points on the y axis. (b) Show that your result reduces to a point-charge potential for $y \gg a$.
63. A 2.0-cm-radius metal sphere carries 75 nC and is surrounded by a concentric spherical conducting shell of radius 10 cm carrying −75 nC. (a) Find the potential difference between the shell and the sphere. (b) How would your answer change if the shell charge were changed to +150 nC?
64. A coaxial cable consists of a 2.0-mm-radius central wire carrying 75 nC/m, and a concentric outer conductor of radius 10 mm carrying −75 nC/m. (a) Find the potential

---

◆ **PROBLEMS**

ActivPhysics can help with these problems:
Activities 11.9, 11.10.

Section 25-2 Potential Difference

1. How much work does it take to move a 50-μC charge against a 12-V potential difference?
2. The potential difference between the two sides of an ordinary electrical outlet is 120 V. How much energy does an electron gain when it moves from one side to the other?
3. It takes 45 J to move a 15-mC charge from point A to point B. What is the potential difference ΔV_{AB}?
4. Show that 1 V/m is the same as 1 N/C.
5. Find the magnitude of the potential difference between two points located 1.4 m apart in a uniform 650 N/C electric field. if a line between the points is parallel to the field.
6. A charge of 3.1 C moves from the positive to the negative terminal of a 9.0-V battery. How much energy does the battery impart to the charge?
7. Two points A and B lie 15 cm apart in a uniform electric field, with the path AB parallel to the field. If the potential difference ΔV_{AB} is 840 V. what is the field strength?
8. Figure 25-37 shows a uniform electric field of magnitude E. Find expressions for (a) the potential difference ΔV_{AB} and (b) ΔV_{BC}. (c) Use your result to determine ΔV_{AC}.

9. A proton, an alpha particle (a bare helium nucleus), and a singly ionized helium atom are accelerated through a potential difference of 100 V. Find the energy each gains.
10. The electric field within the membrane separating the inside and outside of a biological cell is approximately 8.0 MV/m, and is essentially uniform. If the membrane is 10 nm thick, what is the potential difference across the membrane?
11. What is the potential difference between the terminals of a battery that can impart 7.2×10^{-19} J to each electron that moves between the terminals?
12. Electrons in a TV tube are accelerated from rest through a 25-kV potential difference. With what speed do they hit the TV screen?
13. A 12-V car battery stores 2.8 MJ of energy. How much charge can move between the battery terminals before it is totally discharged? Assume the potential difference remains at 12 V, an assumption that is not realistic.
14. What is the charge on an ion that gains 1.6×10^{-15} J when it moves through a potential difference of 2500 V?
15. Two large, flat metal plates are a distance d apart, where d is small compared with the plate size. If the plates carry surface charge densities $\pm \sigma$, show that the magnitude of the potential difference between them is $V = \sigma d/\varepsilon_0$.
16. An electron passes point A moving at 6.5 Mm/s. At point B the electron has come to a complete stop. Find the potential difference ΔV_{AB}.
17. A 5.0-g obj...carri...harge of 3.8... C ...a speed v w... difference ... the same ci...

FIGURE 25-37 Problem 8.

Supplementary Problems

69. A conducting sphere 5.0 cm in radius carries 60 nC. It is surrounded by a concentric spherical conducting shell of radius 15 cm carrying −60 nC. (a) Find the potential at the sphere's surface, taking the zero of potential at infinity. (b) Repeat for the case when the shell also carries +60 nC.
70. Show that the result of Example 25-9 approaches the field of a point charge for $x \gg a$. *Hint:* You will need to apply the binomial theorem to the quantity $1/\sqrt{x^2 + a^2}$.
71. The potential on the axis of a uniformly charged disk at ...: the potential 10 cm ...he disk radius and its

...rge $92e$) decays, emit-
...arge $2e$) and leaving a
...e $90e$). At the instant

76. Repeat the preceding problem for the case $\lambda = \lambda_0(x/\ell)$. Why is your answer for $x \gg \ell$ different? *Hint:* What does this charge distribution resemble at large distances?
77. For the situation of Example 25-10, find an equation for the equipotential with $V = 0$ in the x-y plane. Plot the equipotential, and show that it passes through the points described in Example 25-10 and its exercise.
78. A disk of radius a carries a nonuniform surface charge density given by $\sigma = \sigma_0(r/a)$, where σ_0 is a constant. (a) Find the potential at an arbitrary point on the disk axis, a distance x from the disk center. (b) Use the result of (a) to find the electric field on the disk axis, and (c) show that the field reduces to an expected form for $x \gg a$.
79. An open-ended cylinder of radius a and length $2a$ carries charge q spread uniformly over its surface. Find the potential on the cylinder axis at its center. *Hint:* Treat the cylinder as a stack of charged rings, and integrate.

---

914   Part 4 Cumulative Problems

◆ **PART 4** *Cumulative Problems*

These problems combine material from chapters throughout the entire part or, in addition, from chapters in earlier parts, or they present special challenges.

1. An air-insulated parallel-plate capacitor has plate area 100 cm^2 and spacing 0.50 cm. The capacitor is charged and then disconnected from the charging battery. A thin-walled, nonconducting box of the same dimensions as the capacitor is filled with water at 20.00°C. The box is released at the edge of the capacitor and moves without friction into the capacitor (Fig. 1). When it reaches equilibrium the water temperature is 21.50°. What was the original voltage on the capacitor?

50 T/s while that in the right-hand solenoid is decreasing at 30 T/s. Find the current in the resistance wire shared by both triangles. Which way does the current flow?

FIGURE 3 Cumulative Problem 3.

4. A long solenoid of length ℓ and radius R has a total of N

The Authors

Richard Wolfson is Professor of Physics and George Adams Ellis Professor of the Liberal Arts at Middlebury College, where he has taught since 1976. He did undergraduate work at the Massachusetts Institute of Technology and Swarthmore College and holds the M.S. degree from the University of Michigan and Ph.D. from Dartmouth. He has published widely in scientific journals, including works ranging from medical physics research to experimental plasma physics, electronic circuit design, solar energy engineering, and theoretical astrophysics. He is also an interpreter of science for the nonspecialist, as a contributor to *Scientific American* and author of the book *Nuclear Choices: A Citizen's Guide to Nuclear Technology*. His videotaped course "Einstein's Relativity and the Quantum Revolution," produced by The Teaching Company, brings the key ideas of modern physics to nonscientists. Professor Wolfson has spent sabbatical years as Visiting Scientist at the National Center for Atmospheric Research in Boulder, Colorado, at St. Andrews University in Scotland, and at Stanford University.

Jay M. Pasachoff is Field Memorial Professor of Astronomy and Director of the Hopkins Observatory at Williams College. He was born and brought up in New York City. After attending the Bronx High School of Science, he received his A.B. degree from Harvard College and his A.M. and Ph.D. from Harvard University. He then held postdoctoral fellowships at Harvard and at the California Institute of Technology before going to Williams in 1972. His research has dealt mainly with solar physics, most recently the solar corona as studied at total eclipses, and with nuclear astrophysics, namely, the abundances of the light elements and their formation in the first minutes of the universe. Professor Pasachoff has spent sabbatical leaves at the University of Hawaii, at l'Institut d'Astrophysique in Paris, at the Institute for Advanced Study in Princeton, and at the Harvard-Smithsonian Center for Astrophysics. He is also author or co-author of major texts in physics, calculus, physical science, and astronomy.

Color Key for Figures

The artwork for this third edition is carefully designed to make effective use of color printing as a learning aid. In particular, we have assigned colors to the vector quantities that are so important in physics, and we have used those colors consistently throughout the book. The table below lists some important physical quantities, along with their text and graphic symbols and color assignments. We also include electric circuit symbols, which, to be consistent with usage in engineering, are printed in black.

Vector	Text Symbol	Graphic Symbol
Displacement	$\mathbf{r}, \boldsymbol{\ell}$	
Velocity	$\mathbf{v}$	
Acceleration	$\mathbf{a}$	
Force	$\mathbf{F}$	
Linear momentum	$\mathbf{p}$	
Angular velocity	$\boldsymbol{\omega}$	
Torque	$\boldsymbol{\tau}$	
Angular momentum	$\mathbf{L}$	
Electric field	$\mathbf{E}$	
Magnetic field	$\mathbf{B}$	
Electric dipole moment	$\mathbf{p}$	
Magnetic dipole moment	$\boldsymbol{\mu}$	
Electric charge		
Positive charge	q, Q	
Negative charge	q, Q	
Circuit symbols		
Battery, emf	$\mathcal{E}$	
Resistor	R	
Capacitor	C	
Inductor	L	
Switch	S	

Credits

Page abbreviations are as follows: (T) top, (C) center, (B) bottom, (L) left, (R) right.

588T ©Will and Deni McIntyre/Photo Researchers, Inc.

588B ©Sinclair Stammers/SPL/Photo Researchers, Inc.

591 ©John Wilson White/Addison Wesley Longman

592L Object courtesy of SLAC and Sidney Drell, photo by Oscar Kapp, University of Chicago

592R ©SLAC/SPL/Photo Researchers, Inc.

600 ©Peter Menzel/Stock Boston

610 ©Erik Borg/Addison Wesley Longman

620 ©Hulton Getty

630 Courtesy of Christopher Johnson, University of Utah

633 ©AP/Wide World

634 Courtesy of Hulon Forrester/Video Display Corporation

638 Courtesy of the Museum of Science, Boston

639 ©Tom Sheppard/Tony Stone Images

649L Courtesy of EPRI

649R Courtesy of Environmental Elements Corp

650 Courtesy of Xerox Corporation

652 ©Erik Borg/Addison Wesley Longman

658 Courtesy of Sandia National Laboratory

662 ©Adam Hart/SPL/Photo Researchers, Inc.

663 ©Cliff Holmes

666 ©Erik Borg/Addison Wesley Longman

667 ©1998 PhotoDisc, Inc.

670T ©Erik Borg/Addison Wesley Longman

670B ©Erik Borg/Addison Wesley Longman

671T Courtesy of Lawrence Livermore National Laboratory

671B Courtesy of SurVivaLink Corporation

684 ©David Taylor/SPL/Photo Researchers, Inc.

687 ©Lisas/Lockheed/SPL/Photo Researchers, Inc.

688 Adapted with permission from D.J. Aidley and P.R. Stanfield, *Ion Channels: Molecules in Action,* Cambridge University Press, 1996, p2, Fig.1.1.

691 Courtesy of Don Eigler, IBM Almaden

693T Courtesy of Kitt Peak National Observatory

693C ©Tom Mcugh/Photo Researchers, Inc.

693B Courtesy of Princeton Plasma Physics Laboratory

696 Courtesy of Motorola

697 World record, 13.5 Tesla dipole Magnet, Lawrence Berkeley National Laboratory Superconducting Magnet Group

700B ©Erik Borg/Addison Wesley Longman

707 Courtesy of General Motors

709 ©R. Krubner/H. Armstrong Roberts

710 ©John Wilson White/Addison Wesley Longman, Inc.

714 ©Erik Borg/Addison Wesley Longman

723T Courtesy of Falcon/Simpson Electric Company

723B Courtesy of Tektronix

725 ©Michael Dalton/Fundamental Photographs

732 Courtesy of Survivalink

733 ©Erik Borg/Addison Wesley Longman

734 ©Erik Borg/Addison Wesley Longman

742 Courtesy of Loren Acton

743 ©1986 Richard Megna/Fundamental Photographs

745 Courtesy of Dr. Alexander Kovalenko, JINR

747 ©1986 Richard Megna/Fundamental Photographs

750 Courtesy of NASA

751L ©Ivan Massar

751R ©Fermilab/Peter Arnold, Inc.

752L Courtesy of Jay M. Pasachoff

752R Courtesy of Princeton Plasma Physics Laboratory

753T ©Lionel F. Stevenson/Photo Researchers, Inc.

753B Courtesy of Dr. L.A. Frank, University of Iowa

755 Courtesy of Japan National Railways

756 ©Mitsuhiro Wada/Gamma-Liaison

762T ©John Wilson White/Addison Wesley Longman

762B Courtesy of General Motors

1053L Courtesy of AT&T Bell Laboratories

1054 Courtesy of the Meggers Gallery, AIP

1057T Courtesy of the Institute of Theoretical Physics, Lund, Sweden

1057B Courtesy of Carl D. Anderson/California Institute of Technology

1058 ©AP/Wide World

1060T ©U.S. Navy/SPL/Photo Researchers, Inc.

1060B Courtesy of Ullstein Bilderdienst

1061 Courtesy of Ullstein Bilderdienst

1062 Courtesy of the Stein Collection, AIP

1064L Courtesy of Fermilab Visual Media Services

1064R Courtesy of CERN

1065T Courtesy of Ralph Crane

1065B ©Patrice Loiez/CERN/SPL/Photo Researchers, Inc.

1067 ©Joe Stancampiano and Karl Luttrell/National Geographic Society

1071 ©Dan McCoy/Rainbow

1072R ©Mark Marten/Los Alamos National Laboratory/Photo Researchers, Inc.

Extended

1044 ©Wexler/Burgess/SPL/Photo Researchers, Inc.

1046 Courtesy of The Exploratorium

1057T Courtesy of R. Giovanelli and H.R. Gillett/ CSIRO National Measurement Laboratory, Australia

1057B Courtesy of Alfred Leitner/Rensselaer Polytechnic Institute

1058 Courtesy of the AIP Niels Bohr Library, photo by Paul Ehrenfest

1063L ©Prof. P.M. Motta/SPL/Photo Researchers, Inc.

1063R ©CNRI/SPL/Photo Researchers, Inc.

1064 Courtesy of AT&T Bell Laboratories

1068 Courtesy of the AIP Niels Bohr Library

1074 Courtesy of the Lawrence Livermore National Laboratory

1076 Courtesy of Elisha Huggins, Dartmouth

1077T From C. Jonsson, Zeitscrift fer Physik, Springer-Verlag, Berlin, Heidelberg, New York

1077B Courtesy of the AIP, Meggers Gallery

1079 Courtesy of Paul Ehrenfest

1088 Courtesy of Don Eigler, IBM Almaden

1089L Courtesy of IBM

1089R Courtesy of IBM

1090L Courtesy of Don Eigler, IBM Almaden

1090R Courtesy of R.M. Penner, University of California, Irvine

1094 Courtesy of Fermilab Visual Media Services

1100 ©Ken Eward/Photo Researchers, Inc.

1113 Courtesy of the National Radio Astronomy Observatory

1115T Courtesy of Mike Matthews/JILA

1115B ©Richard Megna/Fundamental Photographs

1121T Courtesy of the Astronomical Data Center (ADC) catalog A6016, by Reader J., Corliss Ch.H.:1981, 'Line Spectra of the Elements', CRC Handbook of Chemistry and Physics; NSRDS-NBS 68

1121B Courtesy of Osram/Sylvania, Inc.

1124 ©SPL/Photo Researchers, Inc.

1126 Courtesy of D.A. Calvert/Royal Greenwich Observatory

1127TL ©Skelton Photography

1127TC ©Dan McCoy/Rainbow

1127TR ©Paul Shambroom/Photo Researchers, Inc.

1127C ©Dagmar Schilling/Peter Arnold, Inc.

1127B ©Dan McCoy/Rainbow

1133 ©Science Source/Photo Researchers, Inc.

1136 ©Geoff Tomplinson/SPL/Photo Researchers, Inc.

1150T ©1998 PhotoDisc, Inc.

1150B ©John Mead/SPL/Photo Researchers, Inc.

1152L ©IBM Research/Peter Arnold, Inc.

1152C Courtesy of Brookhaven National Laboratory and NYU Medi-Cal Center

1153T Courtesy of Conductus

1153B Courtesy of the American Superconductor Corp.

Part Four Electromagnetism

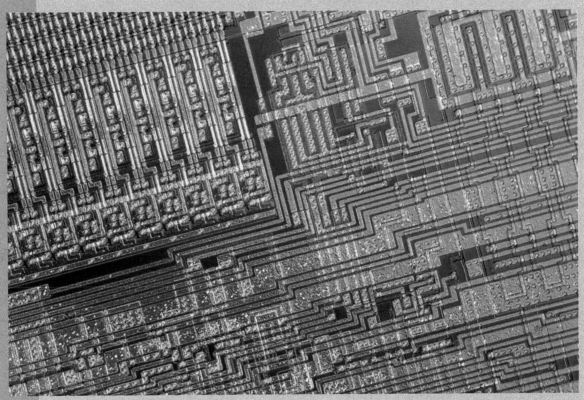

A portion of an integrated circuit, or "chip," magnified 100 times. Integrated circuits are at the heart of computers and many other electronic devices. A single integrated circuit can contain millions of transistors and other electronic components. These miniaturized circuits are but one of a myriad of electromagnetic technologies that we use every day.

Electromagnetism is a fundamental force, and governs the behavior of matter from the atomic scale into the macroscopic world. Electromagnetic technology, from computer microchips to large electric motors and generators, is essential to our technological society. Even our bodies—with their electrochemical nerve impulses, electrically polarized muscle cells, and carefully paced electrical signals controlling heartbeat—rely heavily on electromagnetism.

Four fundamental laws describe electricity and magnetism. Two deal separately with the two phenomena, while the other two reveal profound connections that show electricity and magnetism to be aspects of a single phenomenon—electromagnetism. The twelve chapters in this part will give you a thorough grounding in electromagnetism. You'll come to understand the fundamental laws that govern all electromagnetic phenomena, learn how electromagnetism determines the structure and behavior of nearly all matter, and explore the electromagnetic technologies that play so important a role in your life.

23 Electric Charge, Force, and Field

Lightning strikes at Kitt Peak National Observatory in Arizona relieve the buildup of electric charge in the atmosphere.

What force keeps the molecules in your body together? What force keeps a skyscraper standing or prevents a mountain from spreading into a flat blob? What force holds your car on the road as you round a turn? What force accelerates the electrons that paint the picture on your TV screen? What force underlies the awesome beauty of a thunderstorm?

Remarkably, these and all other forces except gravity that we encounter in our everyday lives—and in nearly all scientific work—are manifestations of a single force: the **electromagnetic force**. The friction, tension, and normal forces of mechanics are ultimately electromagnetic. So are interactions as diverse as the focusing of light in the lens of your eye, the extraction of information from a computer disk, or the formation of a water molecule from separate atoms. Electromagnetism is so important in science and engineering that we devote the next twelve chapters to it.

23-1 ELECTROMAGNETISM

Electromagnetism is among the fundamental forces of nature that we introduced in Chapter 5 (see Fig. 5-9) and is the dominant force in a vast range of natural and technological phenomena. Other than gravity, electromagnetism is the only force most of us will ever deal with.

Three distinct themes motivate our study of electromagnetism:

1. The electromagnetic force is solely responsible for the structure of matter from atoms to objects of roughly human size (Fig. 23-1). Much of physics, all of chemistry, and most of biology deal in this realm. Only at much smaller scales do the color and weak forces become important; only at larger scales is gravity significant.

    The wonderful diversity of chemical compounds is testimony to the rich possibilities contained in the electromagnetic interaction. Even life itself, and the DNA replicating mechanism at its heart, are manifestations of electromagnetism (Fig. 23-1). For students of physical and biological sciences, understanding electromagnetism means understanding the most fundamental basis of these disciplines.

2. We live in a technological world increasingly dominated by devices that operate on electromagnetic principles. Electric lights, motors, batteries, and generators have been essential for over 100 years. More recently, electronic technology has led to the proliferation of devices for storing and processing information, for sensing and measuring, and for sophisticated control of industrial, scientific, medical, automotive, and household systems (Fig. 23-2).

3. Studying electromagnetism leads to an understanding of the nature of light and from there to the theory of relativity. Relativity profoundly alters our ideas of space and time—the very basis of physical reality.

We've been speaking of electromagnetism, yet you're probably more familiar with electricity and magnetism separately. Although we begin with separate studies of these seemingly distinct phenomena, the relation between the two will become increasingly central. Eventually you will understand electricity and magnetism as two aspects of a single phenomenon that is basic to the workings of the universe.

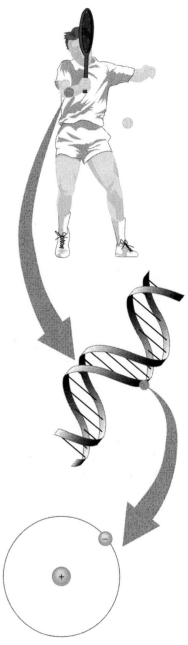

FIGURE 23-1 Electric forces govern the transmission of nerve impulses, shape the DNA molecule, and hold atoms together.

FIGURE 23-2 Inside a computer, components as mundane as the cooling fan motor and as sophisticated as a memory chip work on electromagnetic principles. Blowup shows the computer's microprocessor, which includes millions of electronic components on a single silicon chip.

23-2 ELECTRIC CHARGE

Electric charge is a fundamental property of nature. Of the three building blocks of ordinary matter—the electron, the proton, and the neutron—two carry electric charge. What is electric charge? At the most fundamental level, we don't know. We don't know what mass "really" is either, but we're familiar with it because we've spent our lives pushing objects around. By studying electrical interactions we gain a similar familiarity with charge that is as close as we can get to understanding what it "really" is.

Two Kinds of Charge

Electric charge comes in two varieties, which Benjamin Franklin designated **positive** and **negative**. These are convenient labels, but they have no physical significance. There's nothing "missing" about negative charge. Positive and negative charge are complementary properties, not the presence and absence of something. The utility in the names is mathematical, since it's the algebraic sum of charges—described with positive and negative numbers—that has physical significance.

Quantities of Charge

All electrons carry the same charge, and all protons carry the same charge. The proton's charge has *exactly* the same magnitude as the electron's, but with opposite sign. Given that electrons and protons differ substantially in other properties—like mass—this electrical relation is remarkable. Problem 1 shows how dramatically different our world would be if there were even a slight difference between the magnitudes of the electron and proton charges.

The magnitude of the electron or proton charge is the **elementary charge**, e. Electric charge is **quantized**—that is, it comes only in discrete amounts. In a famous experiment in 1909, the American physicist R. A. Millikan used electric forces to suspend small oil drops. From the electric force he computed the charge on each drop and found it was always a multiple of a basic value we now know as the elementary charge (Fig. 23-3).

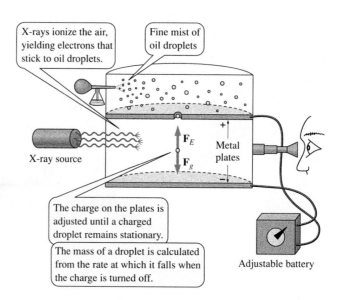

X-rays ionize the air, yielding electrons that stick to oil droplets.

Fine mist of oil droplets

$\mathbf{F}_E$

$\mathbf{F}_g$

X-ray source

Metal plates

The charge on the plates is adjusted until a charged droplet remains stationary.

The mass of a droplet is calculated from the rate at which it falls when the charge is turned off.

Adjustable battery

FIGURE 23-3 Millikan's oil-drop experiment. By balancing the electric force $\mathbf{F}_E$ and gravitational force $\mathbf{F}_g$ on oil drops, Millikan showed that charge is quantized.

Modern elementary particle theories suggest that the most basic unit of charge is actually $\frac{1}{3}e$. Such "fractional charges" reside on quarks, the basic building blocks of protons, neutrons, and many other particles. Quarks always join to produce particles with integer multiples of the full elementary charge, and it seems impossible to isolate individual quarks.

The SI unit of charge is the **coulomb** (C), named for the French physicist Charles Augustin de Coulomb (1736–1806). Although the coulomb's formal definition is in terms of electric current, it's convenient to describe one coulomb as being about 6.25×10^{18} elementary charges, making the elementary charge approximately 1.60×10^{-19} C.

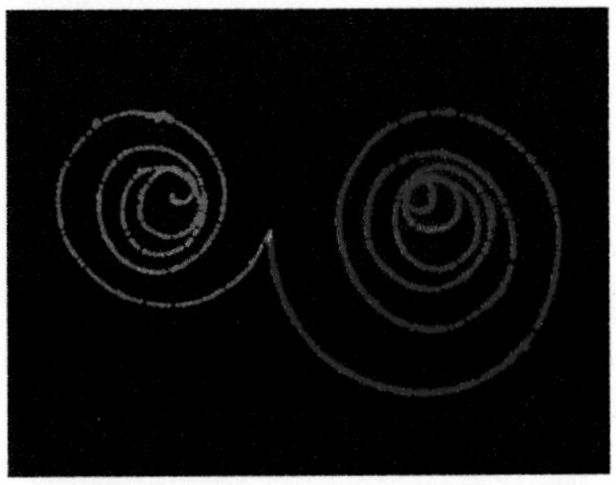

Charge Conservation

Electric charge is a conserved quantity, meaning that the algebraic sum of the electric charges—i.e., the **net charge**—in a closed region remains constant. Charged particles may be created or annihilated, but always in pairs of equal and opposite charge (Fig. 23-4). The net charge always remains the same.

FIGURE 23-4 The creation of an electron and its antiparticle, a positron. The two particles' paths are the oppositely directed spirals that originate in a common point where the pair was created. The net charge remains zero before and after the particle creation. (The curved paths result from a magnetic force.)

23-3 COULOMB'S LAW

You can transfer charge to a balloon by rubbing it on your clothing; you'll then find that the balloon sticks to you. Charge another balloon and the two balloons will repel each other (Fig. 23-5). You're seeing a manifestation of the fundamental fact that unlike charges attract and like charges repel. Socks clinging to other clothes when they come out of a dryer, dust attracted to the front of a TV screen or computer monitor, and the shocks you get when you cross a carpet and touch a doorknob are other common examples where you're directly aware of this electrical interaction.

But electricity would be rather unimportant if the only significant electrical interactions were these obvious ones. In fact, all interactions of everyday matter—from the motion of a car to the movement of a muscle to the growth of a tree—are dominated by the electric force. It's just that matter on the large scale is nearly perfectly neutral, so electrical effects in bulk matter are not obvious. At the molecular or even cellular level the appearance of individual charged particles makes the electrical nature of matter immediately obvious (Fig. 23-6).

The attraction and repulsion of electric charges implies that a force acts between them. Scientists Joseph Priestley and Charles Augustin de Coulomb investigated this force in the late 1700s. They found that the force between two charges acts along the line joining them, with a magnitude proportional to the product of the charges and inversely proportional to the square of the distance

FIGURE 23-5 Two balloons carrying similar electric charge repel each other.

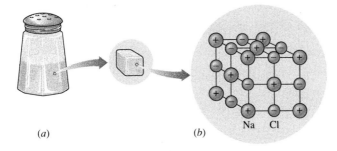

(a) (b)

Na Cl

FIGURE 23-6 (*a*) The salt shaker and even a single salt grain are electrically neutral, so the role of electric forces in these structures is not obvious. (*b*) At the atomic scale, electric forces bind individual sodium and chloride ions together and are, in fact, responsible for the cubical shape of the salt crystal.

$$\mathbf{F}_{12} = \frac{kq_1q_2}{r^2}\hat{\mathbf{r}}$$

FIGURE 23-7 Quantities in Coulomb's law used in calculating the electric force of charge q_1 on q_2. The unit vector $\hat{\mathbf{r}}$ always points in the direction from q_1 toward q_2, regardless of the signs of the charges. The force $\mathbf{F}_{12}$ points in the same direction as $\hat{\mathbf{r}}$ if the two charges have the same sign, and otherwise in the opposite direction.

ActivPhysics
11.1
Electric Force: Coulomb's Law

between them. These results are summarized in **Coulomb's law**:

$$\mathbf{F}_{12} = \frac{kq_1q_2}{r^2}\hat{\mathbf{r}} \qquad \text{Coulomb's law}. \qquad (23\text{-}1)$$

Here $\mathbf{F}_{12}$ is the force exerted *by* the charge q_1 *on* the charge q_2 and r is the distance between the two. The quantity k is a proportionality constant whose value in SI units is approximately 9.0×10^9 N·m²/C². The force $\mathbf{F}_{12}$ is a vector, and $\hat{\mathbf{r}}$ is a unit vector giving its direction. Figure 23-7 shows that $\hat{\mathbf{r}}$ lies on the line passing through the two charges and points in the direction *from q_1 toward q_2.*

Coulomb's law is a vector equation that covers all possible combinations of charges and the associated attractive and repulsive forces. If q_1 and q_2 have the same sign—either positive or negative—then the product q_1q_2 is positive, and the force points in the same direction as $\hat{\mathbf{r}}$. The force on q_2 is thus away from q_1, or repulsive, as it should be. But if q_1 and q_2 have opposite signs, then q_1q_2 is negative and the direction of the force is opposite that of $\hat{\mathbf{r}}$—that is, attractive.

What about the force $\mathbf{F}_{21}$ that q_2 exerts on q_1? Equation 23-1 shows it has the same magnitude as $\mathbf{F}_{12}$, but a drawing like Fig. 23-7 gives the opposite direction. Thus the electric force obeys Newton's third law. ActivPhysics Activity 11.1 lets you explore the forces between pairs of electric charges.

EXAMPLE 23-1	*Two Charges*

A 1.0-μC charge is located at $x = 1.0$ cm, and a -1.5-μC charge at $x = 3.0$ cm. (a) What force does the positive charge exert on the negative one? (b) How would the force change if the distance between the charges were tripled?

Solution

(a) A vector from the positive charge toward the negative charge points in the $+x$ direction, so $\hat{\mathbf{r}}$ is simply the unit vector $\hat{\mathbf{i}}$. Then Equation 23-1 becomes

$$\mathbf{F} = \frac{kq_1q_2}{r^2}\hat{\mathbf{r}}$$

$$= \frac{(9.0\times10^9 \text{ N·m}^2/\text{C}^2)(1.0\times10^{-6} \text{ C})(-1.5\times10^{-6} \text{ C})}{(0.020 \text{ m})^2}\hat{\mathbf{i}}$$

$$= -34\hat{\mathbf{i}} \text{ N}.$$

The minus sign shows that the force is in the negative x direction—toward the positive charge, or attractive.

(b) If the distance were tripled the force would drop by a factor of $1/3^2$, to $-3.8\hat{\mathbf{i}}$ N.

Tip

Let the Algebra Take Care of the Signs Equation 23-1 accounts for all aspects of the force calculation. If you correctly take $\hat{\mathbf{r}}$ to be a unit vector pointing *away* from the charge giving rise to the force—whatever its sign—and *toward* the charge being acted on—whatever its sign—then calculation of $\frac{kq_1q_2}{r^2}\hat{\mathbf{r}}$ gives correctly the magnitude and direction of the force. You should, of course, check that your mathematical answer makes sense.

EXERCISE A 10-μC charge is at the origin. Find the force it exerts on a 5-μC charge at the point $x = 4$ m, $y = 3$ m. *Note:* You may need help with this one; see the Math Toolbox following this example.

Answer: $1.44\hat{\mathbf{i}} + 1.08\hat{\mathbf{j}}$ mN

Some problems similar to Example 23-1: 7, 12, 13

Math Toolbox

Finding the Unit Vector In Example 23-1, both charges lay on the x axis and it was obvious that a unit vector from the 1 μC charge toward the -1.5 μC charge is the vector $\hat{\mathbf{i}}$, so in that case $\hat{\mathbf{r}} = \hat{\mathbf{i}}$. But what's $\hat{\mathbf{r}}$ in the exercise with Example 23-1?

Coulomb's law says that $\hat{\mathbf{r}}$ is in the direction from q_1 toward q_2. But that's the same direction as the displacement vector $\mathbf{r}_{12}$ from q_1 to q_2. So $\mathbf{r}_{12}$ has the right direction; it just isn't a *unit* vector. But dividing by its magnitude makes a unit vector, as you can prove in Problem 12. Figure 23-8 shows that $\mathbf{r}_{12} = 4\hat{\mathbf{i}} + 3\hat{\mathbf{j}}$ m, so its magnitude is $r = \sqrt{(4\text{ m})^2 + (3\text{ m})^2} = 5$ m. Then the unit vector from q_1 toward q_2 is

$$\hat{\mathbf{r}} = \frac{4\hat{\mathbf{i}} + 3\hat{\mathbf{j}}\text{ m}}{5\text{ m}} = 0.80\hat{\mathbf{i}} + 0.60\hat{\mathbf{j}}.$$

Then we're ready to calculate the force, using Coulomb's law (Equation 23-1):

$$\mathbf{F}_{12} = \frac{kq_1q_2}{r^2}\hat{\mathbf{r}} = \frac{(9.0\times10^9\text{ N·m}^2/\text{C}^2)(10\ \mu\text{C})(5.0\ \mu\text{C})}{(5.0\text{ m})^2}(0.80\hat{\mathbf{i}} + 0.60\hat{\mathbf{j}})$$

$$= 1.44\hat{\mathbf{i}} + 1.08\hat{\mathbf{j}}\text{ mN}.$$

And that's it: a full vector expression for the force. More generally, given the vector $\mathbf{r}_{12}$ from q_1 to q_2, we can write the unit vector as

$$\hat{\mathbf{r}} = \frac{\mathbf{r}_{12}}{r}, \tag{23-2a}$$

where r is the magnitude of $\mathbf{r}_{12}$—i.e., the distance between the charges.

Equivalently, you can find the unit vector using trigonometry. Let θ be the angle that the vector $\mathbf{r}_{12}$ from q_1 to q_2 makes with the positive x axis, as marked in Fig. 23-8. Then the unit vector is

$$\hat{\mathbf{r}} = \cos\theta\,\hat{\mathbf{i}} + \sin\theta\,\hat{\mathbf{j}}. \tag{23-2b}$$

You can see this is a unit vector because it has magnitude $\sin^2\theta + \cos^2\theta = 1$, and the geometry of Fig. 23-8 shows clearly that $\hat{\mathbf{r}}$ as defined in Equation 23-2b is in the direction of $\mathbf{r}_{12}$. Finally, with the hypotenuse $r_{12} = 5$ in Fig. 23-8, the figure shows that $\cos\theta = 4/5$ and $\sin\theta = 3/5$. Thus $\hat{\mathbf{r}} = 0.80\hat{\mathbf{i}} + 0.60\hat{\mathbf{j}}$, as before. The methods of Equations 23-2a and 23-2b are completely equivalent. Equation 23-2a may seem less familiar, but it gives the unit vector directly without the intermediary of trigonometry.

Still another approach is to use Equation 23-1 to find just the magnitude of the force, then figure out whether the force is attractive or repulsive, and then find its components in a chosen coordinate system. This method is completely equivalent to our more elegant and straightforward approach using unit vectors.

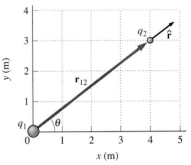

FIGURE 23-8 The two charges in the exercise with Example 23-1. You could get from q_1 to q_2 by going 4 m in the x direction and then 3 m in the y direction, so the displacement vector $\mathbf{r}_{12}$ is $\mathbf{r}_{12} = 4\hat{\mathbf{i}} + 3\hat{\mathbf{j}}$ m. The unit vector $\hat{\mathbf{r}}$ in Coulomb's law has the same direction as $\mathbf{r}_{12}$ but magnitude 1, so it's given by $\mathbf{r}_{12}$ divided by $\mathbf{r}_{12}$'s magnitude r, here $\sqrt{(4\text{ m})^2 + (3\text{ m})^2} = 5$ m. More generally, the unit vector in the direction from q_1 toward q_2 is $\hat{\mathbf{r}} = \mathbf{r}_{12}/r$. Equivalently, the unit vector is $\hat{\mathbf{r}} = \cos\theta\,\hat{\mathbf{i}} + \sin\theta\,\hat{\mathbf{j}}$, with θ the angle between $\mathbf{r}_{12}$ and the positive x axis.

Coulomb's law for the electric force is similar to Newton's law for the gravitational force. Both forces show the same inverse-square decrease with distance, and both are proportional to the product of the interacting charges or masses. But there is an important difference: There's only one kind of mass (even antimatter has "positive mass"), and the gravitational force it produces is always attractive. That means large concentrations of mass give rise to large gravitational forces. But charge comes in two varieties that attract each other, so large concentrations of charge tend to be electrically neutral and therefore give rise to weak electric forces. The electric force between individual particles is vastly stronger than the gravitational force between the same particles (see Problem 6), and it's only because of the nearly complete cancellation of positive and negative charge in bulk matter that gravity becomes important on the macroscopic scale.

Got It!

Charge q_1 is located at $x = 1$ m, $y = 0$. What should you use for the unit vector $\hat{\mathbf{r}}$ in Coulomb's law if you're calculating the force q_1 exerts on a charge q_2 located at (a) the origin and (b) the point $x = 0$, $y = 1$ m? Explain why you can answer this question without being told the signs of either charge.

Point Charges and the Superposition Principle

Coulomb's law is strictly true only for **point charges**—charged objects of negligible size. Electrons and protons can usually be treated as point charges; so, approximately, can any two charged objects if their separation is large compared to their size. But often we're interested in the electrical effects of **charge distributions**—arrangements of charge spread over space. The DNA molecule shown in Fig. 23-1 is a very complicated charge distribution. Other charge distributions include water molecules, the innards of a TV tube, a memory cell in a computer memory chip, your heart, and a thundercloud. We need to know how to combine the effects of two or more charges to find the electrical effects of such charge distributions.

Figure 23-9 shows two charges q_1 and q_2 which constitute a simple charge distribution. We want to know the net force on a third charge q_3 from the combination of q_1 and q_2. To find that net force, you might calculate the forces $\mathbf{F}_{12}$ and $\mathbf{F}_{13}$ from Equation 23-1, and then vectorially add them. And you'd be right: the force that q_1 exerts on q_3 is unaffected by the presence of q_2, and vice versa, so you can apply Coulomb's law separately to the pairs q_1q_3 and q_2q_3 and then combine the results. That may seem obvious, but nature needn't have been so simple.

The fact that electric forces add vectorially is called the **superposition principle**. Our confidence in this principle is ultimately based on experiments that show electric and indeed electromagnetic phenomena behave according to the principle. With superposition we can solve relatively complicated problems by breaking them into simpler parts. If the superposition principle did not hold, the mathematical description of electromagnetism would be far more complicated than it is. ActivPhysics Activities 11.2 and 11.3 let you explore the superposition principle.

Although the force that one point charge exerts on another decreases with the inverse square of the distance between them, it's important to recognize that the same is usually not true of the force arising from a charge distribution. The superposition of forces from different charges in a distribution may result in a very different distance dependence of the force due to a charge distribution (see Fig. 23-10). Example 23-2 on the next page provides a case in point.

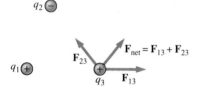

FIGURE 23-9 The superposition principle allows us to add vectorially the forces from two or more charges.

11.2, 11.3
Electric Force:
Superposition Principle

FIGURE 23-10 (*a*) For a charge distribution distant enough to resemble a point charge, the inverse-square law holds approximately. (*b*) Close to charge distribution, the inverse-square law usually does not hold. That's because individual charges in the distribution are located at different distances and directions from the charge experiencing the force.

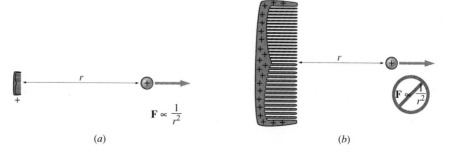

$$\mathbf{F} \propto \frac{1}{r^2}$$

(*a*)

(*b*)

| **EXAMPLE 23-2** | *Raindrops* |

The charging of individual raindrops is ultimately responsible for the electrical activity of a thunderstorm. Suppose two drops with equal charge q are located on the x axis at $\pm a$, as shown in Fig. 23-11. Find the electric force on a third drop with charge Q located at an arbitrary point on the y axis.

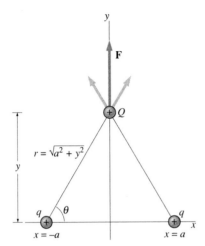

FIGURE 23-11 The force on Q is the vector sum of the forces from the individual charges.

Solution

Charge Q is the same distance $r = \sqrt{a^2 + y^2}$ from the two other drops, so the force from each has the same magnitude. Then it's obvious from Fig. 23-11 that the x components of the two forces cancel, while the y components are the same. Fig. 23-11 and Equation 23-2b show that the y components of the unit vectors from the two charges q toward Q are both given by $\hat{r}_y = \sin\theta = y/\sqrt{a^2 + y^2}$. Then the y component of each force is given by $F_y = (kqQ/r^2)\hat{r}_y$, and the net force on Q becomes

$$\mathbf{F} = F_y\hat{\mathbf{j}} = \left(\frac{2kqQ}{a^2 + y^2}\right)\left(\frac{y}{\sqrt{a^2 + y^2}}\right)\hat{\mathbf{j}} = \frac{2kqQ}{(a^2 + y^2)^{3/2}}\hat{\mathbf{j}},$$

where the factor of two comes from adding the y components of the forces from both charges q.

Does our result make sense? Evaluating $\mathbf{F}$ at $y = 0$ gives zero force. Here, midway between the two charges, Q experi-

ences equal but opposite forces from the two q's, so the net force must be zero. At very large distances such that $y \gg a$, on the other hand, we can neglect a^2 compared with y^2, and the force becomes

$$\mathbf{F} = \frac{k(2q)Q}{y^2}\hat{\mathbf{j}}. \qquad (y \gg a)$$

This is just the force we would expect from a single charge of magnitude $2q$ located a distance y from Q—showing that this system of two charges acts like a single charge $2q$ at distances large compared with the charge separation. But this is true only at distances large compared with the charge separation. In closer, where the detailed arrangement of the individual charges is important, the behavior of the field is more complicated. In fact, our result shows the field initially increasing as y increases, and only later beginning to decrease with increasing y.

In drawing Fig. 23-11 we tacitly assumed that q and Q have the same signs. But our analysis holds even if they don't; in that case the product qQ is negative, and $\mathbf{F}$ therefore points in the opposite direction from $\hat{\mathbf{j}}$.

EXERCISE Find the net force on the charge located at the origin in Fig. 23-12.

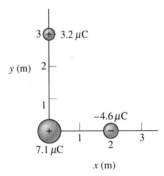

FIGURE 23-12 What is the force on the charge at the origin?

Answer: $73\hat{\mathbf{i}} - 23\hat{\mathbf{j}}$ mN

Some problems similar to Example 23-2: 19–22, 34

| **EXAMPLE 23-3** | *Balancing Forces* |

A positive charge $+2q$ lies on the x axis at $x = -a$, and a charge $-q$ lies at $x = +a$, as shown in Fig. 23-13. Find a point where the electric force on a third charge Q would be zero.

Solution

The point must lie on the x axis since off axis the individual force vectors cannot point in opposite directions. But where on

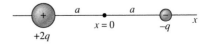

FIGURE 23-13 Where will a third charge experience no net force (Example 23-3)?

the axis? In between the two charges the repulsion of one and attraction of the other would add to give a nonzero net force. To the left of $+2q$, a third charge Q would always be closer to $+2q$ than to $-q$. The force from $+2q$ would always be greater, partly because Q would be closer to it and partly because of its greater charge. So the only place the forces from the two charges might cancel is to the right of $-q$.

So suppose the third charge Q lies at some point x to the right of $-q$, so $x > a$. Then a unit vector from either $+2q$ or $-q$ toward Q points in the $+x$ direction, so is the vector $\hat{\mathbf{i}}$. Summing the two forces as given by Equation 23-1 and setting the result to zero then gives

$$\mathbf{F} = \mathbf{F}_{2q} + \mathbf{F}_{-q} = \frac{k(2q)Q}{(x+a)^2}\hat{\mathbf{i}} + \frac{k(-q)Q}{(x-a)^2}\hat{\mathbf{i}} = \mathbf{0},$$

where the denominators are the distances from any point $x > a$ to the charges located at $x = -a$ and $x = +a$, respectively. Note that Q cancels from the equation, showing that the point we're finding will be a point of zero force for *any* charge, no matter what its sign or magnitude. The quantities k and q also cancel, so the x component of our equation for the net force becomes

$$\frac{2}{(x+a)^2} = \frac{1}{(x-a)^2}.$$

Inverting and taking square roots gives

$$\frac{x+a}{\sqrt{2}} = \pm(x-a).$$

We solve separately for the two possible signs. For the $+$ sign, we have

$$x = a\frac{\sqrt{2}+1}{\sqrt{2}-1} = a\frac{(\sqrt{2}+1)^2}{(\sqrt{2}-1)(\sqrt{2}+1)}$$
$$= (3 + 2\sqrt{2})a = 5.83a.$$

Since this value of x is greater than a, this point does indeed lie to the right of $-q$. So it's the point where the two forces balance. Move a little to the left, and the negative charge dominates, exerting a leftward force on a positive Q. Move a little to the right, and the net positive charge of the whole distribution dominates, exerting a rightward force on a positive Q. In between is the point of zero force.

You can verify that the solution for the minus sign lies to the left of $-q$ and is therefore inconsistent with our choice of direction for the unit vector from $-q$. This second solution is therefore not a meaningful answer.

Tip

Let the Algebra Take Care of Signs Once again, Equation 23-1 tells it all—including the direction of the force once you choose the unit vector correctly. You may be tempted in a problem like Example 23-3 simply to set the magnitudes of the two forces equal and solve for x. That may work if you're careful, but it's safer to remember that you're really solving for a point where *the vector sum of two forces is zero*. You can't go wrong if you write those forces carefully with the correct vector directions and then sum them.

EXERCISE Repeat Example 23-3 with the charge $-q$ changed to $+q$.

Answer: $(3 - 2\sqrt{2})a = 0.17a$

Some problems similar to Example 23-3: 16–18, 32, 34

23-4 THE ELECTRIC FIELD

In Chapter 9 we defined the gravitational field at a point as the gravitational force per unit mass that an object at that point would experience. Even without Chapter 9, you're still familiar with this concept. You know that the force on an object of mass m near Earth's surface has magnitude mg and points downward. So we can think of g as a measure of the *force per unit mass* that any object would experience due to Earth's gravity. Full specification of that force includes its direction, which in this case is downward. So we can picture the gravitational field as a set of vectors giving the magnitude and direction of the gravitational force per unit mass at each point (Fig. 23-14a). In so doing, we've generalized to describe the force Earth would exert on *any* mass, rather than just its force on some particular mass.

It's convenient to do the same thing with the electric force. Rather than finding the force that a charge distribution exerts on some particular charge, we define the **electric field** as the force per unit charge:

> The electric field at any point is the force per unit charge that would be experienced by a charge at that point. Mathematically,

$$\mathbf{E} = \frac{\mathbf{F}}{q}.$$

(23-3a)

We emphasize that the electric field is a continuous entity, existing at every point in space. When we represent the field by vectors, we can't draw one everywhere, but that doesn't mean there isn't field at all points. Furthermore, we draw vectors as extended arrows, but each vector represents the field at only one point, namely the tail end of the vector. Figure 23-14b illustrates this for the electric field of a point charge.

The field concept implies a shift in our thinking about forces. Instead of the "action-at-a-distance" idea that Earth reaches out across empty space to pull on the moon, the gravitational field concept says that Earth creates a gravitational field and that the moon responds to the field at its location. The same is true for the electric field. Instead of thinking of one charge attracting or repelling another, we view a charge as creating an electric field throughout the space surrounding it. A second charge then responds to the field at its immediate location. Although the field only reveals itself through its effect on a charge, we nevertheless consider that the field exists at all points, whether or not there are charges present to feel a force. Right now you probably find the field concept to be a bit abstract, but as you advance in your study of electromagnetism you'll come to appreciate that fields are an essential feature of our universe, every bit as real as matter itself.

We can use Equation 23-3a as a prescription for measuring electric fields. Place a point charge at some point, measure the electric force it experiences, and divide by the charge to get the field. In practice, we need to be careful because the field generally arises from some distribution of charges, which we call the **source charges**. If the charge we're using to probe the field—the **test charge**—is large, the field it creates may disturb the source charges, altering their configuration and thus the field they create. For that reason, it's important to use a very small test charge.

If we know the electric field $\mathbf{E}$ at a point, we can rearrange Equation 23-3a to find the force on any point charge q placed at that point:

$$\mathbf{F} = q\mathbf{E}.$$

(23-3b)

If the charge q is positive, then this force is in the same direction as the field, but if q is negative then the force it experiences is opposite to the field direction.

Equations 23-3 show that the units of electric field are newtons per coulomb. Fields of hundreds to thousands of N/C are commonplace, while fields of 3×10^6 N/C will tear electrons from air molecules. Electric fields within atoms can exceed 10^{12} N/C.

FIGURE 23-14 (a) Representing the gravitational field near Earth's surface as a set of vectors. Each has magnitude $g = 9.8$ N/C and points downward. Each field vector gives the force per unit mass at a single point, namely the tail of the vector. Blowup shows that the field exists everywhere; we just can't draw vectors everywhere. (b) The electric field of a positive point charge points radially outward and its magnitude decreases with distance from the point charge (here the arrow lengths don't accurately reflect the exact inverse-square falloff). Each field vector gives the force per unit charge at a single point, namely the tail of the vector. As the blowup suggests, the field is continuous, with a field vector for each point in space. Figure is a 2-dimensional cross section of the field; in three dimensions, field vectors extend radially outward in all directions.

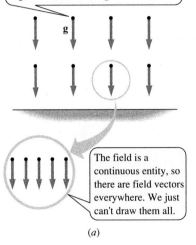

Right at this point the gravitational field is described by the vector **g**. That means a mass m placed here would experience a gravitational force $m\mathbf{g}$.

The field is a continuous entity, so there are field vectors everywhere. We just can't draw them all.

(a)

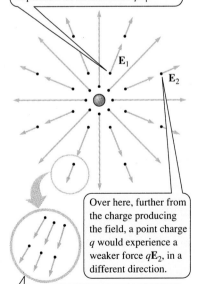

Right at this point the electric field is described by the vector $\mathbf{E}_1$. That means a point charge q placed here would experience an electric force $q\mathbf{E}_1$.

Over here, further from the charge producing the field, a point charge q would experience a weaker force $q\mathbf{E}_2$, in a different direction.

The field is a continuous entity, so there are field vectors everywhere. We just can't draw them all.

(b)

| **EXAMPLE 23-4** | *A Thunderstorm: Force and Field* |

A charged raindrop carrying 10 μC experiences an electric force of 0.30 N in the $+x$ direction. What is the electric field at its location? What would be the force on a -5.0-μC drop at the same location?

Solution

Equation 23-2a defines the electric field; here the force is $0.30\hat{\imath}$ N, so

$$\mathbf{E} = \frac{\mathbf{F}}{q} = \frac{0.30\hat{\imath}\ \text{N}}{10\times10^{-6}\ \text{C}} = 30\hat{\imath}\ \text{kN/C}.$$

Acting on a -5.0-μC charge, this field would result in a force

$$\mathbf{F} = q\mathbf{E} = (-5.0\ \mu\text{C})(30\hat{\imath}\ \text{kN/C}) = -0.15\hat{\imath}\ \text{N}.$$

Tip

The Field Is Independent of the Test Charge You might wonder if the field should point in the $-x$ direction when we talk about putting a negative charge in the field. It doesn't—because the whole point of the field concept is to provide a description that's independent of the particular charge experiencing that force.

The electric field in this example points in the $+x$ direction *no matter what charge* we may choose to put in the field. For a positive charge the force $q\mathbf{E}$ points in the *same* direction as the field; for a negative charge $q < 0$, and the force is *opposite* the field direction. As always, the algebra takes care of the signs—although you should check that your algebraic answers make physical sense.

EXERCISE An electric field $\mathbf{E} = -450\hat{\imath}$ kN/C is used to accelerate electrons in a portion of a TV picture tube, where the x axis points from the back to the front of the tube. Find the force in this field experienced by (a) an electron and (b) an ion carrying $+2$ elementary charges. (c) Which particle will be accelerated toward the front of the tube?

Answers: (a) $7.2\times10^{-14}\hat{\imath}$ N; (b) $-1.4\times10^{-13}\hat{\imath}$ N; (c) the electron

Some problems similar to Example 23-4: 26–28

The Field of a Point Charge

Once we know the field of a charge distribution we can calculate its effect on other charges. The simplest charge distribution is a single point charge. Coulomb's law gives the force on a test charge q_1 located a distance r from a point charge q:

$$\mathbf{F} = \frac{kqq_1}{r^2}\hat{\mathbf{r}},$$

where $\hat{\mathbf{r}}$ is a unit vector pointing *away* from q. The electric field arising from q is the force per unit charge, or

$$\mathbf{E} = \frac{\mathbf{F}}{q_1} = \frac{kq}{r^2}\hat{\mathbf{r}}. \qquad \text{(field of a point charge)} \qquad (23\text{-}4)$$

Since it is so closely related to Coulomb's law for the electric force, we also refer to Equation 23-4 as Coulomb's law. Note that the equation contains no reference to the test charge q_1, since the field of q exists independently of any other charge. Since $\hat{\mathbf{r}}$ always points *away* from q, the direction of $\mathbf{E}$ is radially outward if q is positive and radially inward if q is negative. Figure 23-15 shows some field

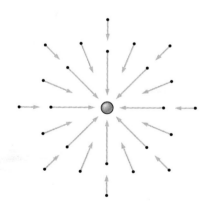

FIGURE 23-15 Field vectors for a negative point charge point radially inward, and their magnitude falls off with increasing distance from the point charge. As in Fig. 23-14*b*, each vector gives the force per unit charge that a test charge would experience when placed at the vector's tail. In three dimensions the vectors would fill all space in a spherically symmetric fashion.

vectors for a negative point charge, analogous to those of the positive point charge in Fig. 23-14b. ActivPhysics Activity 11.4 explores the point charge electric field.

11.4
Electric Field: Point Charge

23-5 ELECTRIC FIELDS OF CHARGE DISTRIBUTIONS

The electric field is the electric force per unit charge. Since the electric force obeys the superposition principle, so does the electric field. That means the field of a charge distribution is the vector sum of the fields of the individual point charges comprising the distribution:

$$\mathbf{E} = \mathbf{E}_1 + \mathbf{E}_2 + \mathbf{E}_3 + \cdots = \sum_i \mathbf{E}_i = \sum_i \frac{kq_i}{r_i^2}\hat{\mathbf{r}}_i, \qquad (23\text{-}5)$$

where the $\mathbf{E}_i$'s are the fields of the point charges q_i located at distances r_i from the point where we're evaluating the field, and where the $\hat{\mathbf{r}}_i$'s are unit vectors pointing *from* each point charge *toward* where we're evaluating the field. In principle, Equation 23-5 gives the electric field of *any* charge distribution. In practice, the process of summing the individual field vectors is often complicated unless the charge distribution contains relatively few charges arranged in a symmetric way.

EXAMPLE 23-5	*Two Protons*

Two protons are 3.6 nm apart. (a) Find the electric field at the point P shown in Fig. 23-16. (b) Find the force on an electron at point P.

Solution
If we take the x axis along the line joining the protons, then $\hat{\mathbf{r}}_1$ is just $\hat{\mathbf{i}}$ and $\hat{\mathbf{r}}_2$ is $-\hat{\mathbf{i}}$, where the subscripts 1 and 2 refer to the left and right protons, respectively. Then Equation 23-5 gives

$$\mathbf{E} = \mathbf{E}_1 + \mathbf{E}_2 = \frac{ke}{r_1^2}\hat{\mathbf{i}} + \frac{ke}{r_2^2}(-\hat{\mathbf{i}}) = ke\left(\frac{1}{r_1^2} - \frac{1}{r_2^2}\right)\hat{\mathbf{i}}$$

$$= (9.0\times10^9 \text{ N·m}^2/\text{C}^2)(1.6\times10^{-19} \text{ C})$$

$$\times\left[\frac{1}{(1.2\times10^{-9} \text{ m})^2} - \frac{1}{(2.4\times10^{-9} \text{ m})^2}\right]\hat{\mathbf{i}}$$

$$= 750\hat{\mathbf{i}} \text{ MN/C}.$$

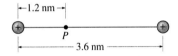

FIGURE 23-16 What is the electric field at P (Example 23-5)?

An electron in this field will experience a force

$$\mathbf{F} = q\mathbf{E} = (-1.6\times10^{-19} \text{ C})(750\times10^6 \,\hat{\mathbf{i}} \text{ N/C})$$

$$= -1.2\times10^{-10}\hat{\mathbf{i}} \text{ N}.$$

EXERCISE Find the magnitude of the electric field (a) 4.8 nm and (b) 200 nm to the right of the right-hand proton in Fig. 23-16. (c) Show that your answer to (b) is nearly equal to the field of a single charge $2e$ located midway between the two protons.

Answers: (a) 82.9 MN/C; (b) 70.7 kN/C

Some problems similar to Example 23-5: 31–34

The Electric Dipole

One of the most important charge distributions is the **electric dipole**, consisting of two point charges of equal magnitude but opposite sign held a fixed distance apart. Many molecules are essentially electric dipoles, so an understanding of

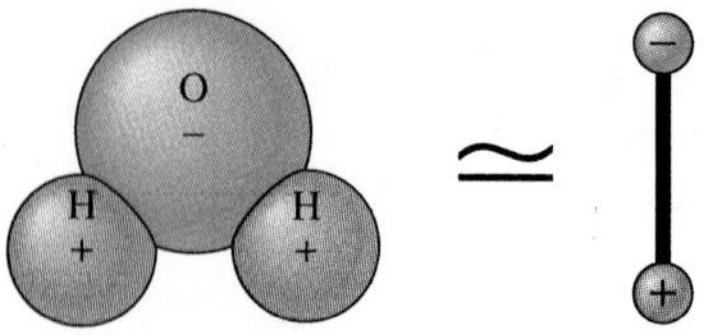

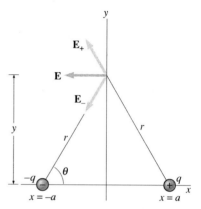

FIGURE 23-17 (left) A water molecule. Electrons spend more time in the vicinity of the single oxygen atom, giving rise to separate regions of negative and positive charge. The molecule therefore approximates the dipole shown at right, and results in an electric field like that of Example 23-6.

the dipole helps explain molecular behavior (Fig. 23-17). During contraction the heart muscle becomes essentially a dipole, and physicians performing electrocardiography are measuring, among other things, the strength and orientation of that dipole. The dipole configuration is also used in a number of technological devices such as radio and TV antennas.

EXAMPLE 23-6	Modeling a Molecule

Solution

A molecule consists of separated regions of positive and negative charge, modeled approximately as a positive charge q at $x = a$ and a negative charge $-q$ at $x = -a$, as shown in Fig. 23-18. Find a general expression for the electric field at any point on the y axis, and an approximate expression valid at large distances ($y \gg a$).

Solution

Figure 23-18 shows the individual field vectors $\mathbf{E}_-$ and $\mathbf{E}_+$, along with their sum. The y components cancel to give a net field parallel to the x axis, so we can get the net field by summing the two x components. Figure 23-18 and Equation 23-2b show that the x component of the unit vector from the negative charge toward the field point is $\cos\theta$, where $\cos\theta = a/r$; the x component of the unit vector from the positive charge is then $-a/r$. So the net field on the y axis becomes

$$\mathbf{E} = \frac{k(-q)}{r^2}\left(\frac{a}{r}\right)\hat{\mathbf{i}} + \frac{kq}{r^2}\left(-\frac{a}{r}\right)\hat{\mathbf{i}} = -\frac{2kqa}{(y^2 + a^2)^{3/2}}\hat{\mathbf{i}},$$

where the two terms in the sum correspond to the negative and positive charges, and where in the last step we used $r = \sqrt{y^2 + a^2}$. Although the x components of the unit vectors from the two charges have opposite signs, so do the charges—and thus the x components of the fields themselves are actually the same, as is obvious in Fig. 23-18.

Does this result make sense? Midway between the charges the fields from each charge point in the same direction and have the same magnitude, so we expect a resultant field twice that of either charge alone. Setting $y = 0$ at the midpoint gives

$$\mathbf{E}(y=0) = -\frac{2kqa}{(a^2)^{3/2}}\hat{\mathbf{i}} = -\frac{k(2q)}{a^2}\hat{\mathbf{i}},$$

which is indeed twice the field of either charge at the distance a.

We're frequently interested in the field far from a dipole, which is why this example asks for an approximate expression for $y \gg a$. (One needn't go very far from a molecule for its size to be insignificant.) Under this approximation we can neglect a^2 compared with y^2 in our expression for the field, giving

$$\mathbf{E} = -\frac{2kqa}{y^3}\hat{\mathbf{i}}, \qquad y \gg a.$$

FIGURE 23-18 An electric dipole. The electric field on the dipole's perpendicular bisector (here the y axis) is parallel to the dipole axis.

We'll see later how forces associated with such molecular electric fields contribute to the van der Waals interaction that we considered in Chapter 20.

Tip

Approximations Making approximations requires some care. Here we're basically asking for the field when y is so large that a is negligible *compared with* y. So we neglect a^2 compared with y^2 when the two are summed, but we *don't* neglect a when it appears in the numerator, where it's not summed with y.

EXERCISE Find (a) a general expression for the dipole field at points on the x axis to the right of $x = a$ in Fig. 23-18, and (b) an approximate expression valid for $x \gg a$.

Answers: (a) $\mathbf{E} = \dfrac{4kqax}{(x^2 - a^2)^2}\hat{\mathbf{i}}$; (b) $\mathbf{E} = \dfrac{4kqa}{x^3}\hat{\mathbf{i}}$

Some problems similar to Example 23-6: 31, 37, 38, 41

The dipole fields in Example 23-6 and its exercise both decrease, at large distances, as the inverse *cube* of distance. Physically, this is because the dipole has zero *net* charge. Its field arises entirely from the slight separation of two opposite charges. Because of this separation the dipole field isn't exactly zero, but it is weaker and more localized than the field of a point charge. Many complicated charge distributions exhibit the essential characteristic of a dipole—namely, they're neutral but consist of separated regions of positive and negative charge—and at large distances such distributions all have essentially the same field configuration (see Problems 46 and 82). ActivPhysics Activity 11.5 explores the dipole field. By placing the two charges in simulation 1 close together you can verify approximately the inverse-cube dependence of the dipole field.

11.5
Electric Field:
Due to a Dipole

At large distances the results of Example 23-6 and its exercise show that the dipole's physical characteristics q and a enter the equations for the electric field only through the product qa. We could double q (that is, double both the positive and the negative charge) and halve a, and the dipole's electric field would remain unchanged. In general, a dipole's electrical properties are characterized completely by its **electric dipole moment**, p, defined as the product of the charge q and the separation d between the two charges making up the dipole:

$$p = qd. \quad \text{(dipole moment)} \qquad (23\text{-}6)$$

In Example 23-6 the charge separation was $d = 2a$, so there the dipole moment was $p = 2aq$. In terms of the dipole moment, the fields we derived in Example 23-6 can then be written

$$\mathbf{E} = -\frac{kp}{y^3}\hat{\mathbf{i}} \qquad \left(\begin{array}{c}\text{dipole field for } y \gg a,\\ \text{on perpendicular bisector}\end{array}\right) \qquad (23\text{-}7a)$$

and

$$\mathbf{E} = \frac{2kp}{x^3}\hat{\mathbf{i}} \qquad \left(\begin{array}{c}\text{dipole field}\\ \text{for } x \gg a, \text{ on axis}\end{array}\right). \qquad (23\text{-}7b)$$

Because the dipole isn't spherically symmetric, its field depends not only on distance but also on orientation; for instance, Equations 23-7a and b show that the field along the dipole axis at a given distance is twice as strong as along the bisector. So it's important to know the orientation of a dipole in space, and therefore we generalize our definition of the dipole moment to make it a vector, of magnitude $p = qd$, and in the direction from the negative toward the positive charge (Fig. 23-19).

FIGURE 23-19 The dipole moment vector has magnitude $p = qd$ given by the product of the charge and separation, and it points from the negative toward the positive charge.

Got It!

Far from a charge distribution, you measure an electric field strength of 800 N/C. What will be the field strength if you double your distance from the charge distribution, if the distribution consists of (a) a point charge or (b) a dipole?

Continuous Charge Distributions

Although any charge distribution ultimately consists of pointlike electrons and protons, it would be impossible in practice to sum all the field vectors from the 10^{23} or so particles in a typical piece of matter. Instead, it's convenient to make the approximation that charge is spread continuously over the distribution. If the charge distribution extends throughout a volume, we describe it in terms of the **volume charge density**, ρ, with units of C/m³. For charge distributions spread over surfaces or lines the corresponding quantities are the **surface charge density**, σ, and **line charge density**, λ. Their units are C/m² and C/m, respectively.

To calculate the field of a continuous charge distribution, we break the charged region into very many small charge elements dq, each small enough that it is essentially a point charge. Each dq then produces an electric field $d\mathbf{E}$ given by Equation 23-3:

$$d\mathbf{E} = \frac{k\,dq}{r^2}\hat{\mathbf{r}}. \tag{23-8a}$$

We then form the vector sum of all the $d\mathbf{E}$'s. In the limit of infinitely many infinitesimally small dq's and their corresponding $d\mathbf{E}$'s, that sum becomes an integral and we have

$$\mathbf{E} = \int d\mathbf{E} = \int \frac{k\,dq}{r^2}\hat{\mathbf{r}}. \tag{23-8b}$$

The limits of this integral are chosen to include the entire charge distribution. Figure 23-20 shows the meaning of Equation 23-8b; note in particular that both the distance r and the direction specified by $\hat{\mathbf{r}}$ generally vary with position.

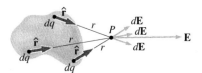

Charge distribution

FIGURE 23-20 The electric field at point P, given by Equation 23-8b, is the sum of the vectors $d\mathbf{E}$ arising from the individual charge elements dq in the entire distribution, each calculated using the appropriate distance r and unit vector $\hat{\mathbf{r}}$.

EXAMPLE 23-7	*A Charged Rod*

Wires, antennas, and similar elongated structures can often be treated as thin rods carrying electric charge. Suppose such a rod of length ℓ carries a positive charge Q distributed uniformly over its length. Find the electric field at point P in Fig. 23-21, a distance a from the end of the rod.

FIGURE 23-21 The field at P is the sum—or integral—of the fields arising from all the infinitesimal charge elements dq along the rod.

Solution

Let the y axis lie along the rod, with origin at P. Consider a small length dy of the rod, containing charge dq, and located a distance y from P. A unit vector from dq toward P is $-\hat{\mathbf{j}}$, so the field at P due to dq is

$$d\mathbf{E} = -\frac{k\,dq}{y^2}\hat{\mathbf{j}}.$$

The net field at P is the sum—that is, the integral—of all the fields $d\mathbf{E}$ arising from all the dq's along the rod:

$$\mathbf{E} = \int d\mathbf{E} = -\hat{\mathbf{j}}\int_{y=a}^{y=a+\ell} \frac{k\,dq}{y^2},$$

where we've chosen the limits to cover the entire rod. To evaluate the integral we must relate dq and y. How? The rod carries total charge Q, distributed uniformly over its length ℓ. The line charge density is therefore $\lambda = Q/\ell$. This is the charge per unit length; a length dy therefore carries charge $dq = \lambda\,dy$, or $dq = Q\,dy/\ell$. Then our integral becomes

$$\mathbf{E} = -\hat{\mathbf{j}}\int_a^{a+\ell} \frac{k(Q\,dy/\ell)}{y^2} = -\frac{kQ}{\ell}\hat{\mathbf{j}}\int_a^{a+\ell}\frac{dy}{y^2}$$

$$= -\frac{kQ}{\ell}\hat{\mathbf{j}}\left[-\frac{1}{y}\right]_a^{a+\ell} = -\frac{kQ}{\ell}\hat{\mathbf{j}}\left(\frac{1}{a} - \frac{1}{a+\ell}\right) = -\frac{kQ}{a(a+\ell)}\hat{\mathbf{j}},$$

where we took k, Q, ℓ, and $\hat{\mathbf{j}}$ outside the integral because they are constants.

Does this result make sense? First consider the direction: The negative sign shows that the field is downward for positive Q and upward for negative Q, as we should expect. Now suppose P is very far from the rod, so $a \gg \ell$. Then our result becomes approximately

$$\mathbf{E} = -\frac{kQ}{a^2}\hat{\mathbf{j}}, \qquad (a \gg \ell),$$

which is just what we expect for the field of a point charge Q. In this case we're so far from the rod that its length becomes negligible, and indeed it acts like a point charge. But as we move closer, the field becomes a more complicated superposition of the fields of all the dq's at different locations along the rod, and the field no longer exhibits the inverse-square dependence of the point-charge field.

Knowing the field of the charged rod, we can use superposition to find the fields of charge distributions involving more than one rod or a combination of rods and point charges (see Problems 44 and 46).

___

Tip

Find a Single Integration Variable Evaluating the integral in Equation 23-8b requires that we relate the charge element dq and the position variable r so we'll have the integral expressed in terms of a single vari-

able. The charge density provides the link needed, since it allows us to write dq as the charge density multiplied by an appropriate element of volume, area, or length:

$$dq = \rho\, dV, \quad dq = \sigma\, dA, \quad \text{or} \quad dq = \lambda\, dx.$$

Which of these we use depends on whether charge is distributed over a volume, area, or length; for the thin rod of Example 23-7, the appropriate charge density was the line charge density λ and the position variable was y, so we had $dq = \lambda\, dy$. Sometimes you'll be given the charge density explicitly, and other times you can compute it from the charge and dimensions of the charge distribution.

EXERCISE A thin rod of length ℓ lies along the y axis with its bottom end at the origin. It carries a line charge density λ that varies with position, being given by $\lambda = Q_0 \dfrac{y^3}{\ell^4}$, where Q_0 is a constant and y is the distance from the origin. Find the magnitude of the electric field at $y = 0$.

Answer: $\dfrac{kQ_0}{2\ell^2}$

Some problems similar to Example 23-7: 43–46, 71, 72, 82

___

Got It!

The point P in Fig. 23-21 is a distance a from the charged rod carrying total charge Q. So why can't you just write kQ/a^2 for the magnitude of the field at P?

___

EXAMPLE 23-8	*A Charged Ring*

A thin ring of radius a is centered on the origin and carries a total charge Q distributed uniformly around the ring, as shown in Fig. 23-22. Find the electric field at a point P located a distance x along the axis of the ring, and show that the result makes sense when $x \gg a$.

Solution

In Example 23-7 the magnitude but not direction of the individual field vectors $d\mathbf{E}$ from all the charge elements dq varied. Here we have the opposite situation: a point on the ring axis is equidistant from all points on the ring, so the field magnitudes dE are the same but their directions vary. Figure 23-22 shows, however, that components perpendicular to the x axis cancel for any pair of charge elements on opposite sides of the ring,

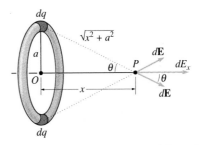

FIGURE 23-22 The electric field of a charged ring points along the ring axis since field components perpendicular to the axis cancel in pairs.

leaving a net field in the x direction. Each charge element contributes an amount dE_x to the field:

$$dE_x = \frac{k\,dq}{r^2}\cos\theta = \frac{k\,dq}{x^2 + a^2}\frac{x}{\sqrt{x^2 + a^2}} = \frac{kx\,dq}{(x^2 + a^2)^{3/2}},$$

where the geometry of Fig. 23-22 gives $r = \sqrt{x^2 + a^2}$ and $\cos\theta = x/\sqrt{x^2 + a^2}$; here $\cos\theta$ is the x component of the unit vector in Equation 23-8a. We now need to integrate this expression over the entire ring. In this integration k, a, and x are all constants—they don't change as we move around the ring. So we have

$$E = E_x = \int_{\text{ring}} dE_x = \int_{\text{ring}} \frac{kx\,dq}{(x^2 + a^2)^{3/2}}$$

$$= \frac{kx}{(x^2 + a^2)^{3/2}}\int_{\text{ring}} dq = \frac{kx\,Q}{(x^2 + a^2)^{3/2}},$$

where the last step follows because $\int_{\text{ring}} dq$ simply means the total charge on the ring. For positive Q this field points away from the ring.

Does this result make sense? At large distances from the ring we can neglect its size a compared with the distance x, and our result reduces to $E = \dfrac{kQ}{x^2}$—just what we would expect for

a point charge Q. As always, a finite-size charge distribution looks essentially like a point charge at distances large compared with its size.

Tip

How Can x Be a Constant? In this exercise x is constant because it's the distance from the center of the ring to the point where we're evaluating the field—that is, it's the distance from the origin to the *field point*, P. In the integration to find the field we're supposed to consider all *source points*—all points where charge is located that contributes to the field at P. Moving around the ring doesn't affect the value of x, so x is a constant for this integration. However, x is arbitrary, so our result holds for *any* value of x.

EXERCISE Find the point on the x axis where the electric field of the ring in Example 23-8 has its greatest magnitude.

Answer: $x = a/\sqrt{2}$

Some problems similar to Example 23-8: 47–50, 76, 83

EXAMPLE 23-9	*A Power Line's Field*

A long, straight electric power line coincides with the x axis and carries a line charge density λ C/m. What is the electric field at a point P on the y axis? Use the approximation that the line is infinitely long.

Solution

Here *both* the direction and magnitude of the field element $d\mathbf{E}$ arising from a charge element on the line vary with the position x of the charge element. But Fig. 23-23 shows that charge

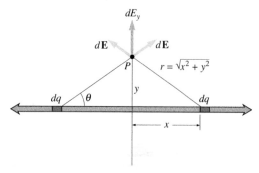

FIGURE 23-23 The field of a charged line is the vector sum of the fields $d\mathbf{E}$ from all the individual charge elements dq along the line. The x components from each pair of charge elements cancel, giving a net field that points directly away from the line.

elements on opposite sides of the y axis give rise to electric fields whose x components cancel. Thus the net field points in the y direction—that is, away from the line if λ is positive. So each charge element contributes an amount dE_y to the net field:

$$dE_y = \frac{k\,dq}{r^2}\sin\theta = \frac{k\lambda\,dx}{x^2 + y^2}\frac{y}{\sqrt{x^2 + y^2}} = \frac{k\lambda y\,dx}{(x^2 + y^2)^{3/2}},$$

where we've written $dq = \lambda\,dx$ and used the geometry of Fig. 23-23 to write $r = \sqrt{x^2 + y^2}$ and $\sin\theta = y/r$. Here, as usual, $\sin\theta$ is the y component of the unit vector $\hat{\mathbf{r}}$. To find the net field, we integrate over the entire line, from $x = -\infty$ to $x = +\infty$. The quantities k, λ, and y don't change as we move along the line, so we have

$$E = E_y = \int_{x=-\infty}^{x=\infty} \frac{k\lambda y\,dx}{(x^2 + y^2)^{3/2}} = k\lambda y \int_{-\infty}^{\infty} \frac{dx}{(x^2 + y^2)^{3/2}}$$

$$= k\lambda y\left[\frac{x}{y^2\sqrt{x^2 + y^2}}\right]_{-\infty}^{\infty} = k\lambda y\left[\frac{1}{y^2} - \left(-\frac{1}{y^2}\right)\right] = \frac{2k\lambda}{y}.$$

(23-9)

Here we evaluated the integral using the integral table in Appendix A and applied the limits $\pm\infty$ by noting that as $x \to \pm\infty$ the term y^2 becomes negligible compared with x^2, giving $x/\sqrt{x^2 + y^2} \to x/\sqrt{x^2} = \pm 1$. The integral could also be evaluated by rewriting it in terms of the angle θ (see Problem 87).

Since the line is infinite in both directions and has cylindrical symmetry, Equation 23-9 holds for *any* point a distance y from the line. Our result thus shows that the electric field of a long line of positive charge points radially away from the line, with magnitude that drops inversely with distance from the line (Fig. 23-24).

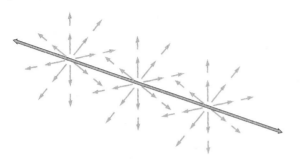

FIGURE 23-24 Field vectors for an infinite line of positive charge point radially outward from the line, with magnitude decreasing inversely with distance.

What about the field at large distances? Shouldn't it resemble that of a point charge, falling with the inverse square of the distance? No: The charged line is infinitely long, so no matter how far away we go it never resembles a point. Its slower dropoff reflects that fact.

Of course our infinite line is an impossibility. But many real charge distributions, including the power line of this example, have long, thin shapes that approximate an infinite line. Equation 23-9 is therefore a good approximation to the field of a *finite* line as long as we're much closer to it than its length, and not too near either end. Very far from a *finite* line, on the other hand, the field does approach that of a point charge.

EXERCISE A thin rod 2.0 m long carries 50 μC distributed uniformly over its length. Find the electric field strength (a) 1.0 cm from the rod axis, not near either end and (b) 500 m from the rod. Make suitable approximations in both cases.

Answers: (a) 45 MN/C; (b) 1.8 N/C

Some problems similar to Example 23-9: 50–54

23-6 MATTER IN ELECTRIC FIELDS

We're ultimately interested in electric fields since they give rise to forces on charged particles. Because matter consists of such particles, much of the behavior of matter is fundamentally determined by electric fields.

Point Charges in Electric Fields

The motion of a single charge in an electric field is governed by the definition of the electric field (Equation 23-3b):

$$\mathbf{F} = q\mathbf{E}$$

and Newton's law: $$\mathbf{F} = m\mathbf{a}.$$

Combining these equations gives the acceleration of a particle with charge q and mass m in an electric field $\mathbf{E}$:

$$\mathbf{a} = \frac{q}{m}\mathbf{E}. \qquad (23\text{-}10)$$

This equation shows that it's the charge-to-mass ratio, q/m, that determines a particle's response to an electric field. Electrons, nearly 2000 times less massive than protons but carrying the same charge, are readily accelerated by electric fields. Many practical devices, from x-ray machines to TV tubes, make use of electrons accelerated in electric fields.

When the electric field is uniform, problems involving the motion of charged particles reduce to the constant-acceleration problems we considered in Chapter 2. We'll see in the next chapter that uniform fields are easily produced by flat, uniformly charged plates. ActivPhysics Activities 11.7 and 11.8 simulate charged-particle motion in uniform electric fields.

ActivPhysics

11.7, 11.8
Motion in an Electric Field

EXAMPLE 23-10	*Inside a Heart Monitor*

A heart monitor used in a hospital's intensive care unit includes a cathode-ray tube that gives continuous visual display of a patient's heartbeat (Fig. 23-25). An electron beam "paints" the display on a phosphor screen at the front of the tube, being "steered" to different parts of the screen by electric forces. Figure 23-26 shows a side view of the "steering" region of the tube. The region is 2.0 cm long and contains a uniform electric field of 1.0 kN/C. (The field is produced by charging two flat metal plates with opposite charges, as we'll see in the next chapter.) Electrons enter this region moving horizontally at 4.0 Mm/s, as shown. In what direction are the electrons moving as they leave the field region?

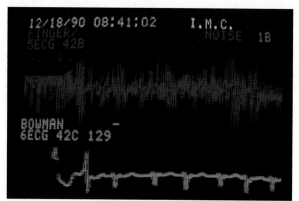

FIGURE 23-25 This heart monitor uses an electron beam deflected by electric fields to display patients' heartbeats.

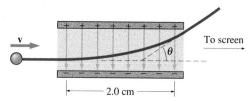

FIGURE 23-26 A uniform electric field deflects an electron from its straight-line path (Example 23-10).

Solution

As usual in two-dimensional motion, the vertical force due to the electric field does not affect the horizontal component of an electron's velocity. Therefore each electron spends a time $t = \Delta x/v_x$ in the field region. During this time it experiences a vertical acceleration qE/m, and therefore gains a vertical velocity component given by

$$v_y = a_y t = \frac{qE_y}{m}\frac{\Delta x}{v_x}$$

$$= \frac{(-1.6\times10^{-19}\text{ C})(-1.0\times10^3\text{ N/C})}{9.11\times10^{-31}\text{ kg}}\left(\frac{2.0\times10^{-2}\text{ m}}{4.0\times10^6\text{ m/s}}\right)$$

$$= 8.78\times10^5\text{ m/s}.$$

Note that the field points downward, as reflected by the minus sign, and combined with the electron's negative charge thus results in an upward velocity. The electron thus leaves the field region moving at an angle of

$$\theta = \tan^{-1}\left(\frac{v_y}{v_x}\right) = \tan^{-1}\left(\frac{8.78\times10^5\text{ m/s}}{4.0\times10^6\text{ m/s}}\right) = 12.4°$$

to the horizontal.

As it traverses the field region the electron describes the parabolic trajectory of an object undergoing constant acceleration in two dimensions; once outside the field it continues in a straight line with its new velocity, as indicated in Fig. 23-26. Field configurations like this one are used to "steer" electron beams not only in heart monitors but also in oscilloscopes and other electronic instrumentation.

EXERCISE What electric field strength would be needed to cause the electron of Example 23-10 to leave the field region at a point 4.6 mm above where it entered?

Answer: 2.1 kN/C

Some problems similar to Example 23-10: 57–61, 75, 76

An application of charge motion in uniform electric fields that's important to biochemists is the process of electrophoresis. Here, charged molecules move through a gel substrate under the influence of a uniform electric field. The drag force of the gel (ultimately electric in origin) counters the $q\mathbf{E}$ force of the electric field, resulting in each molecule having a constant velocity that is greater for molecules of lower mass. The field is applied for a given time, and molecules migrate different distances through the gel. The resulting pattern provides an indication of the different molecular species present (Fig. 23-27). A variation on this technique is the most widely used method of determining the molecular weights of proteins. Electrophoresis is also used to separate particles of all sizes

FIGURE 23-27 Gel electrophoresis of DNA produced these characteristic patterns. Each band marks the final position of a different DNA strand.

in studies of such diverse mixtures as blood and geological sediments. It's sometimes coupled with laser Doppler shift measurements (see Chapter 17) to provide the speeds of the migrating charged particles and give high-precision results in very short times.

When the field is not uniform it's generally difficult to calculate particle trajectories. An important exception is the case of a particle moving at right angles to a field that points radially. In that case—the subject of the following example—the electric force changes the particle's direction but not its speed, so the motion is uniform circular.

| **EXAMPLE 23-11** | *An Electrostatic Analyzer* |

Two curved metal plates are used to establish an electric field given by

$$E = E_0 \frac{b}{r},$$

where $E_0 = 24$ kN/C and $b = 5.0$ cm. The field points toward the center of curvature, as shown in Fig. 23-28, and r is the distance from that center. A beam of protons with a mix of speeds is incident on the device. Find the speed v for which an incident proton will leave the analyzer moving horizontally in Fig. 23-28.

Solution

To exit with its velocity horizontal, a proton must describe a circular arc while inside the analyzer. The field provides the v^2/r acceleration required for that circular motion:

$$a = \frac{v^2}{r} = \frac{eE}{m} = \frac{e}{m} E_0 \frac{b}{r}.$$

Solving for v gives

$$v = \sqrt{\frac{eE_0 b}{m}} = \sqrt{\frac{(1.6 \times 10^{-19}\ \text{C})(2.4 \times 10^4\ \text{N/C})(0.050\ \text{m})}{1.67 \times 10^{-27}\ \text{kg}}}$$

$$= 3.4 \times 10^5\ \text{m/s}.$$

Note that it doesn't matter where the protons enter the analyzer since the $1/r$ decrease in field strength matches the $1/r$ depen-

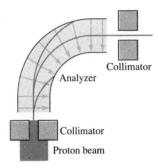

FIGURE 23-28 An electrostatic analyzer, showing the trajectories of protons in the radial electric field. Only those entering with the right speed will emerge at the top moving horizontally. Collimators block protons not moving at right angles to the field.

dence of the acceleration. Devices of this sort have been used on spacecraft to analyze charged particles in interplanetary space.

EXERCISE A proton is in circular motion centered on a long charged wire carrying uniform negative line charge density $-\lambda$. Find its speed. *Hint:* Consult Example 23-9 for the field of the charged wire.

Answer: $v = \sqrt{2k\lambda e/m}$, with m the proton mass

Some problems similar to Example 23-11: 60–64

Dipoles in Electric Fields

Earlier in this chapter we calculated the field of an electric dipole, which consists of two opposite charges of equal magnitude. Here we study a dipole's response to electric fields. Since the dipole configuration provides a simple model for many molecules, our results help explain molecular behavior.

Figure 23-29 shows a dipole with charges $\pm q$ separated by a distance d, located in a uniform electric field. The dipole moment vector **p** has magnitude qd and points from the negative to the positive charge (recall Fig. 23-19). Since the field is uniform, it's the same at both ends of the dipole. Since the dipole charges are equal in magnitude but opposite in sign, they experience equal but opposite forces $\pm q\mathbf{E}$—and therefore there's no net force on the dipole.

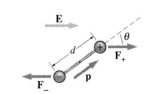

FIGURE 23-29 A dipole in a uniform electric field experiences no net force, but it does experience a torque.

However, Fig. 23-29 shows that the dipole does experience a torque that tends to align it with the field. In Chapter 13 we described torque as the cross product of the position vector with the force: $\boldsymbol{\tau} = \mathbf{r} \times \mathbf{F}$, where the magnitude of the torque vector is $rF \sin\theta$ and its direction is given by the right-hand rule. Figure 23-29 thus shows that the torque about the center of the dipole due to the force on the positive charge has magnitude

$$\tau_+ = rF \sin\theta = \tfrac{1}{2} d\, qE \sin\theta.$$

The torque associated with the negative charge has the same magnitude and both torques are in the same direction since both tend to rotate the dipole in Fig. 23-29 clockwise. Thus the net torque has magnitude $\tau = qdE \sin\theta$; applying the right-hand rule shows that this torque is into the page. But qd is the magnitude of the dipole moment $\mathbf{p}$, and Fig. 23-29 shows that θ is the angle between the dipole moment vector and the electric field $\mathbf{E}$; therefore we can write the torque vectorially as

$$\boldsymbol{\tau} = \mathbf{p} \times \mathbf{E}. \qquad \text{(torque on a dipole)} \qquad (23\text{-}11)$$

Because of this torque, it takes work to rotate a dipole in an electric field. If we start with the dipole oriented at right angles to the field ($\theta = \pi/2$), then Equation 12-22b gives the work required to rotate it to a new angle θ:

$$W = \int_{\pi/2}^{\theta} \tau\, d\theta = \int_{\pi/2}^{\theta} pE \sin\theta\, d\theta = pE\, [-\cos\theta]_{\pi/2}^{\theta} = -pE\cos\theta,$$

where the last step follows because $\cos(\pi/2) = 0$. This work ends up as stored potential energy U. Since the product of two vector magnitudes with the cosine of the angle between the vectors defines the dot product, we can write the potential energy in compact form as

$$U = -\mathbf{p} \cdot \mathbf{E}, \qquad (23\text{-}12)$$

where the zero of potential energy corresponds to the dipole at right angles to the field.

APPLICATION	*Microwave Cooking and Liquid Crystals*

The torque on dipoles in electric fields forms the basis of two widespread contemporary technologies: the microwave oven and the liquid crystal display (LCD).

A microwave oven works by generating an electric field whose direction changes several billion times per second. Water molecules, whose dipole moment is much greater than that of most other molecules, respond by attempting to align with the field. But the field is constantly changing, so the molecules swing rapidly back and forth. As they jostle against each other, the energy they gain from the field is dissipated as heat that cooks the food (see Fig. 23-30).

FIGURE 23-30 Water heats in a microwave oven because individual water molecules act as electric dipoles, experiencing torques in the oven's rapidly reversing electric field.

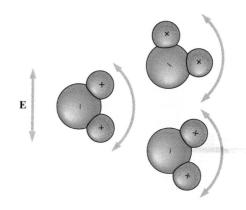

Calculators, laptop computers, gas pumps, watches, and many other devices display numerical and alphabetic information with liquid crystals. This unique state of matter combines the fluidity of a liquid with the order of a solid. The liquid crystal consists of long molecules whose chemical structure gives rise to a dipole-like charge separation. In response to each others' electric fields, the molecules tend to align with each other (see Fig. 23-31). But an external electric field can rotate the liquid crystal dipoles, altering the optical properties of the material. Using optical components we'll study in Chapter 34, different sections of a liquid crystal display can then be made to appear visible or invisible (Fig. 23-32). Liquid crystal displays have the advantage that they consume very little power. On the other hand they generate no light of their own, and therefore an external light source is needed to illuminate the display when it's dark.

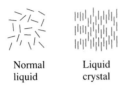

Normal
liquid

Liquid
crystal

FIGURE 23-31 Liquid crystals consist of dipole-like molecules that all align in the same direction, in contrast to the random orientation of molecules in an ordinary liquid. Applying an electric field can change the orientation of the liquid-crystal molecules.

FIGURE 23-32 Changing the orientation of the liquid-crystal molecules alters the optical properties of the liquid crystal, making individual segments of this liquid-crystal display either visible or invisible. (More on liquid-crystal displays in Chapter 34.)

When the electric field is not uniform, the charges at opposite ends of the dipole experience forces that differ in magnitude and/or are not exactly opposite in direction. Then the dipole experiences a net force as well as a torque (Fig. 23-33). An important instance of this effect is the force on a dipole in the field of another dipole (Fig. 23-34). Because the dipole field falls off rapidly with distance and because the dipole responding to the field has closely spaced charges of equal magnitude but opposite sign, the dipole-dipole force is quite weak and falls extremely rapidly with distance. This weak force, which Fig. 23-34 shows to be attractive, is partly responsible for the van der Waals interaction between gas molecules that we considered in Chapter 20. Problems 68 and 85 deal with forces on dipoles in nonuniform fields.

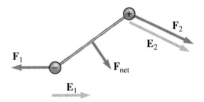

FIGURE 23-33 When the electric field differs in magnitude or direction at the two ends of the dipole, then the dipole experiences a nonzero net force as well as a torque.

Conductors, Insulators, and Dielectrics

Bulk matter contains vast numbers of point charges, namely electrons and protons. In some matter—notably metals, ionic solutions, and ionized gases—individual charges are free to move throughout the material. In such materials—called **conductors**—the application of an electric field results in the ordered motion of electric charge that we call **electric current**. We'll consider the behavior of conductors and related materials called semiconductors in subsequent chapters.

Materials in which charge is not free to move are called **insulators**, since they do not support electric current. Insulators, however, still contain charges—it's just that their charges are bound into neutral molecules. Some molecules, such as water, have intrinsic dipole moments and therefore rotate in response to an applied electric field. Even if they don't have dipole moments, molecules may respond to an electric field by stretching and acquiring **induced dipole**

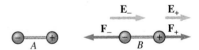

FIGURE 23-34 Dipole B is aligned with the electric field of dipole A. Since the field of A is stronger at the negative end of B, F_- is greater in magnitude than F_+, so dipole B experiences a net force toward dipole A. This is the origin of the van der Waals force between gas molecules.

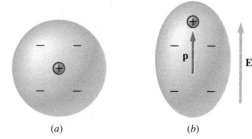

FIGURE 23-35 (*a*) A molecule with no dipole moment has negative charge concentric with positive charge. (*b*) In an applied electric field, the molecule stretches and acquires a dipole moment.

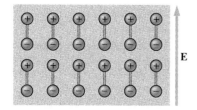

FIGURE 23-36 The alignment of molecular dipoles in a dielectric results in a reduction of the electric field within the dielectric.

moments (Fig. 23-35). In either case, the application of an electric field results in the alignment of molecular dipoles with the field (Fig. 23-36). The fields of the dipoles, pointing from their positive to their negative charges, then reduce the applied electric field within the material. We'll explore the consequences of this effect further in Chapter 26. Materials in which molecules have either intrinsic dipole moments or acquire induced moments are called **dielectrics**.

If the electric field applied to a dielectric becomes too great, individual charges are ripped free, and the material then acts like a conductor. Such **dielectric breakdown** can cause severe damage in electrical equipment (Fig. 23-37). On a larger scale, lightning results from dielectric breakdown in air.

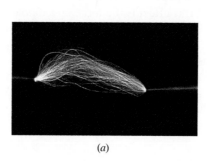

FIGURE 23-37 (*a*) Dielectric breakdown in air results in sparks jumping between two highly charged wires. (*b*) Dielectric breakdown in a solid produced this treelike pattern.

CHAPTER SYNOPSIS

Summary

1. **Electromagnetism** is among the fundamental forces of nature. Electromagnetism comprises electricity and magnetism, seemingly distinct phenomena that are actually intimately related.

2. **Electric charge** is a fundamental property of matter. Charge comes in two types, arbitrarily called positive and negative. Charge is **quantized**, with one elementary charge—the magnitude of the electron or proton charge—equal to 1.60×10^{-19} C, where the coulomb (C) is the SI unit of charge. Charge is also **conserved**, in that the algebraic sum of the charges in a closed system never changes.

3. Charges interact via the **electric force**. This force is proportional to the product of the charges and inversely proportional to the square of the distance between them. **Coulomb's law** provides a mathematical description of the electric force between point charges:

$$\mathbf{F}_{12} = \frac{kq_1 q_2}{r^2} \hat{\mathbf{r}}.$$

4. The **superposition principle** states that the electric force on a charge arising from two or more other charges is the vector sum of the force arising from each according to Coulomb's law. The superposition principle greatly simplifies the calculation of electrical effects of various **charge distributions**.

5. The electric field at a point is a vector giving the electric force per unit charge that would be experienced by a charge at that point:

$$E = \frac{F}{q}.$$

The electric field of a point charge q is therefore

$$E = \frac{kq}{r^2}\hat{r}.$$

6. The superposition principle shows that the electric field of a charge distribution is the sum of the fields of its individual point charges:

$$E = \sum_i E_i = \sum_i \frac{kq_i}{r_i^2}\hat{r}_i.$$

A particularly important charge distribution is the **electric dipole**, consisting of two point charges with equal magnitude but opposite sign, separated by a fixed distance. At large distances from a dipole the field decreases as the inverse cube of the distance.

7. With continuous distributions of charge, the sum over all point charges becomes an integral, giving

$$E = \int dE = \int \frac{k\,dq}{r^2}\hat{r}.$$

For any finite charge distribution with nonzero net charge, the field approaches that of a point charge at large distances.

8. A point charge in an electric field experiences a force $F = qE$; if this is the only force acting, the charge undergoes an acceleration $a = (q/m)E$ in accordance with Newton's law.

9. Because it consists of two equal but opposite point charges, an electric dipole experiences no net force in a uniform electric field. It does, however, experience a torque given by $\tau = p \times E$, where p is the dipole moment vector. A dipole in an electric field has potential energy given by $U = -p \cdot E$, where the zero of potential energy corresponds to the dipole oriented perpendicular to the field. In a nonuniform field, a dipole experiences both a torque and a net force.

Terms You Should Understand

(Pairs are closely related terms whose distinction is important; number in parentheses is chapter section where term first appears.)

electromagnetism (23-1)
electric charge (23-2)
coulomb (23-2)
Coulomb's law (23-3)
superposition principle (23-3)
point charge, charge distribution (23-3)
electric field (23-4)
electric dipole (23-5)
dipole moment (23-5)
volume, surface, and line charge density (23-5)
conductor, insulator, dielectric (23-6)
dielectric breakdown (23-6)

Symbols You Should Recognize

C (23-2)
e (23-2)
k (23-3)
q (23-3)
$\hat{r}$ (23-3)
E (23-4)
p (23-5)
ρ, σ, λ (23-5)

Problems You Should Be Able to Solve

calculating electric forces arising from one or more charges acting on another (23-3)
calculating electric fields of distributions of discrete charges (23-5)
calculating electric fields of continuous charge distributions (23-5)
approximating electric fields at large distances from charge distributions (23-5)
evaluating forces on charges in electric fields (23-4, 23-6)
describing the motion of charged particles in uniform and radial electric fields (23-6)
evaluating torques on dipoles in electric fields (23-6)

Limitations to Keep in Mind

Coulomb's law applies strictly only to one point charge acting on another. The forces and electric fields arising from more than one point charge or from a continuous distribution must be calculated using the superposition principle.

At large distances, the field of a charge distribution approaches that of a point charge only if the distribution is both finite in size and has nonzero net charge.

The dipole field decreases with the inverse cube of the distance only for distances large compared with the dipole's charge separation.

QUESTIONS

1. Discuss this statement: It is precisely because the electric force is so strong that the electrical nature of most everyday interactions is not obvious.
2. The gravitational force between an electron and proton is about 10^{-40} times weaker than the electrical force between the two. Since matter consists largely of electrons and protons, why is the gravitational force ever important?
3. You are given two electric charges. Could you determine whether they had the same or opposite signs? Could you determine the signs of each?
4. In Example 23-3 we found a point where the electric force on a third charge would be zero. Would a charge placed at that point be in stable equilibrium? Why or why not?
5. The gravitational force between an electron and a proton is about 10^{-40} times the electrical force between them. Does this ratio depend on how far apart they are? Explain.
6. In which of the following phenomena does electromagnetism play a dominant role?
    a. Gasoline burns in a car engine.
    b. The moon orbits Earth.
    c. A nerve impulse travels from your brain to a muscle.
    d. Protons and neutrons join to form an atomic nucleus.
    e. A chemist synthesizes a new polymer.
    f. You sit in a chair and the chair doesn't collapse.
7. A free neutron is unstable, and soon decays into other particles. One of the decay products is a proton. Must there be others? If so, what electrical properties must they have?
8. Where in Fig. 23-9 could you put a third charge so it would experience no net force? Would it be in stable or unstable equilibrium?
9. Why should the test charge used to measure an electric field be small?
10. Equation 23-4 gives the electric field of a point charge. Does the direction of $\hat{r}$ depend on whether the charge is positive or negative? Does the direction of $\mathbf{E}$ depend on the sign of the charge?
11. Is the electric force on a charged particle always in the direction of the field? Explain.
12. Why does a dipole produce an electric field at all? After all, the dipole has no net charge.
13. The ring in Example 23-8 carries total charge Q, and the point P is the same distance $r = \sqrt{x^2 + a^2}$ from all parts of the ring. So why isn't the electric field of the ring just kQ/r^2?
14. The field of a dipole decreases with the inverse cube of the distance. Why doesn't this violate our assertion that the field of a finite size charge distribution with nonzero net charge approaches that of a point charge at large distances?
15. A spherical balloon is initially uncharged. If you spread positive charge uniformly over the balloon's surface, would it expand or contract? What would happen if you spread negative charge instead?
16. Suppose someone argued that the force we call gravity is really an electric force, arising from a net electric charge on Earth. How could you disprove this?
17. Two cubical blocks of wood are each 10 cm on a side and carry electric charge spread over their surfaces. If they're 5 cm apart, would you be justified in writing kq_1q_2/r^2 for the force between them? How about if they're 5 m apart? Explain the difference.
18. A deuteron (heavy hydrogen nucleus) has twice the mass but the same charge as a normal hydrogen nucleus (a proton). Both are released from rest in the same uniform electric field. Compare the distances each goes in the same time.
19. Under what circumstances is the path of a charged particle a parabola? A circle?
20. Explain why a nonuniform field is required for a net force on a dipole.
21. Why should there be a force between two dipoles? After all, each has zero net charge.
22. Dipoles A and B are both located in the field of a point charge Q, as shown in Fig. 23-38. Does either experience a net torque? A net force? If each dipole is released from rest, describe qualitatively its subsequent motion.

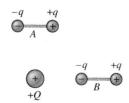

FIGURE 23-38 Question 22.

PROBLEMS

ActivPhysics can help with these problems:
Activities 11.1–11.8

Section 23-2 Electric Charge

1. Suppose the electron and proton charges differed by one part in one billion. Estimate the net charge you would carry.
2. A typical lightning flash delivers about 25 C of negativ charge from cloud to ground. How many electrons are involved?
3. Protons and neutrons are made from combinations of the two most common quarks, the u quark and the d quark. The u quark's charge is $+\frac{2}{3}e$ while the d quark carries

$-\frac{1}{3}e$. How could three of these quarks combine to make (a) a proton and (b) a neutron?

4. A 2-g ping-pong ball rubbed against a wool jacket acquires a net positive charge of 1 μC. Estimate the fraction of the ball's electrons that have been removed.

Section 23-3 Coulomb's Law

5. If the charge imbalance of Problem 1 existed, what would be the approximate force between you and another person 10 m away? Treat the people as point charges, and compare the answer with your weight.

6. Find the ratio of the electrical force between a proton and an electron to the gravitational force between the two. Why doesn't it matter that you aren't told the distance between them?

7. The electron and proton in a hydrogen atom are 52.9 pm apart. What is the magnitude of the electric force between them?

8. How far apart should an electron and proton be so the force of Earth's gravity on the electron is equal to the electric force arising from the proton? Your answer shows why gravity is unimportant on the molecular scale!

9. Two charges, one twice as large as the other, are located 15 cm apart and experience a repulsive force of 95 N. What is the magnitude of the larger charge?

10. Earth carries a net charge of -4.3×10^5 C. The force due to this charge is the same as if it were concentrated at Earth's center. How much charge would you have to place on a 1.0-g mass in order for the electrical and gravitational forces on it to balance?

11. A proton is on the x axis at $x = 1.6$ nm. An electron is on the y axis at $y = 0.85$ nm. Find the net force the two exert on a helium nucleus (charge $+2e$) at the origin.

12. Let $\mathbf{V} = V_x \hat{\mathbf{i}} + V_y \hat{\mathbf{j}}$ be an arbitrary vector, with V its magnitude. Show that $\mathbf{V}/V$ is a unit vector—i.e., that its magnitude is 1.

13. A charge q is at the point $x = 1$ m, $y = 0$. Write expressions for the unit vectors you would use in Coulomb's law if you were finding the force that q exerts on other charges located at (a) $x = 1$ m, $y = 1$ m; (b) the origin; (c) $x = 2$ m, $y = 3$ m. Note that you don't know the sign of q. Why doesn't this matter?

14. A proton is at the origin and an electron is at the point $x = 0.41$ nm, $y = 0.36$ nm. Find the electric force on the proton.

15. A 9.5-μC charge is at $x = 16$ cm, $y = 5.0$ cm, and a -3.2-μC charge is at $x = 4.4$ cm, $y = 11$ cm. Find the force on the negative charge.

16. A charge $3q$ is at the origin, and a charge $-2q$ is on the positive x axis at $x = a$. Where would you place a third charge so it would experience no net electric force?

17. A 60-μC charge is at the origin, and a second charge is on the positive x axis at $x = 75$ cm. If a third charge placed at $x = 50$ cm experiences no net force, what is the second charge?

18. You have two charges $+4q$ and one charge $-q$. (a) How would you place them along a line so there's no net force on any of the three? (b) Is this equilibrium stable or unstable?

19. In Fig. 23-39 take $q_1 = 68$ μC, $q_2 = -34$ μC, and $q_3 = 15$ μC. Find the electric force on q_3.

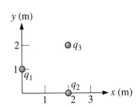

FIGURE 23-39 Problems 19, 20.

20. In Fig. 23-39 take $q_1 = 25$ μC and $q_2 = 20$ μC. If the force on q_1 points in the $-x$ direction, (a) what is q_3 and (b) what is the magnitude of the force on q_1?

21. Four identical charges q form a square of side a. Find the magnitude of the electric force on any of the charges.

22. Three identical charges $+q$ and a fourth charge $-q$ form a square of side a. (a) Find the magnitude of the electric force on a charge Q placed at the center of the square. (b) Describe the direction of this force.

23. Three charges lie in the x-y plane: $q_1 = 55$ μC at $x = 0$, $y = 2.0$ m; q_2 at $x = 3.0$ m, $y = 0$; and q_3 at $x = 4.0$ m, $y = 3.0$ m. If the force on q_3 is $8.0\hat{\mathbf{i}} + 15\hat{\mathbf{j}}$ N, find q_2 and q_3.

24. Two identical small metal spheres initially carry charges q_1 and q_2, respectively. When they're 1.0 m apart they experience a 2.5-N attractive force. Then they're brought together so charge moves from one to the other until they have the same net charge. They're again placed 1.0 m apart, and now they repel with a 2.5-N force. What were the original values of q_1 and q_2?

Section 23-4 The Electric Field

25. An electron placed in an electric field experiences a 6.1×10^{-10} N electric force. What is the field strength?

26. What is the magnitude of the force on a 2.0-μC charge in a 100 N/C electric field?

27. A 68-nC charge experiences a 150-mN force in a certain electric field. Find (a) the field strength and (b) the force that a 35-μC charge would experience in the same field.

28. A -1.0-μC charge experiences a $10\hat{\mathbf{i}}$-N electric force in a certain electric field. What force would a proton experience in the same field?

29. The electron in a hydrogen atom is 0.0529 nm from the proton. What is the proton's electric field strength at this distance?

30. A 65-μC point charge is at the origin. Find the electric field at the points (a) $x = 50$ cm, $y = 0$; (b) $x = 50$ cm, $y = 50$ cm; (c) $x = -25$ cm, $y = 75$ cm.

Section 23-5 Electric Fields of Charge Distributions

31. In Fig. 23-40, point P is midway between the two charges. Find the electric field in the plane of the page (a) 5.0 cm directly above P, (b) 5.0 cm directly to the right of P, and (c) at P.

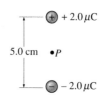

FIGURE 23-40 Problem 31.

32. A 1.0-μC charge and a 2.0-μC charge are 10 cm apart, as shown in Fig. 23-41. Find a point where the electric field is zero.

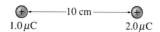

FIGURE 23-41 Problem 32.

33. A proton is at the origin and an ion is at $x = 5.0$ nm. If the electric field is zero at $x = -5$ nm, what is the charge on the ion?

34. For the situation of Example 23-3, (a) write an expression for the electric field as a function of x for points to the right of the charge $-q$ shown in Fig. 23-13. (b) Taking $q = 1.0$ μC and $a = 1.0$ m, plot the field as a function of position for $x = 5$ m to $x = 25$ m.

35. (a) Find an expression for the electric field on the y axis due to the two charges q in Fig. 23-11. (b) At what point is the field on the y axis a maximum?

36. Write an expression for the dipole moment vector of the dipole shown in Fig. 23-18.

37. A dipole lies on the y axis, and consists of an electron at $y = 0.60$ nm and a proton at $y = -0.60$ nm. Find the electric field (a) midway between the two charges, (b) at the point $x = 2.0$ nm, $y = 0$, and (c) at the point $x = -20$ nm, $y = 0$.

38. What is the electric field strength 10 cm from a point dipole with dipole moment 3.8 μC·m (a) on the dipole's perpendicular bisector and (b) on its axis?

39. The dipole moment of the water molecule is 6.2×10^{-30} C·m. What would be the separation distance if the molecule consisted of charges $\pm e$? (The effective charge is actually less because electrons are shared by the oxygen and hydrogen atoms.)

40. You're 1.5 m from a charge distribution whose size is much less than 1 m. You measure an electric field strength of 282 N/C. You move to a distance of 2.0 m and the field strength becomes 119 N/C. What is the net charge of the distribution? *Hint:* Don't try to calculate the charge. Determine instead how the field decreases with distance, and from that infer the charge.

41. Three charges form an equilateral triangle of side a. At one vertex is a charge $+2q$; at the other two vertices are charges $-q$. The triangle is oriented with the charge $2q$ on the positive x axis and both charges $-q$ on the y axis. (a) Find an expression for the electric field on the x axis, in the approximation $x \gg a$. (b) Compare with Equation 23-7b to show that your result in (a) is a dipole field, and give an expression for the magnitude of the triangle's dipole moment.

42. Three identical charges q form an equilateral triangle of side a, with two charges on the x axis and one on the positive y axis. (a) Find an expression for the electric field at points on the y axis above the uppermost charge. (b) Show that your result reduces to the field of a point charge $3q$ for $y \gg a$.

43. A 30-cm-long rod carries a charge of 80 μC spread uniformly over its length. Find the electric field strength on the rod axis, 45 cm from the end of the rod.

44. A thin rod of length ℓ carries charge Q distributed evenly over its length. A point charge with the same charge Q lies a distance b from the end of the rod, as shown in Fig. 23-42. Find a point where the electric field is zero.

FIGURE 23-42 Problem 44.

45. A thin rod of length ℓ has its left end at the origin and its right end at $x = \ell$. It carries a line charge density given by $\lambda = \lambda_0 \dfrac{x^2}{\ell^2} \sin(\pi x/\ell)$, where λ_0 is a constant. Find the electric field strength at the origin.

46. Two identical rods of length ℓ lie on the x axis and carry uniform charges $\pm Q$, as shown in Fig. 23-43. (a) Find an expression for the electric field strength as a function of position x for points to the right of the right-hand rod. (b) Show that your result has the $1/x^3$ dependence of a dipole field for $x \gg \ell$. (c) What is the dipole moment of this configuration? *Hint:* See Equation 23-7b.

FIGURE 23-43 Problem 46.

47. A uniformly charged ring is 1.0 cm in radius. The electric field on the axis 2.0 cm from the center of the ring has magnitude 2.2 MN/C and points toward the ring center. Find the charge on the ring.

48. Figure 23-44 shows a thin, uniformly charged disk of radius R. Imagine the disk divided into rings of varying radii r, as suggested in the figure. (a) Show that the area of such a ring is very nearly $2\pi r\, dr$. (b) If the surface charge density on the disk is σ C/m², use the result of (a) to write an expression for the charge dq on an infinitesimal ring. (c) Use the result of (b) along with the result of Example 23-8 to write the infinitesimal electric field dE of this ring at a point on the disk axis, taken to be the positive x axis. (d) Integrate over all such rings (that is, from $r = 0$ to $r = R$), to show that the net electric field on the disk axis is

$$E = 2\pi k\sigma\left(1 - \frac{x}{\sqrt{x^2 + R^2}}\right).$$

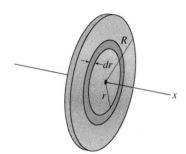

FIGURE 23-44 Problem 48.

49. Use the result of the preceding problem to show that the field of an *infinite,* uniformly charged flat sheet is $2\pi k\sigma$, where σ is the surface charge density. Note that this result is independent of distance from the sheet.

50. A semicircular loop of radius a carries positive charge Q distributed uniformly over its length. Find the electric field at the center of the loop (point P in Fig. 23-45). *Hint:* Divide the loop into charge elements dq as shown in Fig. 23-45, and write dq in terms of the angle $d\theta$. Then integrate over θ to get the net field at P.

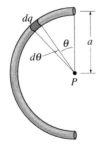

FIGURE 23-45 Problem 50.

51. The electric field 22 cm from a long wire carrying a uniform line charge density is 1.9 kN/C. What will be the field strength 38 cm from the wire?

52. What is the line charge density on a long wire if the electric field 45 cm from the wire has magnitude 260 kN/C and points toward the wire?

53. A straight wire 10 m long carries 25 μC distributed uniformly over its length. (a) What is the line charge density

on the wire? Find the electric field strength (b) 15 cm from the wire axis, not near either end and (c) 350 m from the wire. Make suitable approximations in both cases.

54. Figure 23-46 shows a thin rod of length ℓ carrying charge Q distributed uniformly over its length. (a) What is the line charge density on the rod? (b) What must be the electric field direction on the rod's perpendicular bisector (taken to be the y axis)? (c) Modify the calculation of Example 23-9 to find an expression for the electric field at a point P a distance y along the perpendicular bisector. (d) Show that your result for (c) reduces to the field of a point charge Q for $y \gg \ell$.

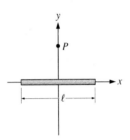

FIGURE 23-46 Problem 54.

Section 23-6 Matter in Electric Fields

55. In his famous 1909 experiment that demonstrated quantization of electric charge, R. A. Millikan suspended small oil drops in an electric field. With a field strength of 20 MN/C, what mass drop can be suspended when the drop carries a net charge of 10 elementary charges?

56. How strong an electric field is needed to accelerate electrons in a TV tube from rest to one-tenth the speed of light in a distance of 5.0 cm?

57. A proton moving to the right at 3.8×10^5 m/s enters a region where a 56 kN/C electric field points to the left. (a) How far will the proton get before its speed reaches zero? (b) Describe its subsequent motion.

58. An oscilloscope display requires that a beam of electrons moving at 8.2 Mm/s be deflected through an angle of 22° by a uniform electric field that occupies a region 5.0 cm long. What should be the field strength?

59. An ink-jet printer works by "steering" charged ink drops to the right place on the page by passing moving drops through a uniform electric field that deflects them by the appropriate amount. Figure 23-47 shows an ink drop approaching the field region, which has length ℓ and width d between the charged plates that establish the field. Find an expression for the minimum speed a drop with mass m and

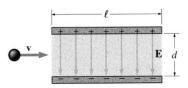

FIGURE 23-47 Problem 59.

charge q must have if it is to get through the region without hitting either plate.

60. An electrostatic analyzer like that of Example 23-11 has $b = 7.5$ cm. What should be the value of E_0 if the device is to select protons moving at 84 km/s?

61. An electron is moving in a circular path around a long, uniformly charged wire carrying 2.5 nC/m. What is the electron's speed?

62. Figure 23-48 shows a device its inventor claims will separate isotopes of a particular element. (Isotopes of the same element have nuclei with the same charge but different masses). Atoms of the element are first stripped completely of their electrons, then accelerated from rest through an electric field chosen to give the desired isotope exactly the right speed to pass through the electrostatic analyzer (see Example 23-11). Prove that the device won't work—that is, that it won't separate different isotopes.

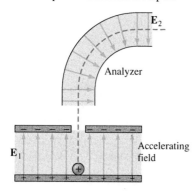

FIGURE 23-48 An isotope separator that won't work (Problem 62).

63. What is the line charge density on a long wire if a 6.8-μg particle carrying 2.1 nC describes a circular orbit about the wire with speed 280 m/s?

64. The electron in a hydrogen atom has kinetic energy 2.18×10^{-18} J. Assuming the electron is in a circular orbit around the central proton, estimate the size of the atom. (Although this problem gives a reasonable answer, the simple model of an electron orbiting a proton is not consonant with the quantum mechanical description of the atom.)

65. A dipole with dipole moment 1.5 nC·m is oriented at 30° to a 4.0-MN/C electric field. (a) What is the magnitude of the torque on the dipole? (b) How much work is required to rotate the dipole until it's antiparallel to the field?

66. A molecule has its dipole moment aligned with a 1.2-kN/C electric field. If it takes 3.1×10^{-27} J to reverse the molecule's orientation, what is its dipole moment?

67. Two identical dipoles, each of charge q and separation a, are a distance x apart as shown in Fig. 23-49. By considering forces between pairs of charges in the different dipoles, calculate the net force between the dipoles. (a) Show that, in the limit $a \ll x$, the force has magnitude $6kp^2/x^4$, where $p = qa$ is the dipole moment. (b) Is the force attractive or repulsive?

FIGURE 23-49 Problem 67.

68. A dipole with charges $\pm q$ and separation $2a$ is located a distance x from a point charge $+Q$, with its dipole moment vector perpendicular to the x axis, as shown in Fig. 23-50. Find expressions for the magnitude of (a) the net torque and (b) the net force on the dipole, both in the limit $x \gg a$. (c) What is the direction of the net force?

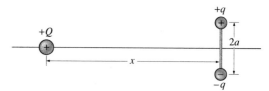

FIGURE 23-50 Problem 68.

Paired Problems

(Both problems in a pair involve the same principles and techniques. If you can get the first problem, you should be able to solve the second one.)

69. An electron is at the origin and an ion with charge $+5e$ is at $x = 10$ nm. Find a point where the electric field is zero.

70. A proton is at the origin and an ion is at $x = 5.0$ nm. If the electric field is zero at $x = -6.83$ nm, what is the charge on the ion?

71. A thin rod of length ℓ has its left end at $x = -\ell$ and its right end at the origin. It carries a line charge density given by $\lambda = \lambda_0 \dfrac{x^2}{\ell^2}$, where λ_0 is a constant. Find the electric field at the origin.

72. Repeat the preceding problem for the case when $\lambda = \lambda_0 \dfrac{x^4}{\ell^4}$.

73. A thin, flexible rod carrying charge Q spread uniformly over its length is bent into a quarter circle of radius a, as shown in Fig. 23-51a. Find the electric field strength at the point P, which is the center of the circle. *Hint:* Consult Problem 50.

74. A thin, flexible rod carrying charge Q spread uniformly over its length is bent into a circular arc of radius a, as shown in Fig. 23-51b. Find the electric field strength at the point P, which is the center of the circular arc.

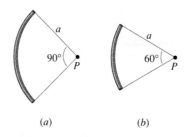

FIGURE 23-51 Problems 73, 74.

75. Ink-jet printers work by deflecting moving ink droplets with an electric field so they hit the right place on the paper. Droplets in a particular printer have mass 1.1×10^{-10} kg, charge 2.1 pC, speed 12 m/s, and pass through a uniform 97-kN/C electric field in order to be deflected through a 10° angle. What is the length of the field region?

76. If the drop speed in the printer of Problem 75 is doubled, what should be done to the electric field to have the drops hit the same point on the paper?

Supplementary Problems

77. A spring of spring constant 100 N/m is stretched 10 cm beyond its 90-cm equilibrium length. If you want to keep it stretched by attaching equal electric charges to the opposite ends, what magnitude of charge should you use?

78. Two small spheres with the same mass m and charge q are suspended from massless strings of length ℓ, as shown in Fig. 23-52. Each string makes an angle θ with the vertical. Show that the charge on each sphere is $q = \pm 2\ell \sin \theta \sqrt{mg \tan \theta / k}$.

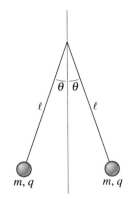

FIGURE 23-52 Problem 78.

79. A charge $-q$ and a charge $\frac{4}{9}q$ are located a distance a apart, as shown in Fig. 23-53. Where would you place a third charge so that all three are in static equilibrium? What should be the sign and magnitude of the third charge?

FIGURE 23-53 Problem 79.

80. Two 34-μC charges are attached to the opposite ends of a spring of spring constant 150 N/m and equilibrium length 50 cm. By how much does the spring stretch?

81. A 3.8-g particle with a 4.0-μC charge experiences a downward force of 0.24 N in a uniform electric field. Find the

electric field, assuming that the gravitational force is *not* negligible.

82. A rod of length 2ℓ lies on the x axis, centered on the origin. It carries a line charge density given by $\lambda = \lambda_0 \dfrac{x}{\ell}$, where λ_0 is a constant. (a) What is the net charge on the rod? (b) Find an expression for electric field strength at all points $x > \ell$. (c) Show that your result has the $1/x^3$ dependence of a dipole field when $x \gg \ell$. *Hint:* For $\ell \ll x$, $\ln\left(\dfrac{x-\ell}{x+\ell}\right)$ becomes approximately $-\dfrac{2\ell}{x} - \dfrac{2\ell^3}{3x^3}$. (d) By comparing with Equation 23-7b, determine the dipole moment of the rod.

83. The electric field on the axis of a uniformly charged ring has magnitude 380 kN/C at a point 5.0 cm from the ring center. The magnitude 15 cm from the center is 160 kN/C; in both cases the field points away from the ring. Find the radius and charge of the ring.

84. Use the binomial theorem to show that, for $x \gg R$, the result of Problem 48 reduces to the field of a point charge whose total charge is the charge density σ times the disk area.

85. A molecule with dipole moment p is located a distance r from a proton, oriented with its dipole moment vector **p** as shown in Fig. 23-54. (a) Use Equation 23-7b to find the force the molecule exerts on the proton. (b) Now find the net force on the molecule in the proton's nonuniform electric field by considering that the molecule consists of two opposite charges $\pm q$, separated by a distance d such that $qd = p$. Take the limit as d becomes very small compared with r, and show that the resulting force has the same magnitude as that of part (a), as required by Newton's third law.

FIGURE 23-54 Problem 85.

86. An *electric quadrupole* consists of two oppositely directed dipoles in close proximity. (a) Calculate the field of the quadrupole shown in Fig. 23-55 for points to the right of $x = a$, and (b) show that for $x \gg a$ the quadrupole field falls off as $1/x^4$.

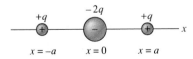

FIGURE 23-55 Problem 86.

87. Derive Equation 23-9 in Example 23-9 by making θ the integration variable, then evaluating the resulting integral.

24 Gauss's Law

Huge sparks jump to the operator's cage in the Hall of Electricity at the Boston Museum of Science. But the operator is unharmed, for reasons that will become evident in this chapter.

W e've seen how it's possible, in principle, to calculate the electric field of any charge distribution by summing the contributions of the many individual charges comprising the distribution. But in practice that process involves a vector integration that becomes difficult for all but the simplest charge distributions. How can we hope to calculate the field of a solid ball of charge, for example, when the individual charge elements are varying distances from the field point and their field vectors point in different directions (Fig. 24-1)?

In this chapter we introduce an elegant way of describing electric fields that makes almost trivial the calculation of fields from certain charge distributions. In the process we will formulate one of the four fundamental laws of electromagnetism—a statement that is equivalent to Coulomb's law but that gives deeper insights into the behavior of the electric field.

24-1 ELECTRIC FIELD LINES

The electric field is a set of vectors defined at all points in space, and we've therefore been representing fields by drawing a number of field vectors. A simpler way to visualize electric fields is with **electric field lines**, continuous lines whose direction is everywhere that of the electric field. To draw a field line, start at some point, and determine the field direction there. Move a small distance in the direction of the field, and evaluate the field direction at the new point. Extending this process in both directions from the starting point traces out an electric field line. The resulting line is a path whose direction at any point is that of the electric field at that point. Drawing many such lines gives a visualization of the overall field structure.

Tracing the field lines of a point charge is particularly simple. Starting at any point near a positive point charge, we find field vectors pointing radially outward from the charge. Move a little way outward, and the field still points in the same direction. So the field lines are straight lines, starting at the point charge and extending radially outward indefinitely (Fig. 24-2).

Field lines show the direction of the field, but what about its magnitude? In Fig. 24-2 the field lines spread apart as they extend farther from the point charge. Coulomb's law tells us that the field weakens farther from the charge. So in Fig. 24-2 the field is stronger where the lines are closer and weaker where they're farther apart. This is generally true, and allows us to infer relative field strength as well as field direction from field line pictures. ActivPhysics Activity 11.4 draws field lines for a point charge.

To trace the field lines of charge distributions, we follow the net field—the vector sum of the field contributions from all the charges in the distribution. Usually the direction of the field varies as we move along a field line, so the line itself is curved. Nevertheless, closeness of the field lines remains a measure of the

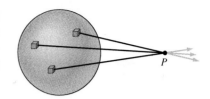

FIGURE 24-1 It would be difficult to find the field of a charged ball by summing vectorially the contributions of all the individual charge elements, three of which are shown here.

11.4
Electric Field: Point Charge

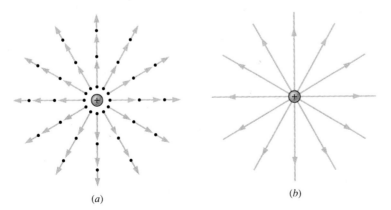

(a)   *(b)*

FIGURE 24-2 Vectors and field lines provide two ways to visualize the electric field. (*a*) The vector picture, introduced in the preceding chapter, uses individual field vectors drawn at selected points. Each vector gives the magnitude and direction of the field at that point, with the length of the arrow representing the magnitude. (*b*) Field lines are continuous lines that have the same direction as the field. For the point charge shown here, the field lines start at the charge and extend to infinity. The field magnitude is larger where the lines are closer together.

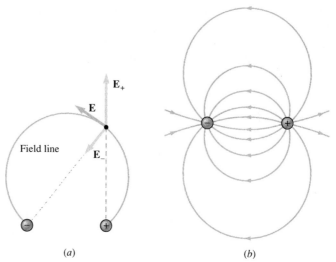

(a)   (b)

FIGURE 24-3 (a) Tracing a field line for an electric dipole. At each point the direction of the field line is that of the *net* electric field $\mathbf{E} = \mathbf{E}_+ + \mathbf{E}_-$. (b) Tracing several field lines gives an overall sense of the dipole field. Near each charge the field has the radial structure of a point-charge field, but farther away the influence of both charges becomes important and the field lines curve. Field is stronger where field lines are closer—namely, near the charges and in the region between them.

field strength. Figure 24-3 shows some field lines for a dipole; you can see immediately from Fig. 24-3b that the field is strongest near the individual charges and in the region directly between them.

You might argue that "closeness of field lines" is vague because the electric field exists everywhere and therefore we can always draw as many field lines as we want. To make the field-line picture more precise, we associate a fixed number of field lines with a charge of given magnitude. In Fig. 24-4, for example, eight field

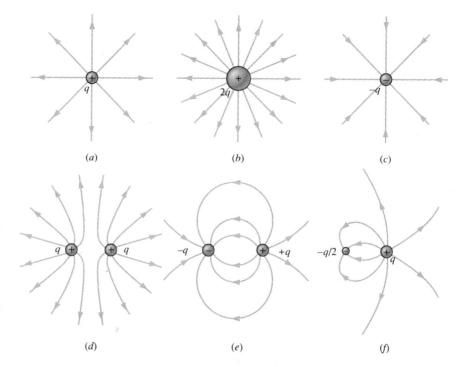

FIGURE 24-4 Field lines for (a) a positive charge q, (b) 2q, (c) −q, (d) two identical charges q, (e) a dipole, consisting of two equal but opposite charges ±q, and (f) opposite and unequal charges q and −q/2. In each drawing eight lines are used to represent a charge of magnitude q. Note in (d) and (f) that the field at large distances begins to resemble that of a single point charge.

lines correspond to a charge of magnitude q. Then eight lines *begin* on the *positive* charge $+q$ (Fig. 24-4a), and 16 on $+2q$ (Fig. 24-4b). Eight lines *end* on the *negative* charge $-q$ in Fig. 24-4c. Figures 24-4d–f show the fields of some two-charge distributions, drawn with the same eight-line convention. Note that field lines always *begin* on *positive* charges and *end* on *negative* charges. Activ-Physics Activity 11.6 draws field lines for other two-charge distributions of your choice.

11.6
Electric Field

24-2 ELECTRIC FLUX

Counting Field Lines

Figure 24-5 shows the charge distributions of Fig. 24-4, each surrounded by several surfaces. (The figure shows only the two-dimensional cross section of each surface.) Each surface is closed, meaning it's impossible to get from inside to outside without crossing the surface. We now ask a simple question: How many field lines emerge from inside each surface?

In Fig. 24-5a the answer for surfaces 1 and 2 is obvious: eight. With surface 3 one field line crosses three times, twice going out and once going in. If we count a field line going inward as negative, then the algebraic sum of field lines is again eight. In fact, any *closed* surface you can draw around $+q$ will have eight field lines emerging from within. That's because eight lines begin on the charge and extend indefinitely outward, so they cross *any* closed surface surrounding the charge.

What about surface 4? Two lines cross going inward and two going outward, so the net number of field lines emerging from this surface is zero. What's different about surface 4 is that it doesn't enclose the charge. By drawing other surfaces you can convince yourself that any surface not enclosing the charge will have as many lines going in as out, and will therefore have zero net field lines emerging.

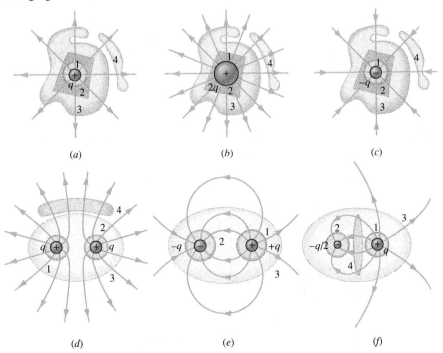

(a)   (b)   (c)

(d)   (e)   (f)

FIGURE 24-5 In all cases, the number of field lines emerging from a closed surface is proportional to the charge enclosed.

Figure 24-5*b* is identical except that now those surfaces enclosing the charge have 16 field lines emerging, reflecting the greater magnitude of the charge. Surfaces that don't enclose the charge still have zero net field lines emerging. Figure 24-5*c* is also like Fig. 24-5*a*, except that now the charge is negative so all field lines point inward. According to our sign convention, -8 field lines emerge from any surface enclosing the charge $-q$.

In Fig. 24-5*d*, surfaces 1 and 2 each enclose one of the charges q, and each has eight field lines emerging. Surface 3 encloses *both* charges, for a total enclosed charge $+2q$, and has 16 field lines emerging. Finally, surface 4 encloses no charge and has zero net field lines emerging.

On to Fig. 24-5*e*, the dipole. Surface 1 encloses charge q and has eight field lines emerging. Surface 2 encloses $-q$ and has -8 field lines emerging. Surface 3 encloses both $+q$ and $-q$, giving zero net charge enclosed. And as many field lines enter surface 3 as leave it, giving zero net field lines emerging.

Finally, in Fig. 24-5*f* eight field lines emerge from surface 1—and that surface encloses $+q$. Surface 2 encloses $-q/2$, and has -4 field lines emerging. Surface 3 encloses both charges, for a net enclosed charge $+q/2$—and four field lines emerge from this surface. Surface 4 encloses no charge and has zero net field lines emerging.

Counting the field lines in Fig. 24-5 leads to a simple statement about how electric fields must behave:

> **The number of electric field lines emerging from any closed surface is proportional to the charge enclosed.**

This statement is very general: It doesn't matter what shape the surface is or whether the enclosed charge is a single point charge or a lot of charges adding to the same net charge. Nor does it matter how the charges are arranged, as long as they're *enclosed* by the surface in question. And the presence of charges *outside* the surface doesn't alter the conclusion about the number of field lines emerging—although it may alter the shape of the individual lines. You can explore this statement as applied to the fields of two-charge distributions using ActivPhysics Activity 11.6.

We'll now rephrase our statement in a more mathematically rigorous way, obtaining one of the four fundamental laws of electromagnetism.

Tip

Remember Fig. 24-5 As we define new terms and write equations involving integrals, remember that the mathematics just reflects in a concise way what's clear from Fig. 24-5—that the number of field lines emerging from a closed surface depends only on the net charge enclosed. Go back to that figure any time you begin to lose the physical significance of the mathematics.

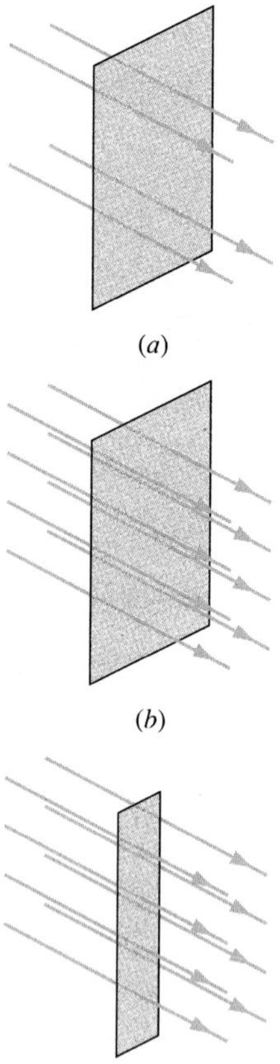

(a)

(b)

(c)

FIGURE 24-6 (*a*) Four field lines cross the surface shown. (*b*) Here the field strength has doubled, and eight lines cross the surface. (*c*) With the same field strength as in (*b*), but with half the area, only four lines cross the surface. In general, the number of field lines crossing a surface is proportional to the surface area and to the field strength.

Electric Flux

We can make the "number of field lines" more rigorous with Fig. 24-6, which shows several flat surfaces in uniform electric fields. Study the figure and its caption, and you'll see that the number of field lines crossing each surface is

FIGURE 24-7 The number of field lines crossing a surface also depends on the surface orientation relative to the field **E**. The orientation is specified by a vector **A** normal to the surface. In (a) the surface is perpendicular to the field, so **A** and **E** are parallel; then $\theta = 0$, $\cos\theta = 1$, and the number of field lines crossing the surface is a maximum. In (b) the surface is parallel to the field, so **A** and **E** are perpendicular; here $\theta = 90°$, $\cos\theta = 0$, and no lines cross the surface. (c) In general, the number of field lines varies as $\cos\theta$, where θ is the angle between **E** and **A**.

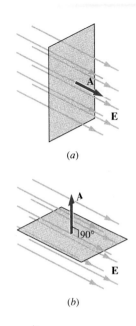

(a)

(b)

proportional to the surface area A and the field strength E. Figure 24-7 shows that it also depends on the orientation of the surface, specified by a vector normal to the surface. As Fig. 24-7 suggests, the number of field lines crossing the surface is proportional to the cosine of the angle between that normal vector **A** and the field **E**. Putting this all together, we have

$$\text{Number of field lines} \propto E\,A\cos\theta.$$

The quantity on the right-hand side of this equation has a definite value that captures the spirit of the more vague expression "number of field lines crossing a surface." We call this quantity the **electric flux**, ϕ, through the surface. If we make the magnitude of the surface normal vector **A** equal to the surface area A, then we can define the flux compactly using the vector dot product:

$$\phi = \mathbf{E} \cdot \mathbf{A}, \tag{24-1}$$

where the dot product, defined in Chapter 7, is the product of the two vector magnitudes with the cosine of the angle between them. Since the units of **E** are N/C, flux is measured in N·m²/C.

For the open surfaces of Fig. 24-6 and 24-7 there's an ambiguity in the sign of ϕ, since we could have taken **A** in either of the two directions along the perpendicular to the surface. But for *closed* surfaces, we unambiguously define the direction of **A** as that of the outward-pointing normal to the surface.

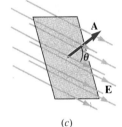

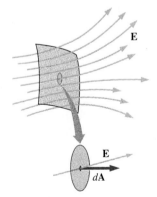

(c)

Tip

The Flux Is Not the Field The flux ϕ and field **E** are related but distinct quantities. The field is a vector defined at each point in space. Flux is a global property of the field, depending not on a single point but on how the field behaves over an extended surface. Unlike field, flux is a scalar quantity; it's simply a quantification of the "amount of field" or "number of field lines" crossing a surface.

What if a surface is curved and/or the field varies with position? Then we divide the surface into many small patches, each small enough that it's essentially flat and that the field is essentially uniform over each (Fig. 24-8). If a patch has area dA, then Equation 24-1 gives the flux through it:

$$d\phi = \mathbf{E} \cdot d\mathbf{A},$$

where the vector $d\mathbf{A}$ is normal to the patch. The total flux through the surface is then the sum over all the patches. If we make the patches arbitrarily small that sum becomes an integral, and the flux is

$$\phi = \int_{\text{surface}} \mathbf{E} \cdot d\mathbf{A}. \tag{24-2}$$

FIGURE 24-8 Even though the surface is curved and the field varies, a small enough patch of surface is essentially flat and the field is uniform over it, so the flux through the patch is $d\phi = \mathbf{E} \cdot d\mathbf{A}$.

FIGURE 24-9 What's the flux through each of the cube faces shown?

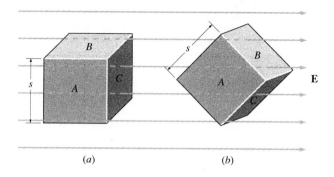

(a)   (b)

The limits of the integral range over the entire surface, picking up contributions from all the patches $d\mathbf{A}$. Although the integral can be difficult to evaluate, we'll find it most useful in cases where its evaluation is almost trivial. Again, remember what Equation 24-2 means: The flux ϕ simply serves as a more precise measure of the "number of field lines" crossing a surface.

Got It!

Figure 24-9 shows a cube of side s in a uniform electric field $\mathbf{E}$. What is the flux through each of the three cube faces A, B, C with the cube oriented as in (a)? Repeat for the orientation in (b), where the cube has been rotated through 45°.

24-3 GAUSS'S LAW

We showed in the preceding section that the number of field lines emerging from a closed surface is proportional to the charge enclosed. Now that we've developed electric flux to express more rigorously the notion "number of field lines," we can state the following:

> **The electric flux through any closed surface is proportional to the charge en-closed by that surface.**

Writing the same thing mathematically gives

$$\phi = \oint \mathbf{E} \cdot d\mathbf{A} \propto q_{\text{enclosed}},$$

where the circle on the integral sign indicates that the integral is over a *closed* surface.

To evaluate the proportionality between flux and enclosed charge, consider a positive point charge q and a spherical surface of radius r centered on the charge (Fig. 24-10a). The flux through this surface is given by Equation 24-2:

$$\phi = \oint \mathbf{E} \cdot d\mathbf{A} = \oint E \, dA \cos\theta.$$

But Fig. 24-10b shows that the surface normal $d\mathbf{A}$ and the electric field $\mathbf{E}$ are parallel at any point on the sphere, so $\cos\theta = 1$. Since the electric field varies as

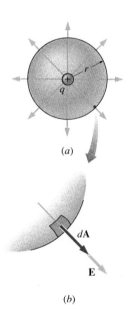

(a)

(b)

FIGURE 24-10 (a) The electric field of a point charge has the same magnitude everywhere on a spherical surface centered on the charge. (b) At each point on the surface the field and the surface normal $d\mathbf{A}$ are parallel.

$1/r^2$ its magnitude is the same everywhere at the fixed radius r of our sphere. Thus, we can take E outside the integral, giving

$$\phi = \oint_{\text{sphere}} E\, dA = E \oint_{\text{sphere}} dA = E(4\pi r^2),$$

where the last step follows because $\oint dA$ just means the surface area of the sphere. Now, the electric field of a point charge is given by Equation 23-4: $E = kq/r^2$. So we have

$$\phi = E(4\pi r^2) = \left(\frac{kq}{r^2}\right)(4\pi r^2) = 4\pi kq.$$

Since the point charge q is the only charge inside our spherical surface, we see that the proportionality constant between flux and enclosed charge is just $4\pi k$.

Before proceeding, we introduce the so-called permittivity constant, ε_0, defined by the relation

$$\varepsilon_0 = \frac{1}{4\pi k}, \tag{24-3}$$

where k is the Coulomb constant. The value of ε_0 is 8.85×10^{-12} C^2/N·m^2.

Tip

Why Two Constants? There's no physics in Equation 24-3; it's just a definition of a new symbol. The SI unit system requires a proportionality constant in Coulomb's law or, equivalently, in the relation between flux and enclosed charge. The value of that constant conveys information about the strength of the electric force. That same information is contained in the constants k and ε_0; both are different ways of expressing the same thing. That there are two constants in use is purely a historical artifact, and we switch now from k to ε_0 only because doing so makes subsequent formulas simpler. It would have been better to define the units of electric charge so that Coulomb's law didn't need a proportionality constant. There are unit systems where that's done—but they aren't the internationally adopted SI system.

In terms of the new constant ε_0, the proportionality $4\pi k$ between flux and enclosed charge becomes $1/\varepsilon_0$. So our statement that the flux through any closed surface is proportional to the net charge enclosed becomes

$$\oint \mathbf{E} \cdot d\mathbf{A} = \frac{q_{\text{enclosed}}}{\varepsilon_0}. \quad \text{(Gauss's law)} \tag{24-4}$$

Here the integral is taken over *any closed surface,* and q_{enclosed} is the charge enclosed *by that surface.*

Equation 24-4 is **Gauss's law**, after the German mathematician Karl Friedrich Gauss (1777–1855). Gauss's law is one of four fundamental relations that govern the behavior of electromagnetic fields throughout the universe. Whether you journey into a star in some remote galaxy, down among the strands of a DNA molecule, or into the microprocessor chip at the heart of your computer, you will

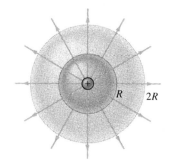

FIGURE 24-11 The outer sphere has twice the radius of the inner sphere, and thus four times the surface area. Since the same number of field lines crosses both spheres, the density of field lines at the outer sphere has one-fourth its value at the inner sphere. Thus the field-line density accurately reflects the inverse-square falloff of the electric field. If the inverse-square law did not hold, we would have to begin new field lines (or stop them) at different distances from the point charge, and the number of field lines crossing a surface would not depend only on the enclosed charge.

find that the flux of the electric field through any closed surface depends only on the enclosed charge. In over a century of experiments, no electric field has ever been observed to violate Gauss's law.

We stress that Gauss's law, although clothed in the mathematical finery of a surface integral, is just a more rigorous way of saying what's clear in Fig. 24-5: that the number of field lines emerging from a closed surface is proportional to the enclosed charge.

Gauss and Coulomb

Gauss's law and Coulomb's law look completely different, but they're actually equivalent. Figure 24-11 shows that the heart of this equivalence is the inverse-square law. The figure shows two spherical surfaces surrounding a point charge q. Gauss's law tells us that the flux through each surface is the same, and is equal to q/ε_0. But why? Because, as our arguments leading to Gauss's law show, the flux through a spherical surface of radius r centered on a point charge is the product of the surface area $4\pi r^2$ with the electric field strength E at the surface. But Coulomb's law says that the electric field drops off as $1/r^2$. As r increases, the surface area grows as r^2, but the $1/r^2$ decrease in field strength just compensates, giving a constant value for the flux that depends only on the enclosed charge. If the inverse-square law (e.g., Coulomb's law) didn't hold, then the flux would not be constant and Gauss's law wouldn't hold either.

It's also the inverse-square law that makes electric field line pictures useful for visualizing fields. Field lines begin or end only on charges; otherwise they go off to infinity. As the field lines of a point charge spread in three dimensions, the number crossing any spherical surface (or any closed surface, for that matter) remains the same. But larger spheres have larger surface areas, in proportion to r^2—and that means the density of field lines drops as $1/r^2$, accurately reflecting the strength of the field. If the inverse-square law didn't hold, we would have to start additional field lines beyond the point charge (or stop them) to represent the field strength quantitatively, and thus the number of field lines crossing a closed surface would not remain the same. Once again, the inverse-square law (Coulomb) and the relation between flux and enclosed charge (Gauss) are intimately connected. Incidentally, field-line pictures printed in a book or drawn on a blackboard generally cannot be quantitatively correct because they don't show the spreading of field lines in all three dimensions.

We've been talking here only about isolated point charges, but we emphasize that Gauss's law applies to *all* electric fields, no matter how complicated the charge distributions producing them. That's because of the superposition principle. We already know that superposition allows us to add vectorially the electric fields described individually by Coulomb's law for the point-charge field. Since Gauss's and Coulomb's law are equivalent, our argument leading to Gauss's law still applies when the field **E** is a superposition of point-charge fields.

Got It!

A spherical surface surrounds an isolated point charge. If a second point charge is brought to a point just outside the surface, will the flux through the surface change? Will the electric field at points on the surface change?

24-4 USING GAUSS'S LAW

Gauss's law is true for *any* surface enclosing *any* charge distribution; it's a universal statement of how electric fields everywhere must behave. In a few specialized cases Gauss's law can be used to calculate the electric field. In those cases, which we treat in this section, Gauss provides a powerful alternative to Coulomb's law, an alternative that makes electric-field calculations much easier. But despite this section's emphasis on using Gauss's law to calculate the field, remember that the law holds *universally,* even in cases where it's not useful for field calculations.

We can use Gauss to calculate the field when it's possible to evaluate the flux integral without actually knowing **E**. That happens only when the charge distribution has sufficient symmetry. We now illustrate the use of Gauss's law for three important symmetries.

Spherical Symmetry

A charge distribution is spherically symmetric if the charge density depends only on the distance from a central point. A point charge, a uniformly charged solid sphere, and a spherical surface carrying uniform surface charge density are all spherically symmetric charge distributions. Spherical symmetry implies that the magnitude of the electric field depends only on the distance r from the center of symmetry, and that the field direction is radial (Fig. 24-12).

Gauss's law relates the electric flux through a closed surface to the enclosed charge. The law holds for *any* surface whatsoever, provided it's a *closed* surface. The surface over which we're evaluating the flux is called a **gaussian surface**; it's not a real, physical surface but just an imaginary, mathematical surface that we envision for the purpose of applying Gauss's law. Although Gauss holds for *any* surface, it's useful for calculating electric fields only for surfaces that share the symmetry of the charge distribution.

In the case of spherical symmetry, the appropriate surface is a sphere of arbitrary radius r centered on the point of symmetry. Two such surfaces are shown in Fig. 24-13. With spherical symmetry, the magnitude E of the electric field must be the same everywhere on such a gaussian sphere. Furthermore, **E** is everywhere in the same direction as the perpendicular to the surface, so $\cos\theta = 1$. Thus, although the direction of **E** and of the surface vary, the product $E\cos\theta$ remains constant and is simply the field magnitude E. Then the flux through a gaussian sphere becomes

$$\phi = \oint \mathbf{E} \cdot d\mathbf{A} = \oint E\cos\theta \, dA = E \oint dA = 4\pi r^2 E, \qquad (24\text{-}5)$$

where the last step follows because $\oint dA$ is just the surface area of the sphere, $4\pi r^2$. This expression for the flux does not depend on the details of the charge distribution, so long as it is spherically symmetric.

Gauss's law says that the flux through the sphere is given by $q_{\text{enclosed}}/\varepsilon_0$, where q_{enclosed} is the net charge enclosed *by the sphere.* Suppose our spherically symmetric charge distribution carries total charge Q and has radius R. That is, whatever the particular distribution of charge for $r \leq R$, there is no charge at $r > R$. For any gaussian sphere with $r > R$, like the surface 1 in Fig. 24-13,

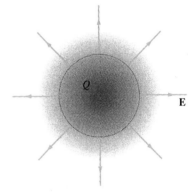

FIGURE 24-12 For a spherically symmetric charge distribution, the field vectors at a given radius all have the same magnitude and point in the radial direction—outward for a positive charge, as shown, or inward for a negative charge.

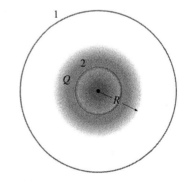

FIGURE 24-13 Two gaussian surfaces surrounding a spherical charge distribution. Surface 1 lies outside the distribution, and encloses all the charge Q. Surface 2 lies inside the distribution, and encloses only part of the charge.

FIGURE 24-14 Hairs on a highly charged person's head trace out the electric field. The essentially spherical head produces a field like that of a point charge.

the enclosed charge is the total charge Q. Equating the flux in Equation 24-5 to Q/ε_0 gives

$$4\pi r^2 E = \frac{Q}{\varepsilon_0},$$

or

$$E = \frac{1}{4\pi\varepsilon_0}\frac{Q}{r^2} = \frac{kQ}{r^2}, \quad (r > R) \tag{24-6}$$

where the last step follows because $1/4\pi\varepsilon_0$ is just the Coulomb constant, k. But this is just the field of a point charge! Equation 24-6 says that *outside* any spherically symmetric distribution of charge, the field is identical to that of a point charge located at the center of symmetry (Fig. 24-14). This is *not* an approximation—it is exactly true right up to the surface $r = R$! Imagine how hard it would have been to calculate this field using the superposition principle! Yet somehow all the charge elements throughout the spherically symmetric distribution produce $d\mathbf{E}$'s that add vectorially to give the same field as a single point charge. Like Gauss's law itself, this result is a manifestation of the inverse-square force law.

The field *inside* the charge distribution depends on how charge is distributed. This is because a gaussian sphere with $r < R$, such as surface 2 of Fig. 24-13, does not enclose the entire charge Q. How much it encloses depends on the charge distribution. In the examples below, we consider two important special cases.

EXAMPLE 24-1	*A Uniformly Charged Sphere*

A total charge Q is spread uniformly throughout a sphere of radius R. What is the electric field at all points in space?

Solution

This charge distribution is spherically symmetric, so the field for $r > R$ is like that of a point charge, given by Equation 24-6.

Inside the charged sphere, our gaussian surface is a sphere like surface 2 in Fig. 24-13. Equation 24-5 for the flux still holds, but now the charge enclosed is some fraction of Q. What fraction? The volume of the sphere is $\frac{4}{3}\pi R^3$, and it contains a total charge Q. Since charge is spread uniformly throughout the sphere, the volume charge density is given by

$$\rho = \frac{Q}{V} = \frac{Q}{\frac{4}{3}\pi R^3}.$$

Then the charge enclosed by our gaussian sphere of radius r is just the volume of that sphere multiplied by the volume charge density:

$$q_{\text{enclosed}} = V\rho = \frac{4}{3}\pi r^3 \frac{Q}{\frac{4}{3}\pi R^3} = Q\frac{r^3}{R^3}.$$

Equating the flux from Equation 24-5 to $q_{\text{enclosed}}/\varepsilon_0$, we have

$$4\pi r^2 E = \frac{Qr^3}{\varepsilon_0 R^3},$$

or

$$E = \frac{1}{4\pi\varepsilon_0}\frac{Qr}{R^3} = \frac{\rho r}{3\varepsilon_0}, \quad (r < R) \tag{24-7}$$

where we've written the field in terms of both the total charge Q and the charge density $\rho = Q/\frac{4}{3}\pi R^3$. Equation 24-7 shows that the field *inside* the charge distribution increases linearly with distance from the center. This result is entirely consistent with the inverse-square law for point charges. Although the field of each charge element decreases as $1/r^2$, in this case the amount of charge enclosed increases more rapidly—as r^3—resulting in a field that increases linearly with r. Figure 24-15 shows the combined results for the fields both inside and outside the sphere. The field direction is, of course, radial, pointing outward if Q is positive and inward if Q is negative.

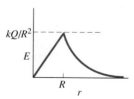

FIGURE 24-15 Field strength versus radial distance for a uniformly charged sphere of radius R. For $r > R$ the field has the inverse-square dependence of a point-charge field.

| EXAMPLE 24-2 | *A Thin Spherical Shell* |

The thin spherical shell of radius R shown in Fig. 24-16 carries a total charge Q distributed uniformly over its surface. What is the electric field inside and outside the shell?

Solution
Since this distribution is spherically symmetric, we already know that the field outside is just the point-charge field of Equation 24-6.

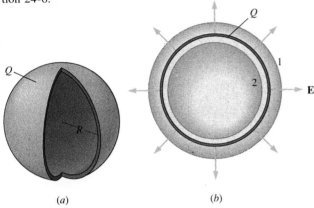

(a)   (b)

FIGURE 24-16 (*a*) A thin spherical shell carries charge Q distributed uniformly over its surface of radius R. (*b*) Cross-sectional view, showing two spherical gaussian surfaces. Surface 1 encloses the entire charge Q, while surface 2 encloses zero charge.

For any gaussian sphere inside the shell, the enclosed charge is zero. Equating the flux from Equation 24-5 to this zero enclosed charge gives

$$4\pi r^2 E = 0$$

so the field is zero everywhere inside the shell! How can this be? Again, it's a manifestation of the inverse-square law. At any point inside the shell, the larger fields of nearby portions of the shell are exactly canceled by the weaker fields of more distant, but more extensive, parts of the shell (Fig. 24-17).

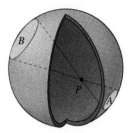

FIGURE 24-17 At any point P inside a charged shell, the field arising from the relatively few but nearby charges in region A is exactly canceled by the field arising from the more numerous but more distant charges in region B.

Got It!

A spherical shell carries a charge Q, uniformly distributed over the shell. If the charge on the shell is doubled, what happens to the electric field (a) inside and (b) outside the shell?

| EXAMPLE 24-3 | *A Point Charge Inside a Shell* |

A point charge $+q$ is at the center of a spherical shell of radius R carrying total charge $-2q$, distributed uniformly over its surface. (a) Draw the electric field lines for this configuration, using eight lines to represent a charge of magnitude q. Find expressions for the field strength for (b) $r < R$ and (c) $r > R$.

Solution
(a) The situation has spherical symmetry and so must the field. Gauss's law tells us that eight field lines must emerge from any surface surrounding $+q$ alone, and that eight field lines must go into any surface surrounding the entire distribution with its net charge $-q$. Fig. 24-18 shows the only way to draw the field that's compatible with Gauss's law. Notice a total of 16 lines end on the charged shell, consistent with its charge of $-2q$.

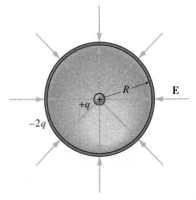

FIGURE 24-18 Field lines for a charge q surrounded by shell carrying $-2q$ (Example 24-3).

(b) For $r < R$ we're inside the shell, so the enclosed charge is just q. Solving Equation 24-4 for E then gives

$$E = \frac{kq}{r^2}.$$

What about the shell? Didn't we forget to take it into account? No! The shell and its charge are *irrelevant* as long as they preserve the spherical symmetry. Example 24-2 showed that the field inside a charged shell *due to the shell itself* is zero. Here we're inside the shell, so the only field we see is that of the point charge.

(c) Outside the shell, a spherical gaussian surface encloses net charge $-q$, so the field we see is that of a point charge $-q$; it has magnitude $E = q/4\pi\varepsilon_0 r^2$, and points radially inward.

What about the field at $r = R$? That's ambiguous; just inside the shell the field points outward, while just outside it points inward. In fact, the field undergoes a discontinuous jump across the infinitesimally thin surface charge layer on the shell.

Tip

Trust Gauss Gauss's law says that the flux—or number of field lines—emerging from any closed surface depends *only* on the *enclosed* charge—not on any other charge that may happen to be outside the surface. (Consult Fig. 24-5 to convince yourself of this.) *When there is enough symmetry* that often means that external charges are totally irrelevant in a field calculation, as is the shell in Example 24-3 for points with $r < R$. *But symmetry matters*: Without enough symmetry, zero net charge inside a gaussian surface is *not* sufficient to ensure that the field on the surface is zero (Fig. 24-19).

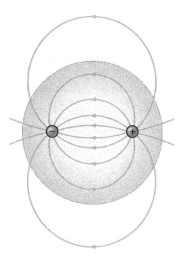

FIGURE 24-19 The net charge enclosed by the gaussian sphere (gray) is zero, but the field on the sphere is not zero. Here the charge distribution—a dipole—is not spherically symmetric, so Equation 24-5 is not a valid expression for the flux.

EXERCISE A solid sphere 10 cm in radius carries a uniform $40\text{-}\mu\text{C}$ charge distributed throughout its volume. It is surrounded by a concentric shell 20 cm in radius, also uniformly charged with $40\ \mu\text{C}$. Find the electric field (a) 5.0 cm, (b) 15 cm, and (c) 30 cm from the center.

Answers: (a) 18 MN/C; (b) 16 MN/C; (c) 8.0 MN/C

Some problems similar to Examples 24-1 through 24-3: 17–26, 66

Strategy

Using Gauss's Law This section illustrated the steps needed to calculate the electric field using Gauss's law:

1. Study the symmetry to see if you can construct a gaussian surface on which the field magnitude and its direction relative to the surface are constant. (With spherical symmetry that surface was spherical.) If you can't find such a surface then Gauss's law, while still true, won't help in calculating the field.
2. Evaluate the flux. This should be easy because your choice of gaussian surface makes $E\cos\theta$ constant over the surface. This term then comes outside the integral, leaving the integral equal to the surface area.
3. Evaluate the *enclosed* charge. This is not the same as the total charge if the gaussian surface lies *within* the charge distribution.
4. Equate the flux to $q_{\text{enclosed}}/\varepsilon_0$, and solve for E. The direction of $\mathbf{E}$ should be evident from the symmetry.

Once steps 1 and 2 are done for a particular symmetry, you'll have an equation like Equation 24-5 for the flux, and you can jump right to step 3 to calculate the field in a specific case—just as we did in Examples 24-1 and 24-2.

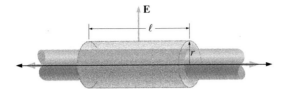

FIGURE 24-20 A positive charge distribution with line symmetry (red) extends infinitely in both directions, and its charge density depends only on the perpendicular distance from the symmetry axis. A cylindrical gaussian surface (gray) of length ℓ and radius r surrounds the charge distribution. Symmetry requires that the electric field on the surface point radially outward, and that the field magnitude E be constant over the surface. With a negative charge the field would point radially inward.

Line Symmetry

A charge distribution has line symmetry when its charge density depends only on the perpendicular distance r from a line, called the symmetry axis (Fig. 24-20). Symmetry then requires that the field point radially and that the field magnitude depend only on distance from the axis. An appropriate gaussian surface is the cylinder of length ℓ and radius r shown in Fig. 24-20. Being radial, field lines don't cross the circular ends of the cylinder, so there's no flux through these ends. The field is everywhere perpendicular to the curved part of the surface, so $\cos\theta = 1$ in the expression for flux through this part. Since the field magnitude is constant at the fixed radius r of the curved surface, the flux becomes

$$\phi = \int \mathbf{E} \cdot d\mathbf{A} = \int E\, dA \cos\theta = E \int dA = 2\pi r \ell E, \qquad (24\text{-}8)$$

where the last step follows because the cylinder "unrolls" into a rectangular sheet of length ℓ and width $2\pi r$ (Fig. 24-21). Since there is no flux through the cylinder ends, Equation 24-8 gives the total flux through our entire gaussian surface. Solving for the electric field in any situation with line symmetry then amounts to equating the flux given in Equation 24-8 to the enclosed charge divided by ε_0, then solving for E—exactly as we did for spherical symmetry using the analogous flux equation, Equation 24-5. There is one quantity in Equation 24-8 that has no analog in Equation 24-5, namely the length ℓ of the gaussian cylinder. As the following examples show, however, that length also appears in the calculation of the enclosed charge, so it always cancels from the final result.

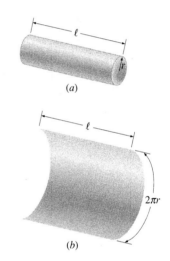

FIGURE 24-21 (*a*) A cylindrical gaussian surface. (*b*) Unrolling the cylinder gives a flat sheet of area $2\pi r \ell$.

EXAMPLE 24-4	*An Infinite Line of Charge*

Use Gauss's law to calculate the electric field of an infinite line carrying line charge density λ.

Solution

This is the same problem we solved in Example 23-9 through a tedious Coulomb's law calculation. With line charge density λ, the charge enclosed by a gaussian cylinder of length ℓ is $q_{\text{enclosed}} = \lambda \ell$. Setting the flux given in Equation 24-8 to $q_{\text{enclosed}}/\varepsilon_0$ and solving for E then gives

$$E = \frac{\lambda \ell}{2\pi \varepsilon_0 r \ell} = \frac{\lambda}{2\pi \varepsilon_0 r}.$$

Since $1/2\pi\varepsilon_0 = 2k$, this is the same result we found in Example 23-9. The Gauss's law calculation is far simpler; symmetry and an intelligent choice of gaussian surface helped us bypass the entire integration of Example 23-9.

Although this problem dealt with an infinitesimally thin charged line, you can see that the same result must hold *outside* any charge distribution with line symmetry. And, as we argued in Example 23-9, the result is a good approximation for long, thin structures of finite length provided we're not too far away nor too close to the ends.

| **EXAMPLE 24-5** | *A Hollow Pipe* |

A thin-walled pipe 3.0 m long and 2.0 cm in radius carries a net charge $q = 5.7\ \mu C$, distributed uniformly over its surface. Find the electric field (a) 8.0 mm and (b) 8.0 cm from the pipe axis, not near either end.

Solution

Since the pipe is much longer than its diameter, we can approximate its field as that of an infinitely long charge distribution with line symmetry.

(a) A point 8.0 mm from the axis lies inside the pipe. An 8.0-mm-radius gaussian cylinder therefore encloses zero net charge; equating the flux from Equation 24-8 to zero then shows that the field at this radius—and indeed anywhere deep within the hollow pipe—is zero.

(b) For a point outside the pipe, a gaussian cylinder of length ℓ encloses charge $\lambda \ell$, where the line charge density λ is $5.7\ \mu C/3.0$ m $= 1.9\ \mu C/m$. Setting the flux from Equation 24-8 to this $q_{enclosed}$ and solving for E then gives

$$E = \frac{q_{enclosed}}{2\pi\varepsilon_0 r \ell} = \frac{\lambda}{2\pi\varepsilon_0 r}$$

$$= \frac{1.9\times10^{-6}\ C/m}{(2\pi)(8.85\times10^{-12}\ C^2/N\cdot m^2)(8.0\times10^{-2}\ m)}$$

$$= 4.3\times10^5\ N/C.$$

In this region the field points radially outward and falls inversely with distance from the axis.

> **Tip**
>
> *That's Distance from the Symmetry Axis* The distance r that arises in applying Gauss's law to situations with spherical or line symmetry is always the distance *from the point or line of symmetry*—as you can see from the derivations of Equations 24-4 and 24-8. Equations for the field are therefore most simply expressed in terms of that distance—*not* in terms of distance from the edge of the charge distribution.

EXERCISE Suppose the pipe in Example 24-5 were surrounded concentrically by a second pipe of the same length and 5.0 cm in diameter. What should be (a) the total charge and (b) the surface charge density (assumed uniform) on this outer pipe in order that there be no electric field outside the entire structure?

Answers: (a) $-5.7\ \mu C$; (b) $-12\ \mu C/m^2$

Some problems similar to Examples 24-4 and 24-5: 28, 29, 31, 32

Plane Symmetry

A charge distribution has plane symmetry when its charge density depends only on the distance from a plane. The only electric-field direction consistent with this symmetry is perpendicular to the symmetry plane (Fig. 24-22). We can evaluate the flux integral in Gauss's law using a gaussian surface with sides perpendicular to the symmetry plane, ends of area A parallel to the plane, and which straddles the symmetry plane to extend equal distances on either side of it (Fig. 24-22). Since no field lines cross the sides, the flux through them is zero. Symmetry of the situation implies that the field magnitude E cannot depend on position parallel to the symmetry plane. Therefore E is uniform over each end of the gaussian cylinder so, with the field perpendicular to the ends, the flux through each end is just EA, where A is the end area. Since the ends are the same distance from the symmetry plane, they must have the same field strength E. The total flux through the gaussian surface is therefore

$$\phi = 2EA. \qquad (24\text{-}9)$$

This equation holds for any charge distribution with plane symmetry; to find the field we evaluate the charge enclosed by the gaussian surface, then apply Gauss's law.

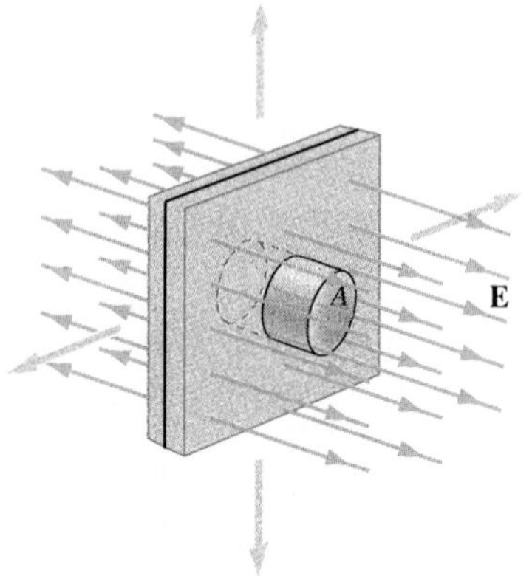

FIGURE 24-22 A charge distribution with plane symmetry. The charge density depends only on the distance from the plane of symmetry (black), and extends infinitely in both directions parallel to that plane. Also shown are the electric field and a gaussian surface with its sides perpendicular and ends parallel to the plane. Dashed lines show that the gaussian surface extends equal distances on both sides of the symmetry plane.

EXAMPLE 24-6	*A Sheet of Charge*

An infinite sheet of charge carries a uniform surface charge density σ. What is the electric field arising from this sheet?

Solution

Since the surface charge density is uniform, this charge distribution has plane symmetry. Figure 24-23 shows the sheet and an appropriate gaussian surface. The sheet area enclosed by the gaussian surface is clearly equal to the end area A. The surface charge density—charge per unit area—is σ, so the enclosed charge is $q_{enclosed} = \sigma A$. Setting $q_{enclosed}/\varepsilon_0$ to the flux $\phi = 2EA$ given by Equation 24-9 and solving for E then gives

$$E = \frac{\sigma}{2\varepsilon_0}. \qquad (24\text{-}10)$$

This simple result says that the field strength does not depend on distance from the sheet. How can this be? By symmetry, the field must point perpendicular to the sheet. There is no charge anywhere but on the sheet, so that's the only place where field lines can begin or end. Therefore the density of field lines—the measure of field strength—is the same everywhere. Figure 24-24 shows how this result is fully consistent with Coulomb's law.

Although this example treated only an infinitesimally thin sheet of charge, we would find a uniform electric field *outside* any charge distribution with plane symmetry. The field *inside* such a distribution would depend on how the charge density varies in the direction perpendicular to the symmetry plane (see Problem 36).

Perfect plane symmetry requires a charge distribution that is infinite in extent. But close to any large, flat, uniformly charged surface and not near an edge, the assumption of plane symmetry becomes a good approximation, and Equation 24-10 becomes reasonably accurate. We make the same approximation when we treat the acceleration of Earth's gravity as a constant; we're neglecting Earth's curvature and therefore its finite size, and approximating its gravitational field as the uniform field of an infinite sheet of mass.

EXERCISE An electron close to a large, flat sheet of charge is repelled from the sheet with a 1.8×10^{-12} N force. Find the surface charge density on the sheet.

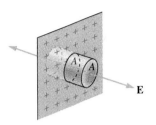

FIGURE 24-23 The area of the charged sheet enclosed by the gaussian surface is the same as the area A of its ends; the enclosed charge is therefore σA.

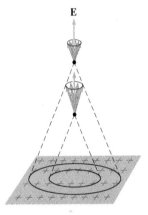

FIGURE 24-24 As we rise above an infinite sheet, the amount of charge within a given angular region increases just enough to compensate for the inverse-square decrease in field strengths of the individual charges. The result is a field that does not depend on distance from the sheet.

Answer: $-200 \ \mu C/m^2$

Some problems similar to Example 24-6: 34–37

24-5 FIELDS OF ARBITRARY CHARGE DISTRIBUTIONS

The examples of Section 24-4 show how easy Gauss's law can sometimes make problems that would be difficult to solve using Coulomb's law. In each case the symmetry allowed us to construct a gaussian surface on which $E\cos\theta$ was constant. Only then could we take E outside the integral and solve for it. But many situations do not possess the symmetry needed to apply Gauss's law in calculating the field. Try, for example, to calculate the field of a dipole using Gauss's law. The attempt fails because it is impossible to draw an appropriate surface.

FIGURE 24-25 The fields of a dipole, a point charge, a charged line, and a charged plane.

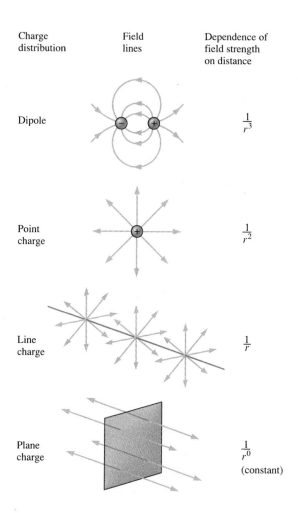

Charge distribution	Field lines	Dependence of field strength on distance
Dipole		$\dfrac{1}{r^3}$
Point charge		$\dfrac{1}{r^2}$
Line charge		$\dfrac{1}{r}$
Plane charge		$\dfrac{1}{r^0}$ (constant)

We can understand the fields associated with more complicated charge distributions by considering the fields of simpler distributions that we have already calculated using either Coulomb's law or Gauss's law. Figure 24-25 summarizes the fields of a dipole, a point charge, a uniformly charged line, and a uniformly charged plane. For the last three, note the simple relation between the number of dimensions in the charge distribution and the way the field strength depends on distance. The plane has two dimensions and its field strength is independent of distance. The line has one dimension and its field falls as $1/r$. The point has no dimensions and its field falls as $1/r^2$. In a sense, the dipole continues this progression, for it consists of two opposite point charges whose effects very nearly cancel. No wonder its field falls even faster, as $1/r^3$. In fact, one can construct a hierarchy of charge distributions whose fields fall off ever faster as dipoles nearly cancel dipoles, and so on. Such distributions are useful in the mathematical analysis of complicated charge distributions such as complex molecules or radio antennas.

Frequently we have a charge distribution that lacks the symmetry required to make Gauss's law useful and for which a Coulomb's law calculation would be impossibly difficult. Good thinking coupled with knowledge of simpler charge distributions can go a long way toward providing a reasonable approximation to the field. Consider, for example, the uniformly charged disk shown in Fig. 24-26. For points much closer to the disk surface than to the edge, the disk looks almost

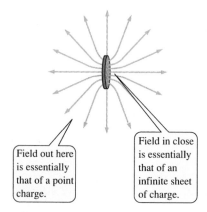

Field out here is essentially that of a point charge.

Field in close is essentially that of an infinite sheet of charge.

FIGURE 24-26 The field of a uniformly charged disk.

like an infinite flat plane of charge. For these points the field is approximately that of an infinite plane—a field that points directly away from the plane and does not fall off with distance. Far from the disk, meanwhile, its exact size and shape are unimportant. Its field closely resembles that of a single charged point: far from the disk the field points radially outward in all directions and falls off as the inverse square of the distance from the disk. The field at intermediate distances is harder to determine. But somehow the infinite-plane field lines close to the disk must connect smoothly to the point-charge field lines far away. If we sketch these in, as in Fig. 24-26, we have a rough picture of the field everywhere. Don't underestimate the value of a simple approximation like this one! It can often tell all we need to know about a situation and may provide a much clearer understanding than would a detailed calculation.

Got It!

A uniformly charged sheet measures 1 m on each side, and you're told the total charge Q. What expressions would you use to get approximate values for the field magnitude (a) 1 cm from the sheet (but not near an edge) and (b) 1 km from the sheet?

24-6 GAUSS'S LAW AND CONDUCTORS

Electrostatic Equilibrium

In the preceding chapter we defined electrical conductors as materials containing free charges—like the free electrons in metals. Figure 24-27 shows what happens when an electric field is applied to a piece of conducting material. Free charges respond to the electric force $q\mathbf{E}$ by moving—in the direction of the field if they are positive, opposite the field if negative. The resulting charge separation gives rise to an electric field within the material that is opposite to the applied field. As more charge moves this internal field becomes stronger until its magnitude eventually equals that of the applied field. At that point free charges within the conductor experience zero net force, and the conductor is in **electrostatic equilibrium**. Although individual charges continue to move about in random thermal motion, there is no longer any net motion of charge. Once equilibrium is reached the internal and applied fields are equal but opposite, and therefore,

❚ **The electric field is zero inside a conductor in electrostatic equilibrium.**

It could not be otherwise: Since a conductor contains free charges, the presence of any internal electric field would result in bulk charge motion, and we would not have equilibrium. This result does not depend on the size or shape of the conductor, the magnitude or direction of the applied field, or even the nature of the material as long as it's a conductor. This ability of a conductor to cancel applied fields is the basis of shielding—the use of conductive enclosures to keep out unwanted electric fields.

This discussion of equilibrium is a macroscopic one; it considers only overall average fields within the material. At the atomic and molecular level there are still strong electric fields near individual electrons and protons. But the *average* field, taken over distances many times the separation between individual charges, is zero in electrostatic equilibrium.

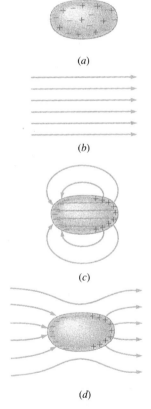

(a)

(b)

(c)

(d)

FIGURE 24-27 (a) A piece of conducting material contains positive and negative charge. (b) A uniform electric field, arising from charges outside the region shown. (c) Charges in the conductor separate in response to the field, resulting in an internal field that cancels the applied field. (d) The net field is the vector sum of the applied field and the field resulting from the redistribution of charge within the conductor. Note that field lines, as always, begin and end on charges.

FIGURE 24-28 Excess charge accumulates at the surface of a charged conductor. In this elongated conductor, mutual repulsion of the excess electrons results in the greatest charge accumulation at the opposite ends.

Gaussian surface

Material surface

FIGURE 24-29 Since the electric field inside the conductor is zero, a gaussian surface within the conductor encloses zero net charge. Any excess charge therefore resides on the conductor surface.

Charged Conductors

Although they contain free charges, conductors are normally electrically neutral since they include equal numbers of electrons and protons. But suppose we give a conductor a nonzero net charge, for example, by injecting excess electrons into its interior. There will be a mutual repulsion among the electrons and, because these are *excess* electrons, there is no compensating attraction from protons. We might expect, therefore, that the electrons will move as far apart as possible— namely to the surface of the conductor (Fig. 24-28). (Electrons might even leave the material—but that only occurs with very high charge densities.)

We now use Gauss's law to prove rigorously that excess charge *must* be at the surface of a conductor in electrostatic equilibrium. Figure 24-29 shows a piece of conducting material with a gaussian surface drawn just below the material surface. In equilibrium there is no electric field within the conductor, and thus the field is zero everywhere on the gaussian surface. The flux, $\oint \mathbf{E} \cdot d\mathbf{A}$, through the gaussian surface is therefore also zero. But Gauss's law says that the flux through a closed surface is proportional to the net charge enclosed, and therefore the net charge within our gaussian surface must be zero. This is true no matter where the gaussian surface is as long as it is *inside* the conductor. We can move the gaussian surface arbitrarily close to the conductor surface and it still encloses no net charge. If there is a net charge on the conductor it lies outside the gaussian surface, and therefore we conclude that

If a conductor in electrostatic equilibrium carries a net charge, all excess charge resides on the conductor surface.

EXAMPLE 24-7	*A Hollow Conductor*

An irregularly shaped conductor has a hollow cavity, as shown in Fig. 24-30. The conductor carries a net charge of 1.0 μC. A 2.0-μC point charge is inside the cavity, not touching the conductor. Find the net charge on the cavity wall and on the outer surface of the conductor, assuming electrostatic equilibrium.

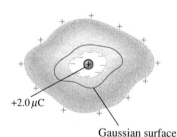

+2.0 μC

Gaussian surface

FIGURE 24-30 A conductor with a hollow cavity containing a charge. The gaussian surface shown encloses no net charge, so the charge on the inner wall must be equal but opposite that of the charge within the cavity.

Solution

The electric field is zero everywhere within the conductor, and therefore is zero at all points on the gaussian surface shown in Fig. 24-30. The flux through this surface is thus zero, and Gauss's law tells us that the surface therefore encloses zero net charge. But there is a 2.0-μC charge within the cavity. In order for the gaussian surface to enclose zero net charge, the cavity wall must therefore carry −2.0 μC.

Since the conductor's net charge is 1.0 μC and there is −2.0 μC on its inner wall, the outer surface of the conductor surface must carry 3.0 μC.

EXERCISE A point charge +q is placed inside a hollow conducting shell carrying a net charge −3q. What is the total charge on the outside surface of the shell?

Answer: −2q

Some problems similar to Example 24-7: 46–49

Got It!

A piece of conductor carries a net charge $+Q$. There's a hollow cavity within the conductor, and in it is a point charge $-Q$. In equilibrium, is there any charge on the outer surface of the conductor?

Experimental Tests of Gauss's Law

The fact that excess charge resides only on a conductor surface provides a very sensitive test of Gauss's law, and thus of the inverse-square law for the electric field. Figure 24-31 shows a charged conducting ball being placed inside a hollow, initially neutral conductor. When the two conductors touch, all the excess charge flows to the outer surface of the hollow conductor, leaving no net charge on the ball. In practice the experiment is often done in reverse, with an uncharged conducting ball placed within a hollow conductor. The outer conductor is then charged, and sensitive instruments used detect any charge moving to the ball. Absence of such charge motion confirms the inverse-square law. Recent experiments of this type show that the exponent 2 appearing in the inverse-square law is indeed 2 to within 3×10^{-16}. Such tests are far more sensitive than direct measurements of how the electric force varies with distance.

The Field at a Conductor Surface

There can be no electric field *within* a conductor in electrostatic equilibrium, but there *may* be a field right *at* the conductor surface. Such a field, though, cannot have a component parallel to the surface; if it did, charge would move along the surface and we would not have equilibrium. So the field at a conductor surface must be perpendicular to the surface (Fig. 24-32a).

We can compute the field strength by considering a small gaussian surface that straddles the conductor surface, as shown in Fig. 24-32b. We make the gaussian surface so small that curvature of the conductor becomes negligible, and we orient the gaussian surface with its sides perpendicular and its top parallel to the conductor surface. Since the field is perpendicular to the conductor, there is then no flux through the sides of the gaussian surface. Since the field is zero inside the conductor, there is also no flux through the inner end of the gaussian surface. The only

FIGURE 24-31 Experimental test of Gauss's law. When the small charged conductor contacts the interior of the hollow conductor, all its charge moves to the outside of the hollow conductor.

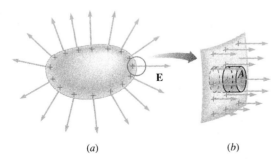

(a)   (b)

FIGURE 24-32 (a) The electric field at the surface of a charged conductor is perpendicular to the conductor surface. (b) A small gaussian surface straddles the conductor surface.

FIGURE 24-33 During thunderstorms, a large charge density builds up at the pointed tip of the Empire State Building. The associated electric field can be strong enough to cause dielectric breakdown in the surrounding air, initiating frequent lightning strikes.

flux is through the outer end, whose area is A. Since the field is essentially uniform and perpendicular to this end, the flux is just EA. The only charge enclosed is right at the conductor surface, where it occupies the same area A. If the surface charge density is σ, then the enclosed charge is σA. Gauss's law equates the flux to $q_{enclosed}/\varepsilon_0$, so we have

$$EA = \frac{\sigma A}{\varepsilon_0}$$

or

$$E = \frac{\sigma}{\varepsilon_0}. \qquad \text{(field at conductor surface)} \qquad (24\text{-}11)$$

This result applies to any conductor in electrostatic equilibrium and shows that large electric fields develop where the charge density is high. Engineers designing electrical devices must avoid high charge densities whose associated fields could lead to sparks, arcing, and breakdown of electrical insulation (Fig. 24-33).

EXAMPLE 24-8	Earth's Field

Earth, which is an electrical conductor, carries a net charge of -4.3×10^5 C distributed approximately uniformly over its surface. Find the surface charge density, and use Equation 24-11 to calculate the electric field at Earth's surface.

Solution

Let Q be Earth's charge and R_E its radius (which is given inside the front cover and in Appendix E). Then the surface charge density is

$$\sigma = \frac{Q}{A} = \frac{Q}{4\pi R_E^2} = \frac{-4.3\times10^5 \text{ C}}{(4\pi)(6.37\times10^6 \text{ m})^2}$$

$$= -8.43\times10^{-10} \text{ C/m}^2.$$

Equation 24-11 then gives the electric field at Earth's surface:

$$E = \frac{\sigma}{\varepsilon_0} = \frac{-8.43\times10^{-10} \text{ C/m}^2}{8.85\times10^{-12} \text{ C}^2/\text{N}\cdot\text{m}^2} = -95 \text{ N/C},$$

where the minus sign indicates that the field direction is downward. This modest field is present near Earth's surface in fair weather; in thunderstorms the local field exceeds this value by many orders of magnitude.

Does our result make sense? We could also treat Earth as a spherical charge distribution, whence its surface field strength would be $E = Q/4\pi\varepsilon_0 R_E^2$. Using the symbolic form of our result for σ in Equation 24-11 gives precisely this expression, showing that these two approaches to the field are indeed consistent.

EXERCISE Dielectric breakdown of air occurs with fields of about 3×10^6 N/C, and results in sparks jumping through the air. What is the maximum surface charge density permissible on a conductor if dielectric breakdown of the surrounding air is to be avoided?

Answer: 27 μC/m^2

Some problems similar to Example 24-8: 43, 44, 51

Equation 24-11 gives a field that depends only on the local charge density. Does that mean the field at any point on a conductor surface arises only from the charge right at that point? No! As always, the field at any point is the vector sum of contributions from all charge elements making up the charge distribution. Remarkably, Gauss's law requires that charges on a conductor arrange themselves in such a way that the field at any point on the conductor surface depends only on

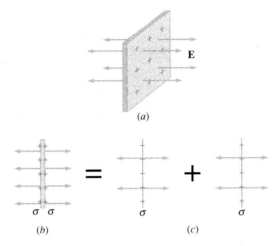

(a)

(b)   (c)

FIGURE 24-34 (a) An isolated, charged conducting plate. Its field points outward from both faces. (b) Edge-on view of the plate. If the plate is isolated, symmetry requires that there be equal charge densities on both faces. (c) The field anywhere is the sum of the fields of the two faces, each treated as a single charged sheet. Within the plate the fields cancel, while outside they sum to give a net field σ/ε_0.

the surface charge density right at that point—even though that field arises from *all* the charges on the surface (as well as from charges elsewhere if there are such)!

Consider a thin, flat, isolated, conducting sheet that has charge density σ on one of its two faces (Fig. 24-34a). Equation 24-11 shows immediately that the field at the surface of this plate is σ/ε_0. But if the plate is large and flat we can approximate it as an infinite sheet of charge—for which we found earlier (Equation 24-10 in Example 24-6) that the field should be $\sigma/2\varepsilon_0$. Is there a contradiction here? No! If the plate is isolated from other conductors or charges, then symmetry requires that charge spread itself evenly over *both* faces. If one face has charge density σ, so must the other—so we really have *two* charge sheets, each with density σ (Fig. 24-34b). Each gives rise to a field of magnitude $\sigma/2\varepsilon_0$, and *outside* the conductor those fields superpose to give the net field σ/ε_0 (Fig. 24-34c). *Inside* the conductor they also superpose, but here their directions are opposite and the result is that there is no field inside the conductor. Application of Equation 24-11 skips all these details. But because Equation 24-11 was derived on the assumption that the field inside the conductor is zero, it "knows" about charges everywhere on the conductor—and in this case that means on the second face of the conductor.

Equation 24-11 also applies to the pair of oppositely charged conducting plates shown in Fig. 24-35; the result, for the field between the plates, is σ/ε_0, where σ is the surface charge density on either plate. Why not $2\sigma/\varepsilon_0$? Again, Equation 24-11 always gives the field at a conductor surface—and it takes into account other charges that may be present. In this case neither plate is isolated, so the symmetry is broken, and charge builds up only on the inner faces of the two plates. Now each plate is a single charge layer, giving rise to a field $\sigma/2\varepsilon_0$, and between the plates the fields sum to Equation 24-11's result, σ/ε_0. Beyond the plates the fields sum to zero—a result that also follows from Equation 24-11 because now there is zero surface charge on the outer faces.

$+\sigma$ $-\sigma$

FIGURE 24-35 Edge view of two parallel conducting plates carrying opposite charges. Electrical attraction brings the excess charges to the inner faces. Each face constitutes a charge layer whose surface charge density has magnitude σ; between the plates their fields add to give field strength σ/ε_0.

CHAPTER SYNOPSIS

Summary

1. **Electric field lines** provide a visual representation of the electric field. The direction of a field line is that of the electric field, and the closeness of field lines is a measure of field strength. Electric field lines begin and end only on charges.

2. **Electric flux** quantifies the notion "number of field lines crossing a surface." Flux is the integral of the electric field over the surface:

$$\phi = \int \mathbf{E} \cdot d\mathbf{A},$$

where $d\mathbf{A}$ is an infinitesimal vector perpendicular to the surface at each point.

3. **Gauss's law** is a fundamental relation governing the behavior of electric fields throughout the universe. Gauss's law states that the electric flux emerging from any closed surface is proportional to the charge enclosed:

$$\oint \mathbf{E} \cdot d\mathbf{A} = \frac{q_{enclosed}}{\varepsilon_0},$$

where $\varepsilon_0 = 1/4\pi k$.

4. Gauss's law is true for any surface and any distribution of charge, but it proves useful in calculating the electric field only in cases with sufficient symmetry—in particular, spherical symmetry, line symmetry, and plane symmetry. Table 24-1 lists some fields calculated with Gauss's law. The fields of more realistic charge distributions are often approximated by the fields associated with these symmetries.

5. There is no electric field inside a conductor in **electrostatic equilibrium**. Gauss's law shows that any excess charge on the conductor resides on the conductor surface, and that the field at the conductor surface is perpendicular to the surface and has magnitude σ/ε_0, with σ the surface charge density.

TABLE 24-1 *Some Results from Gauss's Law*

CHARGE DISTRIBUTION	FIELD	WHERE VALID	DERIVED IN . . .
Any spherically symmetric	$E = \dfrac{kQ}{r^2} = \dfrac{Q}{4\pi\varepsilon_0 r^2}$	Outside the charge distribution	Section 24-4
Solid, uniformly charged sphere of radius R	$E = \dfrac{kQr}{r^3}$ $= \dfrac{Qr}{4\pi\varepsilon_0 r^3} = \dfrac{\rho r}{3\varepsilon_0}$	Inside $(r < R)$	Example 24-1
Uniform spherical shell of charge	$E = 0$	Inside	Example 24-2
Any cylindrically symmetric distribution with line charge density λ	$E = \dfrac{2k\lambda}{r} = \dfrac{\lambda}{2\pi e_0 r}$	Outside the charge distribution	Section 24-4
Solid, charged cylinder of radius R, uniform volume charge density ρ	$E = \dfrac{\rho r}{2\varepsilon_0 r}$	Inside $(r < R)$	Problem 24-31
Hollow, uniformly charged pipe	$E = 0$	Inside	Example 24-5
Infinite flat sheet, uniform surface charge density σ	$E = \dfrac{\sigma}{2\varepsilon_0}$	Outside	Example 24-6
Conductor in electrostatic equilibrium	$E = 0$	Inside	Section 24-6
Conductor in electrostatic equilibrium	$E = \dfrac{\sigma}{\varepsilon_0}$	At conductor surface	Section 24-6

Terms You Should Understand

(Pairs are closely related terms whose distinction is important; number in parentheses is chapter section where term first appears.)

electric field lines (24-1)
electric flux (24-2)
Gauss's law (24-3)
electrostatic equilibrium (24-6)

Symbols You Should Recognize

ϕ (24-2)
$\mathbf{A}, d\mathbf{A}$ (24-2)
$\int$ (24-2)

$\oint \mathbf{E} \cdot d\mathbf{A}$ (24-2)

k, ε_0 (24-3)
σ (24-6)

Problems You Should Be Able to Solve

drawing and interpreting field line patterns for simple charge distributions (24-1)
calculating electric flux (24-2)
using Gauss's law to calculate electric fields with spherical, line, or plane symmetry (24-4)
describing charge distributions in electrostatic equilibrium (24-6)
calculating electric fields at conductor surfaces (24-6)

Limitations to Keep in Mind

Gauss's law is universally true, but it can be used to calculate electric fields only with sufficient symmetry.

QUESTIONS

1. Can electric field lines ever cross? Why or why not?
2. If identical charged particles are placed at points *A* and *B* in Fig. 24-36, which will experience the greater force?

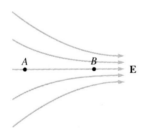

FIGURE 24-36 Question 2.

3. The electric flux through a closed surface is zero. Must the electric field be zero on that surface? If not, give an example.
4. If the flux of the gravitational field through a closed surface is zero, what can you conclude about the region interior to the surface?
5. Under what conditions can the electric flux through a surface be written as *EA*, where *A* is the surface area?
6. Eight field lines emerge from a closed surface surrounding an isolated point charge. Would this fact change if a second identical charge were brought to a point just *outside* the surface? If not, would anything change? Explain.
7. In what sense is Gauss's law equivalent to the inverse-square law?
8. If a charged particle were released from rest on a curved field line, would its subsequent motion follow the field line? Explain.
9. Gauss' law describes the flux of the electric field through a surface that may enclose charge. Must the field in Gauss's law arise only from charges within the closed surface?

10. In a certain region the electric field points to the right and its magnitude increases as you move to the right, as shown in Fig. 24-37. Does the region contain net positive charge, net negative charge, or zero net charge?

FIGURE 24-37 Question 10. (Left ends mark the beginnings of the field lines, which extend indefinitely to the right.)

11. A point charge is located a fixed distance from a uniformly charged sphere, outside the sphere. If the sphere shrinks in size without losing any charge, what happens to the force on the point charge?
12. In applying Equation 24-6 for the field outside a spherically symmetric charge distribution, is *r* the distance from the center or from the edge of the distribution?
13. The field of an infinite line of charge falls as $1/r$. How is this not a violation of the inverse-square law?
14. Why can't you use Gauss's law to determine the field of a uniformly charged cube? Why wouldn't it work to draw a cubical gaussian surface?
15. You're sitting inside an uncharged hollow spherical shell. Suddenly someone dumps a billion coulombs of charge on the shell, distributed uniformly. What happens to the electric field at your location?
16. Why is it that the field inside a uniformly charged sphere actually increases with distance from the center? How is this consistent with Coulomb's law?

17. There is a nonzero flux through each of the surfaces in Fig. 24-6, yet there is no charge in the region shown. Why is this not a violation of Gauss's law?

18. Does Gauss's law apply to a spherical surface not centered on a point charge, as shown in Fig. 24-38? Would this be a useful surface to use in calculating the electric field?

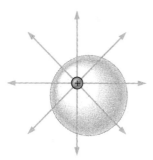

FIGURE 24-38 Question 18.

19. An insulating sphere carries charge spread uniformly throughout its volume. A conducting sphere has the same radius and net charge, but of course the charge is spread over its surface only. How do the electric fields outside these two charge distributions compare?

20. Why must the electric field be zero inside a conductor in electrostatic equilibrium?

21. Why must the electric field at the surface of a conductor in electrostatic equilibrium be perpendicular to the surface?

22. Where in Fig. 24-28 would you find the strongest electric field?

23. The electric field of a flat sheet of charge is $\sigma/2\varepsilon_0$. Yet the field of a flat conducting sheet—even a thin one, like a piece of aluminum foil—is σ/ε_0. Explain this apparent discrepancy.

24. A metal contains free electrons not bound to individual atoms. Does Gauss's law require that all these free electrons be on the metal surface?

PROBLEMS

ActivPhysics can help with these problems:
Activities 11.4–11.6

Section 24-1 Electric Field Lines

1. What is the net charge shown in Fig. 24-39? The magnitude of the middle charge is 3 μC.

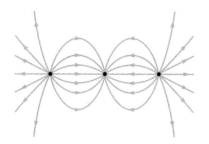

FIGURE 24-39 Problem 1.

2. A charge $+2q$ and a charge $-q$ are near each other. Sketch some field lines for this charge distribution, using the convention of eight lines for a charge of magnitude q.

3. Two charges $+q$ and a charge $-q$ are at the vertices of an equilateral triangle. Sketch some field lines for this charge distribution.

4. The net charge shown in Fig. 24-40 is $+Q$. Identify each of the charges A, B, C shown.

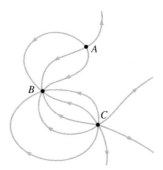

FIGURE 24-40 Problem 4.

Section 24-2 Electric Flux

5. A flat surface with area 2.0 m^2 is in a uniform electric field of 850 N/C. What is the electric flux through the surface when it is (a) at right angles to the field, (b) at 45° to the field, and (c) parallel to the field?

6. What is the electric field strength in a region where the flux through a 1.0 cm $\times$ 1.0 cm flat surface is 65 N·m^2/C, if the field is uniform and the surface is at right angles to the field?

7. A flat surface with area 0.14 m^2 lies in the x-y plane, in a uniform electric field given by $\mathbf{E} = 5.1\hat{\mathbf{i}} + 2.1\hat{\mathbf{j}} + 3.5\hat{\mathbf{k}}$ kN/C. Find the flux through this surface.

8. The electric field on the surface of a 10-cm-diameter sphere is perpendicular to the sphere and has magnitude 47 kN/C. What is the electric flux through the sphere?

9. What is the flux through the hemispherical open surface of radius R shown in Fig. 24-41? The uniform field has magnitude E. *Hint:* Don't do a messy integral! Imagine closing the surface with a flat, circular piece across the open end. What would be the flux through the entire closed surface? And what's the flux through the flat end? So what's the answer?

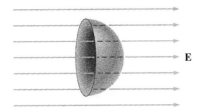

FIGURE 24-41 Problem 9.

10. The electric field shown in Fig. 24-42 is given by $\mathbf{E} = E_0 \dfrac{y}{a}\hat{\mathbf{k}}$, where E_0 and a are constants. Find the flux through the square of side a shown.

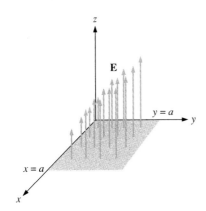

FIGURE 24-42 Problem 10.

Section 24-3 Gauss's Law

11. What is the electric flux through each closed surface shown in Fig. 24-43?

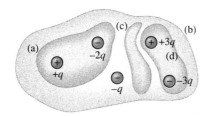

FIGURE 24-43 Problem 11.

12. A 6.8-μC charge and a -4.7 μC charge are inside an uncharged sphere. What is the electric flux through the sphere?

13. A 2.6-μC charge is at the center of a cube 7.5 cm on each side. What is the electric flux through one face of the cube? *Hint:* Think about symmetry, and don't do an integral.

14. If the charge in the preceding problem is still inside the cube but not at the center, (a) what is the flux through the *entire* cube? (b) Could you still calculate the flux through one face without doing an integral?

15. A dipole consists of two charges ± 6.1 μC located 1.2 cm apart. What is the electric flux through each surface shown in Fig. 24-44?

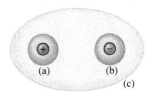

FIGURE 24-44 Problem 15.

16. The electric field in a certain region is given by $\mathbf{E} = 40x\hat{\mathbf{i}}$ N/C, with x in meters. What is the volume charge density in the region? *Hint:* Apply Gauss's law to a cube 1 meter on a side.

Section 24-4 Using Gauss's Law

17. The electric field at the surface of a uniformly charged sphere of radius 5.0 cm is 90 kN/C. What would be the field strength 10 cm from the surface?

18. A solid sphere 25 cm in radius carries 14 μC, distributed uniformly throughout its volume. Find the electric field strength (a) 15 cm, (b) 25 cm, and (c) 50 cm from the sphere's center.

19. A crude model for the hydrogen atom treats it as a point charge $+e$ (the proton) surrounded by a uniform cloud of negative charge with total charge $-e$ and radius 0.0529 nm. What would be the electric field strength inside such an atom, halfway from the proton to the edge of the charge cloud?

20. Positive charge is spread uniformly over the surface of a spherical balloon 70 cm in radius, resulting in an electric field of 26 kN/C at the balloon's surface. Find the field strength (a) 50 cm from the balloon's center and (b) 190 cm from the center. (c) What is the net charge on the balloon?

21. A 10-nC point charge is located at the center of a thin spherical shell of radius 8.0 cm carrying -20 nC distributed uniformly over its surface. What are the magnitude and direction of the electric field (a) 2.0 cm, (b) 6.0 cm, and (c) 15 cm from the point charge?

22. A solid sphere 2.0 cm in radius carries a uniform volume charge density. The electric field 1.0 cm from the sphere's center has magnitude 39 kN/C. (a) At what other distance does the field have this magnitude? (b) What is the net charge on the sphere?

23. A point charge $-2Q$ is at the center of a spherical shell of radius R carrying charge Q spread uniformly over its surface. What is the electric field at (a) $r = \frac{1}{2}R$ and (b) $r = 2R$? (c) How would your answers change if the charge on the shell were doubled?

24. A spherical shell of radius 15 cm carries 4.8 μC, distributed uniformly over its surface. At the center of the shell is a point charge. (a) If the electric field at the surface of the sphere is 750 kN/C and points outward, what is the charge of the point charge? (b) What is the field just inside the shell?

25. A spherical shell 30 cm in diameter carries a total charge 85 μC distributed uniformly over its surface. A 1.0-μC point charge is located at the center of the shell. What is the electric field strength (a) 5.0 cm from the center and (b) 45 cm from the center? (c) How would your answers change if the charge on the shell were doubled?

26. The thick, spherical shell of inner radius a and outer radius b shown in Fig. 24-45 carries a uniform volume charge density ρ. Find an expression for the electric field strength in the region $a < r < b$, and show that your result is consistent with Equation 24-7 when $a = 0$.

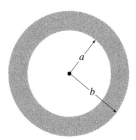

FIGURE 24-45 Problems 26, 32.

27. How should the charge density within a solid sphere vary with distance from the center in order that the magnitude of the electric field in the sphere be constant?

28. A long, thin wire carrying 5.6 nC/m runs down the center of a long, thin-walled, hollow pipe with radius 1.0 cm carrying -4.2 nC/m spread uniformly over its surface. Find the electric field (a) 0.50 cm from the wire and (b) 1.5 cm from the wire.

29. A long solid rod 4.5 cm in radius carries a uniform volume charge density. If the electric field strength at the surface of the rod (not near either end) is 16 kN/C, what is the volume charge density?

30. The electric field strength outside a charge distribution and 18 cm from its center has magnitude 55 kN/C. At 23 cm

the field strength is 43 kN/C. Does the distribution have spherical or line symmetry?

31. An infinitely long rod of radius R carries a uniform volume charge density ρ. Show that the electric field strengths outside and inside the rod are given, respectively, by $E = \rho R^2/2\varepsilon_0 r$ and $E = \rho r/2\varepsilon_0$, where r is the distance from the rod axis.

32. Repeat Problem 26, assuming that Fig. 24-45 represents the cross section of a long, thick-walled pipe. Now the case $a = 0$ should be consistent with the result of Problem 31 for the interior of the rod.

33. A long, thin wire carries a uniform line charge density $\lambda = -6.8 \ \mu$C/m. It is surrounded by a thick concentric cylindrical shell of inner radius 2.5 cm and outer radius 3.5 cm. What uniform volume charge density in the shell will result in zero electric field outside the shell?

34. A square nonconducting plate measures 4.5 m on a side and carries charge spread uniformly over its surface. The electric field 10 cm from the plate and not near an edge has magnitude 430 N/C and points toward the plate. Find (a) the surface charge density on the plate and (b) the total charge on the plate. (c) What is the electric field strength 20 cm from the plate?

35. If you "painted" positive charge on the floor, what surface charge density would be necessary in order to suspend a 15-μC, 5.0-g particle above the floor?

36. A slab of charge extends infinitely in two dimensions and has thickness d in the third dimension, as shown in Fig. 24-46. The slab carries a uniform volume charge density ρ. Find expressions for the electric field strength (a) inside and (b) outside the slab, as functions of the distance x from the center plane.

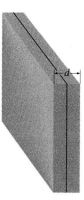

FIGURE 24-46 Section of an infinite slab of charge (Problem 36).

37. Figure 24-47 shows sections of three infinite flat sheets of charge, each carrying surface charge density with the same magnitude σ. Find the magnitude and direction of the electric field in each of the four regions shown.

FIGURE 24-47 Problem 37.

Section 24-5 Fields of Arbitrary Charge Distributions

38. A rod 50 cm long and 1.0 cm in radius carries a 2.0-μC charge distributed uniformly over its length. What is the approximate magnitude of the electric field (a) 4.0 mm from the rod surface, not near either end, and (b) 23 m from the rod?

39. A nonconducting square plate 75 cm on a side carries a uniform surface charge density. The electric field strength 1 cm from the plate, not near an edge, is 45 kN/C. What is the approximate field strength 15 m from the plate?

40. Two circular plates 10 cm in diameter and 2.0 mm apart carry equal but opposite charges ± 0.50 μC distributed uniformly over their facing surfaces. What is the electric field strength (a) between the plates but not near either edge? (b) 2.5 m from the plates on a plane passing midway between them? *Hint* for (b): See Example 23-6.

41. The electric field strength on the axis of a uniformly charged disk is given by $E = 2\pi k\sigma(1 - x/\sqrt{x^2 + a^2})$, with σ the surface charge density, a the disk radius, and x the distance from the disk center. If $a = 20$ cm, (a) for what range of x values does treating the disk as an infinite sheet give an approximation to the field that is good to within 10%? (b) For what range of x values is the point-charge approximation good to 10%?

42. A nonconducting square 2.0 cm on a side carries a 45-nC charge spread uniformly over its surface. The x axis runs through the plate center, perpendicular to the plate, with $x = 0$ at the plate center. A -45-nC point charge is at $x = 5.0$ cm. Find approximate values for the electric field strength on the x axis at (a) $x = 1.0$ mm; (b) $x = 4.8$ cm; (c) $x = 2.5$ m. *Hint* for (c): Consult Example 23-6.

Section 24-6 Gauss's Law and Conductors

43. What is the electric field strength just outside the surface of a conducting sphere carrying surface charge density 1.4 μC/m^2?

44. Calculate the acceleration of a proton at the surface of a conductor carrying surface charge density 0.60 C/m^2.

45. A net charge of 5.0 μC is applied on one side of a solid metal sphere 2.0 cm in diameter. After electrostatic equilibrium is reached, what are (a) the volume charge density inside the sphere and (b) the surface charge density on the sphere? Assume there are no other charges or conductors nearby. (c) Which of your answers depends on this assumption, and why?

46. A point charge $+q$ lies at the center of a spherical conducting shell carrying a net charge $\frac{3}{2}q$. Sketch the field lines both inside and outside the shell, using 8 field lines to represent a charge of magnitude q.

47. A 250-nC point charge is placed at the center of an uncharged spherical conducting shell 20 cm in radius. (a) What is the surface charge density on the outer surface of the shell? (b) What is the electric field strength at the shell's outer surface?

48. A point charge is placed at the center of an uncharged spherical conducting shell of inner radius 2.5 cm and outer radius 4.0 cm (Fig. 24-48). As a result, the outer surface of the shell acquires a surface charge density $\sigma = 71$ nC/cm^2. Find (a) the value of the point charge and (b) the surface charge density on the inner wall of the shell.

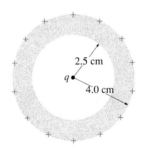

FIGURE 24-48 Problem 48.

49. An irregular conductor containing an irregular, empty cavity carries a net charge Q. (a) Show that the electric field inside the cavity must be zero. (b) If you put a point charge inside the cavity, what value must it have in order to make the surface charge density on the outer surface of the conductor everywhere zero?

50. A neutral dime is placed in a uniform electric field of 6.2×10^5 N/C, with its faces perpendicular to the field. (a) What is the approximate charge density on the faces of the dime? (b) What is the total charge on each face? (Measure a dime!)

51. A total charge of 18 μC is applied to a thin, square metal plate 75 cm on a side. Find the electric field strength near the plate's surface.

52. Two closely spaced parallel metal plates carry surface charge densities ± 95 nC/m^2 on their facing surfaces, with no charge on their outer surfaces. Find the electric field

strength (a) between the plates and (b) outside the plates. Treat the plates as infinite in extent.

53. A conducting sphere 2.0 cm in radius is concentric with a spherical conducting shell with inner radius 8.0 cm and outer radius 10 cm. The small sphere carries 50 nC charge and the shell has no net charge. Find the electric field strength (a) 1.0 cm, (b) 5.0 cm, (c) 9.0 cm, and (d) 15 cm from the center.

54. A coaxial cable consists of an inner wire and a concentric cylindrical outer conductor (Fig. 24-49). If the conductors carry equal but opposite charges, show that there is no net charge on the *outside* of the outer conductor.

FIGURE 24-49 Problem 54.

Paired Problems

(Both problems in a pair involve the same principles and techniques. If you can get the first problem, you should be able to solve the second one.)

55. A point charge $-q$ is at the center of a spherical shell carrying charge $+2q$. That shell, in turn, is concentric with a larger shell carrying charge $-\frac{3}{2}q$. Draw a cross section of this structure, and sketch the electric field lines using the convention that 8 lines correspond to a charge of magnitude q.

56. A point charge $-q$ is at the center of a spherical shell carrying charge $-\frac{3}{2}q$. That shell, in turn, is concentric with a larger shell carrying charge $+2q$. Draw a cross section of this structure, and sketch the electric field lines using the convention that 8 lines correspond to a charge of magnitude q.

57. A point charge q is at the center of a spherical shell of radius R carrying charge $2q$ spread uniformly over its surface. Write expressions for the electric field strength at (a) $\frac{1}{2}R$ and (b) $2R$.

58. A point charge q is at the center of a spherical shell of radius R carrying charge $5q$. At what other distance does the electric field have the same value it does at a point halfway from the center to the shell?

59. A long, thin hollow pipe 4.0 cm in diameter carries charge at a density of $-2.6 \, \mu C/m$, uniformly distributed over the pipe. It is concentric with 10-cm diameter pipe carrying $+2.6 \, \mu C/m$, also uniformly distributed. Find the magnitude of the electric field at (a) 0.50 cm, (b) 3.5 cm, and (c) 12 cm from the axis of the pipes.

60. Two concentric hollow pipes are 5.0 cm and 12 cm in diameter, respectively. Both carry uniformly distributed electric charges. The electric field 4.0 cm from their common axis is 630 kN/C, radially outward. The field 10 cm from their common axis is 126 kN/C, radially outward. (a) Find the linear charge densities on the two pipes. (b) How would the electric field strengths at 4.0 cm and 10 cm change if the charge density on the outer pipe were doubled?

61. An early (and incorrect) model for the atom pictured its positive charge as spread uniformly throughout the spherical atomic volume. For a hydrogen atom of radius 0.0529 nm, what would be the electric field due to such a distribution of positive charge (a) 0.020 nm from the center and (b) 0.20 nm from the center?

62. A solid sphere of radius R carries a charge spread uniformly throughout its volume. At what point outside the sphere is the electric field strength equal to that at a point halfway from the center to the edge? Express your answer as a distance from the center.

63. A sphere of radius $2a$ has a hole of radius a, as shown in Fig. 24-50. The solid portion carries a uniform volume charge density ρ. Find an expression for the electric field strength within the solid portion, as a function of the distance r from the center.

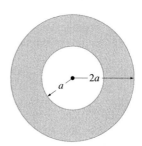

FIGURE 24-50 Problems 63, 64.

64. Repeat the previous problem, now considering that the figure represents the cross section of a thick cylindrical pipe.

Supplementary Problems

65. Repeat Problem 10 for the case $\mathbf{E} = E_0 \left(\frac{y}{a}\right)^2 \hat{\mathbf{k}}$.

66. The volume charge density inside a solid sphere of radius a is given by $\rho = \rho_0 r/a$, where ρ_0 is a constant. Find (a) the total charge and (b) the electric field strength within the sphere, as a function of distance r from the center.

67. A proton is released from rest 1.0 cm from a large sheet carrying a surface charge density of $-24 \, nC/m^2$. How much later does it strike the sheet?

68. Fig. 24-51 shows a rectangular box with sides $2a$ and length ℓ surrounding a line of charge with uniform line charge density λ. The line passes directly through the center of the box faces. Using an expression for the field of a line charge, integrate over strips of width dx as shown to find the electric flux through one face of the box. Multiply by 4 to get the total flux through the box, and show that your result is consistent with Gauss's law.

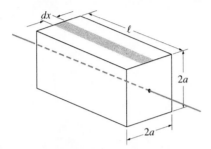

FIGURE 24-51 Problem 68.

69. Repeat Problem 36 for the case when the charge density in the slab is given by $\rho = \rho_0 |x/d|$, where ρ_0 is a constant.

70. The charge density within a uniformly charged sphere of radius R is given by $\rho = \rho_0 - ar^2$, where ρ_0 and a are constants, and r is the distance from the center. Find an expression for a such that the electric field outside the sphere is zero.

71. A small object of mass m and charge q is attached by a thread of length ℓ to a large, flat, nonconducting plate carrying a uniform surface charge density σ with the same sign as q (Fig. 24-52). If the object is displaced slightly sideways from its equilibrium, show that it undergoes simple harmonic motion with period $T = 2\pi \sqrt{2\epsilon_0 m\ell/q\sigma}$. Assume the gravitational force is negligible.

FIGURE 24-52 Problem 71.

72. An infinitely long nonconducting rod of radius R carries a volume charge density given by $\rho = \rho_0(r/R)$, where ρ_0 is a constant. Find the electric field strength (a) inside and (b) outside the rod, as functions of the distance r from the rod axis.

73. A thick spherical shell of inner radius a and outer radius b carries a charge density given by $\rho = \dfrac{ce^{-r/a}}{r^2}$, where a and c are constants. Find expressions for the electric field strength for (a) $r < a$, (b) $a < r < b$, and (c) $r > b$.

74. A solid sphere of radius R carries a nonuniform volume charge density given by $\rho = \pi^2 \rho_0 \sin(\pi r/R)$, where r is the distance from the center and ρ_0 is a positive constant. Find the magnitude and direction of the electric field at the sphere's surface.

75. A solid sphere of radius R carries a uniform volume charge density ρ. A hole of radius $R/2$ occupies a region from the center to the edge of the sphere, as shown in Fig. 24-53. Show that the electric field everywhere in the hole points horizontally and has magnitude $\rho R/6\epsilon_0$. *Hint:* Treat the hole as a superposition of two charged spheres of opposite charge.

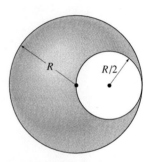

FIGURE 24-53 Problem 75.

76. You're 5.0 m from a charge distribution and you measure an electric field strength of 850 N/C. At 2.5 m the field strength has increased to about 3.4 kN/C. When you're 5.0 mm from the center of the distribution the field strength is 42.5 MN/C, and it increases to 85 MN/C at 2.5 mm. Describe the distribution as fully as you can, including its shape, any dimensions you can find, its total charge, and any appropriate charge density.

77. Two flat, parallel, closely spaced metal plates of area 0.080 m² carry total charges of $-2.1\ \mu$C and $+3.8\ \mu$C. Find the surface charge densities on the inner and outer faces of each plate.

78. Since the gravitational force of a point mass goes as $1/r^2$, the gravitational field **g** also obeys a form of Gauss's law. (a) Formulate this law, and (b) use it to find an expression for the gravitational field strength *within* Earth, as a function of distance r from the center. Treat Earth as a sphere of uniform density.

25 Electric Potential

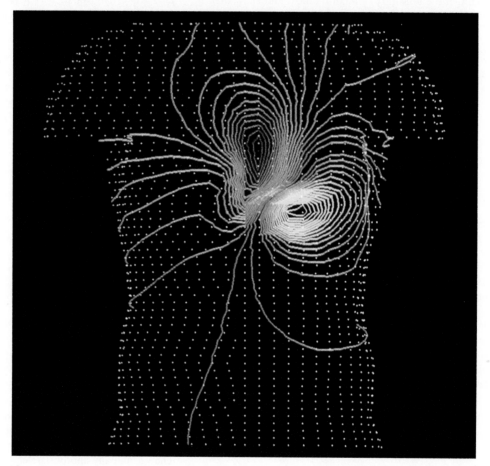

Lines of constant electric potential on the surface of the human body reflect the electric dipole structure of the heart.

You have to do work to lift your book against Earth's gravitational field. The work you do gets stored as potential energy, which is released if you lower the book. In Chapter 8 we introduced the term **conservative** to describe a force or field that, like gravity, "gives back" all the stored energy. With conservative forces we could associate a potential energy, and then use the powerful conservation of energy principle to solve practical problems.

The electric field of a static charge distribution is also conservative—an experimental fact that's also suggested theoretically by the similarity between Coulomb's law and Newton's law of universal gravitation. Because the electric field is conservative, it is meaningful to talk about potential energy in electrostatic systems. If you do work moving a charge against the electric force, for example, that work ends up stored as electric potential energy.

In this chapter we deal with electric potential, a useful and easily measured quantity that derives from the concept of potential energy. We'll see how the use of electric potential can provide a simpler approach to calculating electric fields, and how electric potential relates to the properties of everyday devices like batteries.

25-1 POTENTIAL ENERGY, WORK, AND THE ELECTRIC FIELD

In Chapter 8 we defined potential energy difference ΔU_{AB} as the negative of the work W_{AB} done by a conservative force $\mathbf{F}$ on an object moved from point A to point B:

$$\Delta U_{AB} = U_B - U_A = -W_{AB} = -\int_A^B \mathbf{F} \cdot d\boldsymbol{\ell}, \qquad (25\text{-}1)$$

where $d\boldsymbol{\ell}$ is a small element of the path from A to B. We also showed that this potential energy difference is independent of the path taken between points A and B (Fig. 25-1).

We'll now look at potential energy changes associated with moving charged objects in an electric field. First, consider a positive charge q being moved between two points A and B a distance ℓ apart in a uniform electric field $\mathbf{E}$, as shown in Fig. 25-2. A conservative electric force $q\mathbf{E}$ acts on the charge, and since the field is uniform that force doesn't vary as we move from A to B. Therefore, we can dispense with the integral and write

$$\Delta U_{AB} = -W_{AB} = -\mathbf{F} \cdot \boldsymbol{\ell} = -q\mathbf{E} \cdot \boldsymbol{\ell} = -qE\ell \cos(180°) = qE\ell,$$

where $\boldsymbol{\ell}$ is a vector from A to B and where the factor $\cos 180° = -1$ appears because the vectors $\mathbf{E}$ and $\boldsymbol{\ell}$ are in opposite directions. Does this result make sense? Pushing a positive charge against the electric field is like pushing a car up a hill: We do positive work, gravity does negative work, and the gravitational potential energy increases. Here we must do positive work to move the charge from A to B, the electric field does negative work, and the electric potential energy change—the *negative* of the work done by the conservative electric force—is positive. Let go of the charge and the field will accelerate it back toward B, changing potential to kinetic energy, just as gravity would accelerate the car back down the hill.

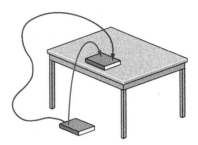

FIGURE 25-1 The gravitational field is conservative, and therefore the net work required to move between two points is independent of the path taken.

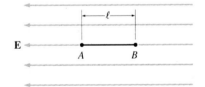

FIGURE 25-2 The work required to move a charge q from A to B in a *uniform* electric field is $qE\ell$.

25-2 POTENTIAL DIFFERENCE

We've just found the potential energy change in moving a charge q from point A to point B in Fig. 25-2. If we had moved a charge $2q$ the potential energy change would have been twice as great, and it would have required twice as much work; $\frac{1}{4}q$ would have one-fourth the potential energy change and would require one-fourth the work. Since the potential energy change is directly proportional to the charge it's convenient to consider the *potential energy change per unit charge* involved in moving between two points. We call this quantity the **electric potential difference**, ΔV. Mathematically, we express the potential difference by writing $\mathbf{F} = q\mathbf{E}$ in Equation 25-1 and dividing by q:

$$\Delta V_{AB} = \frac{\Delta U_{AB}}{q} = -\frac{1}{q}\int_A^B q\mathbf{E} \cdot d\boldsymbol{\ell} = -\int_A^B \mathbf{E} \cdot d\boldsymbol{\ell}.$$

Then our definition of potential difference becomes:

> **The electric potential difference from point A to point B is the potential energy change per unit charge in moving from A to B:**
>
> $$\Delta V_{AB} = -\int_A^B \mathbf{E} \cdot d\boldsymbol{\ell}. \qquad \text{(electric potential difference)} \quad (25\text{-}2a)$$

Here we use the Δ and the subscripts AB to show explicitly that we're talking about a *change* or *difference* from one point to another. We'll sometimes use just the symbol V for potential difference, in cases where the starting point A is understood. Note that potential difference, although computed from the dot product of vectors, is itself a scalar quantity.

The change from potential energy to electric potential is analogous to the change we made in Chapter 23 when we introduced the electric field as the electric force *per unit charge;* similarly, electric potential difference is the change in potential energy *per unit charge.* Again, the reason is the same: we want to express the electrical properties of a system in terms that don't involve the specific charges we may put in the vicinity of that system. Table 25-1 summarizes the relations among force and field, potential energy and electric potential.

In the special case of a uniform field, Equation 25-2a reduces to

$$\Delta V_{AB} = -\mathbf{E} \cdot \boldsymbol{\ell}, \qquad \text{(uniform field)} \qquad (25\text{-}2b)$$

where $\boldsymbol{\ell}$ is a vector from A to B. Figure 25-2 shows the special case when the field $\mathbf{E}$ and path $\boldsymbol{\ell}$ are in opposite directions; here, Equation 25-2b gives $\Delta V_{AB} = E\ell$.

Equations 25-2 show that potential difference can be positive or negative, depending on whether the path goes against or with the field. Moving a positive charge through a positive potential difference is like going uphill: We must do work on the charge, and its potential energy increases. Moving a positive charge through a negative potential difference is like going downhill: We do negative work or, equivalently, the field does work on the charge, and its potential energy decreases. In both cases the opposite is true for a negative charge; even though the potential difference remains the same, the work and potential energy reverse because of the negative sign on the charge.

We emphasize that potential difference is a property *of two points;* it doesn't depend on the path taken between those points. In Fig. 25-2, considering a straight path from A to B made the calculation of potential difference easy, but we would have found the same result—albeit with much more work—using any path (Fig. 25-3).

TABLE 25-1 *Force and Field, Potential Energy and Potential*

GENERAL QUANTITY	ELECTRICAL QUANTITY
Force $\mathbf{F}$ (Unit: N)	Electric field $\mathbf{E} = \dfrac{\mathbf{F}}{q}$ (Unit: N/C or V/m)
Potential energy difference ΔU $\Delta U =$ $-\int_A^B \mathbf{F} \cdot d\boldsymbol{\ell}$ (Unit: J)	Electric potential difference $\Delta V = \dfrac{\Delta U}{q}$ $\Delta V =$ $-\int_A^B \mathbf{E} \cdot d\boldsymbol{\ell}$ (Unit: J/C or V)

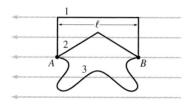

FIGURE 25-3 The potential difference ΔV_{AB} depends only on the points A and B, not on the path taken. Application of Equation 25-2a to any of the three paths shown would give the same result, namely $\Delta V_{AB} = E\ell$.

Got It!

What would happen to the potential difference V_{AB} in Fig. 25-2 if (a) the electric field strength were doubled; (b) the length ℓ were doubled; (c) the points were moved so the path lay at right angles to the field; (d) the positions of A and B were interchanged?

The Volt and the Electron Volt

The definition of potential difference shows that its units are joules/coulomb. Potential difference is important enough that 1 J/C has a special name—the **volt** (V). To say that a car has a 12-V battery, for example, means that the battery does 12 J of work on every coulomb that moves between its two terminals. Table 25-2 lists some common potential differences.

We often use the term **voltage** to speak of potential difference, especially in describing electric circuits. Strictly speaking the two terms are not synonymous, since voltage is used even in nonconservative situations that arise when fields change with time. But in common usage this subtle distinction is usually not bothersome.

Tip

Potential Difference Depends on Two Points Specifically, it is the energy per unit charge involved in moving *between those points*. Always think of potential difference in terms of two points. This is ultimately a very practical matter; if you forget it you won't be able to hook up a voltmeter properly, or connect jumper cables safely to your car battery! Figure 25-4 provides a dramatic illustration of this point.

Sometimes we speak of "the potential (or the voltage) at point P." This is *always* a shorthand way of talking, and we *must* have in mind some other point. What we mean is the potential difference going from that other point to point P.

In molecular, atomic, and nuclear systems it's often convenient to measure energy in **electron volts** (eV), defined as follows:

One electron volt is the energy gained by a particle carrying one elementary charge when it moves through a potential difference of one volt.

Since one elementary charge is 1.6×10^{-19} C, 1 eV is 1.6×10^{-19} J. Energy in eV is particularly easy to calculate when charge is given in elementary charges. However, the eV is *not* an SI unit and should be converted to joules before calculating other quantities.

Got It!

A proton (charge e) and an alpha particle (charge $2e$) each move through the same potential difference. Compare the work done on each.

TABLE 25-2 *Typical Potential Differences*

Between human arm and leg due to heart's electrical activity	1 mV
Across biological cell membrane	80 mV
Between terminals of flashlight battery	1.5 V
Car battery	12 V
Across loudspeaker operating at 50 watts	20 V
Electrical outlet, United States	120 V
Electrical outlet, Europe	230 V
Between accelerating electrodes in TV picture tube	30 kV
Between long-distance electric transmission line and ground	365 kV
Between base of thunderstorm cloud and ground	100 MV

FIGURE 25-4 Potential difference depends on *two* points. This parasailer landed on a 138,000-V power line, but he's not being electrocuted because his body is not contacting *two* points with a potential difference between them.

| **EXAMPLE 25-1** | *A TV Picture Tube: Potential Difference, Work, and Energy* |

At the back end of a TV picture tube, a uniform electric field of 600 kN/C extends over a distance of 5.0 cm and points toward the back of the tube (Fig. 25-5). (a) Find the potential difference between the back and the front end of this field region. (b) How much work would it take to move an ion with charge $+2e$ from the back to the front of the field region? (c) What would happen to an electron released at the back of the field region?

Solution

(a) With a uniform field the potential difference is given by Equation 25-2b:

$$V_{AB} = -\mathbf{E} \cdot \boldsymbol{\ell} = E\ell = (600 \times 10^3 \text{ N/C})(0.050 \text{ m})$$
$$= 30 \text{ kV},$$

where the second equality follows because a path from the back toward the front is opposite the field direction, as shown in Fig. 25-2, so $\cos\theta = -1$.

(b) Potential difference is the potential energy change per unit charge, or, equivalently, the work per unit charge needed to move charge between two points. Thus, the work to move the ion of charge $q = 2e$ against the 30-kV potential difference is

$$W_{\text{ion}} = q\Delta V = (2)(1.6 \times 10^{-19} \text{ C})(30 \text{ kV}) = 9.6 \times 10^{-15} \text{ J},$$

where the units work out because 1 V = 1 J/C. Since the ion carries two elementary charges, we could also express this energy as $(2e)(30 \text{ kV}) = 60 \text{ keV}$.

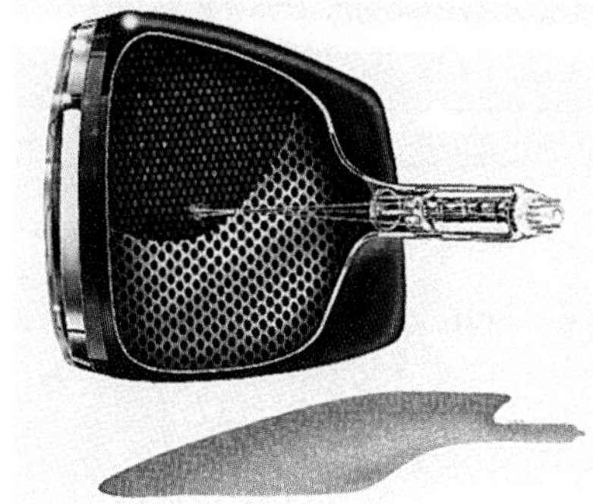

FIGURE 25-5 A potential difference on the order of 30 kV is used to accelerate the electrons that "paint" the picture on the screen of a TV tube, shown here in a cutaway view.

(c) With its negative charge, the electron would *gain* energy given by $e\Delta V$, or 4.8×10^{-15} J (more simply calculated as 30 keV). But energy is conserved, so this gain—an increase in the electron's kinetic energy $\frac{1}{2}mv^2$—comes at the expense of a decrease in potential energy.

EXERCISE A 1.2-μC charge is accelerated through a 3400-V potential difference. How much energy does it gain?

Answer: 4.1 mJ

| **EXAMPLE 25-2** | *Potential of a Charged Sheet* |

An isolated, infinite charged sheet carries a uniform surface charge density σ. (a) Find an expression for the potential difference from the sheet to a point a perpendicular distance x from the sheet. (b) What is the potential difference between two points the same distance from the sheet?

Solution

Equation 24-10 gives $E = \dfrac{\sigma}{2\varepsilon_0}$ for the field of a single, isolated sheet of charge. Since the field is uniform we can apply Equation 25-2b. Moving away from the sheet in either direction is going *with* the field (assuming positive σ), so the dot product in Equation 25-2b is positive and therefore the potential difference is negative. Taking $\ell = x$ in Equation 25-2b then gives

$$\Delta V_{0x} = -Ex = -\frac{\sigma x}{2\varepsilon_0},$$

where the subscript $0x$ means we're taking the potential difference from the sheet ($x = 0$) to the point x. Our result makes two important points. First, the minus sign reaffirms that moving in the direction of the electric field entails a decrease in electric potential. Second, the fact that ΔV is directly proportional to x shows that the potential in a *uniform* field varies *linearly* with distance along the field direction. (Here we're beginning to use the term "potential" as a shorthand for, in this case, "the potential difference between the sheet and another point." When we speak of "the potential," we always mean potential difference between two points, one of which is a common reference point—in this case the position of the charged sheet.)

If, on the other hand, we consider moving charge between two points equidistant from the sheet, then the charge moves perpendicular to the field and there is no change in its potential energy; thus, the potential difference between such points is zero.

EXERCISE Two nonconducting charged sheets carry equal but opposite surface charge densities ± 53 nC/m^2. The negative sheet is located at $x = 0$, the positive sheet at $x = 10$ cm. Find expressions for the potential difference from the negative sheet to the points (a) $x = 2.0$ cm, (b) $x = 5.0$ cm, (c) $x = 25$ cm, and (d) $x = -10$ cm. *Hint:* Think about the different fields *between* and *beyond* the plates.

Answers: (a) 120 V; (b) 300 V; (c) 600 V; (d) 0 V

Some problems similar to Examples 25-1 and 25-2: 5, 7–9, 18

Got It!

Does a proton tend to move in the direction of positive or negative potential difference, as measured from its starting point? How about an electron?

Curved Paths and Nonuniform Fields

Equations 25-2 contain a dot product that accounts for the orientation of the path relative to the field. Figure 25-6, for example, shows several straight paths of the same length ℓ in a uniform electric field. Path AB is the same path we considered in Fig. 25-2; the potential difference between its ends is just $\Delta V_{AB} = E\ell$ because the angle between $\mathbf{E}$ and $\boldsymbol{\ell}$ is 180°. Path AC is at 135° to the field direction, giving a potential difference $\Delta V_{AC} = -E\ell \cos 135° = E\ell/\sqrt{2}$. Finally, path AD is perpendicular to the field, giving $\Delta V_{AD} = 0$. Quite generally, as Fig. 25-6 suggests, the potential difference depends only on the component of the path *along* the field direction. This is analogous to the situation with gravity, where the work mgh needed to lift a mass depends only on the *vertical* distance h and not on any horizontal component of the motion.

If the field is not uniform or the path is not straight, then we must use Equation 25-2a to calculate the potential because the magnitude of $\mathbf{E}$ and/or the angle between $\mathbf{E}$ and the path is changing. Figure 25-7 shows that in such cases we can view the integral in Equation 25-2b as the sum of infinitely many infinitesimal potential differences dV. Each is taken over a path segment $d\boldsymbol{\ell}$ so short that it's essentially straight and the field is essentially uniform over the segment. The limits of the integral are the endpoints of the path, and thus include all the infinitesimal potential differences dVs along the path. Because the electric field is conservative, we can evaluate the integral over any path between the given endpoints. Several examples in the next section illustrate the use of Equation 25-2a.

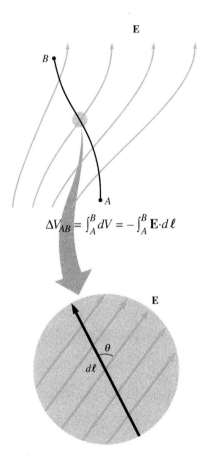

$$\Delta V_{AB} = \int_A^B dV = -\int_A^B \mathbf{E} \cdot d\boldsymbol{\ell}$$

$$dV = -\mathbf{E} \cdot d\boldsymbol{\ell} = -E d\ell \cos\theta$$

FIGURE 25-7 The line integral in Equation 25-2a is the sum of infinitely many infinitesimally small potential differences dV. Each dV is taken over a segment $d\boldsymbol{\ell}$ of the overall path short enough that it's essentially straight and that the electric field is essentially uniform over the segment. Then each dV is given by Equation 25-2b for a straight path in a uniform field: $dV = -\mathbf{E} \cdot d\boldsymbol{\ell}$. Summing—that is, integrating—over the whole path gives Equation 25-2a: $\Delta V_{AB} = -\int_A^B \mathbf{E} \cdot d\boldsymbol{\ell}$.

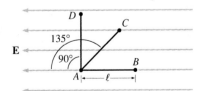

FIGURE 25-6 The potential difference depends only on the component of the path *along* the field. Mathematically, $\Delta V = -\mathbf{E} \cdot \boldsymbol{\ell} = -E\ell \cos\theta$, where the quantity $-\ell \cos\theta$ can be interpreted as the path component along the field.

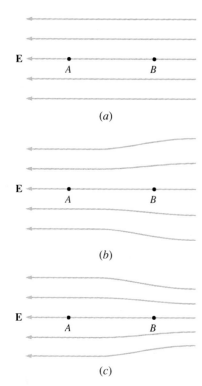

(a)

(b)

(c)

FIGURE 25-8 Which of the potential differences ΔV_{AB} is the lowest? The highest?

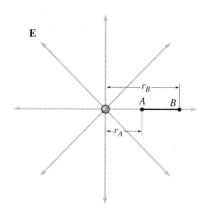

FIGURE 25-9 The potential difference between points A and B is found by integrating between r_A and r_B.

Got It!

Figure 25-8 shows three straight paths AB of the same length, each in a different electric field. The field strength at A is the same in each. Rank the potential differences ΔV_{AB} from lowest to highest.

25-3 CALCULATING POTENTIAL DIFFERENCE

Here we use Equation 25-2a to calculate potential differences for a variety of charge distributions. Most important of these is the point charge. Understanding potential differences in the field of a point charge will deepen your understanding of the concept of electric potential, and provides an easy way to compute potential differences in the fields of more complicated charge distributions.

The Potential of a Point Charge

The electric field of a point charge q is given by Equation 23-3:

$$\mathbf{E} = \frac{kq}{r^2}\hat{\mathbf{r}},$$

where $\hat{\mathbf{r}}$ is a unit vector from the charge toward the point where the field is being evaluated. Consider two points A and B at distances r_A and r_B from a positive point charge, as shown in Fig. 25-9. What is the potential difference between these points? The distance between them is $r_B - r_A$, but we can't just multiply this distance by the electric field because the field varies with position. Instead we integrate, using Equation 25-2a:

$$\Delta V_{AB} = -\int_{r_A}^{r_B} \mathbf{E} \cdot d\boldsymbol{\ell} = -\int_{r_A}^{r_B} \frac{kq}{r^2}\hat{\mathbf{r}} \cdot d\boldsymbol{\ell}.$$

As we move from r_A toward r_B, the path element vectors $d\boldsymbol{\ell}$ correspond to small increments dr in the radial direction, so we write $d\boldsymbol{\ell} = \hat{\mathbf{r}}dr$. Then the potential becomes

$$\Delta V_{AB} = -\int_{r_A}^{r_B} \frac{kq}{r^2}\hat{\mathbf{r}} \cdot \hat{\mathbf{r}}dr = -kq\int_{r_A}^{r_B} r^{-2}\,dr,$$

since the dot product of the unit vector $\hat{\mathbf{r}}$ with itself is simply 1. Evaluating the integral gives

$$\Delta V_{AB} = -kq\left[-\frac{1}{r}\right]_{r_A}^{r_B} = kq\left(\frac{1}{r_B} - \frac{1}{r_A}\right). \qquad (25\text{-}3)$$

Does this result make sense? For $r_B > r_A$ the potential difference is negative, showing that a positive test charge at r_A would "fall down" the potential "hill" toward r_B. Going the other way would require that positive work be done on a positive charge, as it's pushed "up" the potential "hill" against the repulsive force of the charge q. Although we considered q to be positive, our result holds as well for $q < 0$, in which case the sign of the potential difference changes.

Although we derived Equation 25-3 for two points on the same radial line, Fig. 25-10 shows that the result holds for *any* two points in the field of a charge q. It doesn't matter which point is at the greater distance either; if $r_B < r_A$ Equation 25-3 still gives the correct potential difference, which then becomes positive to indicate that work must be done moving a positive test charge *toward* a positive q.

The Zero of Potential

So far we've only talked about potential differences, symbolized by the expression ΔV_{AB}. That's because only differences in potential energy—and thus in electric potential, which is potential energy per unit charge—have physical significance. But as we did with potential energy, it's often convenient to define the **electric potential** at some point as zero and then to measure potential differences relative to that point. We then speak of "the potential at point P," designated $V(P)$ or V_P, and meaning the potential difference V_{0P} *from* our reference point *to* point P. Once we've defined a zero of potential, we can then write potential differences as differences in potential between two points; thus, our terminology ΔV_{AB} can equally well be written $V(B) - V(A)$ or $V_B - V_A$. The choice for the zero of potential is arbitrary and is usually made on the basis of mathematical or physical convenience. In electric power systems, Earth, called "ground," is usually taken as the zero. In automobile electric systems, the car's metal structure makes a convenient zero; this is usually connected electrically to the negative battery terminal. (As we'll soon see, every point on a conductor is at the same potential, so it's appropriate to consider an entire conductor like Earth or a car's metal structure as the "point" of zero potential.)

In dealing with isolated point charges, Equation 25-3 shows that it is convenient to choose the zero of potential at infinity. If we let r_A become arbitrarily large, and drop the subscript on r_B because it can be at any radial distance r, Equation 25-3 becomes

$$V_{\infty r} = V(r) = \frac{kq}{r}. \quad \text{(point-charge potential)} \quad (25\text{-}4)$$

When we call this expression $V(r)$ "the potential of a point charge," we really mean that $V(r)$ is the potential difference going from a point very far from a charge q to a point a distance r from the charge—an interpretation that is consistent with our definition of potential difference as depending on *two* points. Because the field outside any spherically symmetric charge distribution is that of a point charge, Equation 25-4 also gives the potential outside a spherically symmetric charge distribution.

Does it bother you that potential difference can be finite over an infinite distance? The reason lies in the inverse-square dependence of the field, which drops so rapidly that the work done in moving a charge from infinity to the vicinity of a point charge remains finite. We found an analogous result in Chapter 9, where it took only a finite amount of energy—and therefore a finite "escape speed"—to escape completely from a planet's gravitational attraction. As long as a charge distribution is finite in size—so its field at large distances falls at least as fast as $1/r^2$, then it makes sense to take the zero of potential at infinity.

Got It!

You measure a potential difference of 50 V between two points a distance 10 cm apart in the field of a point charge. If you move closer to the charge and measure the potential difference over another 10 cm interval, will it be more, less, or the same?

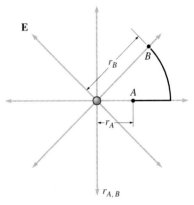

FIGURE 25-10 Here points A and B do not lie on the same radial line. But potential difference is independent of path, and one path between A and B consists of a radial segment and a circular arc. Since **E** is perpendicular to the arc, it takes no work to move a charge along the arc. The potential difference ΔV_{AB} results only from the radial segment, and is therefore given by Equation 25-3. Any other path from A to B would also give the same result.

EXAMPLE 25-3	*A Huge Van de Graaff Generator*

The Hall of Electricity at the Boston Museum of Science contains the world's largest air-insulated Van de Graaff generator, a device that builds up charge on a metal sphere (Fig. 25-11; you may have seen a smaller version used for demonstrations in your physics course). The Boston museum's generator has a sphere of radius $R = 2.3$ m that develops a charge of 640 μC, spread essentially uniformly over its surface. (a) What is the potential at the sphere's surface, with the zero of potential taken at infinity? (b) How much work would it take to bring a proton from infinity to the sphere's surface? (c) What is the potential difference from the sphere's surface to a point located $2R$ from its center?

Solution

(a) The field outside the sphere is that of a point charge Q located at the sphere's center, so the potential difference between infinity and any point *outside* the sphere is given by Equation 25-4. Therefore the potential at the sphere's surface is

$$V(R) = \frac{kQ}{R} = 2.5 \text{ MV},$$

with the numbers given for the museum's device.

(b) This quantity, 2.5 MV, is the work per unit charge needed to move from infinity to the sphere's surface, so the work required for a specific charge q is qV. Since a proton carries one elementary charge e, the work needed to bring the proton to the sphere is 2.5 MeV or 4.0×10^{-13} J.

(c) To get the potential difference from the surface ($r = R$) to $2R$, we could use Equation 25-3 with $r_B = 2R$ and $r_A = R$. But it's perhaps easiest to keep in mind just Equation 25-4 and then find the potential difference by subtracting the potentials at the two points:

$$\Delta V_{R\,2R} = V(2R) - V(R) = \frac{kQ}{2R} - \frac{kQ}{R} = -\frac{kQ}{2R},$$

or -1.25 MV in this example. Does this make sense? Yes: the negative result shows that electric potential decreases as we move in the direction of the electric field—that is, away from the positively charged sphere. Our result also shows that fully half the potential difference between the sphere and infinity

FIGURE 25-11 This Van de Graaff generator at the Boston Museum of Science puts some 640 μC on a 2.3-m-radius sphere, developing a potential difference of several million volts between the sphere and its surroundings. Here, sparks jump to a nearby conductor as the local electric field exceeds the breakdown field in air.

occurs within one radius of the sphere's surface—a consequence of the rapid $1/r^2$ decrease in the field.

You can convince yourself that with a 640-μC charge, the electric field at the sphere's surface is close to the 3 N/C breakdown field in air. Bringing another conductor nearby increases the local field, drawing the sparks shown in Fig. 25-11.

EXERCISE The potential at the surface of a 10-cm-radius sphere is 4.8 kV. (a) What is the charge on the sphere, assuming it's distributed in a spherically symmetric fashion? (b) What is the electric field at its surface? Assume here—and anytime it's not specified—that potential differences are taken from infinity.

Answers: (a) 53 nC; (b) 48 kN/C

Some problems similar to Example 25-3: 19–23, 25, 26, 52, 63, 69

Potentials of Arbitrary Charge Distributions

If we already know the field of a charge distribution, we can calculate potential differences by applying Equation 25-2a, as we did for the point-charge field. Example 25-4 illustrates this approach.

EXAMPLE 25-4	*A Power Line*

A long, straight power line is made from wire with radius $r_A = 1.0$ cm and carries a line charge density $\lambda = 2.6\ \mu C/m$ (Fig. 25-12). Assuming no other charges are present, what is the potential difference between the surface of the wire and the ground, a distance $r_B = 22$ m below?

Solution

We treat the wire as an infinitely long, charged rod. In the preceding chapter we used Gauss's law to show that the electric field outside any cylindrically symmetric charge distribution is the same as that of a line charge, namely

$$\mathbf{E} = \frac{\lambda}{2\pi\varepsilon_0 r}\hat{\mathbf{r}}.$$

We want to evaluate the potential difference in this field from the wire surface at r_A to the ground at r_B, as suggested in Fig. 25-12b. For a straight path between these points, we can again write $d\boldsymbol{\ell} = \hat{\mathbf{r}}\,dr$ just as we did in evaluating the point-charge potential. Then Equation 25-2a becomes

$$\Delta V_{AB} = -\int_{r_A}^{r_B}\mathbf{E}\cdot d\boldsymbol{\ell} = -\int_{r_A}^{r_B}\frac{\lambda}{2\pi\varepsilon_0 r}\hat{\mathbf{r}}\cdot\hat{\mathbf{r}}\,dr$$

$$= -\frac{\lambda}{2\pi\varepsilon_0}\int_{r_A}^{r_B}\frac{dr}{r} = -\frac{\lambda}{2\pi\varepsilon_0}\ln r\,\Big|_{r_A}^{r_B} \qquad (25\text{-}5)$$

$$= \frac{\lambda}{2\pi\varepsilon_0}\ln\left(\frac{r_A}{r_B}\right),$$

where the last step follows because $\ln x - \ln y = \ln(x/y)$. For the numbers of this example, this result gives $\Delta V = -360$ kV, a value typical of long-distance electric power transmission lines. Why negative? Because the charge on the wire is positive, so moving away from the wire means moving in the direction of the field—which is always the direction of lower potential.

Note that we cannot let r_B go to infinity in the case of a truly infinite wire, for that would give an infinite potential difference. Physically, this reflects the fact that the charge distribution is itself of infinite extent. Mathematically, it reflects the slow $1/r$ decrease in field strength.

The calculation in this example is not entirely accurate, because the nearby presence of other wires and of charges drawn to the surface of the ground alters the field somewhat.

(a)

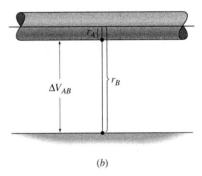

(b)

FIGURE 25-12 (a) A long, straight power line can be approximated as an infinite charged rod whose field is that of a line charge. (b) We want the potential difference from the wire surface, a distance r_A from the wire's axis, to the ground a distance r_B below. The wire carries uniform line charge density λ, and extends indefinitely to left and right. Diagram is not to scale, and we're ignoring the presence of other nearby wires.

Nevertheless, the example correctly illustrates the logarithmic dependence of potential on position in the $1/r$ field of a line charge.

EXERCISE An infinitely long rod of radius R carries a uniform volume charge density ρ; Problem 24-31 shows that the electric field *inside* this rod points radially outward and has magnitude $E = \rho r/2\varepsilon_0$. Use Equation 25-2a to find the potential difference from the rod's surface to its axis.

Answer: $\rho R^2/4\varepsilon_0$

Some problems similar to Example 25-4: 28, 29, 64, 73

Finding Potential Differences Using Superposition

When we don't know the field of a charge distribution, or the field is too complicated to integrate easily, we can find the potential using superposition. This often provides an easier approach to calculating the field as well.

Consider a charge q being brought from infinity to a point P in the vicinity of some other charges. We want to know the potential at P—by which we mean the work per unit charge required to move from infinity to P. The superposition principle states that the electric field of a charge distribution is the sum of the fields of the individual charges comprising the distribution. Therefore the work per unit charge—that is, the potential difference—between infinity and P is just the sum of the potential differences associated with the individual point charges. Mathematically, we find $V(P)$ by summing Equation 25-4 over the individual point charges q_i:

$$V(P) = \sum_i \frac{kq_i}{r_i}, \tag{25-6}$$

where the r_i's are the distances from each of the charges to the point P. Equation 25-6 has one enormous advantage over its counterpart for the electric field, Equation 23-4. Electric potential is a *scalar,* so the sum in Equation 25-6 is a scalar sum, and there's no need to consider angles, vector components, or unit vectors.

EXAMPLE 25-5	*The Dipole Potential*

The dipole of Fig. 25-13 consists of two point charges $\pm q$ separated by a distance $2a$. Find the potential at an arbitrary point P, taking the zero of potential at infinity.

Solution

Note first that this is a more ambitious example than the dipole field calculations in Chapter 23, which for mathematical simplicity were restricted to the dipole axis and perpendicular bisector. Here, since potential is a scalar, we can easily calculate the dipole potential *anywhere.* To do so, we sum the potentials of the individual point charges, as Equation 25-6 suggests:

$$V(P) = \sum_i \frac{kq_i}{r_i} = \frac{kq}{r_1} + \frac{k(-q)}{r_2} = kq\left(\frac{1}{r_1} - \frac{1}{r_2}\right)$$
$$= \frac{kq(r_2 - r_1)}{r_1 r_2},$$

where r_1 and r_2 are the distances from P to the positive and negative charges, respectively.

We're often interested in the electrical effects of a dipole at distances great compared with the separation of its two charges. For example, we saw in Chapter 23 how many molecules can be modeled as dipoles, and how effects such as the van der Waals force involve interactions among distant molecules. If r is the distance from the dipole's center to P, then in the limit $r \gg a$ the quantity $r_1 r_2$ becomes approximately r^2, and, as Fig. 25-13 shows, $r_2 - r_1 \simeq 2a\cos\theta$. Then the dipole potential for $r \gg a$ becomes

$$V(r, \theta) = \frac{k(2aq)\cos\theta}{r^2} = \frac{kp\cos\theta}{r^2}, \tag{25-7}$$

with $p = 2aq$ the dipole moment.

Note that the dipole potential drops more rapidly with distance than the point-charge potential, just as the dipole field drops more rapidly with distance than the point-charge field Note also that Equation 25-7 gives $V = 0$ along the perpendic-

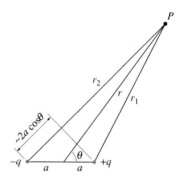

FIGURE 25-13 A dipole and a point P where its potential is to be evaluated. When P is far from the dipole, then r_2 is longer than r_1 by approximately $2a\cos\theta$. (The angle whose vertex is $-q$ is very nearly θ.)

ular bisector of the dipole ($\theta = 90°$). That makes sense because a charge approaching the dipole along its bisector moves at right angles to the dipole field, so no work need be done. Since potential difference is path independent, that means it takes no net work to move on *any* path from infinity to a point on the dipole's bisector (see Question 20).

Figure 25-14 shows a three-dimensional plot of the dipole potential (Equation 25-7) in the plane of Fig. 25-13. The positive charge corresponds to a "hill" of high potential and the negative charge to a deep "hole." Points on the right side of the diagram are closer to the positive charge and are therefore elevated relative to the zero of potential; this is reflected in the positive value of $\cos\theta$ for $\theta < 90°$ in Equation 25-7. Points on the left side are closer to the negative charge and are all depressed relative to zero potential; here $\cos\theta$ in Equation 25-7 is negative. The perpendicular bisector, with $\cos\theta = 0$ and therefore $V = 0$, is a level, straight line, neither elevated nor depressed.

FIGURE 25-14 Three-dimensional plot of potential as a function of position in the plane of Fig. 25-13. Edges of the diagram are at nearly the zero of potential; perpendicular bisector is at exactly $V = 0$.

EXERCISE The dipole moment of a water molecule is 6.2×10^{-30} C·m. (a) Find the potential difference $V_B - V_A$ between two points on the axis of the molecular dipole, where points A and B are 8.2 nm and 5.1 nm, respectively, from the center. Both points are closer to the positive end. (b) How much work would it take to move a proton from A to B?

Answers: (a) 1.32 mV; (b) 1.32 meV $= 2.1 \times 10^{-22}$ J

Some problems similar to Example 25-5: 31–34, 74

Continuous Charge Distributions

We can calculate the potential of a continuous charge distribution by considering it to be made up of infinitely many infinitesimal charge elements dq. Each acts like a point charge and therefore contributes to the potential at some point P an amount dV given by

$$dV = \frac{k\, dq}{r},$$

where the zero of potential is at infinity. The potential at P is the sum—in this case an integral—of the contributions dV from all the charge elements:

$$V = \int dV = \int \frac{k\, dq}{r}, \qquad (25\text{-}8)$$

where the integration is over the entire charge distribution.

The examples that follow illustrate the use of Equation 25-8 for some charge distributions whose simple shapes make the integration reasonably straightforward. Simple cases such as these can often serve as approximations to more complicated charge distributions.

EXAMPLE 25-6	*A Charged Ring*

A total charge Q is distributed uniformly around a thin ring of radius a, as shown in Fig. 25-15. What is the potential on the axis of this charged ring?

Solution

Let x be the distance from the center of the ring to some arbitrary point P on the axis. The distance from each point on the ring to P is the same, and is given by $r = \sqrt{x^2 + a^2}$. The potential on the axis is the sum of the potentials dV of all the charge elements dq around the ring, as described by

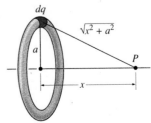

FIGURE 25-15 A charged ring (Example 25-6).

Equation 25-8:

$$V(x) = k \int_{ring} \frac{dq}{r} = \frac{k}{\sqrt{x^2 + a^2}} \int_{ring} dq \,,$$

where we've taken $r = \sqrt{x^2 + a^2}$ outside the integral because it's the same for all charge elements. The remaining integral is just the total charge Q, so we have

$$V(x) = \frac{kQ}{\sqrt{x^2 + a^2}} \,. \qquad (25\text{-}9)$$

Does this result make sense? At great distances from the ring ($x \gg a$), a^2 in the denominator becomes negligible, and our result becomes

$$V(x) = \frac{kQ}{x} \,,$$

which is just the potential of a point charge Q—as we would expect when we're so far from the ring that its size is no longer significant. At the center of the ring, on the other hand, Equation 25-9 gives

$$V(o) = \frac{kQ}{a} \,.$$

Here we're a distance a from all parts of the ring, and, since potential is a *scalar* the directions to those parts don't matter. The result is therefore the same as being a distance a from a point charge Q.

EXAMPLE 25-7	*A Charged Disk*

A charged disk of radius a carries a total charge Q distributed uniformly over its surface. What is the potential at a point P on the disk axis, a distance x from the disk?

Solution

To use Equation 25-8, we must divide the disk into charge elements dq. In the preceding example we found the potential of a charged ring, so we can take the charge elements of our disk to be thin rings (see Fig. 25-16), and integrate over all the rings that make up the disk. If a ring-shaped charge element has charge dq and radius r, then Equation 25-9 gives its potential dV a distance x from the disk center:

$$dV = \frac{k \, dq}{\sqrt{x^2 + r^2}} \,.$$

Then the potential of the entire disk is

$$V(x) = \int_{ring} dV = \int_{r=0}^{r=a} \frac{k \, dq}{\sqrt{x^2 + r^2}} \,.$$

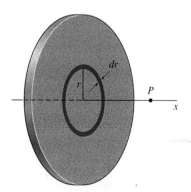

FIGURE 25-16 A charged disk, showing a ring-shaped charge element dq of radius r and width dr.

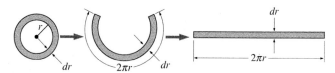

FIGURE 25-17 Unwinding the thin ring gives a strip of width dr and length $2\pi r$.

To evaluate this integral, we must relate r and dq. "Unwinding" the ring gives a strip of area $2\pi r \, dr$ (Fig. 25-17). The surface charge density σ is the total charge divided by the disk area: $\sigma = Q/\pi a^2$. Then the charge dq on our infinitesimal ring of area $2\pi r \, dr$ is

$$dq = \sigma 2\pi r \, dr = \frac{Q}{\pi a^2} 2\pi r \, dr = \frac{2Q}{a^2} r \, dr \,.$$

Using this result in the integral for the potential gives

$$V(x) = \int_0^a \frac{2kQ}{a^2} \frac{r \, dr}{\sqrt{x^2 + r^2}} = \frac{kQ}{a^2} \int_0^a \frac{2r \, dr}{\sqrt{x^2 + r^2}} \,.$$

Note that $2r \, dr = d(r^2) = d(x^2 + r^2)$ since x is a constant with respect to the integration. The integral therefore has the form $u^{-1/2} \, du$, where $u = x^2 + r^2$, and the result is $2u^{1/2}$ or

$$V(x) = \frac{2kQ}{a^2} \sqrt{x^2 + r^2} \, \Big|_{r=0}^{r=a} = \frac{2kQ}{a^2} (\sqrt{x^2 + a^2} - |x|) \,.$$

Figure 25-18 shows that this complicated-looking result makes sense: Close to the sheet, the potential resembles that of an infinite sheet, while far from the disk it approaches the potential of a point charge. Example 25-9 and Problem 70 explore these limiting cases further.

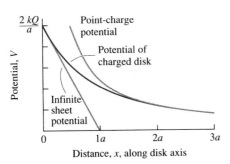

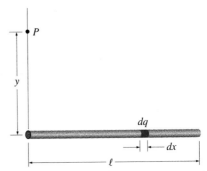

FIGURE 25-18 Charged-disk potential of Equation 25-10 approaches the potential of an infinite sheet for points close to the disk, and that of a point charge far from the disk.

FIGURE 25-19 What is the potential at P? Figure shows a charge element dq, of length dx, to use in the integration for the potential.

EXERCISE Point P in Fig. 25-19 lies a perpendicular distance y from the end of a uniformly charged rod of length ℓ and total charge Q. Find an expression for the potential at P, taking the zero of potential at infinity.

Answer: $V(y) = \dfrac{kQ}{\ell} \ln \left(\dfrac{\ell + \sqrt{\ell^2 + y^2}}{y} \right)$

Some problems similar to Examples 25-6 and 25-7: 36–39, 71, 78

25-4 POTENTIAL DIFFERENCE AND THE ELECTRIC FIELD

Equipotentials

It takes no work to move a charge at right angles to an electric field. Therefore there can be no potential difference between two points on a surface that is everywhere perpendicular to the electric field. Such surfaces are called **equipotential surfaces**, or simply **equipotentials**. Figure 25-20 shows some equipotential surfaces for both uniform and nonuniform electric fields.

Equipotentials are like contour lines that show land elevation on a map (Fig. 25-21). A contour line is a line of constant elevation, and therefore, it takes

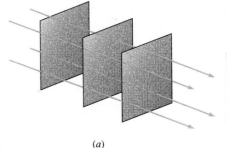

(a)

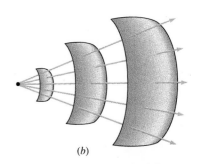

(b)

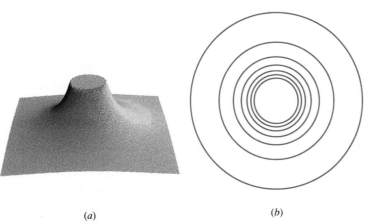

(a)   (b)

FIGURE 25-21 (a) A flat-topped hill and (b) its representation as a contour map. Closely spaced contours indicate steep slopes. Figures can also represent the potential of a uniformly charged spherical shell whose potential is constant inside, where **E** = 0, and falls as $1/r$ outside. In this case (a) is a 3-dimensional plot of the potential in a plane through the center of the sphere, and (b) shows the intersection of the three-dimensional equipotential surfaces (as shown in Fig. 25-20b) with this plane. Closely spaced contours indicate strong electric field.

FIGURE 25-20 (a) Equipotential surfaces in a uniform electric field are planes perpendicular to the field. (b) In a nonuniform field (here that of a point charge) the equipotential surfaces are curved (here they're spherical), but are still perpendicular to the field.

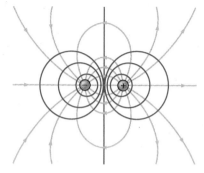

FIGURE 25-22 Equipotentials and field lines for a dipole, in a plane containing the dipole. The two sets of curves are everywhere perpendicular. Equipotentials on the left side represent negative values of potential; those on the right positive values. The perpendicular bisector is the special equipotential on which $V = 0$. In three dimensions it would be a plane and the other equipotentials would be closed surfaces. You should convince yourself that this figure is essentially a contour map of Fig. 25-14.

no work to move along a contour line. Contour lines are usually spaced at even increments of elevation. Where lines are closely spaced, the elevation changes rapidly. Similarly, closely spaced equipotentials indicate large potential differences between nearby points. That, in turn, means it takes a lot of work to move charge between those points—and therefore there must be a large electric field present. Figure 25-21 might just as well represent electric potential, in which case regions with closely spaced equipotentials—steep slopes on the "potential hill"—indicate large electric fields. Similarly, the equipotentials for a dipole (Fig. 25-22) describe the steep "hill" of the positive charge and a correspondingly deep "hole" of the negative charge that we showed in Fig. 25-14. Activ-Physics Activity 11.9 draws equipotentials for common charge distributions.

11.9

Electric Potential

Got It!

Figure 25-23 shows cross sections through two sets of equipotential surfaces. In both figures the potential difference between adjacent equipotentials is the same. Which could represent the potential of a point charge? Explain.

(a)

(b)

FIGURE 25-23 Which equipotential diagram is for a point charge?

Calculating the Field from the Potential

Given electric field lines, we can construct equipotentials. Conversely, given equipotentials we can reconstruct the field by sketching field lines at right angles to the equipotentials. Specifying the potential at each point thus conveys all the information needed to determine the field.

We can quantify the relation between potential and field by writing the potential difference dV between two points separated by an infinitesimal displacement $d\ell$:

$$dV = -\mathbf{E} \cdot d\ell = -E_\ell \, d\ell,$$

where E_ℓ designates the field component in the direction of $d\ell$. Rearranging this equation gives

$$E_\ell = -\frac{dV}{d\ell}. \tag{25-10}$$

This equation confirms our statement that the electric field is strong where potential changes rapidly with distance. The minus sign in Equation 25-10 is the same one that appears in Equation 25-2; here it tells us that if we move in the direction of *increasing* potential, then we must be moving *against* the electric field. If we want to find the field components in a chosen coordinate system, we simply choose $d\ell$ along one of the coordinate axes and apply Equation 25-10; the x component of the field, for example, is given by $E_x = -dV/dx$. (If V is a function of all three coordinates we should, strictly speaking, write E_x in terms of the *partial* derivative, $\partial V/\partial x$, that we introduced in Chapter 16.) ActivPhysics Activity 11.10 explores graphically the relation between potential and electric field.

11.10

Electric Potential, Field, and Force

Equation 25-10 also shows that the units of electric field—introduced in Chapter 23 as N/C—can be written, equivalently, as V/m. You can see from an equipotential diagram why this unit makes sense: where the equipotentials are close, and the field therefore strong, you traverse a greater potential difference in a given distance—i.e., more "volts per meter." In fact, the electric field is sometimes called the "potential gradient," meaning the rate of change of potential with respect to position.

EXAMPLE 25-8	The Field of a Point Charge

Use the point-charge potential of Equation 25-4 to derive the electric field of a point charge.

Solution
The point-charge potential, $V(r) = kq/r$, depends only on r. Therefore the electric field points in the radial direction, and has the form $\mathbf{E} = E_r\hat{\mathbf{r}}$. Choosing $d\ell = dr$ in Equation 25-10

gives the field component:

$$E_r = -\frac{dV}{dr} = -\frac{d}{dr}\left(\frac{kq}{r}\right) = -kq\frac{d(r^{-1})}{dr} = kqr^{-2} = \frac{kq}{r^2}.$$

Thus $\mathbf{E} = \frac{kq}{r^2}\hat{\mathbf{r}}$, as expected.

EXAMPLE 25-9	The Field of a Charged Disk

Use the result of Example 25-7 to find the electric field on the axis of a charged disk.

Solution
Symmetry shows that the field must point along the disk axis, which is the x axis in Fig. 25-16. So the field has only an x component, given by applying Equation 25-10 to the disk potential:

$$E_x = -\frac{dV}{dx} = -\frac{d}{dx}\left(\frac{2kQ}{a^2}(\sqrt{x^2 + a^2} - |x|)\right)$$

$$= \frac{2kQ}{a^2}\left(1 - \frac{|x|}{\sqrt{x^2 + a^2}}\right).$$

To see that this makes sense, consider the case $x \ll a$, for which the field becomes approximately $2kQ/a^2$. Writing Q as the surface density σ times the area πa^2 gives $E_x = 2\pi k\sigma = \sigma/2\varepsilon_0$, which is the field of an infinite charged sheet. Of course—very close to the disk it looks effectively infinite, and its field should be well approximated by that of an infinite sheet. Problem 70 shows that the field far from the disk approaches that of a point charge Q.

EXERCISE Use Equations 25-7 and 25-10 to calculate the electric field on the axis of a point dipole, and show that your result is equivalent to Equation 23-5b.

Some problems similar to Examples 25-8 and 25-9: 47–49, 78

Examples 25-8 and 25-9 show that it is often much easier to calculate the electric field by first finding the potential and then differentiating, rather than doing a vector integration to get the field of a complicated charge distribution.

It's important to recognize that the *values* of the field and potential are not directly related; rather, as Equation 25-10 indicates, the field measures the *rate of change* of the potential. Field and potential are like acceleration and velocity; the *values* of the two are quite independent, with the former depending on the *rate of change* of the latter. Figure 25-24 and Example 25-10 illustrate the relation between potential and field.

Got It!

Is it possible to have a point where the electric field is zero but the potential is not? What about a point where the potential is zero but the field is not?

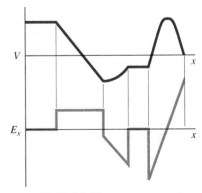

FIGURE 25-24 The x component of the electric field is the negative rate of change of the potential with respect to x.

EXAMPLE 25-10	*Potential and Field*

A positive charge $+2q$ lies at $x = -a$, and a charge $-q$ lies at $x = +a$ as shown in Fig. 25-25. (a) Derive an expression for the potential on the x axis, and find a point on the axis in the region $x > a$ where the potential (with respect to infinity) is zero. (b) Use your expression for potential to find the electric field for $x > a$. Is the electric field zero where the potential is zero? If not, where is the field zero?

Solution

(a) The distance from any point x to the positive charge at $-a$ is $r_+ = |x - (-a)| = |x + a|$; similarly, the distance to the negative charge is $r_- = |x - a|$. Thus, the potential on the axis is

$$V(x) = \frac{k(2q)}{r_+} + \frac{k(-q)}{r_-} = kq\left(\frac{2}{|x+a|} - \frac{1}{|x-a|}\right).$$

We can find where $V = 0$ by setting the quantity in parentheses to zero. For $x > a$ both denominators are positive and we can remove the absolute value signs. For $V = 0$ we then have

$$\frac{2}{x+a} = \frac{1}{x-a}.$$

Solving for x gives $x = 3a$.

(b) The field clearly has only an x component, and Equation 25-10 then gives

$$E_x = -\frac{dV}{dx} = -kq\frac{d}{dx}\left(\frac{2}{x+a} - \frac{1}{x-a}\right)$$

$$= \frac{2kQ}{(x+a)^2} - \frac{kQ}{(x-a)^2}.$$

This result is hardly surprising: It's just the sum of two point-charge fields. We actually solved for the zero-field point in this configuration in Example 23-3; there we found that the electric force would be zero at $x = 5.83a$, which is *not* the same place where the potential is zero.

Figure 25-26 shows the potential of this charge distribution in the region $x > a$, showing clearly the point $x = 3a$ where

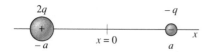

FIGURE 25-25 Two opposite but unequal charges.

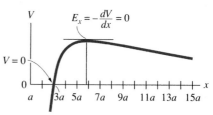

FIGURE 25-26 Potential on the x axis for a charge distribution consisting of $+2q$ at $x = -a$ and $-q$ at $x = +a$. Shown here is the region $x > a$, including the point $x = 3a$ where the potential is zero and the point $x = 5.83a$ where the electric field—proportional to the *slope* of the potential curve—is zero. This graph shows potential along the x axis only in the region to the right of the negative charge. Leftmost part of curve shows the potential "hole" associated with the negative charge.

$V = 0$. Getting a charge to this point from infinity would take no *net* work, although it would require going up and then down a potential "hill." Also clear in Fig. 25-26 is the point $x = 5.83a$ where the electric field is zero. Note that this is the point where the *slope* of the potential curve is zero, *not* where the potential itself is zero.

There are actually two points on the x axis where $V = 0$; the second lies between the charges. Both lie on an equipotential surface of zero potential that surrounds the negative charge.

> **Tip**
>
> *Field and Potential Are Not Proportional* In particular, where one is zero, the other need not be zero. You can see that in Fig. 25-26, where it clearly takes work to get from infinity to the point where $E = 0$. Just because a mountaintop is flat doesn't mean it didn't take work to climb it! Potential depends not on the field at a point but on the field over an entire path from infinity to that point. Similarly, the potential can be zero at points where the field is not, as evidenced by the steep slope of the potential curve in Fig. 25-26 at the point where it crosses zero.

EXERCISE Find the second point on the x axis in Example 25-10 where the potential is zero.

Answer: $x = a/3$

Some problems similar to Example 25-10: 50, 77

25-5 POTENTIALS OF CHARGED CONDUCTORS

There is no electric field inside a conductor in electrostatic equilibrium, as we found in Chapter 24, so it takes no work to move a test charge around inside the conductor. We also found that the field at the conductor surface is perpendicular to the surface, so it takes no work to move a test charge along the surface, either. Therefore the potential difference between two points in or on a conductor must be zero, and thus,

| *A conductor in electrostatic equilibrium is an equipotential.*

Consider an isolated, spherical conductor of radius R carrying charge Q. Since the conductor is isolated, charge is distributed uniformly over its surface, so the field and potential outside the sphere are that of a point charge. Then the potential at its surface is

$$V(R) = \frac{kQ}{R},\qquad\qquad (25\text{-}11)$$

as we found in Example 25-3. The sphere itself is an equipotential, so the potential *difference* between two points *on the sphere* is zero. But that doesn't mean the potential difference between *infinity* and the sphere is zero; since the sphere is charged, it takes work to move charge to its surface from infinity, and that's what Equation 25-11 says.

Now consider two widely separated spheres of different sizes. If we connect them by a thin conducting wire, as shown in Fig. 25-27, then the system constitutes a single conductor, and charge will move through the wire until both spheres are at the same potential. But since the spheres are widely separated, each still has an essentially spherical charge distribution, so Equation 25-11 applies to each. Since the spheres have the same potential, Equation 25-11 implies that

FIGURE 25-27 Two conducting spheres held at the same potential by a conducting wire. The surface charge density is greater on the smaller sphere, in inverse proportion to its radius.

$$\frac{kQ_1}{R_1} = \frac{kQ_2}{R_2},$$

where the subscripts label the two spheres. We can write each charge as the surface area of the sphere multiplied by the surface charge density: $Q = 4\pi R^2 \sigma$. Substituting for the Q's in the above equation and solving for the ratio of surface charge densities then gives

$$\frac{\sigma_1}{\sigma_2} = \frac{R_2}{R_1}.$$

Thus the *smaller* sphere has the *larger* surface charge density. Since the electric field at a conductor surface has magnitude $E = \sigma/\varepsilon_0$, the field must be stronger at the smaller sphere.

This discussion of spherical conductors provides a qualitative description of nonspherical conductors as well. All parts of an irregularly shaped conductor must be at the same potential. Where the conductor surface curves sharply, it is like a small sphere and therefore has a higher surface charge density and a stronger electric field. In general, the field is strongest where the surface curves most sharply.

Because a conductor surface is an equipotential and the electric field is perpendicular to the conductor surface, equipotentials just above the surface must have approximately the same shape as the surface. Because the electric field is stronger where the conductor surface curves sharply, there must be more

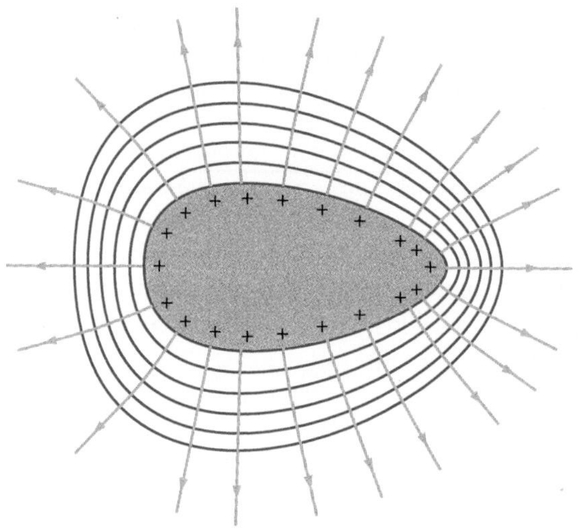

FIGURE 25-28 A charged conductor of irregular shape. Equipotentials near the conductor have approximately its shape, and the field is strongest—and therefore the equipotentials closest—where the conductor curves most sharply.

field lines emerging from such regions. Far from a charged conductor, on the other hand, its field must resemble that of a point charge, with radial field lines and circular equipotentials. With these limiting cases in mind, we can sketch the approximate form for the field of an arbitrarily shaped conductor (Fig. 25-28).

We stress that our conclusion about surface charge density and curvature applies only to *isolated* conductors—those far from any other charges. The field of a nearby charge will modify the charge distribution of a conductor, altering the surface charge distribution (Fig. 25-29).

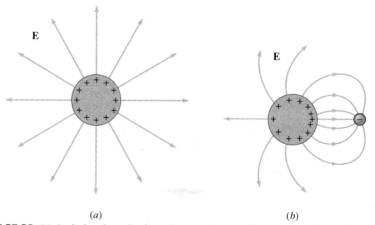

(a) (b)

FIGURE 25-29 (a) An isolated conducting sphere carries a uniform surface charge density and has a spherically symmetric electric field. (b) The presence of a nearby charge distorts the surface charge distribution and therefore the electric field.

APPLICATION	*Corona Discharge, Pollution Control, and Xerography*

The large electric fields that develop where a charged conductor is sharply curved can cause serious problems in electrical equipment; in other applications those fields are put to good use. Fields above 3 MN/C are strong enough to strip electrons from air molecules, making the air a conductor. Breakdown of air is often evidenced by a blue glow around sharply-pointed conductors (Fig. 25-30). Called **corona discharge**, this glow results from the recombination of electrons with atoms. Corona discharge causes loss of power from high-voltage transmission lines, and engineers try to avoid it by eliminating sharp edges on wires and other conducting structures.

Corona discharge is put to good use in the **electrostatic precipitator**, a pollution-control device used especially on coal-burning power plants (Fig. 25-31). A typical precipitator consists of parallel metal plates with thin wires running between them. Application of a high voltage between plates and wires sets up large electric fields near the wires. Exhaust gases flow between the plates and the field ionizes some gas molecules. These charged molecules, in turn, attach themselves to pollutant particles. The charged particles are driven to the collecting plates by the electric field. Every few minutes a mechanical vibrator taps the plates and the particles fall into a hopper, where they can be trucked away to use for fill or in making products such as cinder blocks. A typical power plant produces some 30 pounds of particulates every second, and electrostatic precipitators remove up to 99 percent of this. Since the implementation of the Clean Air Act in the early 1960s, widespread use of electrostatic precipitators has significantly reduced particulate air pollution in the United States. However, precipitators do not remove gases like SO_2 that causes acid rain or CO_2 that contributes to global warming, and they also consume several percent of a power plant's electrical output.

(a)

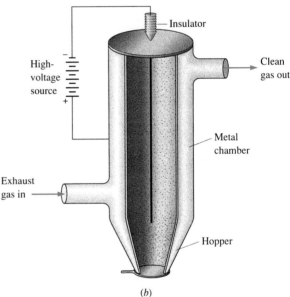

(b)

FIGURE 25-31 (*a*) Electrostatic precipitators at a 1300-MW coal-burning power plant. (*b*) In the electrostatic precipitator, high voltage applied between the metal chamber and the thin central wire results in a strong, nonuniform electric field near the wire. This field ionizes air molecules, which attach to soot particles with the result that the particles are accelerated to the chamber walls. Mechanical vibration then dislodges the particles into the hopper for eventual collection. Parallel metal plates are often used instead of the cylindrical chamber shown here.

Xerography (literally, "dry writing") used in copiers and laser printers is another widespread application of corona discharge. The process starts with the uniform charging of a special photoconductive plate by corona discharge from a thin wire maintained at about 5 kV relative to the plate (Fig. 25-32a). Light, imaged in a copier from the document being copied or from a computer-controlled scanning laser

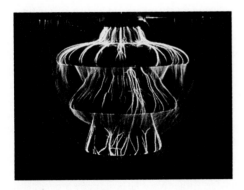

FIGURE 25-30 Corona discharge on a power-line insulator occurs because of strong electric fields that develop where a highly charged conducting wire is attached to the top of the insulator.

FIGURE 25-32 A step-by-step look at the xerography process, widely used in copiers and laser printers.

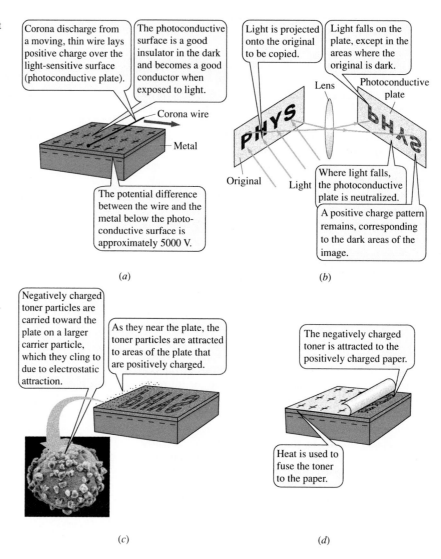

Corona discharge from a moving, thin wire lays positive charge over the light-sensitive surface (photoconductive plate).

The photoconductive surface is a good insulator in the dark and becomes a good conductor when exposed to light.

Corona wire

Metal

The potential difference between the wire and the metal below the photoconductive surface is approximately 5000 V.

(a)

Light is projected onto the original to be copied.

Light falls on the plate, except in the areas where the original is dark.

Lens

Photoconductive plate

Original

Light

Where light falls, the photoconductive plate is neutralized.

A positive charge pattern remains, corresponding to the dark areas of the image.

(b)

Negatively charged toner particles are carried toward the plate on a larger carrier particle, which they cling to due to electrostatic attraction.

As they near the plate, the toner particles are attracted to areas of the plate that are positively charged.

The negatively charged toner is attracted to the positively charged paper.

Heat is used to fuse the toner to the paper.

(c)

(d)

beam in a printer, then strikes the plate. The photoconductive material has the property that it is a good insulator in the dark, but the energy contained in light incident on it can dislodge electrons, creating free charge and making illuminated areas of the material a conductor. These free charges flow to neutralize the surface charge on illuminated areas of the plate, but dark areas retain their charge. At this point, then, the photoconductive plate contains an electrostatic version of the image being reproduced (Fig. 25-32b).

Next, a fine dusting of charged particles called toner is spread over the plate, often delivered on larger so-called carrier particles (Fig. 25-32c). The toner sticks to the charged parts of the photoconductive plate, and is then transferred to a sheet of charged paper (Fig. 25-32d). Finally, heating fuses the toner particles into the paper, making a permanent image.

In practical copiers the photoconductive surface may take the form of a flat plate charged by a moving corona wire, as we've shown in Fig. 25-32, or a moving belt or rotating drum with a fixed wire. The charge spread on the plate may be positive or negative, depending on the particular photoconductive material; inorganic silicon or selenium-based materials are positively charged, as shown in Fig. 25-32, while organic photoconductors, incorporating zinc oxide or cadmium sulfide, are charged negatively. Some copiers, especially smaller ones designed for intermittent use, eliminate the reusable carrier particles that transfer toner to the plate, and instead incorporate magnetic materials within the toner and employ magnets to effect the transfer. Either way, the basic copy process is electrostatic, with toner particles clinging to the unexposed parts of the plate because of the electric force.

CHAPTER SYNOPSIS

Summary

1. The **electric potential difference** between two points is the change in potential energy per unit charge for a charge moved between those points. Its unit is the joule/coulomb, or **volt** (V). Potential difference is a property of two points; because the electric field is conservative, the potential difference between two points is independent of the path taken between them. The potential difference ΔV_{AB} between points A and B is given by

$$\Delta V_{AB} = -\int_A^B \mathbf{E} \cdot d\boldsymbol{\ell}.$$

When the field is uniform, this expression reduces to

$$\Delta V_{AB} = -\mathbf{E} \cdot \boldsymbol{\ell}.$$

2. Defining the potential to be zero at some point allows us to speak of "the potential at a point," meaning the potential difference from the reference point to the point in question. For isolated point charges, a convenient zero is infinitely far from the charge; then the potential at an arbitrary point a distance r from the point charge q is

$$V(r) = \frac{kq}{r}. \qquad \text{(point-charge potential)}$$

The potentials of charge distributions may be found by taking the line integral of the field, if the latter is known, or by summing the potentials of the point charges making up the distribution:

$$V = \sum_i \frac{kq_i}{r_i}, \quad \binom{\text{discrete}}{\text{charges}} \quad \text{or}$$

$$V = \int \frac{k\,dq}{r}. \quad \binom{\text{continuous charge}}{\text{distribution}}$$

3. **Equipotentials** are surfaces over which the potential has a constant value. Equipotentials are everywhere perpendicular to the electric field. The field is strong where equipotentials are closely spaced and vice versa. Mathematically, the field component in a given direction is related to the rate of change of potential with position in that direction:

$$E_\ell = -\frac{dV}{d\ell}.$$

4. A conductor in electrostatic equilibrium is an equipotential. The surface charge density and therefore the electric field at the conductor surface are usually greatest where the conductor curves most sharply. Very strong electric fields

occur at sharp bends; if strong enough, these fields can result in **corona discharge**, in which the surrounding air becomes a conductor and charge leaks off the charged conductor.

Terms You Should Understand

(Pairs are closely related terms whose distinction is important; number in parentheses is chapter section where term first appears.)

conservative field (introduction)
potential difference (25-2)
volt, electron volt (25-2)
line integral (25-2)
equipotential (25-4)
corona discharge (25-5)

Symbols You Should Recognize

ΔV_{AB} (25-2)	$V(P)$ (25-3)
V, eV (25-2)	$d\ell$ (25-2)

Problems You Should Be Able to Solve

calculating the work needed to move a given charge through a given potential difference (25-2)
calculating potential differences in uniform electric fields (25-2)
calculating potential differences using the line integral of a known electric field (25-3)
evaluating potentials by summing or integrating over point charges (25-3)
finding electric field components given potential as a function of position (25-4)
sketching equipotentials of simple charge distributions (25-4)
sketching equipotentials and fields around conductors (25-5)

Limitations to Keep in Mind

Electric potential difference depends on *two points*.
Phrases like "the potential at point P" or "the potential of a point charge" are always shorthand ways of talking about the potential difference between two points. When the second point is not specified, it is often taken to be at infinity.

QUESTIONS

1. Why can a bird perch on a high-voltage power line without getting electrocuted?
2. One proton is accelerated from rest by a uniform electric field, the other by a nonuniform electric field. If they move through the same potential difference, how do their final speeds compare?
3. Would a free electron move toward higher or lower potential?
4. The potential difference from A to B in Fig. 25-33 is zero since the two points are equidistant from the charge Q. How can this be, when a charge moving along the path shown clearly experiences an electric force not perpendicular to the path?

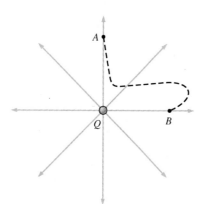

FIGURE 25-33 Question 4.

5. A proton and a positron (a particle with the electron's mass carrying charge $+e$) are accelerated through the same potential difference. How do their final energies compare? Their final speeds?
6. The electric field at the center of a uniformly charged ring is obviously zero, yet Example 25-6 shows that the potential at the center is not zero. How is this possible?
7. Must the potential be zero at any point where the electric field is zero? Explain.
8. Must the electric field be zero at any point where the potential is zero? Explain.
9. The potential is constant throughout an entire volume. What must be true of the electric field within that volume?
10. In considering the potential of an infinite flat sheet, why is it not useful to take the zero of potential at infinity?
11. The potential of a point charge is given by kq/r. Is r the distance between the two points for which this is the potential difference? Explain.
12. "Cherry picker" trucks for working in trees or power lines often carry the warning sign shown in Fig. 25-34. Explain

FIGURE 25-34 Question 12.

how this hazard arises and why it might be more of a danger to someone on the ground than to a worker on the truck.
13. The electric field midway between two equal positive charges is, clearly, zero. Is the potential at this point also zero? (Take the zero of potential at infinity.) Are there any other points (other than infinity) where the potential of this system is zero?
14. Is it possible for equipotential surfaces to intersect? Explain.
15. Is the potential at the center of a hollow, uniformly charged spherical shell higher, lower, or the same as at the surface?
16. A solid sphere contains positive charge uniformly distributed throughout its volume. Is the potential at its center higher, lower, or the same as at the surface?
17. Why do the spheres in Fig. 25-27 need to be far apart for the conclusion that surface charge density is inversely proportional to radius to hold accurately?
18. Figure 25-35 shows a cross section of some equipotential surfaces. Where does the electric field have the greatest magnitude, and in this region what is its approximate direction?

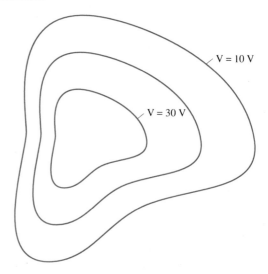

FIGURE 25-35 Question 18.

19. Two equal but opposite charges form a dipole. Describe the equipotential surface on which $V = 0$.
20. Figure 25-36 shows three paths leading from infinity to a point P on the perpendicular bisector of a dipole. For each path, how much work is needed to bring a charge q from infinity to P?
21. The electric potential in a region increases linearly with distance. What can you conclude about the electric field in this region?
22. In Fig. 25-29b the charge density on the conducting sphere is not uniform, yet the field inside must still be zero since the system is in electrostatic equilibrium. How is this possible?

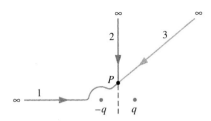

FIGURE 25-36 Question 20.

23. Why is lightning likely to strike an isolated tree?
24. What is the difference between a volt and an electron volt?

PROBLEMS

ActivPhysics can help with these problems:
Activities 11.9, 11.10.

Section 25-2 Potential Difference

1. How much work does it take to move a 50-μC charge against a 12-V potential difference?
2. The potential difference between the two sides of an ordinary electrical outlet is 120 V. How much energy does an electron gain when it moves from one side to the other?
3. It takes 45 J to move a 15-mC charge from point A to point B. What is the potential difference ΔV_{AB}?
4. Show that 1 V/m is the same as 1 N/C.
5. Find the magnitude of the potential difference between two points located 1.4 m apart in a uniform 650 N/C electric field, if a line between the points is parallel to the field.
6. A charge of 3.1 C moves from the positive to the negative terminal of a 9.0-V battery. How much energy does the battery impart to the charge?
7. Two points A and B lie 15 cm apart in a uniform electric field, with the path AB parallel to the field. If the potential difference ΔV_{AB} is 840 V, what is the field strength?
8. Figure 25-37 shows a uniform electric field of magnitude E. Find expressions for (a) the potential difference ΔV_{AB} and (b) ΔV_{BC}. (c) Use your result to determine ΔV_{AC}.

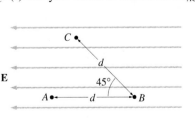

FIGURE 25-37 Problem 8.

9. A proton, an alpha particle (a bare helium nucleus), and a singly ionized helium atom are accelerated through a potential difference of 100 V. Find the energy each gains.
10. The electric field within the membrane separating the inside and outside of a biological cell is approximately 8.0 MV/m, and is essentially uniform. If the membrane is 10 nm thick, what is the potential difference across the membrane?
11. What is the potential difference between the terminals of a battery that can impart 7.2×10^{-19} J to each electron that moves between the terminals?
12. Electrons in a TV tube are accelerated from rest through a 25-kV potential difference. With what speed do they hit the TV screen?
13. A 12-V car battery stores 2.8 MJ of energy. How much charge can move between the battery terminals before it is totally discharged? Assume the potential difference remains at 12 V, an assumption that is not realistic.
14. What is the charge on an ion that gains 1.6×10^{-15} J when it moves through a potential difference of 2500 V?
15. Two large, flat metal plates are a distance d apart, where d is small compared with the plate size. If the plates carry surface charge densities $\pm\sigma$, show that the magnitude of the potential difference between them is $V = \sigma d / \varepsilon_0$.
16. An electron passes point A moving at 6.5 Mm/s. At point B the electron has come to a complete stop. Find the potential difference ΔV_{AB}.
17. A 5.0-g object carries a net charge of 3.8 μC. It acquires a speed v when accelerated from rest through a potential difference V. A 2.0-g object acquires twice the speed under the same circumstances. What is its charge?

Section 25-3 Calculating Potential Difference

Note: In these problems, the zero of potential is taken at infinity unless noted otherwise.

18. An electric field is given by $\mathbf{E} = E_0\hat{\mathbf{j}}$, where E_0 is a constant. Find the potential as a function of position, taking $V = 0$ at $y = 0$.

19. The classical picture of the hydrogen atom has a single electron in orbit a distance 0.0529 nm from the proton. Calculate the electric potential associated with the proton's electric field at this distance.

20. Earth carries an electric charge of -4.3×10^5 C, distributed essentially uniformly over its surface. What is the potential difference between Earth's surface and the base of the ionosphere, about 80 km above the surface?

21. Points A and B lie 20 cm apart on a line extending radially from a point charge Q, and the potentials at these points are $V_A = 280$ V, $V_B = 130$ V. Find Q and the distance r between A and the charge.

22. What is the maximum potential allowable on a 5.0-cm-diameter metal sphere if the electric field at the sphere's surface is not to exceed the 3 MV/m breakdown field in air?

23. A 3.5-cm-diameter isolated metal sphere carries a net charge of 0.86 μC. (a) What is the potential at the sphere's surface? (b) If a proton were released from rest at the sphere's surface, what would be its speed far from the sphere?

24. A sphere of radius R carries a negative charge of magnitude Q, distributed in a spherically symmetric way. Find the "escape speed" for a proton at the sphere's surface—that is, the speed that would enable the proton to escape to arbitrarily large distances.

25. A thin spherical shell of charge has radius R and total charge Q distributed uniformly over its surface. What is the potential at its center?

26. A solid sphere of radius R carries a net charge Q distributed uniformly throughout its volume. Find the potential difference from the sphere's surface to its center. *Hint:* Consult Example 24-1.

27. Find the potential as a function of position in an electric field given by $\mathbf{E} = ax\hat{\mathbf{i}}$, where a is a constant and where $V = 0$ at $x = 0$.

28. A coaxial cable consists of a 2.0-mm-diameter inner conductor and an outer conductor of diameter 1.6 cm and negligible thickness (Fig. 25-38). If the conductors carry line charge densities ± 0.56 nC/m, what is the magnitude of the potential difference between them?

29. The potential difference between the surface of a 3.0-cm-diameter power line and a point 1.0 m distant is 3.9 kV. What is the line charge density on the power line?

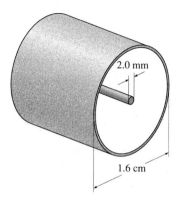

FIGURE 25-38 Problem 28.

30. Three equal charges q form an equilateral triangle of side a. Find the potential at the center of the triangle.

31. A charge $+Q$ lies at the origin, and $-3Q$ at $x = a$. Find two points on the x axis where $V = 0$.

32. Two identical charges q lie on the x axis at $\pm a$. (a) Find an expression for the potential at all points in the x-y plane. (b) Show that your result reduces to the potential of a point charge for distances large compared with a.

33. Find the potential 10 cm from a dipole of moment $p = 2.9$ nC·m (a) on the dipole axis, (b) at 45° to the axis, and (c) on the perpendicular bisector. The dipole separation is much less than 10 cm.

34. Two points A and B lie 55 cm from a dipole of moment $p = 6.4$ nC·m, whose charge separation is much less than 55 cm. A line from the dipole to A makes a 20° angle with the dipole axis, and a line to B makes a 50° angle. Find the potential difference $V_B - V_A$.

35. A hollow, spherical conducting shell of inner radius b and outer radius c surrounds is concentric with a solid conducting sphere of radius a, as shown in Fig. 25-39. The sphere carries a net charge $-Q$ and the shell carries a net charge

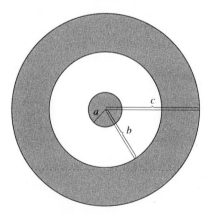

FIGURE 25-39 Problem 35.

+3Q. Both conductors are in electrostatic equilibrium. Find an expression for the potential difference from infinity to the surface of the sphere.

36. A thin plastic rod 20 cm long carries 3.2 nC distributed uniformly over its length. (a) If the rod is bent into a ring, find the potential at its center. (b) If the rod is bent into a semicircle, find the potential at the center (i.e., at the center of the circle of which the semicircle is part).

37. A thin ring of radius R carries a charge $3Q$ distributed uniformly over three-fourths of its circumference, and $-Q$ over the rest. What is the potential at the center of the ring?

38. The potential at the center of a uniformly charged ring is 45 kV, and 15 cm along the ring axis the potential is 33 kV. Find the ring's radius and its total charge.

39. The annulus shown in Fig. 25-40 carries a uniform surface charge density σ. Find an expression for the potential at an arbitrary point P on its axis.

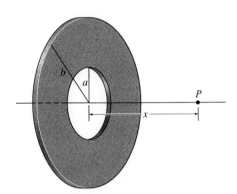

FIGURE 25-40 Problem 39.

40. A thin rod of length ℓ carries a charge Q distributed uniformly over its length. (a) Show that the potential in the plane that perpendicularly bisects the rod is given by

$$V(r) = \frac{2kQ}{\ell} \ln\left[\frac{\ell}{2r} + \sqrt{1 + \frac{\ell^2}{4r^2}}\right],$$

where r is the distance from the rod center. (b) Show that this expression reduces to an expected result when $r \gg \ell$. *Hint:* See Appendix A for a series expansion of the logarithm.

41. (a) Find the potential as a function of position in the electric field $\mathbf{E} = E_0(\hat{\mathbf{i}} + \hat{\mathbf{j}})$, where $E_0 = 150$ V/m. Take the zero of potential at the origin. (b) Find the potential difference from the point $x = 2.0$ m, $y = 1.0$ m to the point $x = 3.5$ m, $y = -1.5$ m.

Section 25-4 Potential Difference and the Electric Field

42. In a uniform electric field, equipotential planes that differ by 1.0 V are 2.5 cm apart. What is the field strength?

43. Figure 25-41 shows a plot of potential versus position along the x axis. Make a plot of the x component of the electric field for this situation.

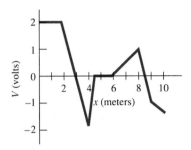

FIGURE 25-41 Problem 43.

44. Figure 25-42 shows some equipotentials in the x-y plane. (a) In what region is the electric field strongest? What are (b) the direction and (c) the magnitude of the field in this region?

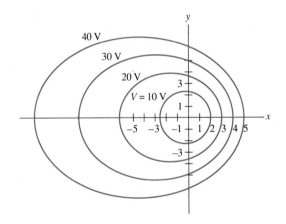

FIGURE 25-42 Problem 44.

45. The potential in a certain region is given by $V = axy$, where a is a constant. (a) Determine the electric field in the region. (b) Sketch some equipotentials and field lines.

46. Sketch some equipotentials and field lines for a distribution consisting of two equal point charges.

47. The electric potential in a region of space is given by $V = 2xy - 3zx + 5y^2$, with V in volts and the coordinates in meters. If point P is at $x = 1$ m, $y = 1$ m, $z = 1$ m, find

(a) the potential at P and (b) the x, y, and z components of the electric field at P.

48. Use Equation 25-7 to calculate the electric field on the perpendicular bisector of a point dipole, and show that your result is equivalent to Equation 23-7a.

49. Use the result of Example 25-6 to determine the on-axis field of a charged ring, and verify that your answer agrees with the result of Example 23-8.

50. A charge $+4q$ is located at the origin and a charge $-q$ is on the x axis at $x = a$. (a) Write an expression for the potential on the x axis for $x > a$. (b) Find a point in this region where $V = 0$. (c) Use the result of (a) to find the electric field on the x axis for $x > a$ and (d) find a point where $\mathbf{E} = \mathbf{0}$.

51. The electric potential in a region is given by $V = -V_0(r/R)$, where V_0 and R are constants, r is the radial distance from the origin, and where the zero of potential is taken at $r = 0$. Find the magnitude and direction of the electric field in this region.

FIGURE 25-43 Problem 56.

58. Two small metal spheres are located 2.0 m apart. One has radius 0.50 cm and carries 0.20 μC. The other has radius 1.0 cm and carries 0.080 μC. (a) What is the potential difference between the spheres? (b) If they were connected by a thin wire, how much charge would move along it, and in which direciton?

Section 25-5 Potentials of Charged Conductors

52. (a) What is the maximum potential (measured from infinity) for the sphere of Example 25-3 before dielectric breakdown of air occurs at the sphere's surface? (Breakdown of air occurs at a field strength of 3 MV/m.) (b) What is the charge on the sphere when it's at this potential?

53. The spark plug in an automobile engine has a center electrode made from wire 2.0 mm in diameter. The electrode is worn to a hemispherical shape, so it behaves approximately like a charged sphere. What is the minimum potential on this electrode that will ensure the plug sparks in air? Neglect the presence of the second electrode.

54. A large metal sphere has three times the diameter of a smaller sphere and carries three times as much charge. Both spheres are isolated, so their surface charge densities are uniform. Compare (a) the potentials and (b) the electric field strengths at their surfaces.

55. Two metal spheres each 1.0 cm in radius are far apart. One sphere carries 38 nC of charge, the other -10 nC. (a) What is the potential on each? (b) If the spheres are connected by a thin wire, what will be the potential on each once equilibrium is reached? (c) How much charge must move between the spheres in order to achieve equilibrium?

56. Sketch some equipotentials and field lines for the isolated, charged conductor shown in Fig. 25-43.

57. Two conducting spheres are each 5.0 cm in diameter and each carries 0.12 μC. They are 8.0 m apart. Determine (a) the potential on each sphere; (b) the field strength at the surface of each sphere; (c) the potential midway between the spheres; (d) the potential difference between the spheres.

Paired Problems

(Both problems in a pair involve the same principles and techniques. If you can get the first problem, you should be able to solve the second one.)

59. Three 50-pC charges sit at the vertices of an equilateral triangle 1.5 mm on a side. How much work would it take to bring a proton from very far away to the midpoint of one of the triangle's sides?

60. Repeat the preceding problem for the case when one of the charges is -50 pC and the proton is brought to the midpoint of the side between the two positive charges.

61. A pair of equal charges q lies on the x axis at $x = \pm a$. (a) Find expressions for the potential at points on the x axis for which $x > a$ and (b) show that your result reduces to a point-charge potential for $x \gg a$.

62. (a) For the charge distribution of the preceding problem, find an expression for the potential at *all* points on the y axis. (b) Show that your result reduces to a point-charge potential for $y \gg a$.

63. A 2.0-cm-radius metal sphere carries 75 nC and is surrounded by a concentric spherical conducting shell of radius 10 cm carrying -75 nC. (a) Find the potential difference between the shell and the sphere. (b) How would your answer change if the shell charge were changed to $+150$ nC?

64. A coaxial cable consists of a 2.0-mm-radius central wire carrying 75 nC/m, and a concentric outer conductor of radius 10 mm carrying -75 nC/m. (a) Find the potential

difference between the outer and inner conductor. (b) How would your answer change if the outer conductor were charged to $+150$ nC/m?

65. On the x axis, the electric field of a certain charge distribution is given by $\mathbf{E} = a/x^4\hat{\mathbf{i}}$, where $a = 55$ V·m^3. Find the potential difference from the point $x = 1.3$ m to the point $x = 2.8$ m.

66. A sphere of radius R carries a nonuniform but spherically symmetric volume charge density that results in an electric field in the sphere given by $\mathbf{E} = E_0(r/R)^2\hat{\mathbf{r}}$, where E_0 is a constant. Find the potential difference from the sphere's surface to its center.

67. The potential as a function of position in a certain region is given by $V(x) = 3x - 2x^2 - x^3$, with x in meters and V in volts. Find (a) all points on the x axis where $V = 0$, (b) an expression for the electric field, and (c) all points on the x axis where $\mathbf{E} = 0$.

68. The potential in a certain region is given by $V(x, y) = -[2x^2 + (y - 1)^2 - 1]$. Find (a) a point where $V = 0$, (b) an expression for the electric field, and (c) a point in the x-y plane where $\mathbf{E} = 0$.

Supplementary Problems

69. A conducting sphere 5.0 cm in radius carries 60 nC. It is surrounded by a concentric spherical conducting shell of radius 15 cm carrying -60 nC. (a) Find the potential at the sphere's surface, taking the zero of potential at infinity. (b) Repeat for the case when the shell also carries $+60$ nC.

70. Show that the result of Example 25-9 approaches the field of a point charge for $x \gg a$. *Hint:* You will need to apply the binomial theorem to the quantity $1/\sqrt{x^2 + a^2}$.

71. The potential on the axis of a uniformly charged disk at 5.0 cm from the disk center is 150 V; the potential 10 cm from the disk center is 110 V. Find the disk radius and its total charge.

72. A uranium nucleus (mass 238 u, charge 92e) decays, emitting an alpha particle (mass 4 u, charge 2e) and leaving a thorium nucleus (mass 234 u, charge 90e). At the instant the alpha particle leaves the nucleus, the centers of the two are 7.4 fm apart and are essentially at rest. Find their speeds when they are a great distance apart. Treat each particle as a spherical charge distribution.

73. A power line consists of two parallel wires 3.0 cm in diameter spaced 2.0 m apart. If the potential difference between the wires is 4.0 kV, what is the charge per unit length on each wire? The wires carry equal but opposite charges. *Hint:* The wires are far enough apart that they don't greatly affect each other's fields.

74. For the dipole of Example 25-5, show that the electric field at an arbitrary point far from the dipole can be written

$$\mathbf{E} = \frac{kp}{r^3}[(3\cos^2\theta - 1)\hat{\mathbf{i}} + 3\sin\theta\cos\theta\hat{\mathbf{j}}].$$

75. A thin rod of length ℓ lies on the x axis with its center at the origin. It carries a line charge density given by $\lambda = \lambda_0(x/\ell)^2$, where λ_0 is a constant. (a) Find an expression for the potential on the x axis for $x > \ell/2$. (b) Integrate the charge density to find the total charge on the rod. (c) Show that your answer for (a) reduces to the potential of a point charge whose charge is the answer to (b), for $x \gg \ell$.

76. Repeat the preceding problem for the case $\lambda = \lambda_0(x/\ell)$. Why is your answer for $x \gg \ell$ different? *Hint:* What does this charge distribution resemble at large distances?

77. For the situation of Example 25-10, find an equation for the equipotential with $V = 0$ in the x-y plane. Plot the equipotential, and show that it passes through the points described in Example 25-10 and its exercise.

78. A disk of radius a carries a nonuniform surface charge density given by $\sigma = \sigma_0(r/a)$, where σ_0 is a constant. (a) Find the potential at an arbitrary point on the disk axis, a distance x from the disk center. (b) Use the result of (a) to find the electric field on the disk axis, and (c) show that the field reduces to an expected form for $x \gg a$.

79. An open-ended cylinder of radius a and length $2a$ carries charge q spread uniformly over its surface. Find the potential on the cylinder axis at its center. *Hint:* Treat the cylinder as a stack of charged rings, and integrate.

26 Electrostatic Energy and Capacitors

A test firing of the Particle Beam Fusion Accelerator at Sandia National Laboratories involves the sudden release of energy stored in electric fields.

Suppose you hold two positive charges in your outstretched arms (Fig. 26-1). Bringing them closer takes work, as you move each charge against the other's electric field. That work is stored as potential energy associated with the new distribution of charge you create by moving the charges closer together. Because the static electric field is conservative, you could recover the stored energy by releasing the charges and letting them accelerate.

The example of Fig. 26-1 is trivial, but its implications are not. Energy storage in configurations of electric charge is a vital aspect of the natural and technological worlds. The energy produced in chemical reactions—including the metabolizing of food and the burning of coal, oil, and other fuels—is electrical energy released in the rearrangement of molecular charge distributions. Energy storage in systems of charged conductors is essential to the workings of electronic equipment and is important in devices that require large amounts of energy delivered in a short time. In this chapter we explore the energy of charge distributions and their electric fields, and we introduce a practical device—the capacitor—whose function is electrical energy storage.

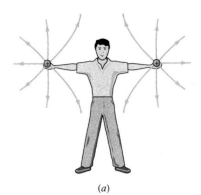

(a)

(b)

26-1 ENERGY OF A CHARGE DISTRIBUTION

In the preceding chapter we defined the electric potential difference between two points as the change in potential energy per unit charge associated with moving charge between those points. To move charge between the two points takes work equal to the change in potential energy—equal, that is, to the electric potential difference multiplied by the charge being moved. In the simple case of two point charges, suppose charge q_1 is initially an infinite distance from a fixed charge q_2. You can assemble a new charge distribution by moving q_1 to a distance r from q_2. Equation 25-4 gives the electric potential difference from infinity to any point a distance r from q_2:

$$V_{\infty r} = \frac{kq_2}{r}.$$

Multiplying by q_1 gives the work you must do to bring q_1 in from infinity—that is, to assemble the new charge distribution. Since that work, W, gets stored as potential energy, U, we can write

$$W = U = \frac{kq_1q_2}{r}, \tag{26-1}$$

where we've taken the zero of potential energy when the charges are infinitely far apart.

Equation 26-1 gives the **electrostatic potential energy** of two point charges. The equation shows that the potential energy is positive if the charges have the same sign and negative if they have opposite signs. In the latter case, it would take positive work to separate the charges. We would have obtained the same potential energy had we moved q_2 in the field of q_1, showing that the potential energy of a charge distribution is independent of how it is assembled.

These considerations hold for any charge distribution. In general, it takes work to assemble a charge distribution and that work is stored as potential energy. The potential energy can be positive, zero, or negative. Because the electric force obeys the superposition principle, the potential energy is independent of how the charge distribution is assembled: the total energy is simply the sum of the potential energies of every charge pair making up the distribution.

FIGURE 26-1 (*a*) Widely separated charges exert little force on each other. (*b*) Moving them together takes work, which is stored as potential energy. Note how the bending of the field lines suggests the repulsive force.

11.11
Electrical Potential Energy and Potential

| **EXAMPLE 26-1** | *The Energy of a Charge Distribution* |

Three point charges each carrying $+q$ and a fourth carrying $-q/2$ are initially infinitely far apart. They are brought together to form the square charge distribution shown in Fig. 26-2. What is the electrostatic potential energy of this charge distribution?

Solution

We can assemble the charge distribution in any order. Assume that the positive charge at the upper left is brought in first. This takes no work because no other charge is present. Next the positive charge q at the upper right is brought to a distance a from the first positive charge. Equation 26-1 tells us that the work required is

$$W_2 = k\frac{q^2}{a}.$$

Now the third positive charge is brought to its place at the lower left. This point is a distance a from the first charge q and $\sqrt{2}a$ from the second, so the work required is

$$W_3 = k\left(\frac{q^2}{a} + \frac{q^2}{\sqrt{2}a}\right).$$

Finally, the negative charge $-q/2$ is brought to a point a distance a from the second and third charges and $\sqrt{2}a$ from the first charge. The work required is again the sum of the potential differences multiplied by the charge $-q/2$:

$$W_4 = k\left(-\frac{q^2}{2a} - \frac{q^2}{2a} - \frac{q^2}{2\sqrt{2}a}\right).$$

This work is negative, indicating that it would take positive work to remove the negative charge. Adding the work required

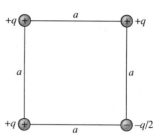

FIGURE 26-2 How much energy is stored in this square charge distribution? (Example 26-1).

to bring in the second, third, and fourth charges gives the electrostatic potential energy of the charge distribution:

$$W = W_2 + W_3 + W_4$$
$$= k\left(\frac{q^2}{a} + \frac{q^2}{a} + \frac{q^2}{\sqrt{2}a} - \frac{q^2}{2a} - \frac{q^2}{2a} - \frac{q^2}{2\sqrt{2}a}\right)$$
$$= \frac{kq^2(2\sqrt{2} + 1)}{2\sqrt{2}a}.$$

That this is a positive quantity indicates that the work needed to assemble the three positive charges is greater than the energy gained bringing in the negative charge.

EXERCISE Repeat Example 26-1 for the case when the charge in the upper left corner is changed to $-q$.

Answer: $-3kq^2[1 - 1/(2\sqrt{2})]/a$

Some problems similar to Example 26-1: 1–4, 7, 79

26-2 TWO ISOLATED CONDUCTORS

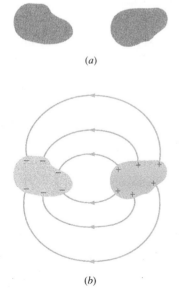

A charge distribution useful for storing electrostatic energy consists of two isolated conductors carrying equal but opposite charges. Figure 26-3 shows two such conductors, each initially uncharged. Imagine moving a small quantity of charge from one conductor to the other, resulting in a net positive charge on one and a net negative charge on the other. This results in an electric field and therefore in a potential difference between the conductors. If we transfer more charge between the conductors, we do work traversing this potential difference. The more charge we move, the harder it gets to transfer additional charge. The work it takes to transfer the charge is stored as potential energy of the charge distribution.

It is generally difficult to calculate the stored potential energy for a pair of irregularly shaped conductors such as those of Fig. 26-3. An important practical case for which the potential energy may be calculated more easily is a pair of identical, flat, parallel conducting plates whose separation is small compared

FIGURE 26-3 A pair of isolated conductors. (*a*) Initially they are uncharged, and there is no potential difference between them. (*b*) When they carry opposite charges, there is an electric field and consequently a potential difference between them.

with their width (Fig. 26-4a). We start with the plates uncharged, and then transfer charge Q from one plate to the other. (In practice, we would accomplish this by connecting the plates to the terminals of a battery.) Charging the plates results in an electric field between them. For closely spaced plates, this field is essentially uniform except very near the edges (Fig. 26-4b), and we may neglect this nonuniform "fringing field."

What is the electric field strength between the plates? In Chapter 24 we used Gauss's law to show that the field near the surface of a conductor carrying surface charge density σ is given by

$$E = \frac{\sigma}{\varepsilon_0}.$$

As we discussed in Section 24-6, charge gathers entirely on the facing surfaces of the two plates, resulting in a charge density of magnitude $\sigma = q/A$, where A is the plate area. So the electric field between the plates is

$$E = \frac{\sigma}{\varepsilon_0} = \frac{q}{\varepsilon_0 A},$$

where q is the magnitude of the charge on either plate. Shouldn't this result be doubled because there are two plates? No! Review the discussion accompanying Figs. 24-34 and 24-35 to convince yourself of this point.

The presence of the electric field means there is a potential difference between the plates. Since the field is uniform, this potential difference is the product of the field strength and the distance d between the plates:

$$V = Ed = \frac{qd}{\varepsilon_0 A},$$

where we're now using V rather than ΔV_{AB} for the potential difference.

Now imagine moving an additional very small positive charge dq from the negative to the positive plate. How much work does this take? That depends on the potential difference between the plates, which, as our expression for V shows, depends on how much charge has already been transferred. Because potential difference is work per unit charge, the work dW required to move the charge dq between the plates is

$$dW = V\, dq = \frac{qd}{\varepsilon_0 A}\, dq.$$

Suppose we start with zero net charge on either plate and gradually transfer a total charge Q from one plate to the other. Each dq that we move requires work dW as given above, so the total work is the sum of all the dW's associated with all the small quantities of charge dq that make up Q. In the limit of infinitely many infinitesimal charges dq, this sum becomes an integral, and we have

$$W = \int_0^Q dW = \int_0^Q \frac{qd}{\varepsilon_0 A}\, dq = \frac{d}{\varepsilon_0 A} \int_0^Q q\, dq.$$

That the variable q remains under the integral sign reflects the physical fact that the continually increasing charge on the plates results in an increasing potential difference and therefore makes it harder to move each additional charge dq. Continuing the integration gives

$$W = \frac{d}{\varepsilon_0 A} \frac{q^2}{2} \bigg|_0^Q = \frac{d}{2\varepsilon_0 A} Q^2.$$

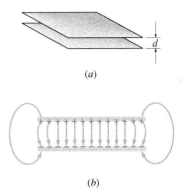

(a)

(b)

FIGURE 26-4 (a) A pair of closely spaced conducting plates. (b) Edge-on view of the plates when oppositely charged. For closely spaced plates the electric field is essentially uniform, except very near the edges, and the field outside the region between the plates is very small. Neglecting these small "fringing fields" is a good approximation.

Thus the work required to charge the plates increases as the square of the charge Q. The work done in charging the plates ends up as stored potential energy of the final charge distribution, so the stored energy is

$$U = W = \frac{d}{2\varepsilon_0 A} Q^2. \tag{26-2}$$

Note that the stored energy in Equation 26-2 depends on the *square* of the charge. Thus a pair of parallel plates on which we can build up lots of charge represents an excellent device for storing electrostatic energy. We'll see later in this chapter how widespread the technological applications of such devices are.

26-3 ENERGY AND THE ELECTRIC FIELD

We've seen that the work required to assemble a distribution of electric charge ends up as electrostatic potential energy. Just where is the energy stored? In Example 26-1, we considered the assembly of four point charges to form a square. Surely the point charges themselves did not change; we only moved them closer together. Similarly, when we charged our pair of metal plates we didn't alter the individual charges; we only moved them from one plate to another. So what has changed in both these cases? The electric field has changed. In the first case we started with four isolated point charges and an electric field that looked like four isolated point-charge fields. We ended with a new charge distribution whose field did not look at all like a point-charge field.

In the case of the parallel plates, we started with uncharged plates and no electric field. As soon as we began transferring charge from one plate to the other, an electric field appeared between the plates, and this field grew in strength as more charge was transferred.

So where is the energy stored? It is stored in the electric field. As we create or alter a charge distribution, we do work and an altered electric field configuration develops. The work done in moving the charges becomes energy stored in the electric field. If that work is positive, the new field configuration contains more energy; if the work is negative, the field has released energy and the new field contains less energy.

Every electric field represents stored energy. Because electric forces are primarily responsible for the behavior of everyday matter, many seemingly different forms of energy storage really involve electric field energy. When you burn gasoline or metabolize food, for example, you are rearranging the charge distributions we call molecules into new configurations whose electric fields contain less energy (Fig. 26-5).

If electric fields store energy, then the amount of stored energy should depend on the field strength. Since the field strength may vary with position, we describe the stored energy in terms of **energy density**, or energy stored per unit volume. We can readily determine the energy density for our parallel plates. There we found that the field strength is given by $E = Q/\varepsilon_0 A$; solving for Q and using the result in Equation 26-2 for the stored energy gives

$$U = \frac{d}{2\varepsilon_0 A} Q^2 = \frac{d}{2\varepsilon_0 A} (\varepsilon_0 A E)^2 = \tfrac{1}{2}\varepsilon_0 E^2 A d.$$

Our assumption that the plates are very close together allowed us to conclude that the field is very nearly uniform between the plates and essentially zero

FIGURE 26-5 Combustion involves the rearrangement of atoms into new molecular structures. Energy released as light and heat comes ultimately from the electric fields associated with the charge distribution in the molecules.

outside the plates. Therefore, the energy U is stored in the region between the plates, and is distributed uniformly because the field is uniform. The volume between the plates is just the plate area times the separation, or Ad, and therefore the energy density u_E is given by $u_E = U/Ad$, or

$$u_E = \tfrac{1}{2}\varepsilon_0 E^2. \quad \text{(electric energy density)} \qquad (26\text{-}3)$$

Although we derived this expression for the uniform field between two parallel plates, it is in fact a universal expression that holds for *any* electric field. At any point where an electric field exists, there is stored energy whose density, in J/m^3, is given by Equation 26-3.

The deepest significance of Equation 26-3 lies in its statement that every electric field represents stored energy. As we observe a variety of physical phenomena, from everyday happenings on Earth to events in distant galaxies, we can understand that the driving energy for many of these phenomena comes from the release of energy stored in electric fields.

EXAMPLE 26-2	*Electrical Energy of a Thunderstorm*

Electric fields inside a thunderstorm (Fig. 26-6) have typical values of 10^5 V/m and get even higher just before electrical energy is unleashed as lightning (recall that 3×10^6 V/m is the field at which air ionizes and becomes a conductor—which is what happens in a lightning strike). The origin of these fields and hence of the energy stored in them is believed to be associated with charge transfer to rising and falling water droplets or ice crystals in the intense updrafts and downdrafts of the thunderstorm. Consider a typical thundercloud that rises to an altitude of 10 km and has a diameter of 20 km. Assuming an average field strength of 10^5 V/m, estimate the total electrostatic energy stored in the cloud. How many gallons of gasoline would you have to burn to release the same amount of energy?

Solution

The energy density is given by Equation 26-3:

$$u_E = \tfrac{1}{2}\varepsilon_0 E^2 = \tfrac{1}{2}(8.85\times10^{-12}\ \text{C}^2/\text{N}\cdot\text{m}^2)(10^5\ \text{V/m})^2$$
$$= 4.4\times10^{-2}\ \text{J/m}^3.$$

(You should verify that the units work out!) We are assuming that this energy density is the same throughout the storm, so we find the total energy by multiplying the energy density by the volume. The storm is roughly cylindrical in shape, so its volume is

$$V = \pi r^2 h = \pi(10\ \text{km})^2(10\ \text{km}) = 3100\ \text{km}^3$$
$$= 3.1\times10^{12}\ \text{m}^3.$$

Then the total stored energy is

$$U = u_E V = (4.4\times10^{-2}\ \text{J/m}^3)(3.1\times10^{12}\ \text{m}^3) = 1.4\times10^{11}\ \text{J}.$$

A gallon of gasoline contains about 10^8 J (see Appendix C), so the electrical energy stored in a thunderstorm at any given instant is equivalent to about 1000 gallons or 4000 L of gasoline. This comparison is not quite fair to the thunderstorm,

FIGURE 26-6 Lightning is the sudden release of energy stored in atmospheric electric fields. The most common form of cloud-to-ground lightning, shown here, involves a negative charge layer at the cloud base, and a corresponding positive charge induced in the ground below. Other charge layers exist within the cloud, so electrostatic energy is stored both below and within the cloud.

though, because its electrical energy is continually dissipated in lightning strikes and at the same time renewed by the violent motion of the air. Problem 77 explores thunderstorm energetics in more detail.

EXERCISE In fair weather, Earth's atmospheric electric field is about 100 V/m. Find the energy stored in each km^3 of the fair-weather atmosphere.

Answer: 44 J

Some problems similar to Example 26-2: 16–18

When the electric field is uniform, as in our thunderstorm example, we can find the stored energy simply by multiplying the energy density by the volume. But when the field changes with position we must resort to calculus. Consider a small volume element dV, so small that the electric field is essentially uniform over this volume. The stored energy dU in the volume element is just the energy density times the volume, or

$$dU = u_E \, dV = \tfrac{1}{2} \varepsilon_0 E^2 \, dV.$$

The total energy U is then the sum of all the dUs. In the limit of infinitesimally small volumes dV and energies dU, this sum becomes an integral:

$$U = \tfrac{1}{2} \varepsilon_0 \int E^2 \, dV, \tag{26-4}$$

where the limits on the integral are chosen to cover the entire region in which the electric field of interest exists.

We derived Equation 26-4 for the electric field energy using our previously determined expression for the work needed to assemble a simple charge distribution. We can also reverse that process, using the electric field of a charge distribution to calculate the energy density and from it the stored energy and therefore the work needed to assemble the distribution. Example 26-3 illustrates this procedure for a case when the energy density varies with position.

EXAMPLE 26-3	*A Shrinking Sphere*

A sphere of radius R_1 carries a total charge Q distributed evenly over its surface (Fig. 26-7a). How much work does it take to shrink the sphere to a smaller radius R_2? Practical applications in which this question might prove important include the behavior of cell membranes, charged bubbles, and raindrops in thunderclouds.

Solution

Shrinking the sphere moves all the charges on its surface closer together, and therefore requires positive work. That work is equal to the change in stored electric field energy given by Equation 26-4. With all charge distributed evenly over the sphere's surface, Gauss's law tells us that there is no electric field within the sphere. Because of the spherical symmetry, Gauss's law also tells us that the field outside the sphere is identical to that of a point charge Q at the sphere's center. This means that the field at and beyond the original radius R_1 does not change as we shrink the sphere. What does change is the field between R_1 and R_2 (Fig. 26-7b). Originally this field was zero. After the sphere has shrunk, this region, too, is filled with a point-charge field. This newly created field is the site of the additional energy stored in shrinking the sphere.

Because the point-charge field between R_1 and R_2 changes with position, we must use the integral form 26-4 to calculate the stored energy. The electric field outside the sphere is that of a point charge:

$$E = \frac{kQ}{r^2},$$

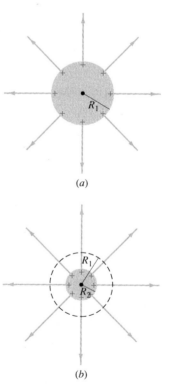

(a)

(b)

FIGURE 26-7 (a) A charged sphere and its electric field. (b) Shrinking the sphere creates new field in the region $R_2 < r < R_1$.

so, from Equation 26-3, the energy density as a function of r is

$$u_E(r) = \tfrac{1}{2}\varepsilon_0 E^2 = \tfrac{1}{2}\varepsilon_0\left(\frac{kQ}{r^2}\right)^2 = \frac{kQ^2}{8\pi r^4},$$

where we used $k = 1/4\pi\varepsilon_0$.

To determine the total stored energy we integrate this energy density over the volume between R_2 and R_1. Because of the spherical symmetry we consider volume elements made of thin spherical shells of thickness dr. Figure 26-8 shows that the volume of the shell is $dV = 4\pi r^2 dr$, so Equation 26-4 becomes

$$U = \int_{R_2}^{R_1} u_E\,dV = \int_{R_2}^{R_1} \frac{kQ^2}{8\pi r^4}\,4\pi r^2\,dr$$

$$= \frac{kQ^2}{2}\int_{R_2}^{R_1} r^{-2}\,dr = \frac{kQ^2}{2}\left(-\frac{1}{r}\right)\Bigg|_{R_2}^{R_1}$$

$$= \frac{kQ^2}{2}\left(\frac{1}{R_2} - \frac{1}{R_1}\right).$$

This is the total energy stored in the new electric field between R_2 and R_1, and is therefore also the work done in shrinking the sphere from R_1 to R_2. If we let R_1 go to infinity, our result becomes the work required to assemble a sphere of radius R_2 carrying surface charge Q, or equivalently, the energy stored in the field of the sphere. Because the stored energy becomes infinite as R_2 approaches zero, our result suggests that the notion of a point charge is an impossible idealization. Problem 90 explores some implications of this result in the theory of elementary particles.

FIGURE 26-8 A thin spherical shell of thickness dr and radius r. Because the shell is very thin, its inner and outer surfaces have essentially the same area, namely $4\pi r^2$. Its volume is therefore $dV = 4\pi r^2\,dr$.

FIGURE 26-9 How much energy is stored in a length ℓ of the cable? (The cable is much longer than the outer conductor radius b.)

EXERCISE A long coaxial cable consists of an inner cylindrical conductor of radius a and an outer cylindrical conducting shell of radius b (Fig. 26-9). The conductors carry equal but opposite line charge densities $\pm\lambda$. Find the electric energy stored in a length ℓ of this cable.

Answer: $k\lambda^2\ell\,\ln(b/a)$

Some problems similar to Example 26-3: 21–23, 26, 27

26-4 CAPACITORS

In electrical and electronic equipment, electrical energy is often stored using a pair of charged conductors. Such a device is called a **capacitor**. Capacitors are typically used for short-term energy storage in situations where it is necessary to release electrical energy quickly. Most practical electronic devices, including radio, TV, computers, and audio equipment, would be virtually impossible to construct without capacitors. When you tune a radio, you're adjusting a capacitor. Your computer's memory stores information in millions of microscopic capacitors. Failure of a capacitor in your car's ignition system could leave you stranded on the highway. And many high-energy experiments in physics and engineering use so much power that, were it not for capacitors, they could not be done without disrupting the supply of electric power to the entire world!

In an uncharged capacitor both conductors are neutral. A capacitor is charged by transferring charge (usually electrons) from one conductor to the other. The work required is supplied by a source of electrical energy—for example, a battery—connected by wires to the capacitor's two conductors. An electric field develops as a result of the separation of positive and negative charge on the two conductors, and the stored energy resides in this field.

Since there's an electric field in a charged capacitor, there's also a potential difference between its two conductors. The more charge, the greater the electric field, and, proportionately, the greater the potential difference. Thus a capacitor's charge and the potential difference between its conductors are proportional. In practice, we impose a potential difference between the two conductors, and a proportionate charge buildup occurs (that's because common electrical energy sources—such as batteries—produce a fixed potential difference rather than a fixed amount of charge). The ratio of charge to potential difference is characteristic of a given capacitor and is called its **capacitance**:

$$C = \frac{Q}{V}. \tag{26-5}$$

Here Q is the magnitude of the charge on either conductor and V the potential difference (or voltage) between the conductors. Clearly the units of capacitance are coulombs/volt. One coulomb/volt is given the name **farad** (F), in honor of the nineteenth century scientist Michael Faraday. One farad is so large a capacitance that the smaller units microfarad (10^{-6} F; abbreviated μF) and picofarad (10^{-12} F; abbreviated pF and often pronounced "puff") are widely used.

Capacitance depends on the physical construction of a capacitor—the shapes of its two conductors, their separation, and the choice of insulating material between them. Although Q and V enter the defining relation 26-5, capacitance is a constant. If V is increased, Q increases proportionately, maintaining the constant ratio C that characterizes the capacitor.

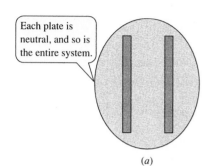

Each plate is neutral, and so is the entire system.

(a)

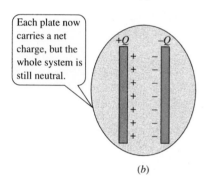

Each plate now carries a net charge, but the whole system is still neutral.

+Q   −Q

(b)

FIGURE 26-10 (a) In an uncharged capacitor both plates are neutral. (b) In a charged capacitor, the two plates carry opposite charges of equal magnitude. The entire system of two plates remains neutral.

Tip

Charged but Neutral When we speak of a "charged capacitor," we mean a capacitor with one conductor positive and the other negative; the net charge on the entire capacitor—i.e., on *both* plates—remains zero. Similarly, when we say "the charge on a capacitor is Q," we mean that one conductor carries $+Q$ and the other $-Q$. Overall, the capacitor remains neutral even when it's "charged" (Fig. 26-10).

Any arrangement of two insulated conductors constitutes a capacitor. Practical capacitors are manufactured in a variety of configurations (Fig. 26-11). Often they are made from two long strips of aluminum foil separated by thin layers of plastic or paper. This foil "sandwich" is then rolled into a compact cylinder, wires attached, and the whole assembly covered with a protective coating. Another common arrangement is the variable capacitor, whose configuration can be altered to change its capacitance. This change can be accomplished mechanically or, as in many modern electronic devices, electrically. Very large capacitances are achieved with so-called electrolytic capacitors, in which a thin insulating layer develops chemically under the influence of the applied voltage. We'll consider the role of insulating materials further in Section 26-7.

FIGURE 26-11 Typical capacitors. The large blue unit is an 18-mF electrolytic capacitor. At top right is an air-insulated variable capacitor in which a set of metal plates rotates with respect to fixed plates in order to change the capacitance. The remaining smaller capacitors range from 43 pF to 10 μF.

Got It!

One capacitor has $\pm 50\ \mu$C on its plates when the voltage between the plates is 6 V. A second capacitor has $\pm 100\ \mu$C on its plates when the voltage between them is 12 V. Compare the two capacitances.

Calculating Capacitance

Capacitance is defined through Equation 26-5 as the ratio of charge to potential difference. To calculate the capacitance of a particular configuration, we assume there is a charge Q on the capacitor and calculate the corresponding potential difference. When the capacitor design includes sufficient symmetry, this calculation is straightforward.

By far the most important capacitor design is the parallel-plate configuration. In Section 26-2 we examined such a capacitor in some detail, although at that time we did not call the configuration a capacitor. There we found that the potential difference between plates of area A separated by a distance d is

$$V = \frac{Qd}{\varepsilon_0 A}.$$

Solving for the ratio $C = Q/V$ gives

$$C = \frac{\varepsilon_0 A}{d}. \qquad \text{(parallel-plate capacitor)} \qquad (26\text{-}6)$$

Equation 26-6 gives the capacitance of a parallel-plate capacitor in terms of the universal constant ε_0 and factors that describe the physical configuration of the capacitor. (Strictly speaking, this expression holds only for capacitors insulated by vacuum. In Section 26-7 we will modify Equation 26-6 to account for other insulating materials.) Note that neither charge nor potential difference enters the final expression for capacitance, showing that the capacitance is indeed a constant, independent of Q and V. Equation 26-6 suggests that the way to make a capacitor with large capacitance is to use two plates of large area but small separation. Incidentally, Equation 26-6 shows that the units of ε_0 may be expressed as farads/meter (F/m); see Problem 32.

APPLICATION	*Microphones, Keyboards, Elevators, Barometers . . .*

Capacitance depends on the geometrical arrangement of two conductors, and capacitance is an electrical quantity that's relatively easy to measure (you'll see why after you're studied Chapter 33). Those facts make capacitors ideal **transducers**—devices that convert physical quantities into electrical signals for measurement and control purposes.

The mechanical displacement of an object can be measured precisely by linking one plate of a capacitor to the object; capacitance changes as the object moves, and the change in capacitance provides a measure of displacement. This principle is used not only in direct displacement measurement, but also in capacitive microphones, where a metal diaphragm forming one capacitor plate vibrates in response to sound waves, changing the capacitance. Similarly, capacitive pressure transducers use the deflection of a capacitor-plate diaphragm to measure changes in air pressure. And, in an application you may use literally thousands of times a day, pressing a key on a computer keyboard varies the spacing of capacitor plates, changing the capacitance and signaling the computer that the key has been pressed (Fig. 26-12).

Contact or even nearby presence of a conducting object can change the charge distribution on capacitor plates, effectively

FIGURE 26-12 The keys of a computer keyboard move capacitor plates, altering the capacitance and signaling which key has been pressed.

altering the capacitance. "Touch sensitive" buttons in elevators and other applications work on this principle; as your finger approaches the button, charge movement in your body alters the charge on a capacitor behind the button, signaling your floor choice to the elevator. Lamps that turn on or off at the touch of a finger work on the same principle.

| **EXAMPLE 26-4** | *A Parallel-Plate Capacitor* |

A capacitor consists of two circular metal plates of radius 10 cm separated by an air gap of 5.0 mm (Fig. 26-13). What is its capacitance? When a 12-volt battery is connected to the capacitor, how much charge appears on the plates?

Solution

Since the plate spacing is much smaller than the plate size, Equation 26-6 holds and the capacitance is

$$C = \frac{\varepsilon_0 A}{d} = \frac{\varepsilon_0 \pi r^2}{d} = \frac{(8.85 \times 10^{-12} \text{ F/m})(\pi)(0.10 \text{ m})^2}{5.0 \times 10^{-3} \text{ m}}$$

$$= 5.6 \times 10^{-11} \text{ F} = 56 \text{ pF}.$$

Equation 26-5 defines capacitance as the ratio of charge to potential difference. We can rewrite this defining relation to solve for the charge:

$$Q = CV = (56 \text{ pF})(12 \text{ V}) = 670 \text{ pC}.$$

What this really means, of course, is that the positive plate carries 670 pC and the negative plate −670 pC. Overall, the capacitor remains neutral. Note that by working with the capacitance in pF, the charge automatically comes out in pC.

EXERCISE A parallel-plate capacitor is to be made from two square pieces of aluminum foil each 8.0 cm on a side. (a) What

FIGURE 26-13 A parallel-plate capacitor connected to a battery. Drawing is not to scale (Example 26-4).

should be the spacing between them if the capacitance is to be 47 pF? (b) What applied voltage will put ±95 nC on the plates?

Answers: (a) 1.2 mm; (b) 2.0 kV

Some problems similar to Example 26-5: 35, 36, 67

| **EXAMPLE 26-5** | *A Cylindrical Capacitor* |

A capacitor consists of two long concentric metal cylinders of length L, as shown in Fig. 26-14. The inner and outer cylinders have radii a and b, respectively. What is the capacitance?

Solution

Equation 26-6 does not apply to this configuration because the field between the cylinders is not uniform. To find the capacitance, we need a relation between charge and potential difference for the cylindrical configuration. In Example 25-4, we found that the potential difference between two points outside a charge distribution with line symmetry can be written

$$V(a) - V(b) = \frac{\lambda}{2\pi\varepsilon_0} \ln\left(\frac{b}{a}\right),$$

where λ is the line charge density. Because our capacitor is long compared with its diameter, this expression is a good approximation to the potential difference due to the field of the inner conductor. What about the outer conductor? Recall (Example 24-5) that the electric field inside an empty, hollow pipe is zero; therefore, the outer conductor contributes nothing to the electric field or the potential difference between the conductors. If the magnitude of the charge on either conductor is Q, then the line charge density is $\lambda = Q/L$, and our expression for

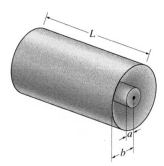

FIGURE 26-14 A cylindrical capacitor (Example 26-5).

potential difference becomes

$$V = V(a) - V(b) = \frac{Q}{2\pi\varepsilon_0 L} \ln\left(\frac{b}{a}\right).$$

Capacitance is the ratio of charge to potential difference, so we have

$$C = \frac{Q}{V} = \frac{Q}{(q/2\pi\varepsilon_0 L)\ln(b/a)} = \frac{2\pi\varepsilon_0 L}{\ln(b/a)}. \quad (26\text{-}7)$$

Does this result make sense? We already found that the capacitance of a parallel-plate capacitor increases with increasing plate area or with decreasing plate separation. With the cylindrical capacitor we can increase the area of both conductors by increasing the length L of the capacitor, and indeed Equation 26-7 shows the capacitance increasing proportionately. We can decrease the spacing of the conductors by making the radii a and b more nearly equal. This makes b/a closer to one, and $\ln(b/a)$ closer to zero, again increasing the capacitance. Although the geometries of the cylindrical and parallel-plate capacitors are quite different, the same physical considerations apply to both: a large capacitance is achieved with large conductor areas and small separation. When the separation is very small, the curvature of the cylindrical capacitor cannot matter, and Equation 26-7 should reduce to Equation 26-6 for the parallel-plate capacitor (see Problem 84).

EXERCISE A conducting sphere of radius R is enclosed in a concentric spherical conducting shell of radius $\frac{3}{2}R$. What is the capacitance of this configuration?

Answer: $3R/k$

Some problems similar to Example 26-5: 35, 36, 67

Working Voltage

The most important consideration in using a capacitor is whether its capacitance is right for the particular application. But it's also important not to exceed a capacitor's **working voltage**, a safety rating set somewhat below the potential difference that would cause dielectric breakdown of the material between the capacitor plates.

Large capacitances are most easily achieved using small plate separations, as Equation 26-6 suggests. But a small plate separation implies a large electric field for a given voltage. Thus in practical capacitors there is a trade-off between capacitance and working voltage. High working voltage and high capacitance together require large plate separation to keep the electric field small and avoid dielectric breakdown, while at the same time requiring large plate area to keep the capacitance up. Thus large, high-voltage capacitors are physically bulky and expensive to build. Often economics as well as physics dictates the final design of a circuit involving capacitors.

26-5 ENERGY STORAGE IN CAPACITORS

In Section 26-3 we found that any electric field represents stored energy. The example that guided us to that conclusion was a parallel-plate capacitor. For that configuration, the stored energy U is given by Equation 26-2:

$$U = \frac{d}{2\varepsilon_0 A} Q^2.$$

Since $\varepsilon_0 A/d$ is the capacitance of the parallel-plate capacitor, this stored energy may be written

$$U = \frac{Q^2}{2C}. \qquad \text{(energy in a capacitor)} \qquad (26\text{-}8a)$$

It is usually easier to measure voltage than charge. To express the stored energy in terms of voltage, we can solve the equation defining capacitance, $C = Q/V$, for Q and use the result in Equation 26-8a:

$$U = \frac{Q^2}{2C} = \frac{(CV)^2}{2C} = \tfrac{1}{2} CV^2. \qquad \text{(energy in capacitor)} \qquad (26\text{-}8b)$$

Although Equations 26-8a and b were derived for a parallel-plate capacitor, they hold for any capacitor regardless of its configuration (see Problem 49).

FIGURE 26-15 The large black cylinders are 4700-μF electrolytic capacitors used in the power supply of a stereo amplifier. They store and release electrical energy to smooth out the voltage variations of the power line, and can retain significant charge after the stereo has been turned off.

That the stored energy depends on the *square* of the potential difference implies that more energy can be stored in a small capacitor at high voltage than in a larger one at low voltage. Practically, the difficulties of handling high voltages mitigate this conclusion somewhat, but the fact remains that the stored energy in a capacitor increases rapidly with increasing voltage.

Capacitors can store energy for significant times. In VCRs, for example, capacitors maintain program memory in the event of a power failure lasting up to an hour or so. Large capacitors used to produce steady direct current in TVs, stereos, and other electronic devices may retain their charge after the device is turned off (Fig. 26-15); before beginning work, repair technicians routinely discharge these capacitors by connecting a screwdriver across their terminals (Fig. 26-16). However, capacitors cannot store arbitrarily large amounts of energy indefinitely. One reason is that all capacitors "leak" charge through their imperfect insulation, gradually losing their energy; another is that dielectric breakdown sets a limit on the magnitude of the electric field in a capacitor. In Problem 18, for example, you can show that the maximum energy density for an electric field in air is far less than the energy density stored in gasoline. Thus you'll not see electric cars powered by the energy stored in capacitors. Capacitors do excel as energy storage devices in situations that call for rapid delivery of stored energy. We'll look at several such applications after Example 26-6.

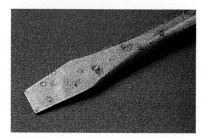

FIGURE 26-16 This screwdriver has been used repeatedly to discharge a large capacitor. Steel vaporized in each of the pitted areas.

EXAMPLE 26-6	*Which Capacitor?*

A 100-μF capacitor has a working voltage of 20 V, while a 1.0-μF capacitor has a 300-V working voltage. Which can store the most energy? The most charge?

Solution

Applying Equation 26-8b with V set to the working voltage gives

$$U_{100\,\mu F} = \tfrac{1}{2}CV^2 = \tfrac{1}{2}(100\ \mu F)(20\ V)^2 = 20\times10^3\ \mu J = 20\ mJ$$

and

$$U_{1.0\,\mu F} = \tfrac{1}{2}CV^2 = \tfrac{1}{2}(1.0\ \mu F)(300\ V)^2$$
$$= 45\times10^3\ \mu J = 45\ mJ\,.$$

Because of its higher working voltage, the smaller capacitor can store more energy. On the other hand, the larger capacitor stores more charge, as shown by solving the defining relation $C = Q/V$:

$$Q_{100\,\mu F} = CV = (100\ \mu F)(20\ V) = 2000\ \mu C = 2.0\ mC$$

and

$$Q_{1.0\,\mu F} = CV = (1.0\ \mu F)(300\ V) = 300\ \mu C = 0.30\ mC\,.$$

Again, these numbers refer to the magnitude of the charge on each plate; overall, each capacitor remains neutral.

EXERCISE The "memory" capacitor in a VCR stores 25 J of energy with a potential difference of 3.5 V. (a) What is its capacitance? (b) What is the magnitude of the charge on each plate?

Answers: (a) 4.1 F; (b) 14 C

Some problems similar to Example 26-6: 38–41, 43, 44

Got It!

You need to replace a capacitor with one that can store more energy. Which will allow a greater increase in stored energy, a replacement capacitor with twice the capacitance and the same working voltage, or one with the same capacitance but twice the working voltage?

APPLICATION	*Camera Flashes, Toilet Flushes, Defibrillators, and Fusion*

You've probably used a camera equipped with a flash. After you snap a picture, you have to wait about 10 seconds before the flash is ready again. Why? Because the power required by the flash is far greater than a small battery could supply. So the battery is used to charge a capacitor at a slow rate. Once the capacitor is charged its stored energy can be dumped suddenly into the flash tube, producing a short burst of intense light. You can't use the flash again until the capacitor is recharged. The capacitor acts as a reservoir, accumulating energy slowly and then releasing it quickly. The average power—averaged over the relatively long capacitor-charging time—is modest and well within the battery's capability. The instantaneous power, during the millisecond or so of the flash, is much larger—and that's why the capacitor is needed. Problem 45 explores the camera flash.

The camera flash and its capacitor are analogous to a situation you encounter every day with household plumbing. Flushing a toilet requires a large amount of water in a short time—far more than typical household plumbing could supply in that time. So the water is accumulated gradually in the toilet tank, then suddenly dumped when needed for flushing. In this analogy the household plumbing corresponds to the small battery of the camera flash. The toilet tank, which gradually accumulates water, corresponds to the capacitor, which gradually accumulates electrical energy. Of course you need to wait between flushes for the toilet tank to fill, just as you need to wait between flash pictures for the capacitor to charge.

Professional photographers needing to take flash pictures in rapid succession often carry around a large, heavy battery pack capable of supplying the flash power directly. Similarly, institutional buildings with large, high-pressure water pipes often have toilets without tanks that can be flushed in rapid succession.

The example of the camera flash, scaled up in size, shows how large amounts of power may be obtained for brief intervals. An analogous medical application is the defibrillator, used to restore rhythmic beating of a heart undergoing the random, ineffectual muscle contractions called fibrillation. Successful defibrillation requires the delivery of several hundred joules of electrical energy in a few milliseconds (Fig. 26-17)—an impossibility for a battery-powered instrument that needs portability for use in medical emergencies. So, just as in the camera, capacitors are used to store the energy and make it available for instant use. Problem 44 explores the energetics of defibrillation.

At a grander scale, experiments involving high-powered lasers for nuclear fusion research require more power than all

FIGURE 26-17 A defibrillator delivers several hundred joules of electrical energy to restore the heart's normal beating. That energy is stored in capacitors which discharge in a few milliseconds.

FIGURE 26-18 This huge capacitor bank stores 60 MJ of energy to drive the Nova laser fusion experiment at Lawrence Livermore National Laboratory. The capacitors can discharge a significant fraction of their energy in 1 ns.

the world's electric generating stations produce (Fig. 26-18). The required energy is accumulated in huge banks of capacitors, which are suddenly discharged to provide energy to the laser. Think here about the difference between energy and power! The pulsed laser is only on for about 10^{-9} seconds, so although it consumes energy at an enormous rate while on, it does not use all that much total energy (see Problem 46). The laser is not fired very often, so there's plenty of time to charge the capacitors. The *average* power consumption of the experiment is modest.

26-6 CONNECTING CAPACITORS

Often a single capacitor with a desired combination of capacitance and working voltage is not available. But we can obtain the combination by connecting two or more capacitors together; that's how the large capacitance needed for laser fusion

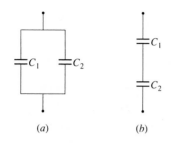

(a)   (b)

FIGURE 26-19 Connecting capacitors together. (a) Parallel; (b) series. $\perp$ is the standard circuit symbol for a capacitor.

is achieved, for example. There are only two ways to connect two capacitors (and indeed any electrical components with only two wires coming from them). Called **parallel** and **series**, these two possible connections are shown in Fig. 26-19. We would like to know the equivalent capacitance of each combination.

Capacitors in Parallel

Consider first the parallel combination of Fig. 26-19a. If we impose a potential difference V across the two wires coming from the combination, what will be the potential difference across each capacitor? The key to answering this question is the recognition that the wires connecting the capacitors are conductors and that in electrostatic equilibrium there can be no potential difference between any points connected to the same wire.* Thus all points connected directly together—including the top plates of each capacitor—are at the same potential. Similarly, the bottom plates and the wires connecting them are all at the same potential. Therefore, the potential differences across the two capacitors are equal. This is a very important point in the practical understanding of electric circuits, and applies to any two circuit components that are connected in parallel:

▎ **The potential differences across two electrical components in parallel are equal.**

Recognizing this simple fact is essential in developing your understanding of electric circuits!

The equivalent capacitance is the ratio of the total charge on both capacitors to the voltage across the parallel combination. Solving the defining relation $C = Q/V$ for charge, we can write the charges on the two capacitors as

$$Q_1 = C_1 V \quad \text{and} \quad Q_2 = C_2 V.$$

The potential difference V is the *same* in both cases because the capacitors are connected in *parallel*. Thus the total charge is

$$Q = Q_1 + Q_2 = C_1 V + C_2 V = (C_1 + C_2)V.$$

Taking the ratio of total charge Q to the voltage V across the parallel combination gives the equivalent capacitance:

$$C = C_1 + C_2. \quad \text{(parallel capacitors)} \tag{26-9a}$$

Equation 26-9a is frequently stated as "capacitors in parallel add." You can understand this result physically by considering two parallel-plate capacitors with equal spacing. Connecting them in parallel amounts to adding their plate areas, giving a larger capacitance. Although we derived Equation 26-9a for two parallel capacitors, the result that parallel capacitances add is easily extended to three or more capacitors (see Problem 56):

$$C = C_1 + C_2 + C_3 + \cdots \quad \text{(parallel capacitors)} \tag{26-9b}$$

What about the working voltage of the parallel combination? Both capacitors experience the full potential difference V, so the working voltage of the combination is that of whichever capacitor has the lower working voltage.

Capacitors in Series

Suppose we charge the series capacitor system of Fig. 26-19b, putting $+Q$ on the upper plate of C_1 and $-Q$ on the lower plate of C_2. The positive charge on the

---

* Even when we relax the equilibrium assumption, this conclusion will still hold in the approximation that the wires are perfect conductors.

uppermost plate attracts $-Q$ to the lower plate of C_1 and the negative charge $-Q$ on the lowermost plate attracts $+Q$ to the upper plate of C_2 (Fig. 26-20). Note that this leaves the middle two plates together with zero net charge, which must be the case since these two plates are not connected to any external source of charge. With charge of magnitude Q on every plate, we can conclude that

▌ **Capacitors in series carry the same charge.**

To find the equivalent capacitance, we first solve the relation $C = Q/V$ for the voltages across the two capacitors:

$$V_1 = \frac{Q}{C_1} \quad \text{and} \quad V_2 = \frac{Q}{C_2}.$$

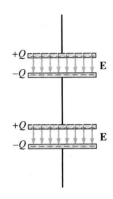

FIGURE 26-20 Capacitors in series carry the same charge.

Here there's no need to label the Q's since series capacitors carry the same charge. But now the voltages need not be the same. Since the electric fields in the two capacitors point the same way (Fig. 26-20), the voltage across the series combination is just

$$V = V_1 + V_2.$$

Inserting our expressions for the individual potential difference gives

$$V = \frac{Q}{C_1} + \frac{Q}{C_2} = Q\left(\frac{1}{C_1} + \frac{1}{C_2}\right).$$

Dividing by Q gives V/Q, which the relation $C = Q/V$ shows is the reciprocal of the equivalent capacitance:

$$\frac{1}{C} = \frac{1}{C_1} + \frac{1}{C_2}. \qquad \text{(series capacitors)} \qquad \text{(26-10a)}$$

This result is frequently described by saying that "capacitors in series add reciprocally." The result is easily extended to three or more capacitors (see Problem 56):

$$\frac{1}{C} = \frac{1}{C_1} + \frac{1}{C_2} + \frac{1}{C_3} + \cdots. \qquad \text{(series capacitors)} \qquad \text{(26-10b)}$$

Equations 26-10 show that the combined capacitance of two series capacitors is less than the capacitance of either. You can make physical sense of this by considering parallel-plate capacitors with equal plate areas. Putting them in series effectively adds the plate separations of the two capacitors, yielding a smaller overall capacitance.

What about the voltage rating of a series combination? The full applied voltage V is the sum of the voltages across each capacitor, so each can be rated for less than the full applied voltage. The fraction of the applied voltage that appears across each capacitor depends on the relative capacitances.

Got It!

You have two identical capacitors, each with capacitance C. How would you connect the two to get equivalent capacitances of (a) $2C$ and (b) $\frac{1}{2}C$? (c) Which equivalent capacitor has the higher working voltage?

EXAMPLE 26-7	*Connecting Capacitors*

(a) Find the equivalent capacitance of the combination shown in Fig. 26-21a. (b) If the maximum voltage applied between points A and B is 100 V, what should be the working voltage of C_2?

Solution

This is a problem about an electric circuit—an assemblage of interconnected electrical components, in this case four capacitors. The way to handle many such circuit problems is to reduce the circuit to a simpler one by recognizing combinations of series and parallel components, as shown in Fig. 26-21. Here C_3 and C_4 are in parallel, so they add to give an equivalent capacitance of 4.0 μF; the circuit then looks like Fig. 26-21b. This parallel combination C_{34} is in series with C_2; solving

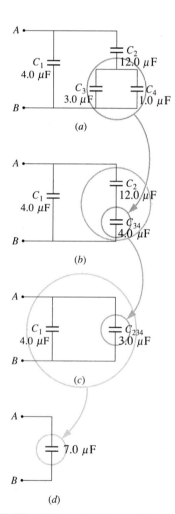

(a)

(b)

(c)

(d)

FIGURE 26-21 What is the equivalent capacitance (Example 26-7)? Analyzing the circuit involves reducing parallel and series combinations using Equations 26-9 and 26-10.

Equation 26-10a then gives

$$C_{234} = \frac{C_2 C_{34}}{C_2 + C_{34}} = \frac{(12\ \mu\text{F})(4.0\ \mu\text{F})}{12\ \mu\text{F} + 4.0\ \mu\text{F}} = 3.0\ \mu\text{F}.$$

Now the circuit looks like Fig. 26-21c, with C_1 and C_{234} in parallel. The equivalent capacitance of the entire circuit is their sum, or 7.0 μF (Fig. 26-21d).

To find the working voltage needed for C_2, we need to know the voltage across C_2 with 100 V across the entire combination. Since C_1 and the combination C_{234} are in parallel and connected to points A and B, both these capacitors experience the full 100 V. We can then use the defining relation $C = Q/V$ to find the charge on C_{234}:

$$Q_{234} = C_{234} V = (3.0\ \mu\text{F})(100\ \text{V}) = 300\ \mu\text{C}.$$

But C_{234} is the series combination of C_2 and C_{34} (Fig. 26-21b, c), and the charge on series capacitors is the same. So $Q_2 = 300\ \mu$C as well. We again use the defining relation $C = Q/V$, now to find the voltage across C_2:

$$V_2 = \frac{Q_2}{C_2} = \frac{300\ \mu\text{C}}{12\ \mu\text{F}} = 25\ \text{V}.$$

This is the required working voltage for C_2.

Tip

Analyzing Circuits This example illustrates a very general approach to circuit analysis. You reduce the circuit to its simplest form by recognizing series and parallel combinations, then gradually build back up to find the quantity of interest. The reduction is essential, even when you're only interested in what's happening with one component. Here, for instance, we wanted to know the voltage on C_2 with 100 V across the whole combination. But to find that we had to analyze the entire circuit, and only then could we focus on C_2.

Tip

Recognize Series and Parallel Parallel components have their two ends, respectively, connected *directly* together, as in Fig. 26-19a. Series components are connected in such a way that if you imagine moving through one component, then the *only* place you can go is into the next component (Fig. 26-19b). Many connections are neither; C_2 and C_3 in Fig. 26-21a, for example, are *not* in series because after you go through C_2 the circuit splits and you could go through either C_3 or C_4. And C_1 and C_2 are *not* in parallel; even though their top plates are connected directly together, their bottom plates are not. The series and parallel formulas we've derived apply *only* to true series and parallel combinations.

EXERCISE (a) With $V_{AB} = 100$ V in Fig. 26-21, what should be C_3's working voltage? (b) What will be the charges on C_1, C_3, and C_4?

Answers: (a) 75 V; (b) $Q_1 = 400$ μC, $Q_3 = 225$ μC, $Q_4 = 75$ μC

Some problems similar to Example 26-7: 52, 54, 57, 58

26-7 CAPACITORS AND DIELECTRICS

The insulating material between the plates of a capacitor serves several purposes. It maintains physical separation of the plates and minimizes charge leakage. Its molecular properties also influence the capacitance. In Chapter 23 we found that electric dipoles tend to align with an applied electric field, and we defined **dielectrics** as materials whose molecules behave as dipoles. The molecular dipole moments may be intrinsic to the molecules, or may be induced by an applied electric field, as we showed in Fig. 23-35. Essentially all insulators are dielectrics.

Suppose we have a parallel-plate capacitor charged to some voltage V_0, with air or vacuum between its plates. What happens if we insert a slab of dielectric material that fills the space between the plates? If the molecules of the dielectric have permanent dipole moments, they'll tend to align with the field, although thermal agitation prevents perfect alignment. If the molecular dipoles are induced by the electric field of the capacitor plates (recall Fig. 23-35), then the induced dipoles form in alignment with the field. Either way, as Fig. 26-22 shows for the case of induced dipoles, the fields of the dipoles themselves *oppose* the capacitor field. The result is a reduction in the net electric field between the plates. How much reduction depends on details of molecular structure and molecular interactions; empirically, though, we find that a given material may be characterized by its **dielectric constant**, κ, which describes the reduction in field. If E_0 is the original field, then the field after insertion of the dielectric will be decreased by a factor $1/\kappa$: $E = E_0/\kappa$.

If the capacitor is not connected to anything, then there's no way for the charge on its plates to change. But the field between the plates has been reduced, and therefore the potential difference $V = Ed$ has decreased by the same factor $1/\kappa$; $V = V_0/\kappa$. But capacitance is the ratio of charge to voltage, so with the dielectric in place we have

$$C = \frac{Q}{V} = \frac{Q}{(V_0/\kappa)} = \frac{\kappa Q}{V_0} = \kappa C_0, \qquad (26\text{-}11)$$

where $C_0 = Q/V_0$ is the original capacitance. Thus insertion of the dielectric increases the capacitance by a factor κ.

Capacitors are among the most difficult electronic components to miniaturize, so the ongoing revolution in microelectronics has spurred a search for suitable dielectrics with large dielectric constants, good insulating properties, and high breakdown fields. Exotic materials such as tantalum oxide and strontium titanate have become widely used in recent years because of their high dielectric constants. In a few unusual applications water, with its dielectric constant of 78, is used as a dielectric. In high-energy experiments where it is necessary to store a large amount of energy for a short time, water's large dielectric

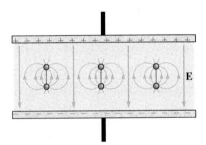

FIGURE 26-22 A capacitor with a dielectric between its plates. Molecular dipoles align with the capacitor's electric field, and their own fields point opposite to the original field. The result is a reduction in field strength.

TABLE 26-1 *Properties of Some Common Dielectrics*

DIELECTRIC MATERIAL	DIELECTRIC CONSTANT	BREAKDOWN FIELD (kV/mm)
Air	1.0006	3
Aluminum oxide	8.4	670
Glass (Pyrex)	5.6	14
Paper	3.5	14
Plexiglass	3.4	40
Polyethylene	2.3	50
Polystyrene	2.6	25
Quartz	3.8	8
Tantalum oxide	26	500
Teflon	2.1	60
Water	78	—

constant outweighs the disadvantage of poor insulating quality. Table 26-1 lists dielectric constants and breakdown fields of selected materials.

In addition to helping build better capacitors, the relation between capacitance and dielectric constant serves as a useful probe of the structure of matter. Introducing a dielectric material between capacitor plates lowers the potential difference and therefore allows us to calculate the dielectric constant. This, in turn, gives information about the density and structure of the individual molecular dipoles. Conversely, we can use the measured dielectric constant to help identify an unknown material.

EXAMPLE 26-8	*Capacitors and Dielectrics*

An air-insulated capacitor is charged by connecting it to a 12-V battery. The battery is then disconnected. When the space between capacitor plates is filled with an unknown plastic, the voltage between the plates drops to 4.6 V. What is the unknown material? If the plate spacing is 0.10 mm, how much voltage can the capacitor withstand with this material between its plates?

Solution

The voltage has dropped by a factor $1/\kappa = 4.6/12 = 1/2.6$. From Table 26-1, we see that a plastic with $\kappa = 2.6$ is polystyrene. With a dielectric breakdown field of 25 kV/mm, the 0.1-mm-thick piece of polystyrene can withstand 2.5 kV.

The rated working voltage would actually be lower, to allow a margin of safety.

EXERCISE An air-insulated capacitor with $C = 25 \ \mu F$ is connected to a 10-V battery and the battery is left connected as a quartz slab is inserted to fill the space between the plates. Find the charge on the capacitor (a) before and (b) after the slab is inserted. *Hint:* The battery maintains a fixed 10 V across the plates, but now charge can move from the battery to the plates.

Answers: (a) 250 μC; (b) 950 μC

Some problems similar to Example 26-8: 64–66

What happens to the energy stored in a capacitor when a dielectric is inserted between its plates? The dielectric increases the capacitance by a factor κ, but it also decreases the potential difference by the same factor. If the energy is initially $U_0 = \frac{1}{2} C_0 V_0^2$, then after the dielectric is inserted it becomes

$$U = \frac{1}{2}(\kappa C_0)\left(\frac{V_0}{\kappa}\right)^2 = \frac{1}{2\kappa} C_0 V_0^2 = \frac{U_0}{\kappa}. \tag{26-12}$$

Since $\kappa > 1$, the energy has decreased. Where has it gone? As the dielectric moves into the capacitor, the electric field causes charge separation and rotation of the molecular dipoles. The dipoles thus gain energy from the field. In a solid the molecules interact strongly, and the energy is quickly dissipated as heat.

FIGURE 26-23 The nonuniform fringing field outside the capacitor is stronger nearer the plates and therefore results in a net force on the molecular dipoles in the dielectric slab. As a result, the dielectric is pulled into the capacitor.

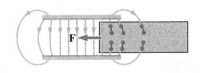

That the energy of a capacitor is lower with a dielectric inserted suggests that some attractive force must pull the dielectric slab into the capacitor. Figure 26-23 shows that this force originates in something we have heretofore intentionally ignored—the nonuniform fringing field beyond the plates of the capacitor. This nonuniform field acts on the dipoles in the dielectric to produce a net force toward the interior of the capacitor (see Problem 81).

CHAPTER SYNOPSIS

Summary

1. The work required to assemble a charge distribution is stored as the **electrostatic potential energy** of the distribution. Electrostatic potential energy resides in the electric field. Whenever an electric field is altered, energy is added to or removed from the field.
   a. The **electric field energy density** is given by

   $$u_E = \tfrac{1}{2}\varepsilon_0 E^2,$$

   where the SI units of u_E are J/m³.
   b. The electrostatic potential energy of a charge distribution may be determined either by computing the work required to assemble the individual charges of the distribution or, knowing the electric field of the distribution, by integrating the energy density over the volume containing the field:

   $$U = \int u_E \, dV = \tfrac{1}{2}\varepsilon_0 \int E^2 \, dV.$$

2. A **capacitor** is an arrangement of two conductors separated by an insulator. Transferring charge from one conductor to the other results in an electric field in the region between the conductors, and energy is stored in the field.
   a. The **capacitance** of a capacitor is the ratio of the charge to the potential difference between its conductors:

   $$C = \frac{Q}{V}.$$

   The capacitance of a parallel-plate capacitor is given by

   $$C = \frac{\varepsilon_0 A}{d},$$

   where A is the plate area and d the spacing. The capacitance of other configurations may be determined by assuming a charge, computing the associated potential difference, and taking the ratio $C = Q/V$.
   b. The energy stored in a capacitor depends on the capacitance and on the square of the potential difference:

   $$U = \tfrac{1}{2}CV^2.$$

   c. Capacitors may be connected in **series** or **parallel**. The capacitances of parallel capacitors add:

   $$C = C_1 + C_2 + C_3 + \cdots. \qquad \text{(parallel capacitors)}$$

   The capacitances of series capacitors add reciprocally:

   $$\frac{1}{C} = \frac{1}{C_1} + \frac{1}{C_2} + \frac{1}{C_3} + \cdots. \qquad \text{(series capacitors)}$$

   d. The **working voltage** of a capacitor is the maximum potential difference that should be applied across the capacitor without risk of dielectric breakdown in the insulating material.
   e. The **dielectric constant**, κ, of the insulating material used in a capacitor affects the capacitance, increasing it by this factor κ.

Terms You Should Understand

(Pairs are closely related terms whose distinction is important; number in parentheses is chapter section where term first appears.)

electrostatic potential energy (26-1)
energy density (26-3)
capacitor (26-4)
capacitance (26-4)
working voltage (26-6)
series, parallel (26-6)
dielectric constant (26-7)

Symbols You Should Recognize

U, u (26-2, 26-3)
C (26-4)
κ (26-7)

Problems You Should Be Able to Solve

calculating the work needed to assemble a distribution of discrete charges (26-1)
calculating electrostatic energy by integrating electric field energy density (26-3)

determining capacitance of simple capacitor configurations (26-4)

evaluating energy stored in capacitors (26-5)

analyzing parallel and series capacitor combinations (26-6)

determining the effect of dielectric materials in capacitors (26-7)

Limitations to Keep in Mind

Equation 26-6 for a parallel-plate capacitor is an approximation that neglects fringing fields at the plate edges; the approximation is good for capacitor plates much larger than their spacing.

QUESTIONS

1. Two positive point charges are initially infinitely far apart. Is it possible, using only a finite amount of work, to move them until they are located a small distance d apart?

2. How does the energy density a certain distance from a negative point charge compare with the energy density the same distance from a positive point charge of equal magnitude?

3. A dipole consists of two equal but opposite charges. Is the total energy stored in the field of the dipole zero? Why or why not?

4. Charge is spread over the surface of a balloon. The balloon is then allowed to expand. What happens to the energy of the electric field? If it is reduced, where does it go? If it is increased, where does the extra energy come from?

5. Why doesn't the superposition principle hold for electric field energy densities? That is, if you double the field strength at some point, why don't you simply double the energy density as well?

6. A student argues that the total energy associated with the electric field of a charged sphere must be infinite because its field extends throughout an infinite volume. Criticize this argument.

7. A capacitor is said to carry a charge Q. What is the net charge on the entire capacitor?

8. Does the capacitance of a capacitor describe the maximum amount of charge it can hold, in the same way that the capacity of a bucket describes the maximum amount of water it can hold? Explain and compare the meanings of capacitance and capacity.

9. A cylinder for storing compressed gas has a fixed volume, yet knowing this volume does not tell how much gas the cylinder can hold. Why not? How is the cylinder like a capacitor? Form analogies between quantities used in describing a capacitor and the amount of gas in the cylinder, the cylinder pressure, and the maximum pressure the cylinder can withstand.

10. A capacitor of capacitance C is charged to a potential difference V and carries charge Q. Why isn't the stored energy given simply by CV^2? After all, the work required to move a charge Q against a potential difference V is QV, and $C = Q/V$, so $Q = CV$.

11. Is a force needed to hold the plates of a charged capacitor in place? Explain.

12. Why do we say that capacitance depends only on the physical configuration of conductors making up a capacitor, not on the charge or potential difference, and yet we define capacitance as $C = Q/V$?

13. Why can't useful capacitors of arbitrarily large capacitance be made by simply reducing the spacing between parallel plates?

14. A solid conducting slab is inserted between the plates of a capacitor, as shown in Fig. 26-24. Does the capacitance increase, decrease, or remain the same?

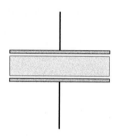

FIGURE 26-24 Question 14.

15. Why is a capacitor needed for energy storage in a camera flash? After all, the battery is the ultimate source of the flash energy, so it should be capable of supplying the needed energy.

16. Two capacitors are connected in series. Is the equivalent capacitance more or less than that of either one?

17. Two capacitors are connected in series; they have capacitances C_1 and C_2, with $C_1 > C_2$. A potential difference V is imposed across the combination. Is the voltage across the two capacitors the same? If not, which has the greater voltage? Is the charge on each the same? If not, which has the greater charge?

18. Explain why the potential differences across parallel capacitors must be the same.

19. Two capacitors are storing equal amounts of energy, yet one has twice the capacitance of the other. How do their voltages compare?

20. Explain why inserting a dielectric between capacitor plates increases the capacitance.

21. An air-insulated parallel-plate capacitor is connected to a battery that imposes a potential difference V across the capacitor. If a dielectric slab is inserted between the capacitor plates, what happens to (a) the potential difference; (b) the capacitor charge; and (c) the capacitance?

22. A capacitor is charged and left connected to the charging battery. If you insert a dielectric slab between the capacitor plates, do you do work on the slab, or does it do work on you? Explain.

PROBLEMS

Section 26-1 Energy of a Charge Distribution

1. Three point charges, each of $+q$, are moved from infinity to the vertices of an equilateral triangle of side ℓ. How much work is required?

2. Repeat the preceding problem for the case of two charges $+q$ and one $-q$.

3. Four 50-μC charges are brought from far apart onto a line where they are spaced at 2.0-cm intervals. How much work does it take to assemble this charge distribution?

4. Repeat Example 26-1 for the case when the negative charge is $-q$ rather than $-q/2$.

5. Suppose two of the charges in Problem 1 are held in place, while the third is allowed to move freely. If this third charge has mass m, what will be its speed when it's far from the other two charges?

6. To a very crude approximation, a water molecule consists of a negatively charged oxygen atom and two "bare" protons, as shown in Fig. 26-25. Calculate the electrostatic energy of this configuration, which is therefore the magnitude of the energy released in forming this molecule from widely separated atoms. Your answer is an overestimate because electrons are actually "shared" among the three atoms, spending more time near the oxygen.

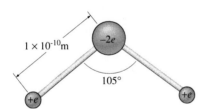

FIGURE 26-25 Problem 6.

7. Four identical charges q, initially widely separated, are brought to the vertices of a tetrahedron of side a (Fig. 26-26). Find the electrostatic energy of this configuration.

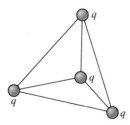

FIGURE 26-26 Problem 7 (All sides have equal length a).

8. A charge Q_0 is at the origin. A second charge, $Q_x = 2Q_0$, is brought to the point $x = a$, $y = 0$. Then a third charge Q_y is brought to the point $x = 0$, $y = a$. If it takes twice as much work to bring in Q_y as it did Q_x, what is Q_y in terms of Q_0?

Section 26-2 Two Isolated Conductors

9. Two square conducting plates 25 cm on a side and 5.0 mm apart carry charges ±1.1 μC. Find (a) the electric field between the plates, (b) the potential difference between the plates, and (c) the stored energy.

10. Two square conducting plates measure 5.0 cm on a side. The plates are parallel, spaced 1.2 mm apart, and initially uncharged. (a) How much work is required to transfer 7.2 μC from one plate to the other? (b) How much work is required to transfer a second 7.2 μC?

11. (a) How much charge must be transferred between the initially uncharged plates of the preceding problem in order to store 15 mJ of energy? (b) What will be the potential difference between the plates?

12. Two parallel, circular metal plates of 15 cm radius are initially uncharged. It takes 6.3 J to transfer 45 μC from one plate to the other. How far apart are the plates?

13. A conducting sphere of radius a is surrounded by a concentric spherical shell of radius b. Both are initially uncharged. How much work does it take to transfer charge from one to the other until they carry charges $\pm Q$?

14. Show that the energy given by Equation 26-2 can be written as the product of the charge transferred with the *average* value of the potential during the transfer.

15. Two conducting spheres of radius a are separated by a distance $\ell \gg a$; since the distance is large, neither sphere affects the other's electric field significantly, and the fields remain spherically symmetric. (a) If the spheres carry equal but opposite charges $\pm q$, show that the potential difference between them is $2kq/a$. (b) Write an expression for the work dW involved in moving an infinitesimal charge dq from the negative to the positive sphere. (c) Integrate your expression to find the work involved in transferring a charge Q from one sphere to the other, assuming both are initially uncharged.

Section 26-3 Energy and the Electric Field

16. The energy density in a uniform electric field is 3.0 J/m^3. What is the field strength?

17. A car battery stores about 4 MJ of energy. If all this energy were used to create a uniform electric field of 30 kV/m, what volume would it occupy?

18. Air undergoes dielectric breakdown at a field strength of 3 MV/m. Could you store energy in a uniform electric field in air with the same energy density as that of liquid gasoline? (See Appendix C.)

19. Find the electric field energy density at the surface of a proton, taken to be a uniformly charged sphere 1 fm in radius.

20. A pair of closely spaced square conducting plates measure 10 cm on a side. The electric field energy density between the plates is 4.5 kJ/m^3. What is the charge on the plates?

21. The electric field strength as a function of position x in a certain region is given by $E = E_0(x/x_0)$, where $E_0 = 24$ kV/m and $x_0 = 6.0$ m. Find the total energy stored in a cube 1.0 m on a side, located between $x = 0$ and $x = 1.0$ m. (The field strength is independent of y and z.)

22. A sphere of radius R contains charge Q spread uniformly throughout its volume. Find an expression for the electrostatic energy contained within the sphere itself. *Hint:* Consult Example 24-1.

23. A sphere of radius R carries a total charge Q distributed over its surface. Show that the total energy stored in its electric field is $U = kQ^2/2R$.

24. A uranium-235 nucleus contains 92 protons and 143 neutrons, and has a diameter of 6.6 fm. Assuming that the proton charge is distributed uniformly throughout the nucleus, calculate the total electrostatic energy of this configuration. *Hint:* See the preceding two problems.

25. Two 4.0-mm-diameter water drops each carry 15 nC. They are initially separated by a great distance. Find the change in the electrostatic potential energy if they are brought together to form a single spherical drop. Assume all charge resides on the drops' surfaces.

26. A 2.1-mm-diameter wire carries a uniform line charge density $\lambda = 28$ μC/m. How much energy is contained in a space 1.0 m long within one wire diameter of the wire surface?

27. A long, solid rod of radius a carries uniform volume charge density ρ. Find an expression for the electrostatic energy per unit length contained *within* the rod. *Hint:* See Problem 24-31.

Sections 26-4 Capacitors

28. A capacitor's plates hold 1.3 μC when charged to 60 V. What is its capacitance?

29. The "memory" capacitor in a VCR has a capacitance of 4.0 F and is charged to 3.5 V. What is the charge on its plates?

30. What voltage is needed to put 1.6 mC on a 100-μF capacitor?

31. Figure 26-27 shows data from an experiment in which known amounts of charge are placed on a capacitor and the resulting voltage measured. Fit a line to the data, and use it to determine the capacitance.

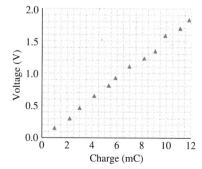

FIGURE 26-27 Problem 31 (data plot).

32. Show that the units of ε_0 may be written as F/m.

33. Find the capacitance of a parallel-plate capacitor consisting of circular plates 20 cm in radius separated by 1.5 mm.

34. A parallel-plate capacitor with 1.1-mm plate spacing has ± 2.3 μC on its plates when charged to 150 V. What is the plate area?

35. Find the capacitance of a 1.0-m-long piece of coaxial cable whose inner conductor radius is 0.80 mm and whose outer conductor radius is 2.2 mm, with air in between.

36. A capacitor consists of a conducting sphere of radius a surrounded by a concentric conducting shell of radius b. Show that its capacitance is $C = \dfrac{ab}{k(b - a)}$.

37. Figure 26-28 shows a capacitor consisting of two electrically connected plates with a third plate between them, spaced so its surfaces are a distance d from the other plates. The plates have area A. Neglecting edge effects, show that the capacitance is $2\varepsilon_0 A/d$.

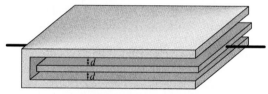

FIGURE 26-28 Problem 37.

Section 26-5 Energy Storage in Capacitors

38. The power supply of a stereo receiver contains a 2500-μF capacitor charged to 35 V. How much energy does it store?

39. Find the capacitance of a capacitor that stores 350 μJ when the potential difference across its plates is 100 V.

40. A certain capacitor stores 40 mJ of energy when charged to 100 V. (a) How much would it store when charged to 25 V? (b) What is its capacitance?

41. Which can store more energy, a 1-μF capacitor rated at 250 V or a 470 pF capacitor rated at 3 kV?

42. A circuit application calls for a 10-μF capacitor that can store 12 mJ. What should be its voltage rating? The capacitors are available with voltage ratings that are multiples of 25 V.

43. A 0.01-μF, 300-V capacitor costs 25¢, a 0.1-μF, 100-V capacitor costs 35¢, and a 30-μF, 5-V capacitor costs 88¢. (a) Which can store the most charge? (b) Which can store the most energy? (c) Which is the most cost-effective energy storage device, as measured by energy stored per unit cost?

44. A medical defibrillator stores 950 J of energy in a 100-μF capacitor. (a) What is the voltage across the capacitor? (b) If the capacitor discharges 300 J of its stored energy in 2.5 ms, what is the power delivered during this time?

45. A camera flashtube requires 5.0 J of energy per flash. The flash duration is 1.0 ms. (a) What is the power used by the flashtube *while it is actually flashing*? (b) If the flashtube operates at 200 V, what size capacitor is needed to supply the flash energy? (c) If the flashtube is fired once every 10 s, what is its *average* power consumption?

46. The NOVA laser fusion experiment at Lawrence Livermore Laboratory in California can deliver 10^{14} W (roughly 100 times the output of all the world's power plants) of light energy when its lasers are on. But the laser pulse lasts only 10^{-9} s. (a) How much energy is delivered in one pulse? (b) The capacitor bank supplying this energy has a total capacitance of 0.26 F. Only about 0.17% (i.e., 0.0017) of the capacitor energy actually appears as light. To what voltage must the capacitor bank be charged?

47. A solid conducting slab is inserted between the plates of a charged capacitor, as shown in Fig. 26-29. The slab thickness is 60% of the plate spacing, and its area is the same as the plates'. (a) What happens to the capacitance? (b) What happens to the stored energy, assuming the capacitor is not connected to anything?

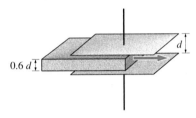

FIGURE 26-29 Problem 47.

48. Consider the two widely separated spheres of Problem 15 as a capacitor. Use energy considerations (i.e., the equation $U = \frac{1}{2}CV^2$ applies to *any* capacitor) and the answers to Problem 15 to find the capacitance.

49. The cylindrical capacitor of Example 26-5 is charged to a voltage V. Obtain an expression for the energy density as a function of radial position in the capacitor, and integrate to show explicitly that the stored energy is $\frac{1}{2}CV^2$.

Section 26-6 Connecting Capacitors

50. You have a 1.0-μF and a 2.0 μF capacitor. What values of capacitance could you get by connecting them in series or parallel?

51. Two capacitors are connected in series and the combination charged to 100 V. If the voltage across each capacitor is 50 V, how do their capacitances compare?

52. (a) What is the equivalent capacitance of the combination shown in Fig. 26-30? (b) If a 100-V battery is connected across the combination, what is the charge on each capacitor? (c) What is the voltage across each?

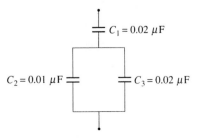

FIGURE 26-30 Problems 52.

53. You're given three capacitors: 1.0 μF, 2.0 μF, and 3.0 μF. Find (a) the maximum, (b) the minimum, and (c) two intermediate values of capacitance you could achieve with various combinations of all three capacitors.

54. What is the equivalent capacitance of the four identical capacitors in Fig. 26-31, measured between A and B?

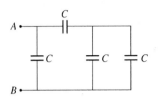

FIGURE 26-31 Problem 54.

55. You have an unlimited supply of 2.0-μF, 50-V capacitors. Describe combinations that would be equivalent to (a) a 2.0-μF, 100-V capacitor and (b) a 0.50-μF, 200-V capacitor.

56. Repeat the derivations for parallel and series capacitors, now using combinations of three capacitors.

57. What is the equivalent capacitance in Fig. 26-32?

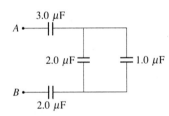

FIGURE 26-32 Problems 57, 58.

58. In Fig. 26-32, find the energy stored in the 1-μF capacitor when a 50-V battery is connected between points A and B.

59. Two capacitors C_1 and C_2 are in series, with a voltage V across the combination. Show that the voltages across the individual capacitors are

$$V_1 = \frac{C_2 V}{C_1 + C_2} \quad \text{and} \quad V_2 = \frac{C_1 V}{C_1 + C_2}.$$

60. A 0.10-μF capacitor rated at 50 V is in series with a 0.20-μF capacitor rated at 200 V. What is the maximum voltage that should be applied across the series combination? *Hint:* See the preceding problem.

61. A variable "trimmer" capacitor used to make fine adjustments has a capacitance range from 10 to 30 pF. The trimmer is in parallel with a capacitor of about 0.001 μF. Over what percentage range can the capacitance of the combination be varied?

62. Capacitors are often marked with a nominal value for the capacitance and a tolerance range within which the actual capacitance lies. For example, a 1-μF, $\pm$20% capacitor has capacitance between 0.8 μF and 1.2 μF. If you connect a 0.01-μF $\pm$ 20% capacitor in series with a 0.02 μF $\pm$ 30% capacitor, in what range will the resulting capacitance lie? Express as a capacitance and its associated tolerance.

63. A 5.0-μF capacitor is charged to 50 V, and a 2.0-μF capacitor is charged to 100 V. The two are disconnected from their charging batteries and connected in parallel, positive to positive. (a) What is the common voltage across each after they are connected? *Hint:* Charge is conserved. (b) Compare the total electrostatic energy before and after the capacitors are connected. Speculate on the discrepancy.

Section 26-7 Capacitors and Dielectrics

64. A parallel-plate capacitor has plates with 50 cm^2 area separated by a 25-μm layer of polyethylene. Find (a) its capacitance and (b) its working voltage.

65. A 470-pF capacitor consists of two circular plates 15 cm in radius, separated by a sheet of polystyrene. (a) What is the thickness of the sheet? (b) What is the working voltage?

66. An electrolytic capacitor is essentially a parallel-plate configuration in which aluminum plates are separated by a thin layer of aluminum oxide created by chemical action when a voltage is applied. If the effective plate area of a 2000-μF capacitor is 2.5 m^2, what are (a) the oxide layer thickness and (b) the working voltage?

67. Repeat Problem 35 for the more realistic case of a cable insulated with polyethylene.

68. An air-insulated parallel-plate capacitor has plate area 76 cm^2 and spacing 1.2 mm. It is charged to 900 V and then disconnected from the charging battery. A plexiglass sheet is then inserted to fill the space between the plates. What are (a) the capacitance, (b) the potential difference between the plates, and (c) the stored energy both before and after the plexiglass is inserted?

69. The capacitor of the preceding problem is connected to its 900-V charging battery and left connected as the plexiglass sheet is inserted, so the potential difference remains at 900 V. What are (a) the charge on the plates and (b) the stored energy both before and after the plexiglass is inserted?

70. The first accurate estimate of the thickness of biological cell membranes used a capacitive technique, in which the capacitance per unit area of cell membrane was determined through a macroscopic measurement of the electrical properties of a suspension of cells; the result was a value of about 1 μF/cm^2 for a wide range of cells. Assuming a dielectric constant of about 3 for the membrane material, find the membrane thickness. (Your answer is the thickness of the bipolar lipid layer alone, and is lower by a factor of about 3 than values based on x-ray techniques; the full membrane may be thicker still.)

Paired Problems

(Both problems in a pair involve the same principles and techniques. If you can get the first problem, you should be able to solve the second one.)

71. A pair of parallel conducting plates of area 0.025 m^2 carrying equal but opposite charges stores 1.6 J in its electric field. When the magnitude of the charge on both plates is increased by 5.0 μC, the stored energy increases to 2.4 J. Find the plate separation.

72. A capacitor stores 50 mJ of energy at voltage V_0. When the voltage is increased by 150 V, the stored energy increases to 75 mJ. Find the capacitance.

73. A 20-μF air-insulated parallel-plate capacitor is charged to 300 V. The capacitor is then disconnected from the charging battery, and its plate separation is doubled. Find the stored energy (a) before and (b) after the plate separation increases. Where does the extra energy come from?

74. Repeat the preceding problem, except that now the capacitor remains connected to the 300-V battery while the plates are separated.

75. In the capacitor network of Fig. 26-33, take $C = 6.0$ μF. Find (a) the equivalent capacitance between A and B and (b) the charge on C when 30 V is applied between A and B.

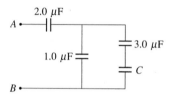

FIGURE 26-33 Problems 75, 76.

76. Take C in Fig. 26-33 as an unknown capacitance. If 100 V is applied between A and B, the network stores 5.8 mJ of energy. Find C.

Supplementary Problems

77. A typical lightning flash transfers 30 C across a potential difference of 30 MV. Assuming such flashes occur every 5 s in the thunderstorm of Example 26-2, roughly how long could the storm continue if its electrical energy were not replenished?

78. A capacitor is constructed from a "sandwich" consisting of two long strips of aluminum foil each 2.0 cm wide and 1.6 m long, separated by two strips of 5.0-μm-thick polyethylene (Fig. 26-34). The capacitor is rolled up to make a compact cylinder. Find its capacitance. *Hint:* Because the strips are thin and closely spaced, you can treat this as a parallel-plate capacitor. But note that each foil layer in the rolled-up capacitor "sees" an oppositely charged layer on *both* sides.

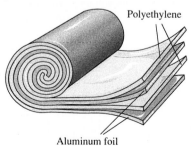

FIGURE 26-34 Problem 78.

79. Six charges $\pm q$, initially widely separated, are positioned to form a hexagon of side a, as shown in Fig. 26-35. What is the electrostatic energy of this configuration?

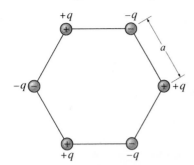

FIGURE 26-35 Problem 79.

80. Show that the result of Problem 36 reduces to that of a parallel-plate capacitor when the separation $b - a$ is much less than the radius a.

81. An air-insulated parallel-plate capacitor of capacitance C_0 is charged to voltage V_0 and then disconnected from the charging battery. A slab of material with dielectric constant κ, whose thickness is essentially equal to the capacitor spacing, is then inserted halfway into the capacitor (Fig. 26-36). Determine (a) the new capacitance, (b) the stored energy, and (c) the force on the slab in terms of C_0, V_0, κ, and the capacitor plate length L.

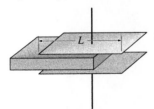

FIGURE 26-36 Problem 81.

82. Repeat parts (b) and (c) of the preceding problem, now assuming the battery remains connected while the slab is inserted.

83. We live inside a giant capacitor! Its plates are Earth's surface and the ionosphere, a conducting layer of the atmosphere beginning at about 60 km altitude. (a) What is its capacitance? *Hint:* You can treat it as either a spherical or a parallel-plate capacitor. Why? (b) The potential difference between Earth and ionosphere is about 6 MV. Find the total energy stored in this planetary capacitor.

84. Show that the result of Example 26-5 reduces to that of a parallel-plate capacitor when the separation $b - a$ is much less than the radius a. *Hint:* See Appendix A for an approximation to the logarithm.

85. Equation 26-2 gives the potential energy of a pair of oppositely charged plates. (a) Differentiate this expression with respect to the plate spacing to find the magnitude of the attractive force between the plates. (b) Compare with the answer you would get by multiplying one plate's charge by the electric field between the plates. Why do your answers differ? Which is right?

86. A solid sphere contains a uniform volume charge density. What fraction of the total electrostatic energy of this configuration is contained *within* the sphere?

87. A small dipole lies on the x axis, centered at the origin. Find an expression for the total electrostatic energy contained in a thin cylindrical volume of diameter d and length ℓ, with its left end a distance ℓ from the dipole center, as shown in Fig. 26-37. Assume that ℓ is much greater than the dipole spacing. *Hint:* Since the cylinder is very thin, you can use the on-axis dipole field (Equation 23-5b) for the field throughout the cylinder.

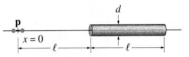

FIGURE 26-37 Problem 87.

88. A coaxial cable 15 m long consists of an inner conductor 1.0 mm in radius and an outer conductor 3.0 mm in radius, separated by polyethylene insulation. What is the electrostatic energy contained within this cable when a potential difference of 300 V is applied between its two conductors?

89. A TV antenna cable consists of two 0.50-mm-diameter wires spaced 12 mm apart. Estimate the capacitance per unit length of this cable, neglecting dielectric effects of the insulation.

90. A classical view of the electron pictures it as a purely electrical entity, whose rest mass energy mc^2 (see Section 8-7) is the energy stored in its electric field. If the electron were a sphere with charge distributed uniformly over its surface, what radius would it have to satisfy this condition? (Your answer for the electron's "size" is not consistent with modern quantum mechanics nor with experiments that suggest the electron is a true point particle.)

91. Use the fact that the static electric field is conservative to argue that there *must* be fringing field at the edges of a parallel plate capacitor. *Hint:* Remember that the plates are equipotentials, and consider the potential differences V_{AB} and V_{CD} in Fig. 26-38. What does your argument say about the strength of the fringing field relative to the field between the plates?

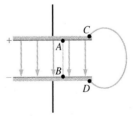

FIGURE 26-38 Problem 91.

27 Electric Current

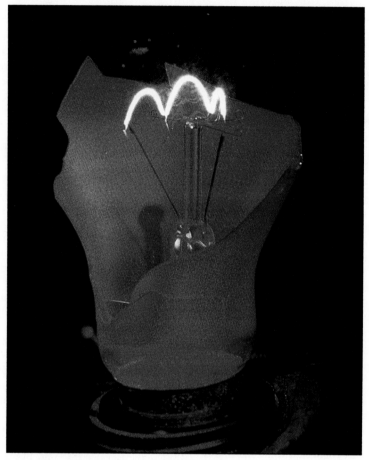

Electrical energy is converted to heat and light as a current of electrons flows through a lightbulb's filament.

So far our discussion of electrical phenomena has been based on the assumption of electrostatic equilibrium. We now relax that assumption, and instead of considering charges at rest, we'll consider situations in which charges are moving. Such motion usually occurs only in materials containing free charges, so our discussion will emphasize electrical conductors.

27-1 ELECTRIC CURRENT

Moving electric charge constitutes **electric current**. Electric currents are essential to many technological and natural processes. Currents flowing in light bulbs, toasters, and electric stoves produce heat and light. Currents in electric motors run our computers' disk drives, our refrigerators and washing machines, subway and railroad locomotives, and, increasingly, even advanced-technology electric cars. Your computer can plot a graph for your physics lab or search for a word in your English paper; fundamentally, these processes involve electric currents within the microchips at the heart of computers and other modern electronic devices. Currents in your body help your brain process information, regulate your heartbeat, and tell your muscles to move. Electric eels sense and kill their prey with electric currents they send through the surrounding water. A lightning strike is a strong but brief flow of current through the atmosphere. Currents in Earth's liquid outer core produce the planetary magnetic field that protects us from cosmic radiation, and currents in the ionized gases making up the stars greatly influence stellar behavior.

The measure of current is the net rate at which charge crosses a given area. Accordingly, its units are coulombs per second (C/s). This unit is given the special name **ampere** (A) after the French physicist André Marie Ampère:

$$1\ A = 1\ C/s.$$

In electronics, biomedical applications, and many other practical situations currents are small enough that the milliampere (mA) and microampere (μA) are frequently used. When the current I is steady we write

$$I = \frac{\Delta q}{\Delta t}, \qquad \text{(steady current)} \qquad (27\text{-}1a)$$

where Δq is the net charge crossing the given area in time Δt. If the current is not steady, we consider the ratio of charge to time for arbitrarily small time intervals, giving an instantaneous current that may vary with time:

$$I = \frac{dq}{dt}. \qquad \text{(instantaneous current)} \qquad (27\text{-}1b)$$

The direction of current is the direction in which *positive* charge flows. If the moving charge is negative, as with electrons in a metal, then the current is opposite the charge motion. You can blame Benjamin Franklin for this confusing situation! It was Franklin who assigned the names "positive" and "negative" to the two kinds of electric charge. Had Franklin known that free charges in metals are electrons, he might well have reversed his terminology.

An electric current may consist of only one sign of charge in motion, or it may involve both positive and negative charge. In that case the current is determined by the *net* charge motion—that is, by the algebraic sum of the currents associated with both kinds of charge (Fig. 27-1). That's why the bulk motion of a neutral object—even though it contains many coulombs of positive and of negative charge—does not constitute a current (Fig. 27-1b).

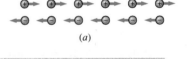

(a)

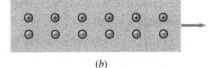

(b)

FIGURE 27-1 (a) Protons moving to the right constitute a current to the right. Since electrons are negative, *leftward* moving electrons also constitute a current to the *right*. The result in this case is a net current to the right. (b) In this bulk motion of neutral matter, the protons constitute a current to the right. But the negative electrons, also moving to the right, constitute a current to the *left*. So the net current is zero. Bulk motion of a *charged* object would, however, constitute a current.

Got It!

In which of the following situations is there a nonzero net current, and in which direction is that current flowing? (a) A beam of electrons moves from left to right; (b) a beam of protons moves upward; (c) in a solution, positive ions move to the left and negative ions to the right; (d) blood, carrying positive and negative ions at the same velocity, flows upward through a vein in your leg; (e) a metal car with no net charge moves westward on a highway.

A Microscopic Look at Current

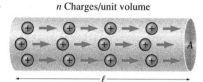

v_d →
n Charges/unit volume

FIGURE 27-2 A conductor of cross-sectional area A containing n charge carriers per unit volume. Each moves with speed v_d and carries charge q. The total charge in a region of length ℓ is $nA\ell q$, and the current is therefore $nAqv_d$. Although we show positive charge moving, in the most common conductors—metals—charges carrying the current are actually negative electrons.

Current —the rate at which charge crosses a given area—depends on the speed of the charge carriers, their density, and the charge carried by each. Consider a conductor containing n charges per unit volume, each carrying charge q and moving with speed v_d, as shown in Fig. 27-2. The quantity n is called the **number density**, and v_d is the **drift speed**. In some cases—a beam of electrons, for example—v_d is the actual particle speed. More commonly, v_d represents the time-average speed of the charge carriers, averaging out the effects of much faster but random thermal motion and collisions. If A is the conductor's cross-sectional area, then a length ℓ has volume $A\ell$ and therefore contains $nA\ell$ charges. Since each carries charge q, the total charge is $\Delta Q = nA\ell q$. With drift speed v_d, the length ℓ of charge moves past a given point in time $\Delta t = \ell/v_d$, so the current is

$$I = \frac{\Delta Q}{\Delta t} = \frac{nA\ell q}{\ell/v_d} = nAqv_d. \qquad (27\text{-}2)$$

EXAMPLE 27-1	*Current in a Wire*

A copper wire with a cross-sectional area of 1.0 mm² carries a current of 5.0 A. The charge carriers in copper are electrons, and each copper atom contributes, on average, 1.3 free electrons. What is the drift speed of the electrons?

Solution

The density of copper (see inside back cover) is 8920 kg/m³, and the periodic table (also inside back cover) lists copper's atomic weight as 63.55—meaning that the mass per atom is 63.55 u. So the number density of copper atoms is

$$n = \frac{8920 \text{ kg/m}^3}{(63.55 \text{ u/atom})(1.66\times10^{-27} \text{ kg/u})}$$

$$= 8.46\times10^{28} \text{ atoms/m}^3.$$

Since each atom contributes 1.3 free electrons, the electron density is $(1.3)(8.46\times10^{28} \text{ m}^{-3}) = 1.10\times10^{29} \text{ m}^{-3}$. Solving Equation 27-2 for v_d then gives

$$v_d = \frac{I}{nAq} = \frac{5.0 \text{ A}}{(1.10\times10^{29} \text{ m}^{-3})(1.0\times10^{-6} \text{ m}^2)(1.6\times10^{-19}\text{C})}$$

$$= 0.284 \text{ mm/s}.$$

This remarkably small value is typical of drift speeds in metallic conductors.

EXERCISE A thin layer of gold, 0.10 mm wide and 3.2 μm thick, is used for connections to an integrated circuit. Find (a) the free electron density in gold and (b) the drift speed of electrons in the gold layer when it carries a current of 140 μA. The density of gold is 1.93×10^4 kg/m³, and each gold atom contributes, on average, 1.5 free electrons.

Answers: (a) 8.85×10^{28} m^{-3}; (b) 31 μm/s

Some problems similar to Example 27-1: 8, 55, 56

How can the drift speed be so small? When you turn on a light switch, the light comes on immediately, not several thousand seconds later as the result of Example 27-1 might imply. Here it's important to distinguish between the speed of the electrons and that of the electrical signal in the wire. As soon as electrons at one end of the wire begin moving, their electric fields affect adjacent electrons, which also begin moving. This effect propagates down the wire at what is in fact nearly the speed of light, so the current begins everywhere almost simultaneously. The same thing happens when you turn on a garden hose full of water: Water comes out the far end even though water at the faucet has not had time to travel down the hose.

Current Density

In many cases electric currents are not neatly confined in a wire. Examples include currents in Earth, in the atmosphere, in chemical solutions, and in the ionized gases that make up the stars and indeed much of the matter in the universe (Fig. 27-3). In these situations the current is spread over a rather ill-defined area, and its magnitude and direction may vary from point to point. It's useful to characterize such diffuse currents in terms of **current density**, J, defined as the current per unit area at a given point. Dividing Equation 27-2 by the area gives

$$J = \frac{I}{A} = nqv_d. \qquad (27\text{-}3a)$$

The flow of charge can vary in both magnitude and direction, so current density is more generally written as a vector quantity:

$$\mathbf{J} = nq\mathbf{v}_d, \qquad (27\text{-}3b)$$

where $\mathbf{v}_d$ is the drift velocity.

If current density is uniform, as in a wire, then the total current is simply the product of the current density with the wire's cross-sectional area. When the current density varies with position, then integration is necessary to calculate the total current. Problem 65 explores this case.

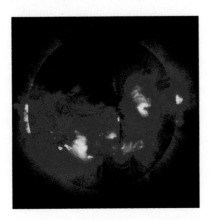

FIGURE 27-3 Strong electric currents flow in the bright yellow loops of ionized gas that arch above the Sun's surface in this image made with an orbiting x-ray telescope on the Japanese satellite Yohkoh.

EXAMPLE 27-2	*Through the Cell Membrane*

An ion channel is a narrow pore, formed from a special protein molecule, that allows specific ions to pass through a biological cell membrane (Fig. 27-4). A particular channel carries a current of 1.8 pA, with the charges being singly ionized potassium (K^+). The channel has a circular cross section 0.30 nm in diameter. (a) If the channel is open for 1.0 ms, how many ions pass through it? (b) What is the magnitude of the current density in the channel?

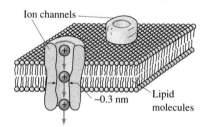

FIGURE 27-4 Diagram of a cell membrane, showing two ion channels. An ion current is passing through the frontmost channel, shown in cutaway. The current is driven in part by the electric field associated with the charge distribution on the lipid molecules that make up the membrane.

Solution

(a) A current of 1.8 pA means 1.8 pC/s, so the total charge passing through the channel in 1.0 ms is (1.8 pC/s)(1.0 ms) = 1.8 fC, where we use the SI prefixes p = 10^{-12}, m = 10^{-3}, and f = 10^{-15}. Each ion carries one elementary charge, so the number of ions in 1 ms is

$$N = \frac{1.8 \times 10^{-15}\,\text{C}}{1.6 \times 10^{-19}\,\text{C/ion}} = 1.1 \times 10^4 \text{ ions} .$$

(b) Current density is current per unit area, so

$$J = \frac{I}{A} = \frac{I}{\pi r^2} = \frac{1.8 \times 10^{-12}\,\text{A}}{(\pi)(0.15 \times 10^{-9}\,\text{m})^2} = 2.5 \times 10^7\,\text{A/m}^2 .$$

This value is about four times the maximum safe current density in copper wire used in household wiring! (See the exercise with this example.) Of course, the ion channel is so narrow that the total current is minuscule.

Tip

Don't Just Plug In! Do you search for an equation as soon as you start a problem? Think first! If you really know what the concepts mean, you may not always need equations. Here we solved the problem entirely by knowing the meanings of the terms *current* and *current density*.

EXERCISE The maximum safe current density in copper wire used in household wiring is about 6 MA/m². (Beyond this level the wire overheats.) What is the minimum safe wire diameter in a circuit that can carry up to 15 A?

Answer: 1.8 mm

Some problems similar to Example 27-2: 2, 5–7, 10, 11

27-2 CONDUCTION MECHANISMS

What causes electric current? Electric charges experience forces in electric fields, so applying a field to a conductor should result in a current. (The simplest way to produce such a field is to connect a battery—a device that provides a fixed potential difference between two points—across the conductor.) You might think that it would suffice to apply the field briefly to get the charges moving; Newton's law suggests they would then keep moving. In most conductors, however, charges do not move unimpeded. They bump into things—usually ions— and quickly lose any energy they've gained from the field. To sustain a current in most materials, it is therefore necessary to maintain an electric field within the material. Having such a field does not violate our conclusion that there can be no electric field in a conductor in electrostatic equilibrium since we're explicitly considering moving charges and are therefore no longer talking about equilibrium.

Although it is generally true that electric fields result in currents, the detailed relation between current and field depends on the type of conductor. In addition to metals, important conductors include ionic solutions, plasmas (ionized gases), semiconductors, and superconductors, all of which we will consider briefly in this section.

In most materials the current density and the electric field are in the same direction, and we can therefore characterize the relation between the two using the equation

$$\mathbf{J} = \sigma\mathbf{E}, \tag{27-4a}$$

where σ is called the **conductivity** of the material. Equation 27-4a shows that conductivity is the ratio of the magnitude of the current density to the magnitude of the electric field.

Ohm's Law: A Microscopic View

For many common conductors, including metals, the conductivity σ is independent of the electric field. Such materials are called **ohmic**, and for these materials Equation 27-4a is one way of stating what is known as **Ohm's law**, namely that the current density at any point in a conductor is proportional to the electric field at that point. In **nonohmic** materials, in contrast, conductivity does depend on field, and therefore $\mathbf{J}$ and $\mathbf{E}$ are not directly proportional.

You may already be familiar with the *macroscopic* version of Ohm's law, which makes the equivalent statement that the total current through a piece of material is proportional to the potential difference, or voltage, across it. In Equation 27-4a we have the *microscopic* version of Ohm's law, which describes what happens at a single point in a material in terms of the electric field and current density at that point. The macroscopic version, in contrast, links the current (a quantity related to current density) and voltage (related, as we saw in Chapter 25, to the electric field) associated with an entire piece of material. We'll derive the macroscopic version in section 27-3, and will find it very useful for analyzing electric circuits. But the microscopic version remains important for many applications in biophysics, geophysics, astrophysics, semiconductor engineering, and other areas where electric fields in conducting materials may vary with position, and where we therefore need to know what's going on at each point.

The conductivity σ tells how large a current density will result from a given electric field; it's thus a measure of how easy it is for an electric field to cause free charges in a material to move. A perfect conductor would have $\sigma = \infty$; a perfect insulator, $\sigma = 0$. A lot of subtle physics goes into determining the conductivity, as we'll soon see for metallic conductors. An equivalent quantity for describing the relation between current density and electric field in a material is the material's **resistivity**, ρ, defined as the reciprocal of the conductivity:

$$\rho = \frac{1}{\sigma},$$

so Equation 27-4a can also be written

$$\mathbf{J} = \frac{\mathbf{E}}{\rho}. \tag{27-4b}$$

Where conductivity tells how *easy* it is for a field to cause current in a material, its reciprocal, resistivity, tells how *hard* it is. Thus the larger the resistivity, the greater the electric field needed to produce a given current density. You may be familiar with electrical *resistance,* which we'll soon see is an electrical property of specific objects that relates to the underlying *resistivity* of the materials they're made from.

TABLE 27-1 *Resistivities*

MATERIAL	RESISTIVITY ($\Omega \cdot m$)
Metallic conductors (at 20°C)	
Aluminum	2.65×10^{-8}
Copper	1.68×10^{-8}
Gold	2.24×10^{-8}
Iron	9.71×10^{-8}
Mercury	9.84×10^{-7}
Silver	1.59×10^{-8}
Ionic solutions (in water at 18°C)	
1-molar copper sulfate ($CuSO_4$)	3.9×10^{-4}
1-molar hydrochloric acid (HCl)	1.7×10^{-2}
1-molar sodium chloride (NaCl)	1.4×10^{-4}
Water, pure (H_2O)	2.6×10^{5}
Blood, human	0.70
Sea water (typical value)	0.22
Semiconductors (pure, at 20°C)	
Germanium	0.45
Silicon	640
Insulators	
Ceramics	$10^{11}-10^{14}$
Glass	$10^{10}-10^{14}$
Polystyrene	$10^{15}-10^{17}$
Rubber	$10^{13}-10^{16}$
Wood (dry)	$10^{8}-10^{14}$

Equation 27-4b shows that the units of resistivity are V·m/A. One V/A is given the name **ohm** (symbol Ω), after the German physicist Georg Ohm (1789–1854), whose experiments clarified the relation between voltage and current. Thus the SI units of resistivity can be written $\Omega \cdot m$. Reciprocally, the units of conductivity are $(\Omega \cdot m)^{-1}$.

Conductivity and resistivity vary dramatically among different materials; indeed, their measurable range is one of the broadest of any physical quantity, spanning some 24 orders of magnitude. Table 27-1 lists some typical resistivities. In addition to telling us how well materials conduct electricity, measurement of resistivity or conductivity can also provide information on structure or composition. Some devices for routine blood analysis, for example, make use of conductivity measurements, while measurement of blood conductivity in laboratory animals has been used experimentally to assess changes in metabolic activity.

EXAMPLE 27-3	*Household Wiring: The Electric Field*

A 1.8-mm-diameter copper wire carries 15 A to a household appliance. What is the electric field in the wire?

Solution

The current density is $J = I/A$; using this result in Equation 27-4b and solving for E gives

$$E = \frac{I\rho}{A} = \frac{(15 \text{ A})(1.68 \times 10^{-8}\ \Omega \cdot m)}{(\pi)(0.90 \times 10^{-3}\ m)^2} = 99 \text{ mV/m},$$

where we found the resistivity of copper in Table 27-1. This result is much smaller than the fields we've been discussing in electrostatic situations. Because copper is such a good conductor, only a very small field is needed to drive even a substantial current. In analyzing electric circuits we will often make the approximation that the fields and therefore potential differences in copper wires are essentially zero.

EXERCISE A uniform electric field of 0.76 V/m drives a 10-A current in an iron wire. Find the wire diameter.

Answer: 1.3 mm

Some problems similar to Example 27-3: 17–19

Conduction in Metals

Metals are good conductors because they contain large numbers of free electrons, which respond readily to electric fields. Each atom in the metal contributes, on average, about one electron to this "sea" of free electrons. The resulting positive ions combine in a regular structure, called the crystal lattice (Fig. 27-5). In the absence of an electric field, electrons move randomly through the lattice at high speeds of typically 10^6 m/s. They collide frequently with the ions, bouncing off in random directions. There's no net flow of electrons in any one direction, so there's no electric current. And because the whole system is in thermal equilibrium, there's no net energy transfer from electrons to ions or vice versa.

We'll use this simple description of a metal to develop an understanding of what happens when we apply an electric field to a metal—i.e., the conduction process. Although this will help you see why metals obey Ohm's law, be aware that our explanation is incomplete; a full description of metallic conduction necessarily involves quantum mechanics.

Applying an electric field to a metal gives the negative electrons an acceleration in the direction opposite the field. But the electrons are already whizzing around at high speed, colliding frequently with the ions. So an electron doesn't gain much energy or speed from the electric field before it collides with an ion. When it does, it gives up whatever energy it gained from the field, and rebounds with a random velocity. But the field is still there, and the electron again accelerates (Fig. 27-6). The result is that the electrons acquire an additional, very small average velocity in the direction opposite the field. This is the drift velocity $\mathbf{v}_d$ that we introduced earlier. Unlike their random thermal velocities, all electrons share a common drift velocity, and thus their motion constitutes a net current that is proportional to $\mathbf{v}_d$.

The electrons' behavior in metallic conduction is somewhat like driving through stop-and-go city traffic; you spend a lot of time accelerating, but soon you have to stop again. As a result, you acquire a rather slow average speed through the city. But this analogy is imperfect: your car accelerates from rest at each red light, while the electrons' acceleration introduces only a minuscule velocity change compared with their already high thermal velocity.

What happens to the energy the electrons gain from the field? They give it up in collisions with the ions, ultimately increasing the internal energy of the material. We saw in Chapter 21 that temperature is a measure of internal energy, so the metal's temperature increases when a current flows through it. That's the ultimate cause of heating in electric stoves, hair dryers, water heaters, toasters, and myriad other everyday devices.

So now we have the electrons drifting slowly in a direction opposite the electric field, with velocity $\mathbf{v}_d$. That drift velocity depends on two things: the acceleration of the electrons and the rate at which they undergo collisions. The electric force $-e\mathbf{E}$ gives an acceleration $\mathbf{a} = \mathbf{F}/m = -e\mathbf{E}/m$, with m the electron mass and $-e$ its charge. If we pick a random electron and ask when it last underwent a collision, the answer will be some mean time τ called the **collision time**. During that time the electron has been accelerating with acceleration $\mathbf{a} = -e\mathbf{E}/m$, and therefore its average velocity due to the presence of the electric field—i.e., the drift velocity $\mathbf{v}_d$—will be

$$\mathbf{v}_d = -\frac{e\mathbf{E}}{m}\tau.$$

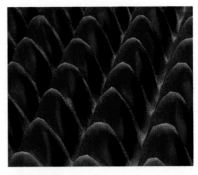

FIGURE 27-5 Atoms of a metal form a regular structure, or crystal lattice. This image, made with a scanning tunneling microscope that uses the quantum mechanical behavior of electrons to image individual atoms, shows the arrangement of atoms at the surface of a metallic nickel crystal.

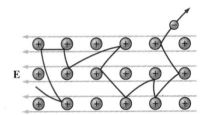

FIGURE 27-6 The path of an electron moving through a metal. The motion is almost completely random, but in the presence of an electric field there is a very slight drift antiparallel to the field.

Of course the electron also has its random thermal motion, but over many collisions this averages to zero while the velocity resulting from the electric field does not. Using our expression for the drift velocity in Equation 27-3b gives

$$\mathbf{J} = nq\,\mathbf{v}_d = n(-e)\mathbf{v}_d = \frac{ne^2\mathbf{E}}{m}\tau.$$

Comparing this expression with Equation 27-4a shows that the conductivity is

$$\sigma = \frac{ne^2}{m}\tau. \qquad (27\text{-}5)$$

The collision time τ depends on several factors. Obviously, the spacing of ions in the crystal lattice influences how often collisions occur. Less obvious is the fact that the presence of impurities—i.e., atoms of other materials—has a dramatic influence on electron-ion collisions and thus on conductivity. And, also obviously, τ depends on how fast the electrons are moving; the faster they go, the more frequent their collisions, and the lower τ should be. The electrons have two kinds of motion: their random thermal motion and the drift velocity $\mathbf{v}_d$ acquired from the electric field. In Example 27-1 we found that a typical drift speed is on the order 1 mm/s, while thermal speeds are around 10^6 m/s. The drift speed is therefore completely negligible in determining the collision time. That means the collision time and hence the conductivity are essentially independent of the applied electric field—and that makes Equation 27-4a a linear relation for metallic conductors. In other words, metals obey Ohm's law. We stress that this conclusion is only approximate, and that Ohm's law, unlike Gauss's law, is *not* an exact, universal statement that holds everywhere and for all materials.

Although the conductivity of a metal is independent of the applied electric field, it does depend on other factors, especially temperature. From Chapter 20 we know that classical physics gives a thermal speed proportional to the square root of the temperature, so we might expect conductivity to be proportional to $1/\sqrt{T}$ and thus resistivity to $\sqrt{T}$. Experiment, however, shows that resistivity is very nearly proportional to temperature rather than to its square root. We show this relation for copper in Fig. 27-7, and explore it further in Problem 25. Here we've reached the limits of classical physics, which cannot describe fully the behavior of the free electrons in a metal. Readers of the extended version of this text will explore quantum mechanics and how it deals with electrical conduction.

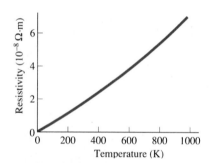

FIGURE 27-7 Resistivity of copper—the inverse of conductivity—shows a nearly linear dependence on temperature, in contrast to the classical prediction of a $\sqrt{T}$ dependence.

EXAMPLE 27-4	*Conductivity and Collision Time*

Copper at room temperature contains 1.1×10^{29} free electrons per cubic meter. What is the collision time for these electrons?

Solution

Writing $\sigma = 1/\rho$ and solving Equation 27-5 for the collision time gives

$$\tau = \frac{m}{ne^2\rho}$$

$$= \frac{9.11\times10^{-31}\ \text{kg}}{(1.1\times10^{29}\ \text{m}^{-3})(1.6\times10^{-19}\ \text{C})^2(1.68\times10^{-8}\ \Omega\!\cdot\!\text{m})}$$

$$= 1.9\times10^{-14}\ \text{s},$$

where we found the resistivity of copper in Table 27-1. Problem 66 uses this result to estimate the mean thermal speed of the electrons.

EXERCISE Sodium contains 2.5×10^{28} free electrons per cubic meter, and the collision time is 3.4×10^{-14}s. What is the resistivity of sodium?

Answer: $4.2\times10^{-8}\ \Omega\!\cdot\!\text{m}$

Some problems similar to Example 27-4: 21, 66

| APPLICATION | *Noise in Electronic Equipment* |

Although the time-average current associated with random thermal motion of charge carriers is zero, at any given instant random fluctuations may result in more charge carriers moving in one direction than in another. The result is a very small current, whose sign and magnitude fluctuate randomly. Called thermal noise, this current may disturb or even overwhelm currents of interest in sensitive electronic instruments. Thermal motion decreases at low temperatures, and sensitive circuits such as the amplifiers in radio telescopes are often cooled to liquid helium temperatures, around 4 K (Fig. 27-8). That way, the very weak signals reaching Earth from cosmic sources are not overwhelmed by thermal noise. Ultimately thermal noise limits our ability to detect and study very weak electrical signals.

FIGURE 27-8 This 12-m radio telescope at Kitt Peak National Observatory uses amplifiers cooled to 4 K with liquid helium in order to reduce electrical noise.

Ionic Solutions

An ionic solution contains positive and negative ions that respond to an electric field by moving in opposite directions, resulting in a net current. Conductivity of the solution is limited by collisions between the ions and neutral atoms. In addition to heating the solution, some of the energy of these collisions may go into chemical reactions that store energy—as in charging a rechargable battery.

Conduction in ionic solutions is essential to life, as the flow of sodium, potassium, and other ions through cell membranes occurs through the process of ionic conduction. Electric eels set up currents in the surrounding water, using ionic conduction to sense and kill their prey (Fig. 27-9). Technological processes that use ionic conduction include electroplating of thin layers of one material onto another, and electrolysis of water to produce hydrogen and oxygen gas. Ionic conduction also plays an important role in the corrosion of metals, for example those exposed to salt solutions. And the presence of an ionic solution—sweat—increases our vulnerability to electric shock. Table 27-1 includes the resistivities of some ionic solutions. Note that these solutions are poorer conductors than metals.

FIGURE 27-9 The electric eel sets up currents in the surrounding water, and can sense the presence of nearby objects by subtle variations in conductivity. It uses larger currents to kill its prey.

Plasmas

Plasma is ionized gas that conducts because it contains free electrons and positive ions. It takes substantial energy to ionize atoms, so plasmas usually occur only in high-temperature environments. The few examples of plasmas on Earth occur in fluorescent lamps, neon signs, devices for fusion research, the ionosphere, flames, and lightning flashes (Fig. 27-10). Yet most of the matter in the universe is probably in the plasma state; the stars, in particular, are almost entirely plasma.

The electrical properties of plasma make it so different from ordinary gas that plasma is often called "the fourth state of matter." Some plasmas, especially in astrophysical situations, are so diffuse that collisions between particles are rare. These "collisionless" plasmas are sometimes far better conductors than metals, and they can sustain large electric currents with very modest electric fields.

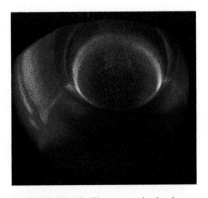

FIGURE 27-10 Plasma, or ionized gas, is an excellent electrical conductor. Photo shows glowing plasma in the Tokamak Fusion Test Reactor at the Princeton Plasma Physics Laboratory.

Semiconductors

Even in the best insulators, random thermal motions occasionally dislodge electrons, giving these materials very modest conductivity. This effect is usually insignificant at normal temperatures. But a few materials—notably the element silicon—have more electrons dislodged by thermal motion even at room temperature, and therefore exhibit significant conductivity. Because their conductivity lies between that of insulators and that of good conductors, such materials are called **semiconductors**. The electrical properties of semiconductors make possible the microelectronic technology that plays a pervasive role in modern civilization. Here we give a qualitative description of semiconductors based on classical physics; the extended version of this text revisits semiconductors from a quantum perspective in Chapter 42.

Conduction in semiconductors involves not only electrons dislodged from their places in the material structure, but also the "holes" left behind by those electrons. Nudged by the electric field, an adjacent electron can "fall" into the hole, with the effective result that the hole has moved in the direction of the field (Fig. 27-11). Thus holes act as positive charge carriers, and a pure semiconductor such as silicon contains equal numbers of negative charge carriers (free electrons) and positive charge carriers (holes).

A pure semiconductor has rather low conductivity and is useful only in a few applications. The key to semiconductor technology lies in the control of conductivity by adding very small amounts of impurities—a process called **doping**. Adding an element with five electrons in its outermost shell—as opposed to silicon's four—results in large numbers of free electrons and a much more conductive material whose charge carriers are predominantly negative (Fig. 27-12). Since its charge carriers are negative, such a material is called an **N-type** semiconductor. In contrast, doping with an element containing only three outermost electrons results in a **P-type** semiconductor, whose charge carriers are predominantly positive holes.

The key element in nearly all semiconductor devices is the **PN junction**, where P- and N-type semiconductors meet. When such a junction forms, free

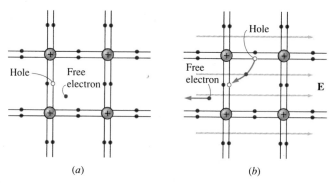

(a)   (b)

FIGURE 27-11 (a) Structure of a silicon crystal, showing each atom bound to each of its neighbors by two shared electrons. Thermal motion has dislodged one of the electrons from the crystal structure, leaving behind a hole. (b) In the presence of an electric field, the free electron drifts opposite the field direction. In addition, a nearby bound electron falls into the hole, effectively moving the hole in the direction of the field. Holes thus act as positive charge carriers.

FIGURE 27-12 (*a*) An arsenic atom, showing its five valence electrons. (*b*) Incorporated into a silicon crystal, the arsenic atom does its best to fit into the crystal structure. One of its electrons cannot participate in the bonding, but moves throughout the crystal lattice as a free conduction electron. Because its free charge carriers are predominantly electrons, the arsenic-doped silicon is an *N*-type semiconductor. Doping with aluminum, which has three valence electrons, would result similarly in excess holes, making a *P*-type material. In either case the material remains neutral; *P* and *N* refer to the sign of the free charges, not to a net charge on the material.

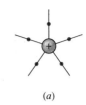

(*a*)

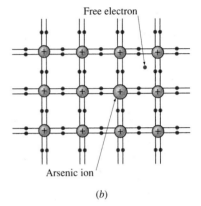

(*b*)

electrons, abundant in the *N*-type material but rare in the *P*, diffuse across the junction and combine with ions on the *P* side of the junction (Fig. 27-13*a*). Similarly, holes diffuse the other way and combine with electrons. (This diffusion process is similar to what happens when you open a bottle of perfume or drop food coloring into water; molecules of the substance spread from regions of high concentration to regions of low concentration.) Eventually diffusion stops because buildup of charge on opposite sides of the junction results in an electric field opposing further diffusion. But by now the junction region is depleted of free charges, and is therefore a poor conductor.

A single *PN* junction does conduct, but only in one direction. Applying a potential difference with positive at the *N*-type material only reinforces the charge depletion at the junction, further reducing its conductivity (Fig. 27-13*b*) and preventing significant current from flowing. This situation is called **reverse bias**. In contrast, making the *P*-type material positive reduces the internal electric field, shrinking the depleted region and greatly increasing its conductivity (Fig. 27-13*c*). A substantial current thus flows in this case of **forward bias**. We'll see in Chapter 33 how this "one-way" property of the *PN* junction is used to convert alternating current from household power sources into the direct current needed to power electronic devices.

The wide range of semiconductor devices in use today results largely from carefully engineered combinations of *PN* junctions. The following application presents one of the most important such devices.

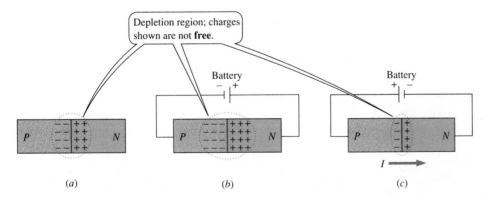

(*a*)   (*b*)   (*c*)

FIGURE 27-13 (*a*) When a *PN* junction is first established, electrons diffuse from the *N*-type material into the *P*, where they combine with holes. The result is a net negative charge to the left of the junction, but few free charges. Similarly, holes diffuse the other way, resulting in net positive charge and few free charges to the right of the junction. (*b*) Applying a potential difference from *N* to *P* reinforces the depletion, and very little current flows. (*c*) Applying a potential difference from *P* to *N* narrows the depletion region and results in substantial current flow.

| APPLICATION | *Transistors and Integrated Circuits* |

Few inventions have revolutionized human society as much as the transistor. Transistors are the basis of all modern electronic devices, from stereo amplifiers to automobile ignition systems to VCRs, laboratory instruments, and computers.

Figure 27-14 shows a widely used type of transistor, called the field effect transistor (FET). This particular FET consists of a slab of *P*-type material with two embedded *N*-type regions. Wires connect these *N*-type regions to external circuitry, but normally no current can flow through the transistor in either direction because one of the two *PN* junctions will be reverse biased. Coated on top of the *P* region is a layer of silicon dioxide (SiO_2), an excellent insulator, and over that is a metal layer called the *gate*. Suppose the gate is charged positively, by connecting it to a battery. This charge will repel positive holes in the *P*-type channel below the gate, and attract electrons. As a result, the channel becomes temporarily *N*-type, and the *PN* junctions disappear. The transistor therefore conducts electric current (Fig. 27-14*b*).

Varying the gate charge continuously varies the conductivity and therefore the current; the transistor then functions as an *amplifier,* in which a weak signal applied to the gate controls a stronger signal in the form of the current through the transistor.

Audio and video systems all contain amplifying transistors; ultimately, for example, the weak signal from a microphone or guitar pickup is amplified enough to drive a loudspeaker. In digital circuits like computers, in contrast, the transistor functions as a switch, with its drain–source channel either fully "on" (conducting) or "off" (nonconducting).

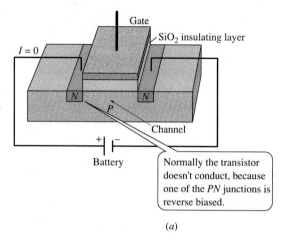

> Normally the transistor doesn't conduct, because one of the *PN* junctions is reverse biased.

(*a*)

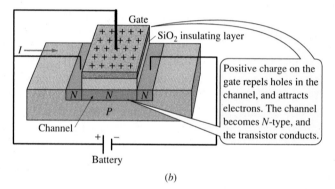

> Positive charge on the gate repels holes in the channel, and attracts electrons. The channel becomes *N*-type, and the transistor conducts.

(*b*)

FIGURE 27-14 A field-effect transistor, or FET. (*a*) Normally current flow between the *N*-type regions is impossible, because one of the two *PN* junctions is necessarily reverse biased. (*b*) Positive charge on the gate makes the channel temporarily *N*-type, allowing current to flow.

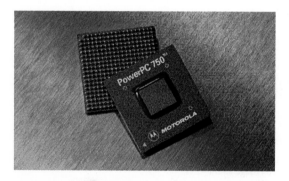

FIGURE 27-15 The PowerPC chip is a complex integrated circuit at the heart of Apple's Macintosh computers.

A transistor is fabricated from a single piece of silicon. By exposing various parts of the surface to dopant chemicals, oxygen, and metal atoms, the various *N* and *P* regions as well as the SiO_2 insulator and metallic gate are formed. The same process is used to produce entire circuits containing millions of transistors (Fig. 27-15). These **integrated circuits**—also called **chips**—make possible the complexity, miniaturization, and sophistication of modern electronic devices.

Superconductors

In 1911 the Dutch physicist H. Kamerlingh Onnes, studying the electrical properties of mercury at very low temperatures, found a sudden drop in resistivity at a temperature of 4.2 K. The resistivity below this temperature proved immeasurably low. Subsequent research has identified thousands of substances that become **superconductors** at sufficiently low temperatures. Currents in superconductors persist for years without any measurable decrease, suggesting that the resistivity of a superconductor is truly zero (Fig. 27-16).

For decades the known superconductors were largely metals and metal alloys that required cooling in liquid helium to achieve their superconductivity. Then, in 1986, physicists J. Georg Bednorz and K. Alex Müller of IBM's Zurich research laboratory made the stunning discovery that a class of ceramic materials becomes superconducting at temperatures around 100 K—high enough that these materials superconduct when cooled with liquid nitrogen. A flurry of research followed, soon pushing the highest superconducting temperature to well over 100 K. Bednorz and Müller received the 1987 Nobel Prize in physics, only a year after their discovery. The search for higher temperature superconductors continues, with the highest reported temperatures now over 160 K. Sporadic reports of superconductivity at or close to room temperature have appeared in the literature, but so far none have met the test of repeatability. Development of a room-temperature superconductor would revolutionize electromagnetic technology.

Superconductivity offers loss-free flow of electric current. Electromagnets made from metal and metal alloy superconductors cooled with liquid helium have been used for years in such applications as nuclear magnetic resonance spectrometers (your chemistry lab may have one) and, more recently, in magnetic resonance imagers used in medicine. Electric current in these devices, once started, continues forever with no power source—as long as the liquid helium is regularly replenished (Fig. 27-17).

The liquid nitrogen coolant adequate for high-temperature superconductors is far less expensive than liquid helium, so scientists and engineers are developing a wide array of commercial applications of these materials. Devices based on thin films of high-T superconductors measure weak magnetic fields in biomedical and geophysical applications, sense radiant energy, and produce and process microwaves. Finally, high-T superconducting wires are now commercially available in kilometer lengths.

Although superconductivity was discovered in 1911, a satisfactory explanation of the phenomenon was not given until 1957. In that year John Bardeen, Leon Cooper, and J. Robert Schrieffer showed how superconductivity in the traditional low-temperature materials arises from a quantum-mechanical interaction among the conduction electrons. In a way that has no analog in classical physics, all the electrons move coherently through the crystal lattice, with no energy loss. Their theory earned Bardeen, Cooper, and Schrieffer the 1972 Nobel Prize in physics. A comprehensive theory of the newer, high-temperature superconducting materials has yet to be fully developed. Readers of the extended version of this text will revisit superconductivity in Chapter 42.

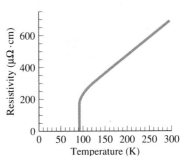

FIGURE 27-16 Resistivity versus temperature for a thin film of yttrium-barium-copper-oxide. Below the 93-K transition temperature the resistivity is truly zero.

FIGURE 27-17 This superconducting electromagnet at Lawrence Berkeley Laboratory is among the strongest of its kind. It uses 14 miles of niobium-tin superconducting wire, and is cooled with liquid helium.

27-3 RESISTANCE AND OHM'S LAW

How much current does it take to run this hair dryer? Do I risk a fatal shock if I touch this wire? How long an extension cord can I use with this electric saw? Why are these jumper cables so thick? How long will it take to recharge my dead battery? Is the wiring in my house safe, or could it overheat and cause a fire? All these questions are ultimately about the total electric current flowing in wires, bodies, batteries, and other objects. The answer in each case depends on two things: the voltage (i.e., potential difference), V, applied across the object, and the **resistance**, R, that the object offers to the flow of electric current.

The macroscopic version of Ohm's law—with which you may already be familiar—relates voltage, current, and resistance. Ohm's law states that the current through an object is proportional to the voltage across it and inversely proportional to the object's resistance:

$$I = \frac{V}{R}. \quad \text{(Ohm's law)} \qquad (27\text{-}6)$$

Ohm's law in this form makes good sense, for it shows that a given voltage can push more current through a lower resistance. It's worth noting two extreme cases: An **open circuit** is a nonconducting gap with infinite resistance. No matter what the voltage across an open circuit, Equation 27-6 shows that no current can flow. A common example of an open circuit is a switch in its "off" position. A **short circuit**, in contrast, has zero resistance. In a short circuit, current of any magnitude is possible without any voltage or electric field. A closed switch approximates a short circuit. An unintentional short circuit is often dangerous; short circuits in household wiring, for example, are a leading cause of fires because they allow large currents to flow, resulting in excessive heating. All real situations, with the exception of superconductors, lie between the extremes of short and open circuits.

We can understand how the macroscopic version of Ohm's law, Equation 27-6, follows from the microscopic version by considering the cylindrical conductor shown in Fig. 27-18. Suppose there is a uniform electric field **E** within the conductor. Then there must be a uniform current density given by Equation 27-4b:

$$\mathbf{J} = \frac{\mathbf{E}}{\rho},$$

where ρ is the resistivity of the material. Then the total current is

$$I = JA = \frac{EA}{\rho},$$

where A is the conductor's cross-sectional area. If the conductor has length ℓ then the potential difference between its ends is

$$V = E\ell,$$

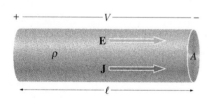

FIGURE 27-18 A cylindrical conductor made from a material with resistivity ρ. The uniform electric field **E** drives a uniform current density **J**, giving a total current $I = JA$ through the conductor's cross-sectional area A. The electric field is associated with a potential difference V across the length ℓ of the conductor.

since the electric field is uniform. Solving to get $E = V/\ell$ and using the result in our expression for I gives

$$I = \frac{VA}{\ell\rho} = \frac{V}{(\rho\ell/A)}.$$

Comparison with the macroscopic Ohm's law, Equation 27-6, lets us identify the resistance with the term $\rho\ell/A$. Thus resistance depends on the resistivity ρ and the geometry—length and area—of the particular piece of material:

$$R = \frac{\rho\ell}{A}. \tag{27-7}$$

We derived this expression for a conductor of uniform cross section; although Ohm's law still holds for a nonuniform conductor, integration is required to calculate the resistance (see Problems 71 and 72). Incidentally, Equations 27-6 and 27-7 both show that the units of resistance are ohms (Ω).

We emphasize again that neither the microscopic nor the macroscopic version of Ohm's law is fundamental, but rather that each is an empirical law that provides a good description of electrical conductivity in some materials. Table 27-2 summarizes the relation between microscopic and macroscopic quantities in Ohm's law.

TABLE 27-2 *Microscopic and Macroscopic Quantities and Ohm's Law*

MICROSCOPIC QUANTITY	MACROSCOPIC QUANTITY	RELATION
Electric field, **E**	Voltage, V	**E** is defined at each point in a material; V is the integral of **E** over a path containing many points. In a uniform field, $V = E\ell$.
Current density, **J**	Current, I	**J** is defined at each point in a material; I is the integral of **J** over an area containing many points. With uniform current density, $I = JA$.
Resistivity, ρ	Resistance, R	ρ is a property of a given material; R is a property of a particular piece of the material. In a piece of uniform cross section, $R = \dfrac{\rho\ell}{A}$.
Ohm's law $$\mathbf{J} = \frac{\mathbf{E}}{\rho}$$	Ohm's law $$I = \frac{V}{R}$$	Microscopic version relates current density to electric field at a point in a material of specified resistivity; macroscopic version relates current through to voltage across a given piece of material with specified resistance.

EXAMPLE 27-5	*Resistance and Ohm's Law*

A copper wire 0.50 cm in diameter and 70 cm long is used to connect a car battery to the starter motor. What is the wire's resistance? If the starter motor draws a current of 170 A, what is the potential difference across the wire?

Solution
Table 27-1 gives 1.68×10^{-8} $\Omega \cdot m$ for the resistivity of copper. Then Equation 27-6 gives

$$R = \frac{\rho \ell}{A} = \frac{(1.68 \times 10^{-8} \; \Omega \cdot m)(0.70 \; m)}{(\pi)(0.25 \times 10^{-2} \; m)^2} = 6.0 \times 10^{-4} \; \Omega \,.$$

This low resistance is necessary because the starter motor draws such a large current. We now apply Ohm's law to find the voltage across the wire:

$$V = IR = (170 \; A)(6.0 \times 10^{-4} \; \Omega) = 0.10 \; V \,.$$

This is small compared with the 12 volts available from the car battery, showing that the wire is well chosen for this application (Fig. 27-19). A larger voltage difference—which would occur with a thinner wire—would mean a significant reduction in current to the motor.

FIGURE 27-19 Thick jumper cables are necessary to carry the large current used by a car's starter motor.

EXERCISE What should be the diameter of an aluminum wire that carries 15 A when the voltage across 1.0 m of the wire is 0.25 V?

Answer: 1.4 mm

Some problems similar to Example 27-5: 30, 35, 36, 38

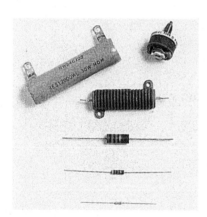

FIGURE 27-20 Typical resistors. The large unit at the upper left is a wire-wound resistor that can dissipate 30 watts. At upper right is a variable resistor, in which a rotating contact can be positioned at different points on a coil of resistance wire. Colored stripes on the smaller resistors code their resistance values. The smallest resistor shown is a carbon-film resistor that can dissipate at most $\frac{1}{4}$ watt.

A **resistor** is a piece of conductor made to have a specific resistance. Heating elements used in electric stoves, hair dryers, irons, space heaters, and the like are all essentially resistors; so are the filaments of ordinary incandescent light bulbs. In all these cases the resistance—ultimately resulting from collisions between conduction electrons and lattice ions—provides a means of turning electrical energy into heat. Resistors are also used to set appropriate values of current and voltage in electronic circuits; for this purpose, they are made in a wide range of resistances. Resistors are rated not only by their resistance but also by the maximum power they can dissipate without overheating. Figure 27-20 shows some typical resistors.

Got It!

Figure 27-21 shows three pieces of wire. (1) and (2) are made from the same material, while (3) is made from a material with twice the resistivity. (a) Which has the greatest resistance? (b) If the same voltage is applied across each, which will pass the greatest current?

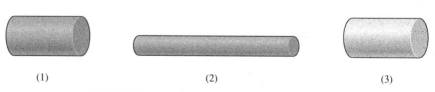

(1)   (2)   (3)

FIGURE 27-21 Which wire has the greatest resistance?

27-4 ELECTRIC POWER

Suppose a potential difference V is imposed across a resistor, driving a current I through it. The quantity V is the energy gained per unit charge as charge "falls" through the potential difference. In a resistor, that energy is dissipated through collisions, heating the material. So V is also the energy per unit charge going into heating. Meanwhile, the current I is the rate at which charge flows through the resistor. Then the energy per unit time—that is, the power dissipated in heating the resistor—is the product of the energy per unit charge times the rate at which charge moves through the conductor:

$$P = IV. \quad \text{(electric power)} \qquad (27\text{-}8)$$

Although we developed Equation 27-8 for power dissipated as heat in a resistance, it holds any time electrical energy is being converted to some other form. If, for example, we measure 5 V across an electric motor and 2 A through the motor, we can conclude that the motor is converting electrical to mechanical energy at the rate of 10 W (actually somewhat less because some of the power goes into heating).

Solving Ohm's law for V and putting the result in Equation 27-8 gives

$$P = I^2R; \qquad (27\text{-}9a)$$

solving instead for I gives

$$P = \frac{V^2}{R}. \qquad (27\text{-}9b)$$

These are useful forms when we know the resistance and either the voltage or current. Although they may seem contradictory, the forms are equivalent and both are equivalent to the more general Equation 27-8 for the case when current and voltage are related by Ohm's law.

Tip

Think about What's Constant Equation 27-9a seems to imply that power increases with increasing resistance, while Equation 27-9b seems to suggest the opposite. Both implications are correct—*if I* in Equation 27-9a and V in Equation 27-9b are constants. But there's no contradiction because I and V can't both be constant while the resistance R—the ratio of V to I—changes. In most cases we work with sources of constant voltage—for example, the power company promises to maintain 120 V between the two contacts in a household electrical outlet—and in this case the power dissipated is inversely proportional to the resistance we connect across that voltage, as shown by Equation 27-9b. See Question 20 for more on this point.

| **EXAMPLE 27-6** | *A Light Bulb* |

The voltage in typical household wiring is 120 V. How much current does a 100-W light bulb draw? What is the bulb's resistance under these conditions?

Solution

Solving Equation 27-8 for *I* gives

$$I = \frac{P}{V} = \frac{100 \text{ W}}{120 \text{ V}} = 0.833 \text{ A} \,.$$

Since we know the current, we can determine the resistance directly from Ohm's law:

$$R = \frac{V}{I} = \frac{120 \text{ V}}{0.833 \text{ A}} = 144 \text{ }\Omega \,.$$

We could have bypassed the calculation of current and obtained *R* directly from Equation 27-9b:

$$R = \frac{V^2}{P} = \frac{(120 \text{ V})^2}{100 \text{ W}} = 144 \text{ }\Omega \,.$$

Finally, had we known the current but not the voltage, we could have used Equation 27-9a:

$$R = \frac{P}{I^2} = \frac{100 \text{ W}}{(0.833 \text{ A})^2} = 144 \text{ }\Omega \,.$$

The three approaches are equivalent. Use of Equation 27-9a or b merely amounts to solving symbolically for *V* or *I* before using Equation 27-8.

Because a light bulb filament undergoes a huge temperature change when turned on, its resistance is not independent of voltage and current. Our value 144 Ω holds when the light is on. When off, it is cool, and its resistance is much lower.

EXERCISE A power line has 0.20 Ω resistance per kilometer of length. If it carries 300 A of current, find (a) the voltage across 1.0 km of the wire and (b) the power dissipated in each km of wire.

Answers: (a) 60 V; (b) 18 kW

Some problems similar to Example 27-6: 44–46

The exercise with Example 27-6 suggests that high currents result in significant power loss even in wires of low resistance—as the quadratic dependence of power on current in Equation 27-9b confirms. That result has important implications for electric power transmission, showing that power companies are better off transmitting a given power $P = IV$ at high voltage and low current rather than vice versa. We'll examine this situation in more detail in Chapter 33, once we've seen how to effect transformations among different voltage levels (see the Application: Electric Power Distribution, on page 873).

The Kilowatt-Hour

The SI unit of power is the watt (W), defined as 1 J/s and thus reflecting the definition of power as energy per time. We could equally well have defined the watt first, then defined the Joule as 1 W·s. The **kilowatt-hour** (kWh), a unit commonly used for electrical energy, is in fact defined in an analogous way. Just as 1 joule is the energy used by a device consuming 1 watt for 1 second, so a kilowatt-hour is the energy used by a device consuming 1 kW for 1 hour. Your household electric bill shows your electrical energy consumption in kWh; your cost for 1 kWh of electrical energy is typically in the range from 5¢ to 15¢. Since there are 3600 s in an hour, 1 kWh is equal to (1000 W)(3600 s) = 3.6 MJ. Burning a 100-W light bulb for 1 hour, for example, uses 100 watt-hours or 0.1 kWh. Although it is usually used only with electrical energy, the kWh is a perfectly good non-SI unit for describing any kind of energy; for example, it's useful to remember that the energy content of a gallon of oil or gasoline is about 40 kWh. If all that energy could be converted to electrical energy, it could power a 100-W light bulb for 400 hours.

CHAPTER SYNOPSIS

Summary

1. **Electric current** is a net flow of electric charge, specified as the charge per unit time crossing a given area:

$$I = \frac{dq}{dt}.$$

If a material contains n free charges q per unit volume, moving with average speed v_d (called the **drift speed**), then the current through an area A perpendicular to the flow is

$$I = nqAv_d.$$

Current density is a vector specifying the current per unit area:

$$\mathbf{J} = nq\mathbf{v}_d.$$

2. **Conductivity**, σ, is a property of a given material describing the ratio of current density to electric field in the material:

$$\mathbf{J} = \sigma\mathbf{E}.$$

For **ohmic** materials conductivity is independent of electric field and this relation constitutes the microscopic version of **Ohm's law.**

   Resistivity, ρ, is the inverse of conductivity.

3. Conduction mechanisms vary with material, and include:
   a. **Metals**, in which the charge carriers are free electrons. Metals are ohmic materials in which resistivity arises from collisions of free electrons with ions.
   b. **Ionic solutions** are conductors because of the presence of negative and positive ions that can move through the solution.
   c. **Plasmas** are ionized gases, often with extremely high conductivity. Plasmas are rare on Earth but comprise much of the matter in the universe.
   d. **Semiconductors** conduct only poorly in their pure state, but their electrical properties can be radically altered by doping with impurities. Charge carriers in semiconductors can be electrons, positive "holes," or both. Semiconductors are the basis of modern electronic technology.
   e. **Superconductors** exhibit zero resistivity at sufficiently low temperatures, and consequently require no electric field or potential difference to drive a current.

4. The macroscopic version of **Ohm's law** relates current I, voltage V, and **resistance** R:

$$I = \frac{V}{R}.$$

Resistance depends on resistivity and physical dimensions. For an object of resistivity ρ, length ℓ, and uniform cross-sectional area A, the resistance is $R = \rho\ell/A$.

5. The rate at which electrical energy is converted to other forms—i.e., the power, P—is the product of the current I through a device and the potential difference V across it:

$$P = IV.$$

In a resistance the electrical energy is converted to heat, and the power can be written in the two equivalent forms

$$P = I^2R \quad \text{and} \quad P = \frac{V^2}{R}.$$

Terms You Should Understand

(Pairs are closely related terms whose distinction is important; number in parentheses is chapter section where term first appears.)

electric current, current density (27-1)
ampere (27-1)
drift speed, drift velocity (27-1)
conductivity, resistivity (27-2)
ohm (27-2)
ohmic, nonohmic materials (27-2)
Ohm's law (27-2, 27-3)
plasma (27-2)
semiconductor (27-2)
superconductor (27-2)
resistance (27-3)
open circuit, short circuit (27-3)

Symbols You Should Recognize

I (27-1)	σ, ρ (27-2)
v_d (27-1)	Ω (27-2)
$\mathbf{J}$ (27-1)	R (27-3)

Problems You Should Be Able to Solve

calculating current from drift speed and material properties (27-1)
relating current and current density (27-1)
relating electric field, current density, and conductivity or resistivity (27-2)
calculating resistance from resistivity and dimensions (27-3)
using Ohm's law to relate current, voltage, and resistance (27-3)
calculating electric power (27-4)

Limitations to Keep in Mind

Ohm's law is not a universal statement but an approximate empirical relation that holds with high accuracy for some materials, such as metals.

QUESTIONS

1. If you physically move an electrical conductor, does this constitute a current?

2. In previous chapters we've stressed the absence of electric fields inside conductors in equilibrium. Why now do we allow such fields?

3. A wire carries a steady current. If the wire diameter decreases in the direction of the current, what happens to the current density?

4. When you talk on the telephone, your voice is heard almost immediately at the other end. Yet the drift speed of electrons in the telephone wire is on the order of millimeters per second. Explain the apparent discrepancy.

5. What is the difference between current and current density?

6. A constant electric field generally produces a constant drift velocity. How is this consistent with Newton's assertion that force results in acceleration, not velocity?

7. When caught in the open in a lightning storm, it is better to crouch low with the feet close together rather than lie flat on the ground. Why?

8. Why does the conductivity of a metal depend on the *square* of the electron charge?

9. What are *P*- and *N*-type semiconductors? Does either carry a net electric charge?

10. Good conductors of electricity are often good conductors of heat. Why might this be?

11. Why can current persist forever in a superconductor with no applied voltage?

12. A plasma contains equal densities of free electrons and protons. Do you expect each to contribute equally to the net current? Explain.

13. Does an electric stove burner draw more current when it is first turned on or when it's fully hot?

14. A person and a cow are standing in a field when lightning strikes the ground nearby. Why is the cow more likely to be electrocuted?

15. You put a 1.5-V battery across a piece of material and a 100-mA current flows through the material. With a 9-V battery the current increases to 400 mA. Is the material ohmic or not?

16. The resistance of a metal increases with increasing temperature, while the resistance of a semiconductor decreases. Why the difference?

17. How does the fact that the drift speed of electrons in a metal is much less than their thermal speed imply that metals are ohmic conductors?

18. A 50-W and a 100-W light bulb are both designed to operate at 120 V. Which has the lower resistance?

19. A power line with a small but nonzero resistance is used to carry 450 MW of electric power from a nuclear power plant to a city. Is it most efficient to transmit this power at high voltage and low current or vice versa? Explain.

20. Equation 27-9a suggests that no power can be dissipated in a superconductor, since $R = 0$. But Equation 27-9b suggests the power should be infinite. Which is right, and why?

21. A motor made with superconducting wire and frictionless bearings is turning at constant speed and doing no mechanical work. Make an argument showing that the motor cannot be drawing current, even if it's connected to a battery. What would happen if the motor started to do mechanical work, like lifting a weight?

22. The resistivity of a pure semiconductor decreases with increasing temperature. Speculate on what might happen if a fixed voltage were applied across a piece of such material.

PROBLEMS

Section 27-1 Electric Current

1. A wire carries 1.5 A. How many electrons pass through the wire in each second?

2. In an ionic solution, 4.1×10^{15} ions, each carrying charge $+2e$, pass to the right each second; 3.6×10^{15} ions, each carrying $-e$, pass to the left in the same time. What is the net current?

3. A 12-V car battery is rated at 80 ampere-hours, meaning it can supply 80 A of current for 1 hour before it becomes discharged. If you accidentally leave the headlights on until the battery discharges, how much charge moves through the lights?

4. The electron beam that "paints" the image on a computer screen contains 5.0×10^6 electrons per cm of its length. If the electrons move toward the screen at 6.0×10^7 m/s, how much current does the beam carry? What is the direction of this current?

5. Microbiologists measure total current due to potassium ions (K^+) moving through a cell membrane of a rock crab neuron cell to be 30 nA. How many ions pass through the membrane each second?

6. An ion channel in a cell membrane carries 2.4 pA when it's open, but it's only open 20% of the time. (a) What is the average current in the channel? (b) If the channel opens for 1.0 ms, how many singly ionized ions pass through it in this time?

7. The National Electrical Code specifies a maximum current of 10 A in 16-gauge (0.129 cm diameter) copper wire. What is the corresponding current density?

8. Each atom in aluminum contributes about 3.5 conduction electrons. What is the drift speed in a 0.21-cm-diameter aluminum wire carrying 20 A?

9. What is the drift speed in a silver wire carrying a current density of 150 A/mm²? Each silver atom contributes 1.3 free electrons.

10. The filament of the light bulb in Example 27-6 has a diameter of 0.050 mm. What is the current density in the filament? Compare with the current density in a 12-gauge wire (diameter 0.21 cm) supplying current to the light bulb.

11. A gold film in an integrated circuit measures 2.5 μm thick by 0.18 mm wide. It carries a current density of 6.8×10^5 A/m². What is the total current?

12. A piece of copper wire joins a piece of aluminum wire whose diameter is twice that of the copper. The same current flows in both wires. The density of conduction electrons in copper is 1.1×10^{29} m⁻³; in aluminum it is 2.1×10^{29} m⁻³. Compare (a) the drift speeds and (b) the current densities in each.

13. A plasma used in fusion research contains 5.0×10^{18} electrons and an equal number of protons per cubic meter. Under the influence of an electric field the electrons drift in one direction at 40 m/s, while the protons drift in the opposite direction at 6.5 m/s. (a) What is the current density? (b) What fraction of the current is carried by the electrons?

14. In Fig. 27-22, a 100-mA current flows through a copper wire 0.10 mm in diameter, a 1.0-cm-diameter glass tube containing a salt solution, and a vacuum tube where the current is carried by an electron beam 1.0 mm in diameter. The density of conduction electrons in copper is 1.1×10^{29} m⁻³. The current in the solution is carried equally by positive and negative ions with charges $\pm 2e$; the density of each ion species is 6.1×10^{23} m⁻³. The electron density in the beam is 2.2×10^{16} m⁻³. Find the drift speed in each region.

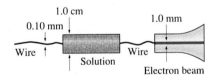

FIGURE 27-22 Problem 14.

15. In a study of proteins mediating cell membrane transport, microbiologists measure current versus time through the cell membranes of oocytes (nearly mature egg cells) taken from the African clawed frog, *Xenopus*. The measured current versus time is given approximately by $I = 60t + 200t^2 + 4.0t^3$, with t in seconds and I in nA. Find the total charge that flows through the cell membrane in the interval from $t = 0$ to $t = 5.0$ s.

Section 27-2 Conduction Mechanisms

16. The electric field in an aluminum wire is 0.085 V/m. What is the current density in the wire?

17. What electric field is necessary to drive a 7.5-A current through a silver wire 0.95 mm in diameter?

18. A cylindrical tube of sea water carries a total electric current of 350 mA. If the electric field in the water is 21 V/m, what is the diameter of the tube?

19. A 1.0-cm-diameter rod carries a 50-A current when the electric field in the rod is 1.4 V/m. What is the resistivity of the rod material?

20. There is a potential difference of 2.5 V between opposite ends of a 6.0-m-long iron wire. (a) Assuming a uniform electric field in the wire, what is the current density? (b) If the wire diameter is 1.0 mm, what is the total current?

21. Use Table 27-1 to determine the conductivity of (a) copper and (b) sea water.

22. The maximum safe current in 12-gauge (0.21-cm-diameter) copper wire is 20 A. What are (a) the current density and (b) the electric field under these conditions?

23. The free-electron density in aluminum is 2.1×10^{29} m⁻³. What is the collision time in aluminum?

24. A pure silicon crystal contains 4.9×10^{28} atoms/m³. At room temperature, the density of electron-hole pairs is 1×10^{16} m⁻³. In what concentration (aluminum atoms per silicon atom) must aluminum be added to give a conductivity 1000 times that of pure silicon? Assume that each aluminum atom contributes one extra hole, and that the conductivity is proportional to the density of charge carriers.

25. The resistivity of copper as a function of temperature is given approximately by $\rho = \rho_0[1 + \alpha(T - T_0)]$, where ρ_0 is the value listed in Table 27-1 for 20°C, $T_0 = 20$°C, and $\alpha = 4.3 \times 10^{-3}$°C⁻¹. Find the temperature at which copper's resistivity is twice its room-temperature value.

26. Manganin is an alloy whose resistivity hardly changes with temperature; its resistivity is given by the same equation as in the previous problem, but with $\rho_0 = 48.8 \times 10^{-8}$ Ω·m and $\alpha = 2.0 \times 10^{-6}$°C⁻¹. At what temperature does manganin have a resistivity 10 times that of copper?

Section 27-3 Resistance and Ohm's Law

27. What is the resistance of a heating coil that draws 4.8 A when the voltage across it is 120 V?

28. What voltage does it take to drive 300 mA through a 1.2-kΩ resistance?

29. What is the current in a 47-kΩ resistor with 110 V across it?

30. The "third rail" that carries the electric power to a subway train is a rectangular iron bar whose cross section measures 10 cm × 15 cm, as shown in Fig. 27-23. What is the resistance of a 5.0-km piece of this rail?

FIGURE 27-23 A "third rail" (Problem 30).

31. What current flows when a 45-V potential difference is imposed across a 1.8-kΩ resistor?

32. A silver and an iron wire of the same length and diameter carry the same current. How do the voltages across the two compare?

33. The presence of a few ions makes air a conductor, albeit a poor one. If the total resistance between the ionosphere and Earth is 200 Ω, how much current flows as a result of a 300-kV potential difference between Earth and ionosphere?

34. A uniform wire of resistance R is stretched until its length doubles. Assuming its density and resistivity remain constant, what is its new resistance?

35. A cylindrical iron rod measures 88 cm long and 0.25 cm in diameter. (a) Find its resistance. If a 1.5-V potential difference is applied between the ends of the rod, find (b) the current, (c) the current density, and (d) the electric field in the rod.

36. You have a cylindrical piece of material 2.4 cm long and 2.0 mm in diameter. When you attach a 9-V battery to the ends of the piece, a current of 2.6 mA results. Which material from Table 27-1 do you have?

37. How must the diameters of copper and aluminum wire be related if they are to have the same resistance per unit length?

38. Extension cords are often made from 18-gauge copper wire (diameter 1.0 mm). (a) What is the resistance per unit length of this wire? (b) An electric saw that draws 7.0 A is operated at the end of an 8.0-m-long extension cord. What is the potential difference between the wall outlet and the saw?

39. Engineers call for a power line with a resistance per unit length of 50 mΩ/km. What wire diameter is required if the line is made of (a) copper or (b) aluminum? (c) If the costs of copper and aluminum wire are $1.53/kg and $1.34/kg, which material is more economical? The densities of copper and aluminum are 8.9 g/cm³ and 2.7 g/cm³, respectively.

40. A solid, rectangular iron bar measures 0.50 cm by 1.0 cm by 20 cm. Find the resistance between each of the three pairs of opposing faces, assuming that the faces in question are equipotentials.

41. Corrosion at battery terminals results in increased resistance, and is a frequent cause of hard starting in cars. In an effort to diagnose hard starting, a mechanic measures the voltage between the battery terminal and the wire carrying current to the starter motor. While the motor is cranking, this voltage is 4.2 V. If the motor draws 125 A, what is the resistance at the battery terminal?

42. A clear plastic trough 2.5 cm wide, 5.0 cm high, and 15 cm long has the insides of its two long sides coated with metal, as shown in Fig. 27-24. If a 60-V potential difference is applied between these sides, how much current flows when the trough contains (a) pure water and (b) sea water?

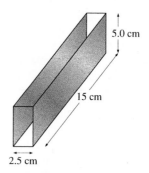

5.0 cm

15 cm

2.5 cm

FIGURE 27-24 Problem 42.

Section 27-4 Electric Power

43. A car's starter motor draws 125 A with 11 V across its terminals. What is its power consumption?

44. A 4.5-W flashlight bulb draws 750 mA. (a) At what voltage does it operate? (b) What is its resistance?

45. A watch uses energy at the rate of 240 μW. How much current does it draw from its 1.5-V battery?

46. An electric stove burner with 35 Ω resistance consumes 1.5 kW of power. At what voltage does it operate?

47. What is the resistance of a standard 120-V, 60-W light bulb?

48. Use the numbers from Problem 33 to find the electric power dissipation in Earth's atmosphere. If we could harness this power, would it make a dent in humanity's 10^{12}-W electric power consumption?

49. If the electrons of Problem 4 are accelerated through a potential difference of 10 kV, how much power must be supplied to produce the electron beam?

50. The "instant on" feature of all the television sets in the United States requires the continuous power output of a typical large power plant—about 1000 MW. If there are 10^8 TVs in the United States, how much current does the "instant on" circuit of each draw from the 120-V power line?

51. How much total energy could the 12-V battery of Problem 3 supply?

52. During a "brownout," the power line voltage drops from 120 V to 105 V. By how much does the thermal power output of a 1500-W stove burner drop, assuming its resistance remains constant?

53. Two cylindrical resistors are made from the same material and have the same length. When connected across the same battery, one dissipates twice as much power as the other. How do their diameters compare?

54. Your author's house uses approximately 110 kWh of electrical energy each week. If that energy is supplied at 240 V, what average resistance does the house present to the power line?

55. A 2000-horsepower electric railroad locomotive gets its power from an overhead wire with 0.20 Ω/km. The potential difference between wire and track is 10 kV. Current returns through the track, whose resistance is negligible. (a) How much current does the locomotive draw? (b) How far from the power plant can the train go before 1% of the energy is lost in the wire?

56. A 100% efficient electric motor is lifting a 15-N weight at 25 cm/s. If the motor is connected to a 6.0-V battery, how much current does it draw?

Paired Problems

(Both problems in a pair involve the same principles and techniques. If you can get the first problem, you should be able to solve the second one.)

57. Electrons in a fine silver wire 20 μm in diameter drift at 0.14 mm/s. What is the current in the wire? Each silver atom contributes 1.3 free electrons.

58. A potassium slab carries a current density of 470 kA/m², and the drift speed of the electrons is 0.20 mm/s. If the density of potassium is 860 kg/m³, what is the average number of free electrons contributed by each atom?

59. What is the resistance of a column of mercury 0.75 m long and 1.0 mm in diameter?

60. An integrated circuit design calls for a 470-Ω resistor. The resistor is to be 10 μm long, 1.4 μm wide, and 0.85 μm thick, with connections made at the ends 10 μm apart. Its resistivity is to be set by the appropriate amount of doping. What should that resistivity be?

61. A power plant produces 1000 MW to supply a city 40 km away. Current flows from the power plant on a single wire of resistance 0.050 Ω/km, through the city, and returns via the ground, assumed to have negligible resistance. At the power plant the voltage between the wire and ground is 115 kV. (a) What is the current in the wire? (b) What fraction of the power is lost in transmission?

62. What should be the power line voltage in the preceding problem if the transmission loss is not to exceed 2%?

63. A 240-V electric motor is 90% efficient, meaning that 90% of the energy supplied to it ends up as mechanical work. If the motor lifts a 200-N weight at 3.1 m/s, how much current does it draw?

64. An 8.5-kN elevator is powered by a 480-V electric motor that draws 24 A. If the motor is 85% efficient, how long does it take to lift the elevator 18 m?

Supplementary Problems

65. A metal bar has a rectangular cross section 5.0 cm by 10 cm, as shown in Fig. 27-25. The bar has a nonuniform conductivity, ranging from zero at the bottom to a maximum at the top. As a result, the current density increases linearly from zero at the bottom to 0.10 A/cm² at the top. What is the total current in the bar?

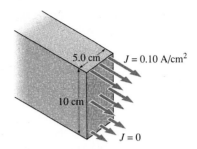

FIGURE 27-25 Problem 65.

66. Metallic copper (atomic weight 64, density 8.9 g/cm²) forms a crystal structure with copper atoms located at the corners of cubes. (a) Use the density and atomic weight to determine the distance between copper atoms. (b) Use your result, and the collision time from Example 27-4, to estimate the mean thermal speed of the electrons in copper. Consider τ to be the mean time between collisions.

67. General Motors' EV1 electric car has a mass of 1500 kg and is powered by 26 12-V batteries connected in series, for a total of 312 V. About 85% of the electrical energy from the batteries ends up as mechanical energy at the drive wheels. How much current do the batteries supply when the car is climbing a 10° slope at 45 km/h? Neglect frictional losses and air resistance.

FIGURE 27-26 General Motors' EV1 electric car is powered by 26 12-V batteries driving a 102 kW (137 horsepower) electric motor. It can accelerate from 0 to 60 mi/h in 9 s, and can travel up to 90 miles before recharging (Problem 67).

68. An immersion-type heating coil is connected to a 120-V outlet and immersed in a 250-ml cup of water initially at 10°C. The water comes to a boil in 85 s. What are (a) the power and (b) the resistance of the heater? Assume no heat loss, and neglect the mass of the heater.

69. A 100-Ω resistor of negligible mass is mounted inside a calorimeter. When a 12-V battery is connected for 5.0 min, the temperature inside the calorimeter rises by 26°C. What is the heat capacity of the calorimeter contents?

70. A parallel-plate capacitor has plates of 10 cm² area separated by a 1.0-mm layer of glass insulation with resistivity

$\rho = 1.2 \times 10^{13}$ $\Omega \cdot$m and dielectric constant $\kappa = 5.6$. The capacitor is charged to 100 V and the charging battery disconnected. (a) What is the initial rate of discharge (i.e., the current through the insulation)? (b) At this rate, how long would it take the capacitor to discharge fully? (The rate does not remain constant; more on this in the next chapter.)

71. Figure 27-27 shows a resistor made from a truncated cone of material with uniform resistivity ρ. Consider the cone to be made of thin slices of thickness dx, like the one shown; Equation 27-6 shows that the resistance of each slab is $dR = \rho \, dx/A$. By integrating over all such slices, show that the resistance between the two flat faces is $R = \rho \ell / \pi ab$. (This method assumes the equipotentials are planes, which is only approximately true.)

72. A circular pan of radius b has a plastic bottom and metallic side wall of height h. It is filled with a solution of resistivity ρ. A metal disk of radius a and height h is placed at the center of the pan, as shown in Fig. 27-28. The side and disk are essentially perfect conductors. Show that the resistance measured from side to disk is $\rho \ln(b/a)/2\pi h$.

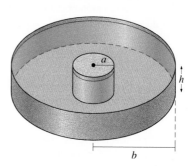

FIGURE 27-28 Problem 72.

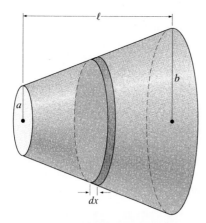

FIGURE 27-27 Problem 71.

73. At some point in a material of resistivity ρ the current density is J. Show that the power per unit volume dissipated at that point is $J^2 \rho$.

74. A thermally insulated container of sea water carries a uniform current density of 75 mA/cm². How long does it take to raise its temperature from 15°C to 20°C? Use the result of the preceding problem, and assume that both the specific heat (assumed the same as pure water) and the resistivity are constant over this range.

Electric Circuits

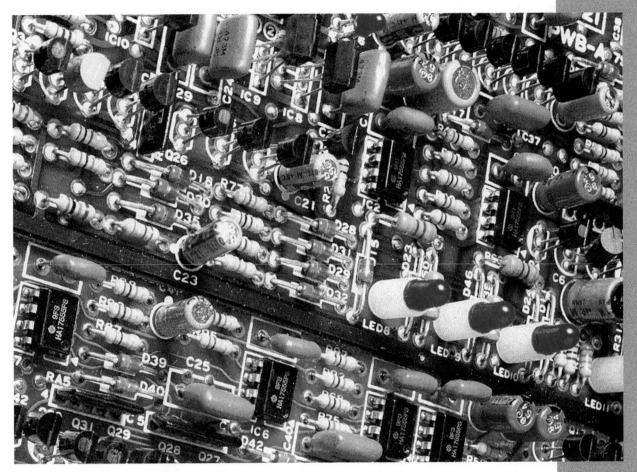

This circuit board is a complex interconnection of electronic components, including resistors, capacitors, transistors, light-emitting diodes, and integrated circuits.

28-1 CIRCUITS AND SYMBOLS

An **electric circuit** is a collection of electrical devices, called **circuit elements**, connected by conductors. Most circuits include a source of electrical energy. You're most familiar with human-made electrical circuits, which range from simple flashlights to computers, but important circuits also exist in nature. Examples include nervous systems in living organisms and Earth's global atmospheric circuit, in which thunderstorms are the batteries and the atmosphere a resistor. Your study of electric circuits should prove immensely practical, for it will help you to understand and to use effectively and safely the growing myriad of electrical and electronic devices you encounter. Basic circuit knowledge can even help you design new devices and troubleshoot old ones.

Circuit symbols

Resistor Capacitor Source Voltmeter Switch
of emf

Ammeter Variable Variable Ground Fuse
resistor capacitor

FIGURE 28-1 Common circuit symbols.

FIGURE 28-2 Chemical reactions in this alkaline battery separate electric charges, resulting in a positive charge at the + end (left) and negative charge at the − end (right).

FIGURE 28-3 A gravitational analog of a source of emf. The person lifting the balls does work against the gravitational field **g** to maintain a steady flow of balls. This represents the energy conversion process in the emf, which does work lifting charge against the electric field. The balls roll down the ramp driven by the gravitational field. They bump into the pegs and dissipate their energy. The ramp and pegs are analogous to an external resistance connected across the emf.

It's often helpful to represent circuits symbolically. We do so using standard symbols for circuit elements, with lines to represent the wires connecting them. We usually assume that the wires are perfect conductors, so all points connected by wires alone are at the same potential; such points are electrically equivalent. Realizing this will greatly facilitate your interpretation of circuit diagrams! Figure 28-1 shows some common circuit symbols. With ActivPhysics you can "build" and simulate circuits using such symbols.

28-2 ELECTROMOTIVE FORCE

In the preceding chapter, we found that an electric field is necessary to drive a current in any conductor with nonzero resistance. But if we simply apply an electric field, say by putting excess charge on one end of the conductor, the charge will quickly redistribute itself until electrostatic equilibrium is reached and the electric field disappears. Somehow we must maintain the electric field, and with it the current, despite the tendency toward equilibrium. To keep current flowing through a conductor with nonzero resistance, we need to maintain a potential difference between the ends of the conductor. Otherwise the conductor would quickly come to electrostatic equilibrium, with no electric field to drive the current.

A device that can maintain a fixed potential difference and thus an electric field, despite the flow of current, is called a source of **electromotive force**, or **emf**. (This name, which has historical origins, is not accurate; emf is not a force but a potential difference.) Most sources of emf have two electrical contacts, or **terminals**, for connection to other circuit elements. A source of emf converts some other form of energy into electrical energy by separating charge to maintain the fixed potential difference between its two terminals. The circuit symbol for a source of emf is shown in Fig. 28-1. The most familiar example is a battery, in which chemical energy drives opposite charges to the two terminals (Fig. 28-2). Others include electric generators, which convert mechanical energy to electrical energy; photovoltaic cells, which convert sunlight; fuel cells, which "burn" hydrogen to produce electrical energy and water; and biological cell membranes, which separate charge to control the movement of ions into the cell.

When a source of emf is connected to an external circuit, current flows through the circuit from the emf's positive to the negative terminal. Energy conversion processes within the emf then "lift" charge against the internal electric field, boosting the charge's energy and thus maintaining a fixed voltage across the emf's terminals. The charge then "falls" through the external circuit, dissipating its energy in the circuit resistance. The process repeats as the charge returns to the negative terminal of the emf, and the result is a steady current and a constant voltage across the emf. Figure 28-3 shows a gravitational analogy for an emf with a resistance connected across it.

Electromotive force is quantified by the work per unit charge done as the emf "lifts" charge against the electric field. The units of emf are therefore volts. An **ideal source of emf**—one with no internal energy losses—maintains the same voltage across its terminals under all conditions. Real sources always have internal energy losses, so the terminal voltage may not equal the rated emf. We discuss this situation in the next section.

28-3 SIMPLE CIRCUITS: SERIES AND PARALLEL RESISTORS

In the circuit of Fig. 28-4 an ideal battery of emf $\mathcal{E}$ drives a current through the resistor R. How much current? The voltage across the battery is its emf $\mathcal{E}$. The battery is connected to the resistor by wires, assumed to have zero resistance. Because they have zero resistance, there is no potential difference across either wire. Therefore the voltage across the resistor is the same as the voltage across the battery, and we can immediately apply Ohm's law to find the current:

$$ I = \frac{\mathcal{E}}{R}. $$

Energetically, this circuit is analogous to Fig. 28-3. Charge gains energy in the amount $\mathcal{E}$ joules per coulomb as it's "lifted" against the electric field inside the battery, then dissipates that energy in heating the resistor.

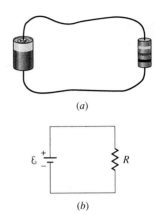

(a)

(b)

FIGURE 28-4 A circuit containing a battery and a resistor. (*a*) Physical circuit. (*b*) Schematic diagram, using the symbols of Fig. 28-1. Colored stripes on small resistors, like that shown here, code for the value of the resistance.

Tip

Don't Get Hung Up about Wires We assume the wires connecting circuit elements to be essentially perfect conductors—so it takes no potential difference between the ends of a wire to drive current through it. Thus all points on a wire are at the same potential, and are electrically equivalent. That means there are many ways to diagram the same circuit; as long as two components are shown as connected by a wire, that's all that matters. Of course real wires have some resistance, but if it's negligible compared with other resistances in the circuit, then we can approximate the wires as being ideal.

Series Resistors

Figure 28-5 shows a circuit containing two resistors in series. What's the current through these resistors? What's the voltage across each? Note that neither resistor is connected directly across the battery, so we can't argue that the voltage across either is the battery voltage. But we *can* argue that the current through the two resistors is the same. Why? Because the resistors are connected in series, so the only place for current to go after it flows through R_1 is through R_2. In a steady state, with no buildup of charge in the circuit, the current through both resistors—and, for that matter, through the battery as well—must be the same. This situation holds whenever circuit elements are in series:

12.1
DC Series Circuits

▎ **The current through each circuit element connected in series is the same.**

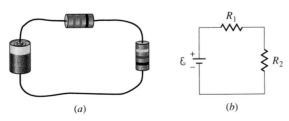

(a)   (b)

FIGURE 28-5 A battery and two resistors in series. (*a*) Physical circuit. (*b*) Schematic diagram.

If I is the current in the circuit of Fig. 28-5, then there must be a voltage $V_1 = IR_1$ across R_1 to drive the current through this resistor. Similarly, the voltage across R_2 is $V_2 = IR_2$. Thus, the voltage across the two resistors together is $V_1 + V_2 = IR_1 + IR_2$. But the battery is connected directly across this series combination, so we have

$$IR_1 + IR_2 = \mathcal{E},$$

or

$$I = \frac{\mathcal{E}}{R_1 + R_2}.$$

Comparison with Ohm's law in the form $I = V/R$ shows that the two resistors in series behave like an equivalent resistance equal to the sum of their resistances. In an obvious generalization to more resistors in series, we have

$$R_{\text{series}} = R_1 + R_2 + R_3 + \cdots \qquad (28\text{-}1)$$

In other words, resistors in series add.

Given the current, we can use Ohm's law in the form $V = IR$ to solve for the voltage across each resistor:

$$V_1 = \frac{R_1}{R_1 + R_2}\mathcal{E} \qquad (28\text{-}2\text{a})$$

and

$$V_2 = \frac{R_2}{R_1 + R_2}\mathcal{E}. \qquad (28\text{-}2\text{b})$$

These expressions show that the battery voltage divides between the two resistors in proportion to their resistance. For this reason a series combination of resistors is called a **voltage divider**. Figure 28-6 depicts the voltages throughout the circuit of Fig. 28-5, and shows explicitly that the resistors divide the battery voltage.

FIGURE 28-6 Voltages in the circuit of Fig. 28-5, with $V = 0$ at the negative battery terminal. Note that there is no potential difference across the wires, since they have negligible resistance, and that potential increases across the battery and decreases across the resistors. Can you tell from the graph which resistance is greater? (Here we've "unrolled" the circuit so we can clearly show the voltage as a function of position around the circuit. But remember that the circuit is a closed loop, so the left and right ends of the graph represent the same physical point, namely the negative battery terminal.)

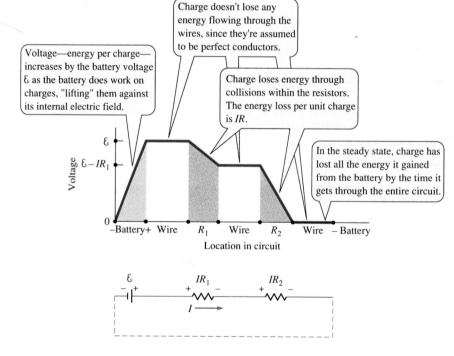

Tip

How Does the Battery Know? How does the battery in Fig. 28-5 "know" how much current to supply? How does it even "know" there are two resistors, and what their values are? For the brief instant when the circuit is first connected, the battery doesn't "know," and some rather complicated action occurs as charge moves from the battery, encounters resistance, and accumulates to establish the potential differences across the resistors. During that brief time the current is not the same everywhere. But very soon the circuit reaches a steady state, with the same current throughout. Later in this chapter, when we consider circuits with capacitors, we'll look in more detail at the approach to the steady state; for now, our analyses assume that circuits have already reached that state.

EXAMPLE 28-1	*Designing a Voltage Divider*

A light bulb with a resistance (when on) of 5.0 Ω is designed to operate at a current of 600 mA. To operate this lamp from a 12-V battery, what resistance should you place in series with it?

Solution

Let R_2 be the lamp and R_1 the unknown series resistor. Since resistors in series add, the current through both resistors is $I = \mathcal{E}/(R_1 + R_2)$, which is supposed to be 600 mA or 0.60 A. Solving for R_1 gives

$$R_1 = \frac{\mathcal{E} - IR_2}{I} = \frac{12 \text{ V} - (0.60 \text{ A})(5.0 \text{ }\Omega)}{0.60 \text{ A}} = 15 \text{ }\Omega.$$

You can also get this result by noting that the light bulb's proper operating voltage is $V = IR_2 = (0.60 \text{ A})(5.0 \text{ }\Omega) = 3.0$ V. This is one-fourth of the battery voltage, so the light bulb's 5-Ω resistance should be one-fourth of the total. That makes the total 20 Ω, leaving 15 Ω for R_1.

EXERCISE Suppose that in Fig. 28-5 $R_1 = 470$ Ω. If the voltage across R_2 is 59% of the battery voltage, find R_2.

Answer: 676 Ω

Some problems similar to Example 28-1: 23–25

Got It!

What is the voltage across the resistor R at the top of each circuit shown in Fig. 28-7? In (a) the second resistor has the same resistance R, and in (b) the gap is an open circuit (infinite resistance). Think about it first, then verify your answers using Equations 28-2.

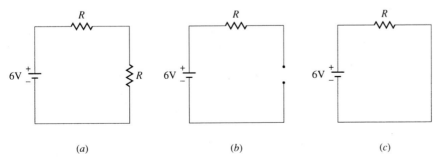

         (a)   (b)   (c)

FIGURE 28-7 What's the voltage across the upper resistor in each circuit?

FIGURE 28-8 A 1.5-V calculator battery and a 1.5-V D-cell flashlight battery have the same voltage, but the internal resistance of the calculator battery is higher.

Real Batteries

What's the difference between the two 1.5-V batteries shown in Fig. 28-8? If both were ideal there would be no difference because both would maintain 1.5 V across their terminals no matter how much current was flowing. But these are real batteries. The rate at which internal chemical reactions take place limits the amount of current each can supply. Not surprisingly, the larger battery can supply more current.

We can model a real battery by considering it to be an ideal emf in series with an **internal resistance**, as shown in Fig. 28-9. Of course this is not how batteries are made since no manufacturer can make an ideal emf! The internal resistance is intrinsic to the battery, and there is no way to circumvent it. Some of the internal resistance is actual resistance of the battery materials, but most represents the limited rate of the chemical reactions that power the battery. The more powerful battery is the one with lower internal resistance; it approaches more closely the ideal of zero internal resistance and can therefore supply more current.

We can understand the effect of internal resistance by considering the circuit of Fig. 28-10. This is just the series circuit of Fig. 28-5, with R_1 the internal resistance R_{int} and R_2 the external resistance R_L. R_L is called the *load resistor* because it is the component to which we wish to deliver electric power; it is the electrical load on the battery. From Equation 28-2b we see that if R_{int} is small compared with R_L, then the voltage across the load resistance will be very close to the battery's internal emf. In this case the battery's behavior is nearly ideal, since it has essentially $\mathcal{E}$ volts across its terminals. But if we lower R_L so it becomes comparable with R_{int}, then the voltage across R_L decreases and the battery no longer seems ideal. As we lower R_L we draw more current from the battery. It takes a higher voltage to drive this current through the fixed resistance R_{int}, so more voltage drops across R_{int}, leaving less across R_L. Even if we short-circuit the battery terminals (which is not good for the battery!) we will not get infinite current—in fact, we will simply have

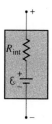

FIGURE 28-9 A real battery modeled as an ideal emf in series with an internal resistance.

$$I = \frac{\mathcal{E}}{R_{int}}. \quad \text{(battery short-circuited)}$$

We conclude that a battery or other source of emf behaves more or less ideally depending on the size of its load resistance relative to its internal resistance. A calculator, for example, has a very high resistance and draws little current. It is quite happy with a small battery whose internal resistance, while high, is still small compared with the calculator's resistance. A car starter motor, on the other hand, draws a large current and thus requires a much larger battery with very low internal resistance.

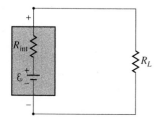

FIGURE 28-10 A real battery connected to an external load. Some voltage drops across the internal resistance, making the voltage across the battery terminals less than the battery's rated voltage.

EXAMPLE 28-2	*Starting a Car*

Your car's starter motor draws 125 A. The car has a 12-V battery, but while the starter motor is running the voltage across the battery terminals measures only 9.5 V. What is the internal resistance of the battery?

Solution

This circuit is just that of Fig. 28-10, with the starter being the load. With 9.5 V across the starter, there must be 2.5 V left across the internal resistance to make a total of 12 V. The current is the same throughout this series circuit, so 125 A is the current through R_{int}. Knowing current and voltage, we apply Ohm's law:

$$R = \frac{V}{I} = \frac{2.5 \text{ V}}{125 \text{ A}} = 0.020 \text{ } \Omega.$$

A battery voltage between 9 and 11 volts is typical of a car being started. A battery voltage much below 9 volts usually indicates a weak battery, a defective starter motor, or very cold weather!

EXERCISE A 9-V battery has an internal resistance of 13 Ω. What is the maximum current that can be drawn from the battery if its terminal voltage is to remain above 8.0 V?

Answer: 77 mA

Some problems similar to Example 28-2: 12, 13, 15, 17

Parallel Resistors

Figure 28-11 shows two resistors in parallel, connected across an ideal battery. What is the equivalent resistance of this parallel combination? Since the two resistors are connected at top and bottom by ideal wires, the voltage across each must be the same. We made this point in Chapter 26 when we discussed parallel capacitors, and it's worth repeating here:

▌ **The voltage across circuit elements in parallel is the same.**

The parallel resistors are connected directly across the battery, so their common voltage is the battery emf $\mathscr{E}$. Applying Ohm's law then gives the current through each resistor:

$$I_1 = \frac{\mathscr{E}}{R_1}$$

and

$$I_2 = \frac{\mathscr{E}}{R_2}.$$

At the point marked A in Fig. 28-11, a current I brings in charge from the battery, while the currents I_1 and I_2 carry charge away. If charge is not to accumulate (see Problem 69), the incoming and outgoing currents must be equal; that is,

$$I = I_1 + I_2.$$

Using our expressions for the two resistor currents gives

$$I = \frac{\mathscr{E}}{R_1} + \frac{\mathscr{E}}{R_2} = \mathscr{E}\left(\frac{1}{R_1} + \frac{1}{R_2}\right).$$

Comparison with Ohm's law in the form $I = V/R$ shows that the equivalent resistance of the parallel combination is given by

$$\frac{1}{R_{parallel}} = \frac{1}{R_1} + \frac{1}{R_2}. \tag{28-3a}$$

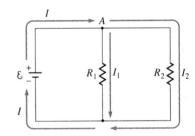

FIGURE 28-11 Parallel resistors connected across a battery. The resistor currents I_1 and I_2 sum to the battery current I.

12.2
DC Parallel Circuits

This result is readily generalized to more than two parallel resistors:

$$\frac{1}{R_{\text{parallel}}} = \frac{1}{R_1} + \frac{1}{R_2} + \frac{1}{R_3} + \cdots. \qquad (28\text{-}3b)$$

In other words, resistors in parallel add reciprocally. Equation 28-3b shows that the resistance of a parallel combination is always lower than that of the lowest resistance in the combination.

An analogy with highway traffic shows why this makes sense: adding a lane to a crowded highway eases congestion (i.e., lowers the overall resistance), allowing a greater traffic flow (e.g., a greater current). Putting one resistor in parallel with another is like adding an extra traffic lane.

When there are only two parallel resistors, we can rewrite Equation 28-3a using a common denominator to obtain

$$R_{\text{parallel}} = \frac{R_1 R_2}{R_1 + R_2}. \qquad (28\text{-}3c)$$

Note that *parallel* resistors combine in the same way as *series* capacitors, and vice versa.

Got It!

What's the equivalent resistance if you connect two identical resistors R (a) in series and (b) in parallel?

EXAMPLE 28-3	*Parallel and Series Resistors*

You have available three 2.0-Ω resistors. What different resistances can you make by combining all three resistors?

Solution

Figure 28-12 shows the four possible combinations. Resistors in series add, so combination (*a*) has 6.0 Ω. Resistors in parallel reciprocally add, so combination (*b*) has

$$\frac{1}{R} = \frac{1}{2.0\ \Omega} + \frac{1}{2.0\ \Omega} + \frac{1}{2.0\ \Omega} = 1.5\ \Omega^{-1},$$

for a resistance of 0.67 Ω. Combination (*c*) has two resistors in series, giving 4.0 Ω. This 4.0-Ω combination is in parallel with 2.0 Ω, so Equation 28-3c gives

$$R = \frac{(2.0\ \Omega)(4.0\ \Omega)}{2.0\ \Omega + 4.0\ \Omega} = 1.3\ \Omega.$$

Finally, combination (*d*) has two resistors in parallel, giving 1.0 Ω. This combination is in series with 2.0 Ω, for a total of 3.0 Ω. Thus you can make combinations ranging from 0.67 Ω to 6.0 Ω with these three equal resistors.

EXERCISE A 270-Ω and a 470-Ω resistor are connected in parallel, and the combination is connected in series with a 150-Ω resistor. Find the equivalent resistance of this combination.

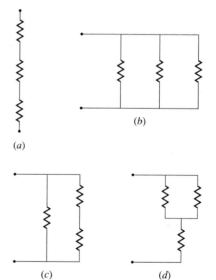

FIGURE 28-12 The four possible combinations of three equal resistors (Example 28-3).

Answer: 321 Ω

Some problems similar to Example 28-3: 16, 18, 19, 59, 60

Analyzing Circuits

Many circuits contain series and parallel combinations of basic circuit elements. We can simplify these circuits by treating each series or parallel combination as a single element, continuing the process until we can determine the voltages and currents throughout the entire circuit. Example 28-4 illustrates this procedure, which is similar to the way we dealt with capacitor combinations in Chapter 26.

12.3

DC Circuit Puzzles

EXAMPLE 28-4	*Analyzing a Circuit*

In the circuit of Fig. 28-13, what is the current through the 2-Ω resistor?

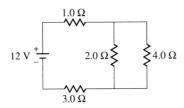

FIGURE 28-13 Circuit for Example 28-4.

Solution

We approach this problem by simplifying the circuit until we can solve for something—in this case the total current. Then we reverse the process, analyzing the circuit details until we can solve for the quantity we want. Figure 28-14 shows the steps in simplifying the circuit. We get from the original circuit, Fig. 28-14a, to Fig. 28-14b by calculating the resistance of the parallel combination of 2 Ω and 4 Ω:

$$R_{\parallel} = \frac{(2.0\ \Omega)(4.0\ \Omega)}{2.0\ \Omega + 4.0\ \Omega} = 1.33\ \Omega .$$

Figure 28-14b shows three resistors in series, which add to get the single-resistor circuit of Fig. 28-14c. From here we can calculate the total current:

$$I = \frac{\mathcal{E}}{R} = \frac{12\ V}{5.33\ \Omega} = 2.25\ A .$$

Where does this current flow? It flows from the battery through the 1-Ω resistor, then on through the parallel combination of the 2-Ω and 4-Ω resistors, then through the 3-Ω resistor and back to the battery. It does *not* all flow through the 2-Ω resistor because there are two paths the current can take when it gets to the parallel combination. However, it does all flow through the parallel combination. We already found that this combination has a resistance of 1.33 Ω, and now we know that 2.25 A flows through the combination. So the voltage across the combination is

$$V = IR = (2.25\ A)(1.33\ \Omega) = 2.99\ V .$$

This same voltage appears across each of the two resistors making up the parallel combination so the current through the 2-Ω resistor is

$$I = \frac{V}{R} = \frac{2.99\ V}{2.0\ \Omega} = 1.5\ A .$$

In solving for this current we effectively reversed our original simplification of the circuit, first considering Fig. 28-14b to get the voltage across the parallel combination, and then going to the full circuit to get the answer. At each stage we applied Ohm's law to solve for either a voltage or a current as needed.

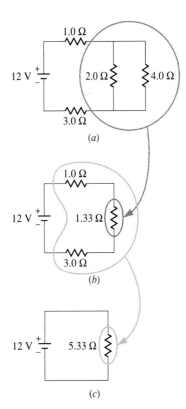

FIGURE 28-14 Simplifying the circuit by forming parallel and series combinations.

Don't Abuse Ohm's Law Ohm's law relates the voltage *across a resistor* to the current *through that resistor*. It does *not* relate arbitrary voltages and currents anywhere in a circuit. Just because there is a 12-V battery in Fig. 28-13, for example, does *not* mean that 12 V appears across the 2-Ω resistor. Be careful, too, with series and parallel combinations. As it stands, the only individual resistors in Fig. 28-13 in either series or parallel are the parallel pair of 2 Ω and 4 Ω. The 1-Ω and 2-Ω resistors are *not* in series because current flowing through the 1-Ω resistor need not all go through the 2-Ω resistor; some can go through the 4-Ω resistor instead. Equations 28-1 and 28-3 apply *only* to combinations that are strictly series or parallel, respectively.

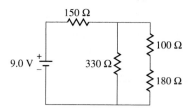

FIGURE 28-15 What is the voltage across the 180-Ω resistor?

EXERCISE In Fig. 28-15, find (a) the current supplied by the battery and (b) the voltage across the 180-Ω resistor.

Answers: (a) 30 mA; (b) 2.9 V

Some problems similar to Example 28-4: 26–28

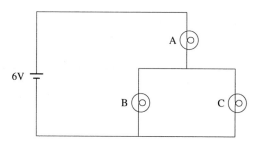

FIGURE 28-16 Which bulb will be brightest? What happens if you disconnect bulb C?

Got It!

Figure 28-16 shows a circuit with a 6-V battery and identical 6-V light bulbs—that is, bulbs that light at full brightness when there's a 6-V potential difference between their terminals. You can treat all three bulbs as being resistors. Which, if any, of the bulbs will be brightest? What will happen to the other two bulbs if you disconnect bulb C?

28-4 KIRCHHOFF'S LAWS AND MULTILOOP CIRCUITS

Some circuits cannot be simplified using series and parallel combinations. This often happens when there is more than one source of emf or when circuit elements are connected in complicated ways. In Fig. 28-17, for example, are

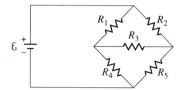

FIGURE 28-17 This circuit cannot be analyzed using series and parallel combinations.

resistors R_1 and R_2 in parallel? No, because R_3 separates their lower ends. Are R_1 and R_3 in series? No, because current flowing out the bottom of R_1 can go through either R_3 or R_4. Solving circuits that aren't reducible to series and parallel combinations usually requires more general techniques than we've used so far.

Kirchhoff's Laws

In Fig. 28-6 we looked at changes in electric potential around the loop comprising a simple series circuit. The result was an increase in potential at the battery, followed by decreases at both resistors that summed to the gain in the battery. If we count the increase as a positive change and the decreases as negative changes, we can state the following:

The sum of the voltage changes across all the circuit elements around any closed loop is zero.

This statement is known as **Kirchhoff's loop law**, and it applies not just to Fig. 28-6 but to *any* closed loop in a circuit. The loop law is ultimately about energy conservation; it says that charge moving around a loop gains as much energy from batteries or other sources as it loses in resistors or other energy-conversion devices.

In analyzing parallel resistors with Fig. 28-11 we noted that the current flowing into point *A* must equal the total current flowing out through the two parallel resistors. This is really a statement about conservation of charge. It applies to any point in a circuit carrying steady currents since under steady-state conditions charge cannot build up or be depleted. The statement is most useful at a point where three or more wires join; such a point, like *A* in Fig. 28-11, is called a **node**. If we count currents flowing into a node as positive, and currents flowing out as negative, then the statement of charge conservation becomes the following:

The sum of the currents at any node is zero.

This is **Kirchhoff's node law**.

Analyzing Multiloop Circuits

Even the most complex circuits can be analyzed using Kirchhoff's laws. Applying the laws amounts to writing equations expressing the loop law and node law for the distinct loops and nodes in the circuit. The number of equations needed is generally one less than the number of loops plus one less than the number of nodes; this is because the quantities in one loop and one node can be expressed entirely in terms of other loops and nodes, making one loop and one node equation each redundant. Here we give just two examples; electrical engineers take entire courses in circuit analysis using these laws.

12.5
Using Kirchhoff's Laws

EXAMPLE 28-5	*Rate the Resistor*

What power dissipation must resistor R_3 of Fig. 28-18a be able to tolerate?

Solution

This is a multiloop circuit in which none of the resistors are in either series or parallel with the others, so we need to use Kirchhoff's laws. In Figure 28-18b we identify three loops and two nodes. It's not always obvious in a multiloop circuit which way the currents flow, so in Fig. 28-18b we've arbitrarily assigned directions to the three currents. If an answer comes out negative, that just means the current is flowing in the opposite direction.

Here we need to know I_3 to find the power dissipation in R_3. Rather than solving symbolically, it will be simpler if we write the equations directly with their numerical values. Let's go counterclockwise around loop 1; starting at node A, the loop law becomes

$$6 - 2I_1 - I_3 = 0, \quad \text{(loop 1)}$$

where we've temporarily dropped the units. Starting from A and going clockwise around loop 2 (remember, the direction is arbitrary), we have

$$9 + 4I_2 - I_3 = 0. \quad \text{(loop 2)}$$

Why did we make the second term positive? Because this quantity is the voltage drop $I_2 R_2$ across the 4-Ω resistor R_2, and we're going through the resistor *against* the direction we've assigned for the current. This implies a voltage *increase* going in this direction. Finally, the node equation at node A reads

$$-I_1 + I_2 + I_3 = 0, \quad \text{(node } A)$$

where the first term is negative because I_1 is indicated as flowing *away* from the node. The equations for node B and loop 3 are redundant, so we're ready to solve the system. The node equation gives $I_1 = I_2 + I_3$; substituting in the loop 1 equation, we have $6 - 2I_2 - 3I_3 = 0$, or

$$I_2 = \tfrac{1}{2}(6 - 3I_3).$$

Finally, we can use this result in the loop 2 equation to get $9 + 2(6 - 3I_3) - I_3 = 0$ or

$$21 - 7I_3 = 0,$$

giving $I_3 = 3$ A. That this answer is positive indicates that I_3 is indeed upward in Fig. 28-18. The power dissipated in R_3 is therefore

$$P_3 = I_3^2 R_3 = (3 \text{ A})^2(1 \text{ }\Omega) = 9 \text{ W},$$

using Equation 27-9a. A 10-W resistor, the next larger size commercially available, would be just adequate.

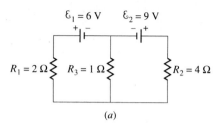

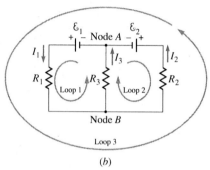

FIGURE 28-18 (a) A circuit that cannot be analyzed using series and parallel combinations. (b) There are 3 loops, 2 nodes, and 3 unknown currents whose direction assignments are, arbitrary (Example 28-5).

Tip

Getting Those Signs Right It really doesn't matter what direction you assign to the currents in a multiloop circuit, so don't spend a lot of time fretting about it; the algebra really will take care of signs. Here we found $I_3 = +3$ A, indicating that our upward direction in Fig. 28-18b was correct. But we found that I_2 was given by $I_2 = \tfrac{1}{2}(6 - 3I_3)$, so, with $I_3 = 3$ A, $I_2 = -1.5$ A. The minus sign says that I_2 is actually flowing downward through R_2, opposite the direction we assigned. Had we assigned a downward direction originally, we would have had a positive answer—but the physical situation would be identical.

The exercise with this example shows that I_2 goes to zero when $\mathscr{E}_2$ drops to 2 V. If $\mathscr{E}_2$ drops lower still, I_2 really will be upward—and then the algebra will give a positive answer.

It also doesn't matter what direction you choose to go around the circuit loops; changing direction will change the sign of *all* terms in the loop equation—leaving the mathematical content of the equation unchanged.

EXERCISE To what value should $\mathscr{E}_2$ in Fig. 28-18 be changed so that the current I_2 becomes zero?

Answer: 2.0 V

EXAMPLE 28-6	*The Cell Membrane: A Microbiological Circuit*

Figure 28-19 shows a simplified version of the so-called Hodgkin-Huxley model, which microbiologists use to describe the flow of ions through cell membranes (Hodgkin and Huxley won the 1963 Nobel Prize for physiology or medicine for development of this model). The batteries labeled $\mathcal{E}_K$, $\mathcal{E}_{Na}$, and $\mathcal{E}_L$ represent, respectively, the electrochemical effects of potassium, sodium, and other ions. (Sodium and potassium dominate, and currents associated with other ions constitute a small "leakage current"; hence the subscript L.) The resistances describe just that—the resistance the cell membrane offers to each ion species passing through it (although the resistances vary with electrical activity of the cell). Find an expression for the voltage across the cell membrane, V_M in Fig. 28-19, in terms of the other quantities shown.

Solution

V_M is clearly the sum of any one battery voltage minus the drop across the corresponding resistor, so we need the current in any one of the resistors. Here we'll go for I_K. We've identified two loops and one node, and marked them on Fig. 28-19, and have assigned directions to all three currents (obviously, they can't all be flowing upward, but once again we'll let the algebra handle that).

All the physics is in writing the loop and node equations. We'll start with the two loop equations, first going clockwise (an arbitrary choice) around loop 1, from the bottom; taking the sum of the voltage differences and setting it to zero gives

$$\mathcal{E}_K - I_K R_K + I_{Na} R_{Na} - \mathcal{E}_{Na} = 0.$$

Here the voltage drop $I_{Na} R_{Na}$ across R_{Na} enters with a positive sign, since we're going *against* the direction we've assigned for the current through this resistor. Similarly, $\mathcal{E}_{Na}$ enters with a negative sign since we're going from the positive to the negative terminal of this battery—that is, in the direction of lower energy per unit charge. Similarly, going clockwise around loop 2 gives

$$\mathcal{E}_{Na} - I_{Na} R_{Na} + I_L R_L - \mathcal{E}_L = 0.$$

Finally, we have an equation for node A. All our currents are assigned as flowing into the node, so

$$I_K + I_{Na} + I_L = 0,$$

which affirms what should be obvious already: that all three currents can't really flow upward, since all three can't have positive signs and satisfy this equation.

We now have three equations in the three unknown currents, and the rest is algebra. You can either solve and substitute for I_L, then I_{Na}, until you finally have one equation in the single unknown I_K, or you can use the methods of linear algebra if

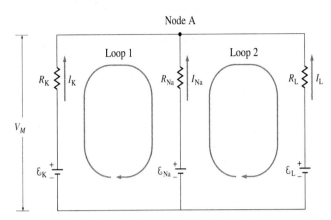

FIGURE 28-19 Simplified version of the Hodgkin-Huxley model for a biological cell membrane.

you've studied them. Either way, we'll skip the algebra and just give the result:

$$I_K = \frac{(\mathcal{E}_K - \mathcal{E}_{Na})R_L + (\mathcal{E}_K - \mathcal{E}_L)R_{Na}}{R_K R_L + R_K R_{Na} + R_L R_{Na}}.$$

The membrane voltage itself is then $V_M = \mathcal{E}_K - R_K I_K$. In typical situations this quantity has a value measured in tens of millivolts.

EXERCISE In Fig. 28-20, find an expression for the current through R_3 in terms of the quantities listed.

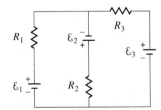

FIGURE 28-20 What's the current through R_3?

Answer: $I_K = \dfrac{(\mathcal{E}_1 - \mathcal{E}_3)R_2 - (\mathcal{E}_2 + \mathcal{E}_3)R_1}{R_1 R_2 + R_1 R_3 + R_2 R_3}$, with a positive value indicating current from left to right in Fig. 28-20.

Some problems similar to Examples 28-5 and 28-6: 32–38

Strategy

Multiloop Circuits Examples 28-5 and 28-6 illustrate the strategy for solving multiloop circuits, for which simple series-parallel reductions don't work. Here we outline the steps in that strategy.

1. Identify circuit nodes and loops.
2. Assign directions to each current. The directions you assign are completely arbitrary, but once you assign them, use those directions consistently throughout.
3. Go around all but one of the loops you've identified, either clockwise or counterclockwise; the direction doesn't matter (you don't need to do all the loops because one is always redundant). As you go, sum the voltage changes across each circuit element you encounter, following these rules (all of which give the energy change per unit charge in traversing the circuit elements):
   a. For batteries traversed from the negative to the positive terminal, the voltage change is $+\mathcal{E}$, where $\mathcal{E}$ is the battery voltage.
   b. For batteries traversed from positive to negative, the voltage change is $-\mathcal{E}$.
   c. For resistors traversed in the direction you've assigned to the current I through the resistor, the voltage change is $-IR$.
   d. For resistors traversed opposite the direction you've assigned to the current I through the resistor, the voltage change is $+IR$.
   e. For other circuit elements (which we haven't yet encountered) use the characteristics of that element to determine the change in voltage across the element.
   For each loop, set the resulting sum to zero, reflecting the fact that charges going around a circuit gain as much energy as they lose. You then have one equation for each circuit loop but one.
4. For all but one node, sum the currents into the node and set the result to zero, reflecting the fact that there's no charge buildup in the steady state. Use the convention that a current whose assigned direction has it flowing *into* the node is positive, while a current flowing *out* of the node is negative. You now have one equation for each node but one; again, the last node is always redundant.
5. You now have as many equations as there are unknown currents. Solve these as a system of simultaneous equations. Use the algebraic signs of your answers to find the actual current directions. If an answer is positive, your assigned direction is correct; if not, the actual current direction is opposite what you've assigned.

28-5 ELECTRICAL MEASURING INSTRUMENTS

12.4

Using Ammeters and Voltmeters

Voltmeters

A **voltmeter** is a device that indicates the potential difference across its two terminals. The indication is usually by a digital readout, although older meters

FIGURE 28-21 (*a*) Most voltmeters today have digital displays, although (*b*) analog—or moving-needle—meters are still found in older instruments. (*c*) An oscilloscope is essentially a pair of voltmeters in which two different voltages are indicated by the horizontal and vertical deflection of an electron beam. When the horizontal voltage varies linearly with time, the result is a plot of the vertical voltage versus time.

(*a*)

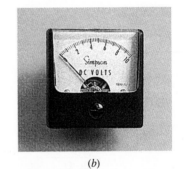

(*b*)

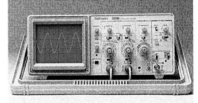

(*c*)

use a moving needle, and oscilloscopes use the deflection of an electron beam (Fig. 28-21). Potential difference—voltage—is a property of two points, and therefore to measure the voltage between two points we connect the two terminals of the voltmeter to those points. So to measure the voltage across resistor R_2 in Fig. 28-22a, we connect the voltmeter *across* R_2, as shown. We do *not* break the circuit and insert the meter, as in Fig. 28-22b, for then we would not be measuring the voltage *across* the resistor; in fact, we would radically alter the circuit.

How good is our voltage measurement? That depends on two things: first, obviously, is the accuracy of the meter in reading the voltage across it. The second is more subtle: unless the voltmeter in Fig. 28-22 has infinite resistance, its presence will alter the circuit and change the voltage across R_2 from what it was without the meter. Even if the meter is perfectly accurate, it still will not read exactly what we want, namely the voltage that was across R_2 before we connected the meter.

An ideal voltmeter, therefore, should have infinite resistance so it doesn't draw any current and therefore doesn't alter the circuit it's measuring. Practically speaking, a voltmeter's resistance should be large compared with resistances in the circuit where the meter is being used. As a rough rule of thumb, you'll get accuracy within 1% if you use a meter whose resistance is 100 times the circuit resistance.

Older moving-needle meters (Fig. 28-21b) fall short of the ideal because they rely on current drawn from the circuit to produce a magnetic force that deflects the needle (more on magnetic force in the next chapter). Modern digital meters (Fig. 28-21a) contain amplifiers that greatly reduce current drawn from the circuit; typical meter resistances are around 10 MΩ and can easily be made much higher. Today's digital meters include amplifier, digital converter, and digital display in a single integrated-circuit package, making them the most economical, reliable, and accurate variety.

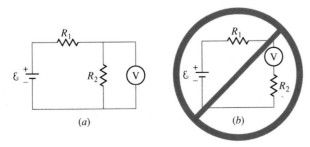

(*a*)   (*b*)

FIGURE 28-22 (*a*) Correct and (*b*) incorrect ways to measure the voltage across R_2.

| **EXAMPLE 28-7** | *Voltmeters* |

You wish to measure the voltage across the 40-Ω resistor of Fig. 28-23. What reading would an ideal voltmeter give? A voltmeter with a resistance of 1000 Ω?

Solution

An ideal voltmeter has infinite resistance and therefore would not alter the circuit, which is a simple voltage divider. Applying Equation 28-2b to this divider circuit gives the voltage across the 40-Ω resistor:

$$V_{40} = \frac{(40\ \Omega)(12\ \text{V})}{80\ \Omega + 40\ \Omega} = 4.0\ \text{V}.$$

Because the meter is connected in parallel with the resistor, this is also the voltage read by the meter.

With the nonideal voltmeter in place, the circuit becomes that of Fig. 28-24. The meter and 40-Ω resistor form a parallel combination whose resistance is given by Equation 28-3c:

$$R_{\parallel} = \frac{(40\ \Omega)(1000\ \Omega)}{40\ \Omega + 1000\ \Omega} = 38.5\ \Omega.$$

The circuit now looks like a voltage divider with $R_{\parallel}$ the lower resistor. Applying Equation 28-2b to this circuit gives

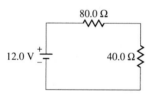

FIGURE 28-23 What is the voltage across the 40-Ω resistor?

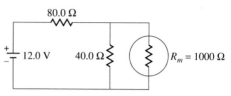

FIGURE 28-24 A nonideal voltmeter alters the circuit, lowering the overall resistance.

$$V_{\parallel} = \frac{(38.5\ \Omega)(12\ \text{V})}{80\ \Omega + 38.5\ \Omega} = 3.9\ \text{V}.$$

This $V_{\parallel}$ is the voltage across the parallel combination consisting of the meter and 40-Ω resistor. Since the voltage across parallel circuit elements is the same, $V_{\parallel}$ is both the meter reading and the voltage across the 40-Ω resistor. And this value is 0.10 V—about 2.5%—lower than the value indicated by an ideal voltmeter.

EXERCISE A 100-kΩ resistor and a 150-kΩ resistor are in series, with a 250-V potential difference across the combination. A digital meter with a 3-significant-digit display and 1.0-MΩ resistance is used to measure the voltage across the 150-kΩ resistor. (a) What does it read? (b) By what percentage does this reading differ from that of an ideal voltmeter?

Answers: (a) 142 V; (b) 5.3%

Some problems similar to Example 28-7: 39, 40, 41, 61

Ammeters

An **ammeter** measures the current flowing *through* itself. To measure the current through a circuit element it is necessary to break the circuit and insert the ammeter in series with that element (Fig. 28-25); only then will all the current through the element also go through the meter. Connecting the meter across the resistor in Fig. 28-25 would be wrong, for then the current through the resistor would not be going through the meter.

FIGURE 28-25 An ammeter goes in series with the circuit element whose current it is to measure. It doesn't matter whether the meter goes (*a*) before or (*b*) after the circuit element, in this case the resistor *R*. (*c*) Connecting it across the resistor is incorrect, since then the resistor current does not flow through the meter. In fact, this connection would probably destroy the meter!

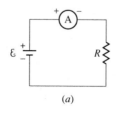

(*a*)

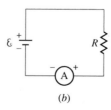

(*b*)

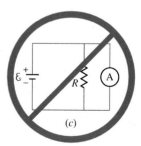

(*c*)

What electrical properties should the ammeter have so it doesn't alter the circuit in which it is connected? If the meter had any resistance, then the total resistance of the circuit would increase with the meter connected in series. This in turn would decrease the current, resulting in an incorrect reading. We conclude that an ideal ammeter should have zero resistance. In practice, ammeter resistance should be much lower than typical resistances in the circuit being measured.

Tip

Watch Your Language When Connecting Meters A voltmeter measures potential difference *between* two points; hence, we connect it *across*—i.e., in parallel with—the circuit element whose voltage we wish to measure. An ammeter measures the current *through* itself; hence, we connect it in *series* with the circuit element whose current we wish to measure. If you get used to voltages appearing *across* things and currents flowing *through* them, you'll have no trouble connecting meters. But if you insist on talking about "the voltage through" something, then you'll be unable to hook up meters accurately or safely. The ways to connect meters, and the words *across* for voltage and *through* for current, go right back to the definitions of potential difference as a property of two points and of current as a flow.

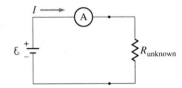

FIGURE 28-26 A simple ohmmeter consists of a known emf and an ammeter. When an unknown resistance is connected across the pair, its resistance may be determined from Ohm's law in the form $R = \mathcal{E}/I$.

Ohmmeters and Multimeters

Often we would like to measure the resistance of a particular circuit element. We can do this by connecting a source of known voltage in series with an ammeter and the unknown resistance, as in Fig. 28-26. Knowing the voltage and measuring the current then allows us to calculate the unknown resistance. A meter used for this purpose can be calibrated directly in ohms even though it is really measuring current; it is then called an **ohmmeter**.

The functions of voltmeter, ammeter, and ohmmeter are often combined in a single instrument called a **multimeter**. Multimeters include switches for selecting the quantity and range to be measured, and may be either analog or digital. Figure 28-27 shows a modern digital multimeter, or DMM.

Potentiometric Measurement

An elegant way to measure voltage is to compare the unknown voltage with an accurate standard, in much the same way that a pan balance weighs an unknown mass by balancing it against standard masses. Figure 28-28 shows how this scheme works. An accurately known emf $\mathcal{E}_0$ is connected across a resistor along which a sliding contact moves, forming a variable voltage divider in which the position of the sliding contact determines the voltage. The output of this voltage divider—called a **potentiometer**—is connected to the unknown voltage through a meter. The potentiometer is adjusted until the meter reads zero, at which point the potentiometer voltage—which can be read off its calibrated dial—must equal the unknown voltage. The great virtue of this method is that when the system is at null—the condition where source and unknown voltages are equal—then there is no current being drawn from the unknown regardless of the meter resistance, and therefore the method has, in principle, no effect on the circuit being measured.

FIGURE 28-27 This digital multimeter measures voltage, current, and resistance.

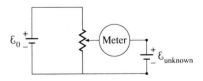

FIGURE 28-28 Potentiometric voltage measurement compares the unknown voltage with an accurately known voltage.

In the past, potentiometric measurements were made with circuits like that of Fig. 28-28, with special batteries of precisely known emf and accurately calibrated potentiometers. Manual adjustment was used to achieve the null condition. Today, nulling is accomplished electronically or electromechanically through a process known as negative feedback. Circuits using the potentiometric technique are the basis of many powerful measurement and control devices.

28-6 CIRCUITS WITH CAPACITORS

So far we've considered only circuits in which current and voltage are steady in all components. When you turn on a flashlight, for example, current starts to flow almost immediately through the bulb, batteries, and connecting metal parts. The current continues to flow steadily until you turn off the switch.

With a capacitor in a circuit, this picture changes. Circuit quantities change more gradually because of the capacitor. Why is this? Recall that a capacitor is a pair of insulated conductors that stores electrical energy when opposite charges are put on the conductors. A capacitor is characterized by its capacitance

$$C = \frac{Q}{V},$$

where Q is the magnitude of the charge on either conductor and V the voltage between the conductors. (See Section 26-4 for a review of capacitors.) Because charge and voltage are proportional in a capacitor, a change in a capacitor's voltage requires a change in its charge. In a circuit, a capacitor's charge changes only when current flows through the wires connecting the capacitor plates to the rest of the circuit. The magnitude of the current is the rate at which charge enters or leaves the capacitor. Since the current in any real circuit is finite, the charge on the capacitor cannot change instantaneously. But a capacitor's voltage is proportional to its charge, so:

▌ **The voltage across a capacitor cannot change instantaneously.**

This simple statement is the key to understanding circuits containing capacitors, so make sure you're clear on what it means. It says that you'll never see the voltage on a capacitor jump abruptly from one value to a different one; mathematically, capacitor voltage V_C must be a continuous function of time, with its derivative always finite. Just how rapidly the voltage can change depends on capacitance and other circuit quantities, as we'll soon see.

We now consider a simple circuit containing a resistor and a capacitor, and therefore called an ***RC* circuit**. *RC* circuits are ubiquitous, appearing everywhere from microbiological structures to stereo amplifiers to giant energy storage systems. We examine separately the two cases in which the capacitor is (1) charging and (2) discharging.

The *RC* Circuit: Charging

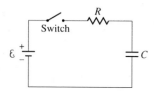

FIGURE 28-29 An *RC* circuit. The switch is closed at time $t = 0$.

Consider the circuit of Fig. 28-29. The capacitor is initially uncharged, so the voltage across it is zero. What happens when we close the switch?

The switch connects the left end of the resistor to the battery's positive terminal, so the left end of the resistor goes to $\mathcal{E}$ volts (here we take the zero of potential at the battery's negative terminal). The right end of the resistor is at the same voltage as the upper capacitor plate. But the voltage across the capacitor cannot change instantaneously, and therefore remains zero just after the switch is closed. With the capacitor plates both at zero volts, the full battery voltage $\mathcal{E}$ appears across the resistor. With $\mathcal{E}$ volts across the resistor, there must be a current $I = \mathcal{E}/R$ through the resistor. This current cannot flow "through" the capacitor but serves instead to pile positive charge on the upper plate, negative charge on the lower. The same current I flows everywhere except in the insulated gap between the capacitor plates.

12.6
Capacitance

Now that current is flowing, charge accumulates on the capacitor, and the capacitor voltage increases in proportion to this charge. As the capacitor voltage rises, the resistor voltage falls because the voltage across the series combination of resistor and capacitor is the battery voltage $\mathcal{E}$. But the current through the resistor is proportional to the resistor voltage, so the resistor current falls as well. This in turn decreases the *rate* at which charge accumulates on the capacitor plates, lowering the rate at which the capacitor voltage increases. The voltage across the capacitor continues to increase, and the current through the resistor to decrease, but at an ever slower rate.

What happens if we wait a long time? As the capacitor voltage approaches the battery voltage, the voltage across the resistor, hence the current through the resistor, and therefore the rate of charge buildup on the capacitor, all become very small. The whole system tends more and more slowly toward a final state in which the capacitor is charged to the full battery voltage and the current in the circuit is zero. Figure 28-30 summarizes the interplay among current, charge, and voltage.

We can analyze this circuit quantitatively using the loop law. Going clockwise around the loop, we first encounter a voltage increase $\mathcal{E}$ across the battery, then a drop IR across the resistor, then a drop V_C from the upper to lower capacitor

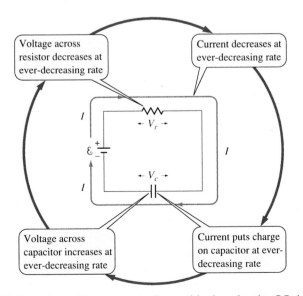

FIGURE 28-30 Interrelationships among circuit quantities in a charging *RC* circuit.

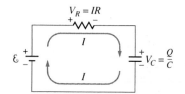

FIGURE 28-31 Voltage changes in a charging RC circuit. Since they sum to zero, the loop equation for this circuit is $\mathcal{E} - (IR) - (Q/C) = 0$.

plate (Fig. 28-31). But the definition of capacitance gives $V_C = Q/C$, so the loop equation becomes

$$\mathcal{E} - IR - \frac{Q}{C} = 0.$$

This equation contains the two unknown quantities I and Q. Can we relate them? Yes, because the current is the rate at which charge is accumulating on the capacitor. That is:

$$I = \frac{dQ}{dt}.$$

To use this relation, we take the time derivative of the loop equation:

$$-R\frac{dI}{dt} - \frac{1}{C}\frac{dQ}{dt} = 0.$$

The battery voltage $\mathcal{E}$ does not appear in this differentiated equation because it is constant and thus its derivative is zero. Using $I = dQ/dt$ and rearranging the equation slightly gives

$$\frac{dI}{dt} = -\frac{I}{RC}. \qquad (28\text{-}4)$$

This equation shows that the rate of change of current is proportional to the current itself, expressing mathematically what Fig. 28-30 shows schematically. Equations like this arise whenever the rate of change of a quantity is proportional to the quantity itself. Population growth, the increase of money in a bank account, and the decay of a radioactive element are all described by similar equations.

Like the equation for simple harmonic motion in Chapter 15, Equation 28-4 is a *differential* equation, so called because the unknown quantity I occurs in a derivative. The solution to a differential equation is not a single number but rather a function expressing the relation between the unknown quantity—in this case current—and the independent variable—in this case time. We can solve this particular differential equation by multiplying both sides by dt/I, in order to collect all terms involving I on one side of the equation. This gives

$$\frac{dI}{I} = -\frac{dt}{RC}.$$

We then integrate both sides, noting that RC is constant:

$$\int_{I_0}^{I} \frac{dI}{I} = -\frac{1}{RC} \int_0^t dt,$$

where $I_0 = \mathcal{E}/R$ is the initial current at the time $t = 0$ just after the switch is closed and where the integration runs from $t = 0$ to some arbitrary time t. The integral on the left is just the natural logarithm, and that on the right is just t. Then we have

$$\ln(I/I_0) = -\frac{t}{RC},$$

where we used $\ln I - \ln I_0 = \ln(I/I_0)$. To get an equation for I we exponentiate both sides, recalling that $e^{\ln x} = x$. This gives

$$\frac{I}{I_0} = e^{-t/RC},$$

or, since $I_0 = \mathscr{E}/R$,

$$I = \frac{\mathscr{E}}{R}e^{-t/RC}. \qquad (28\text{-}5)$$

Thus the current in the circuit decreases exponentially with time, in agreement with our qualitative analysis.

What about the capacitor voltage? The capacitor and resistor voltages must add to the battery voltage $\mathscr{E}$, and the resistor voltage is just $V_R = IR$, or

$$V_R = \mathscr{E}e^{-t/RC}.$$

Thus the capacitor voltage is $V_C = \mathscr{E} - V_R$, or

$$V_C = \mathscr{E}(1 - e^{-t/RC}). \qquad (RC \text{ circuit, charging}) \qquad (28\text{-}6)$$

Equation 28-6 shows the capacitor voltage starting at zero, and rising rapidly at first but with its rate of rise ever slowing, as it gradually approaches the battery voltage $\mathscr{E}$—just as we reasoned in our qualitative analysis. Figure 28-32 shows plots of capacitor voltage, charge, and current using the equations we've just derived.

When is the capacitor fully charged? Never, according to our equations! But the rate at which it approaches full charge is determined by the quantity RC that appears in Equations 28-5 and 28-6. (Problem 45 will convince you that this quantity has the units of time.) Called the **time constant**, RC is a characteristic time for changes to occur in a circuit containing a capacitor. Equation 28-6 shows that in one time constant, the voltage rises to $\mathscr{E}(1 - 1/e)$, or to about two-thirds of the battery voltage. A practical rule of thumb says that in five time constants ($t = 5RC$) a capacitor is 99% charged (see Problem 47). The RC time constant clarifies our statement that the voltage across a capacitor cannot change instantaneously. We can now say that in times small compared with the time constant, the voltage across a capacitor cannot change appreciably. On the other hand, if we wait a long time—many time constants—we will find essentially no current flowing to the capacitor. We've shown quantitatively the role of the time constant RC by marking the time in units of RC on Fig. 28-32.

Resistors and capacitors are available in a wide range of values, so practical values for RC span many orders of magnitude. RC circuits with time constants from microseconds to hours are widely used in electronic devices to control the rates at which electrical quantities vary. For example, circuits with RC many times the sixtieth-of-a-second period of standard AC power are used to produce steady, direct current power for audio and video equipment. Bass and treble controls, or equalizers in more sophisticated audio systems, are simply variable resistances in RC circuits; changing the resistance changes the time constant and therefore the way the circuit handles rapidly changing audio signals. Sometimes, though, the time constant can be a nuisance. Capacitance in audio systems can limit high-frequency response, decreasing the quality of music reproduction. As computers reach speeds in the GHz range—meaning basic operations occur a billion times a second—even tiny, unintentional RC time constants associated with the resistance of wires and the capacitance of nearby conductors must be eliminated.

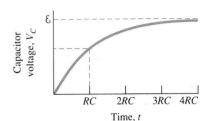

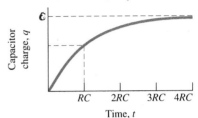

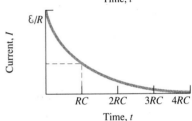

FIGURE 28-32 Time dependence of capacitor voltage, capacitor charge, and current in a charging RC circuit. In one time constant RC the capacitor voltage and charge rise to about 2/3 (actually $1 - 1/e$) of their final value, while the current drops to about 1/3 (actually $1/e$) of its initial value.

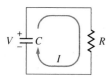

FIGURE 28-33 A discharging RC circuit.

The RC Circuit: Discharging

Suppose we connect a charged capacitor across a resistor, as shown in Fig. 28-33. If the capacitor voltage is initially V_0, then when the circuit is connected this voltage will drive a current $I_0 = V_0/R$ through the resistor. This current transfers charge from the positive to the negative capacitor plate, lowering the charge on the capacitor. Since capacitor charge and voltage are proportional, the capacitor voltage drops, too. So, therefore, does the current, and therefore the rate at which the capacitor discharges. We therefore expect both the voltage and current in this circuit to decay toward zero. In terms of energy, that happens because the energy stored in the capacitor's electric field is gradually dissipated as heat in the resistor.

The loop equation for Fig. 28-33 is particularly simple; going clockwise, we have

$$\frac{Q}{C} - IR = 0\,,$$

where the two terms are the voltage changes across the capacitor and resistor, respectively. Since we've indicated positive current in Fig. 28-33 in the direction that would *reduce* the capacitor charge Q, the rate of change dQ/dt and the current must have opposite signs: $I = -dQ/dt$. Differentiating our loop equation and substituting this expression for I gives

$$\frac{dI}{dt} = -\frac{I}{RC}\,.$$

This is Equation 28-4; the solution is therefore Equation 28-5, but with $I_0 = V_0/R$ instead of $\mathscr{E}/R$:

$$I = \frac{V_0}{R}e^{-t/RC}\,. \tag{28-7}$$

In this circuit the capacitor and resistor voltage are the same since the two are in parallel. Since the resistor voltage and current are proportional, the voltage across the capacitor and resistor is

$$V = V_0 e^{-t/RC}\,. \qquad \text{(RC circuit, discharging)} \tag{28-8}$$

Equations 28-7 and 28-8 show that the capacitor discharges with the same characteristic time constant RC that governs its charging.

12.7

Circuit Time Constant

| **EXAMPLE 28-8** | *A Camera Flash* |

In Chapter 26 we considered an electronic camera flash using a capacitor to store energy. A particular camera flashtube obtains its energy from a 150-μF capacitor and requires 170 V to fire. If the capacitor is charged by a 200-V source through a 30-kΩ resistor, how long must the photographer wait between flashes? What is the peak power drawn from the power source? Assume the capacitor is fully discharged during a flash.

Solution

The time between flashes is the time it takes the capacitor voltage to reach 170 V. To find this time, we solve Equa-

tion 28-6 for the exponential term that contains the time:

$$e^{-t/RC} = 1 - \frac{V_C}{\mathscr{E}}\,.$$

We then take the natural logarithm of both sides, recalling that $\ln e^x = x$, so

$$-\frac{t}{RC} = \ln\!\left(1 - \frac{V_C}{\mathscr{E}}\right)\,.$$

Solving for t and setting $V_C = 170$ V, $\mathscr{E} = 200$ V, $R = 30$ kΩ, and $C = 150\ \mu$F gives

$$t = -RC \ln\left(1 - \frac{V_C}{\mathcal{E}}\right)$$

$$= -(30 \times 10^3 \ \Omega)(150 \times 10^{-6} \ \text{F}) \ln\left(1 - \frac{170 \ \text{V}}{200 \ \text{V}}\right) = 8.5 \ \text{s} \ .$$

Problem 74 explores the question of power in this circuit, and shows that energy from the source cannot all end up in the capacitor.

EXERCISE If the flash lamp in Example 28-8 has an effective resistance of 10 Ω, how long does it take the capacitor voltage to drop to 100 V as it discharges through the lamp?

Answer: 0.80 ms

Some problems similar to Example 28-8: 47–49, 51

RC Circuits: Long- and Short-Term Behavior

It's not always necessary to solve exponential equations in analyzing *RC* circuits. If we're concerned only with times short compared with the time constant, it suffices to remember that the voltage across a capacitor cannot change instantaneously. And after many time constants have passed a capacitor has essentially reached its final voltage, and there will be no current flowing to it. These two conditions are sufficient to analyze circuits on short and long time scales.

EXAMPLE 28-9	*Long- and Short-Time Behavior of an RC Circuit*

In Fig. 28-34*a* the capacitor is initially uncharged. What is the current through R_1 the instant after the switch is closed? A long time after the switch has been closed?

Solution
The capacitor voltage cannot change instantaneously, so just after the switch is closed there can be no voltage across the capacitor and therefore none across R_2. Then the full battery voltage is across R_1, so the current in R_1 is $\mathcal{E}/R_1$. After a very long time the capacitor will be fully charged (to what voltage? —see the exercise below), and no current will flow into it. The capacitor then acts like an open circuit, and we simply have two resistors in series. The current in each is $\mathcal{E}/(R_1 + R_2)$.

How simple this example is! The uncharged capacitor has no voltage across it, so it acts instantaneously like a short circuit. The fully charged capacitor has no current into it, so it acts like an open circuit. To solve the problem we could simply re-draw the circuit, once with the capacitor replaced by a wire (Fig. 28-34*b*), the second time with the capacitor simply erased from the circuit diagram (Fig. 28-34*c*). Only if we wanted to know what was happening at intermediate times would we have to resort to the solution of an equation describing the circuit.

EXERCISE When the capacitor in Example 28-9 is fully charged, what will be the voltage across it?

Answer: $\mathcal{E}R_2/(R_1 + R_2)$

Some problems similar to Example 28-9: 55–57

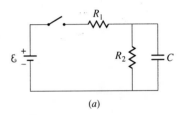

(a)

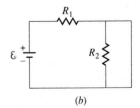

(b)

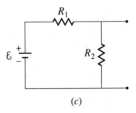

(c)

FIGURE 28-34 (*a*) A circuit with two resistors and a capacitor. (*b*) Just after the switch is closed the voltage across the capacitor is still zero, so the capacitor acts like a short circuit. (*c*) Long after the switch is closed the capacitor is fully charged. No more current flows into it, so it acts like an open circuit.

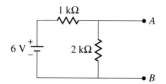

FIGURE 28-35 What's the current in the 2-kΩ resistor when a charged capacitor is connected between points A and B?

FIGURE 28-36 Defibrillation of a heart attack victim uses a current pulse of some 20 A, delivered over a few milliseconds. This high current shocks the heart out of ineffectual, chaotic muscle spasms called fibrillation. It may then restart with its normal rhythm.

Got It!

A capacitor is charged to 12 V and then connected between points A and B in Fig. 28-35, with its positive plate to A. What is the current through the 2-kΩ resistor (a) immediately after the capacitor is connected and (b) a long time (i.e., many time constants) after it's connected?

28-7 ELECTRICAL SAFETY

Whether you find yourself in a laboratory hooking up electronic equipment, or in a hospital connecting instrumentation to a patient, or on a job designing electrical devices, or simply at home plugging in appliances and tools, you should be concerned with electrical safety.

Everyone knows enough to be wary of "high voltage." People with a little more electrical sophistication are fond of saying "it isn't the voltage but the current that kills you." In fact, both points of view are partially correct. Current through the body is dangerous, but as with any resistor it takes voltage to drive that current.

Table 28-1 shows typical effects of electric currents introduced into the body through skin contact. A primary danger is disturbance of the biologically generated electrical signals that pace heartbeat; this is reflected in the lethal zone of 100 to 200 mA at which currents the heart is thrown into fibrillation—uncontrolled spasms of the cardiac muscle. With electrical signals applied internally to local regions of the body, much smaller currents can be lethal. Doctors performing cardiac catheterization, for example, must worry about currents at the microampere level.

Above 200 mA, complete cardiac arrest may occur, breathing may stop, and there may be severe burns both internally and at the points of skin contact. Sometimes such high currents are useful: when a heart is fibrillating, doctors or emergency technicians briefly apply a high enough current to stop the heart (Fig. 28-36). The heart often restarts, beating normally. The figures of Table 28-1 are rough averages, and vary widely from person to person as well as with duration of the shock and whether alternating or direct current is involved. In particular, very young children and people with heart conditions are at higher risk.

Under dry conditions, the typical human being has a resistance from one point to another on unbroken skin of about 10^5 Ω. What voltages are dangerous to such a person? At 10^5 Ω it takes

$$V = IR = (0.1 \text{ A})(10^5 \text{ Ω}) = 10,000 \text{ V}$$

to drive the fatal 100 mA. But a person who is wet or sweaty has a much lower resistance and may be electrocuted by 120-V household electricity. People have been electrocuted at voltages as low as 30 V, although such cases are rare.

It takes current to harm a person, but it takes voltage to drive that current. To be dangerous, an electric circuit must have high voltage *and* be capable of

TABLE 28-1 *Effects of Externally Applied Current on the Human Organism*

CURRENT RANGE	EFFECT
0.5–2 mA	Threshold of sensation
10–15 mA	Involuntary muscle contractions; can't let go
15–100 mA	Severe shock; muscle control lost; breathing difficult
100–200 mA	Fibrillation of heart; death within minutes
>200 mA	Cardiac arrest; breathing stops; severe burns

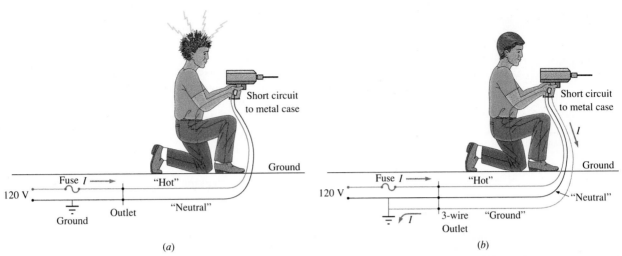

FIGURE 28-37 (*a*) A short circuit in an ungrounded tool could result in a lethal shock. (*b*) With a grounded tool, the short circuit causes a blown fuse or circuit breaker, thereby protecting the operator.

driving sufficient current. For example, a car battery can deliver 300 A, but it cannot electrocute you because its 12 volts will not drive much current through you (although you could get a bad burn, or be struck by vaporizing metal, if you accidentally short-circuit such a powerful battery). On the other hand the 20,000 V that runs your car's spark plugs will not electrocute you either, since the internal resistance of this high-voltage circuit is so high that it cannot deliver more than a few mA.

Because potential difference is a property of two points, receiving an electric shock requires that two parts of the body be in contact with conductors at different potentials. In typical 120-V wiring used throughout North America, one of the two wires is connected physically to the ground. This ground connection is to prevent the wiring from reaching arbitrarily high potentials with respect to the ground, as might otherwise happen in a thunderstorm or if a short circuit occurred in a power line. At the same time it means that an individual contacting the "hot" side of the circuit and any grounded conductor such as the ground, a water pipe, or a bathtub will receive a shock.

A potentially dangerous situation occurs when power tools, instruments, or appliances are used by an operator who is likely to be in contact with a grounded conductor. Examples include working outdoors with an electric drill, in a kitchen with an electric mixer, or in a laboratory with an oscilloscope. Suppose you're using a power tool that is plugged in through a regular two-wire cord. Normally exposed metal parts of the tool are not connected to either wire. Now suppose something goes wrong in the tool and a wire short-circuits to the metal case. If it happens to be the wire that's plugged into the grounded side of the power line there's no problem, but if it's the other wire the metal is suddenly 120 V above ground. If you're standing on the ground, or in a damp basement, or are leaning on the kitchen sink, you will receive a potentially lethal shock (Fig. 28-37*a*).

To avoid this danger many electrical devices have three-wire cords (Fig. 28-38). The third wire runs from exposed metal parts to a grounded wire in the outlet, and normally carries no current. If a short circuit occurs the third wire provides a very low resistance path to ground (Fig. 28-37*b*). A large current will flow and will blow the circuit breaker or fuse, shutting off the current. Held at ground potential by the ground wire, the operator of the device will be safe.

Because many older homes are not wired with grounded outlets, some manufacturers produce two-wire tools and other devices that are "double-insulated"

FIGURE 28-38 Plugs. (Left) grounded; (right) polarized.

FIGURE 28-39 A ground-fault interrupter protects against shock by shutting off the power when it senses small currents leaking to ground. It must then be reset manually by pushing the reset button.

to provide an extra margin of safety. Newer appliances are equipped with "polarized plugs," which can only be plugged in one way (Fig. 28-38), ensuring that exposed metal parts are most likely to end up at ground potential. Finally, electronic devices called ground-fault interrupters (Fig. 28-39) are used in kitchen, bathroom, basement, and other hazardous circuits in new homes. These devices sense a slight imbalance—5 mA or less—in current flowing in the two wires of a circuit, and shut off the circuit in less than a millisecond on the assumption that the excess current is leaking to ground—perhaps through a person. (Do ground-fault interrupters know about the node law?)

CHAPTER SYNOPSIS

Summary

1. A source of **electromotive force (emf)** is a device—like a battery—that converts some form of energy into the electrical energy associated with the buildup of positive and negative charge at its two terminals. An ideal emf maintains a constant potential difference between its terminals, but energy losses in a real emf result in terminal voltage that decreases as more current is drawn from the device.

2. Electric circuits may often be analyzed using series and parallel resistor combinations. Resistors in series add:

$$R_{\text{series}} = R_1 + R_2 + R_3 + \cdots,$$

while resistors in parallel add reciprocally:

$$\frac{1}{R_{\text{parallel}}} = \frac{1}{R_1} + \frac{1}{R_2} + \frac{1}{R_3} + \cdots.$$

3. More complicated circuits may be analyzed using **Kirchhoff's laws**. The **loop law** follows from conservation of energy and states that the sum of the voltage differences around any circuit loop is zero. The **node law** follows from conservation of charge and states that the sum of the currents at any circuit node is zero.

4. Measuring instruments should not alter the circuit they're measuring. An ideal **voltmeter** has infinite resistance, and should be connected in parallel with the component whose voltage is being measured. An ideal **ammeter** has zero resistance, and should be connected in series with the component whose current is being measured.

5. The voltage across a capacitor cannot change instantaneously. Quantities in a resistor-capacitor (RC) circuit change on a characteristic time scale given by the product RC. When an emf $\mathcal{E}$ charges a capacitor C through a resistor R, the capacitor voltage and circuit current vary with time according to

$$V_C = \mathcal{E}(1 - e^{-t/RC})$$

$$I = \frac{\mathcal{E}}{R} e^{-t/RC}.$$

For a discharging capacitor, both voltage and current decrease exponentially with the same time constant RC.

6. **Electrical safety** is a matter of avoiding currents high enough to cause biological damage. The danger of electric shock depends on the current at which such damage occurs, the resistance of the organism, and the voltage available to drive the current.

Terms You Should Understand

(Pairs are closely related terms whose distinction is important; number in parentheses is chapter section where term first appears.)

circuit, circuit element (28-1)
electromotive force (emf) (28-2)
ideal, real emfs (28-2, 28-3)
voltage divider (28-3)
internal resistance (28-3)
Kirchhoff's loop and node laws (28-4)
voltmeter, ammeter, ohmmeter (28-5)
RC circuit (28-6)
time constant (28-6)

Symbols You Should Recognize

electric circuit symbols (Fig. 28-1)
$\mathcal{E}$ (28-1)

Problems You Should Be Able to Solve

analyzing simple circuits with series and parallel resistors (28-3)
analyzing circuits with the loop and node laws (28-4)
determining the effects of nonideal measuring instruments (28-5)
analyzing charging and discharging RC circuits (28-6)
quickly determining short- and long-term behavior of RC circuits (28-6)
assessing electrical hazards (28-7)

Limitations to Keep in Mind

Real circuit elements deviate from their idealizations. Thus the voltage across a real battery may not be exactly its rated voltage, and voltage drops occur in real wires. Attention to circuit design will minimize these nonideal effects.

Electrical measuring instruments may affect the circuits they are measuring.

Currents may be far more dangerous than Table 28-1 implies if they are introduced beneath the skin.

QUESTIONS

1. In each of the circuits of Fig. 28-40, which, if any, of the resistors are in series? In parallel?

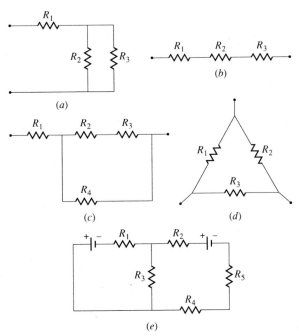

(a)

(b)

(c)

(d)

(e)

FIGURE 28-40 Question 1.

2. Are the electrical outlets in a home connected in series or parallel? How do you know?
3. In which of the circuits of Fig. 28-41 does the battery supply the same current? All the resistors have the same resistance.

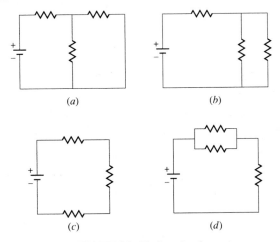

(a)

(b)

(c)

(d)

FIGURE 28-41 Question 3.

4. Can the voltage across a battery's terminals differ from the rated voltage of the battery? Explain.
5. Can the voltage across a battery's terminals be higher than the rated voltage of the battery? Explain.
6. In some cities, streetlights are wired in such a way that when one light burns out, they all go out. Are the lights in series or parallel?
7. If you know the battery voltage in Fig. 28-42, can you determine the voltage between points B and C without knowing the resistance R?

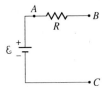

FIGURE 28-42 Questions 7, 16.

8. When the switch in Fig 28-43 is open, what is the voltage across the resistor? Across the switch?

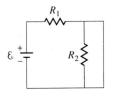

FIGURE 28-43 Question 8.

9. Two identical resistors in series dissipate equal power. How can this be, when electric charge loses energy in flowing through the first resistor?
10. What is the current through resistor R_2 in Fig. 28-44? Assume all the wires are ideal.

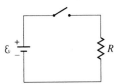

FIGURE 28-44 Question 10.

11. The resistors in Fig. 28-45 all have the same resistance. If an ideal voltmeter is connected between points A and B, what will it read?

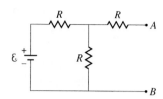

FIGURE 28-45 Question 11.

12. When a large electrical load such as a washing machine, oven, or oil burner comes on, lights throughout a house often dim. Why is this? *Hint:* Think about real wires.

13. If the node law were not obeyed at some node in an electric circuit, what would happen to the voltage at that node?

14. How would you connect a pair of equal resistors across an ideal battery in order to get the most power dissipation in the resistors?

15. You have a battery whose voltage and internal resistance are unknown. Using an ideal voltmeter and an ideal ammeter, how would you determine both these battery characteristics?

16. An ideal voltmeter is used to measure the voltages between points A and C and between B and C in the circuit of Fig. 28-42. How do the measurements compare?

17. You wish to measure the resistance R_2 in Fig. 28-46 with an ohmmeter. Can you do so while R_2 is in the circuit? Why or why not?

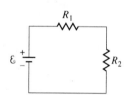

FIGURE 28-46 Question 17.

18. A student who is confused about voltage and current hooks a nearly ideal ammeter across a car battery. What happens?

19. A student who is confused about voltage and current tries to measure the voltage across a lighted light bulb by inserting a voltmeter in series with the bulb. What happens to the bulb? Explain.

20. Four identical light bulbs are connected to a battery as shown in Fig. 28-47. How does the brightness of each compare? Explain.

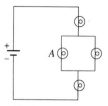

FIGURE 28-47 Questions 20, 21.

21. Suppose bulb A in Fig. 28-47 is unscrewed from its socket. How will the brightness of the three remaining bulbs change? How does the brightness of the three compare?

22. What does it mean for a capacitor to be "fully charged"?

23. Is the current into a charging capacitor in an RC circuit greatest when the capacitor voltage is greatest or when it is smallest?

24. If it takes forever to charge a capacitor fully, why is the RC time constant of any significance in describing the charging?

25. The two resistors in Fig. 28-48 have equal resistance. If the circuit has been connected for a long time, what is the voltage across the capacitor?

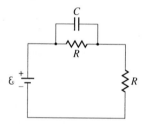

FIGURE 28-48 Question 25.

26. In one time constant, a charging capacitor reaches approximately $\frac{2}{3}$ of full charge. In one time constant, the voltage across a discharging capacitor falls to approximately $\frac{1}{3}$ of its original value. What is the origin of the approximate numerical factors $\frac{2}{3}$ and $\frac{1}{3}$ in these statements?

27. What's wrong with this news report: "A power-line worker was seriously injured when 4000 volts passed through his body"?

PROBLEMS

ActivPhysics can help with these problems:
Section 12, "DC Circuits."

Section 28-1 Circuits and Symbols

1. Sketch a circuit diagram for a circuit that includes a resistor R_1 connected to the positive terminal of a battery, a pair of parallel resistors R_2 and R_3 connected to the lower-voltage end of R_1, then returned to the battery's negative terminal, and a capacitor across R_2.

2. A circuit consists of two batteries, a resistor, and a capacitor, all in series. Sketch this circuit. Does the description allow any flexibility in how you draw the circuit?

3. Resistors R_1 and R_2 are connected in series, and this series combination is in parallel with R_3. This parallel combination is connected across a battery whose internal resistance is R_{int}. Draw a diagram representing this circuit.

Section 28-2 Electromotive Force

4. What is the emf of a battery that delivers 27 J of energy as it moves 3.0 C between its terminals?

5. A 1.5-V battery stores 4.5 kJ of energy. How long can it light a flashlight bulb that draws 0.60 A?

6. If you accidentally leave your car headlights (current drain 5 A) on for an hour, how much of the 12-V battery's chemical energy is used up?

7. A battery stores 50 W·h of chemical energy. If it uses up this energy moving 3.0×10^4 C through a circuit, what is its voltage?

Section 28-3 Simple Circuits: Series and Parallel Resistors

8. A 47-kΩ resistor and a 39-kΩ resistor are in parallel, and the pair is in series with a 22-kΩ resistor. What is the resistance of the combination?

9. What resistance should be placed in parallel with a 56-kΩ resistor to make an equivalent resistance of 45 kΩ?

10. In Fig. 28-49 all resistors have the same value, R. What will be the resistance measured (a) between A and B or (b) between A and C?

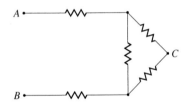

FIGURE 28-49 Problems 10, 11.

11. In Fig. 28-49, take all resistors to be 1.0 Ω. If a 6.0-V battery is connected between points A and B, what will be the current in the vertical resistor?

12. A defective starter motor in a car draws 300 A from the car's 12-V battery, dropping the battery terminal voltage to only 6 V. A good starter motor should draw only 100 A. What will the battery terminal voltage be with a good starter?

13. What is the internal resistance of the battery in the preceding problem?

14. Three 1.5-V batteries, with internal resistances of 0.01 Ω, 0.1 Ω, and 1 Ω, each have 1-Ω resistors connected across their terminals. To three significant figures, what is the voltage across each resistor?

15. When a 9-V battery is temporarily short-circuited, a 200-mA current flows. What is the internal resistance of the battery?

16. What possible resistance combinations can you form using three resistors whose values are 1.0 Ω, 2.0 Ω, and 3.0 Ω? (Use all three resistors.)

17. A partially discharged car battery can be modeled as a 9-V emf in series with an internal resistance of 0.08 Ω. Jumper cables are used to connect this battery to a fully charged battery, modeled as a 12-V emf in series with a 0.02-Ω internal resistance. How much current flows through the discharged battery?

18. You have a number of 50-Ω resistors, each capable of dissipating 0.50 W without overheating. How many resistors would you need, and how would you connect them, so as to make a 50-Ω combination that could be connected safely across a 12-V battery?

19. What is the equivalent resistance between A and B in each of the circuits shown in Fig. 28-50? *Hint*: In (c), think about symmetry and the current that would flow through R_2.

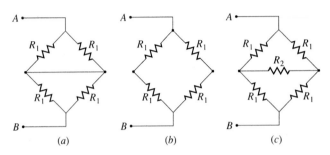

FIGURE 28-50 Problem 19.

20. A 6.0-V battery has an internal resistance of 2.5 Ω. If the battery is short circuited, what is the rate of energy dissipation in its internal resistance?

21. How many 100-W, 120-V light bulbs can be connected in parallel before they blow a 20-A circuit breaker?

22. What is the current through the 3-Ω resistor in the circuit of Fig. 28-51? *Hint*: This is trivial. Can you see why?

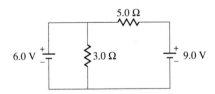

FIGURE 28-51 Problem 22.

23. Take $\mathscr{E} = 12$ V and $R_1 = 270$ Ω in the voltage divider of Fig. 28-5. (a) What should be the value of R_2 in order that 4.5 V appear across R_2? (b) What will be the power dissipation in R_2?

24. A voltage divider consists of two 1.0-kΩ resistors connected in series across a 160-V emf. If a 10-kΩ resistor is connected across one of the 1.0-kΩ resistors, what will be the voltage across it?

25. In the circuit of Fig. 28-52, R_1 is a variable resistor, and the other two resistors have equal resistances R. (a) Find an expression for the voltage across R_1, and (b) sketch a graph of this quantity as a function of R_1 as R_1 varies from 0 to $10R$. (c) What is the limiting value as $R_1 \to \infty$?

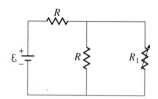

FIGURE 28-52 Problem 25.

26. In the circuit of Fig. 28-53 find (a) the current supplied by the battery and (b) the current through the 6-Ω resistor.

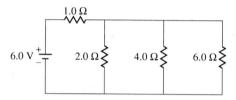

FIGURE 28-53 Problems 26, 27.

27. In the circuit of Fig. 28-53, how much power is being dissipated in the 4-Ω resistor?

28. A 50-Ω resistor is connected across a battery, and a 26-mA current flows. When the 50-Ω resistor is replaced with a 22-Ω resistor, a 43-mA current flows. What are the battery's voltage and internal resistance?

Section 28-4 Kirchhoff's Laws and Multiloop Circuits

29. In the circuit of Fig. 28-54 it makes no difference whether the switch is open or closed. What is $\mathcal{E}_3$ in terms of the other quantities shown?

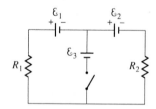

FIGURE 28-54 Problem 29.

30. What is the current through the ammeter in Fig. 28-55?

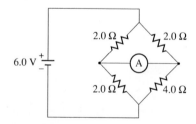

FIGURE 28-55 Problem 30.

31. In Fig. 28-56, what is the equivalent resistance measured between points A and B?

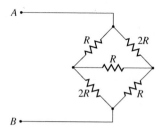

FIGURE 28-56 Problem 31.

32. Find all three currents in the circuit of Fig. 28-18, but now with $\mathcal{E}_2 = 1.0$ V.

33. Find all three currents in the circuit of Fig. 28-18 with the values given, but with battery $\mathcal{E}_2$ reversed.

34. In Fig. 28-57, take $\mathcal{E}_1 = 6.0$ V, $\mathcal{E}_2 = 1.5$ V, $\mathcal{E}_3 = 4.5$ V, $R_1 = 270$ Ω, $R_2 = 150$ Ω, $R_3 = 560$ Ω, and $R_4 = 820$ Ω. Find the current in R_3, and give its direction.

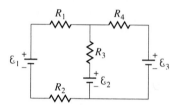

FIGURE 28-57 Problems 34, 35, 36.

35. With all the values except $\mathcal{E}_2$ in Fig. 28-57 as given in the preceding problem, find the condition on $\mathcal{E}_2$ that will make the current in R_3 flow upward.

36. Suppose that all resistors in Fig. 28-57 have the same value R and that $\mathcal{E}_1 = \mathcal{E}_3 = \mathcal{E}$ and $\mathcal{E}_2 = 2\mathcal{E}$. Find expressions for the currents in the four resistors, and give their directions.

37. Figure 28-58 shows a portion of a circuit used to model the electrical behavior of long, cylindrical biological cells such as muscle cells or the axons of neurons. Find the current through the emf $\mathcal{E}_3$, given that all resistors have the same value $R = 1.5$ MΩ and that $\mathcal{E}_1 = 75$ mV, $\mathcal{E}_2 = 45$ mV, and $\mathcal{E}_3 = 20$ mV. Be sure to specify the direction of the current.

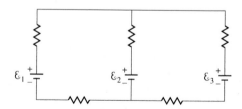

FIGURE 28-58 Problems 37, 38.

38. An electrochemical impulse traveling along the cell modeled in Fig. 28-58 changes the value of emf $\mathcal{E}_3$ so that now it supplies an upward current of 40 nA. Assuming the rest of the circuit remains as described in the preceding problem, what is the new value of $\mathcal{E}_3$?

Section 28-5 Electrical Measuring Instruments

39. A voltmeter with 200-kΩ resistance is used to measure the voltage across the 10-kΩ resistor in Fig. 28-59. By what percentage is the measurement in error because of the finite meter resistance?

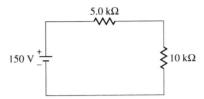

FIGURE 28-59 Problems 39, 40.

40. An ammeter with 100-Ω resistance is inserted in the circuit of Fig. 28-59. By what percentage is the measurement in error because of the nonzero meter resistance?
41. A neophyte mechanic foolishly connects an ammeter with 0.1-Ω resistance directly across a 12-V car battery whose internal resistance is 0.01 Ω. What is the power dissipation in the meter? No wonder it gets destroyed!
42. The voltage across the 30-kΩ resistor in Fig. 28-60 is measured with (a) a 50-kΩ voltmeter, (b) a 250-kΩ voltmeter, and (c) a digital meter with 10-MΩ resistance. To two significant figures, what does each read?

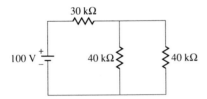

FIGURE 28-60 Problem 42.

43. In Fig. 28-61 what are the meter readings when (a) an ideal voltmeter or (b) an ideal ammeter is connected between points A and B?

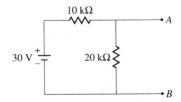

FIGURE 28-61 Problem 43.

44. A resistor draws 1.00 A from an ideal 12.0-V battery. (a) If an ammeter with 0.10-Ω resistance is inserted in the circuit, what will it read? (b) If this current is used to calculate the resistance, how will the calculated value compare with the actual value?

Section 28-6 Circuits with Capacitors

45. Show that the quantity RC has the units of time (seconds).

46. If capacitance is given in μF, what will be the units of the RC time constant when resistance is given in (a) Ω, (b) kΩ, (c) MΩ? Your answers eliminate the need for tedious power-of-10 conversions.
47. Show that a capacitor is charged to approximately 99% of the applied voltage in five time constants.
48. An uncharged 10-μF capacitor and a 470-kΩ resistor are connected in series, and 250 V applied across the combination. How long does it take the capacitor voltage to reach 200 V?
49. Figure 28-62 shows the voltage across a capacitor that is charging through a 4700-Ω resistor in the circuit of Fig. 28-29. Use the graph to determine (a) the battery voltage, (b) the time constant, and (c) the capacitance.

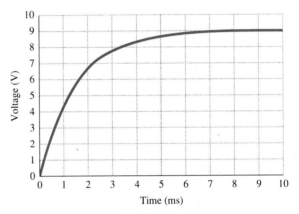

FIGURE 28-62 Problem 49.

50. The voltage across a charging capacitor in an RC circuit rises to $1 - 1/e$ of the battery voltage in 5.0 ms. (a) How long will it take to reach $1 - 1/e^3$ of the battery voltage? (b) If the capacitor is charging through a 22-kΩ resistor, what is its capacitance?
51. A 1.0-μF capacitor is charged to 10.0 V. It is then connected across a 500-kΩ resistor. How long does it take (a) for the capacitor voltage to reach 5.0 V and (b) for the energy stored in the capacitor to decrease to half its initial value?
52. A capacitor used to provide steady voltages in the power supply of a stereo amplifier charges rapidly to 35 V every 1/60 of a second. It must then hold that voltage to within 1.0 V for the next 1/60 s while it discharges through the amplifier circuit. If the circuit draws 1.2 A from the 35-V supply (a) what is its effective resistance and (b) what value of capacitance is needed?
53. A capacitor is charged until it holds 5.0 J of energy. It is then connected across a 10-kΩ resistor. In 8.6 ms, the resistor dissipates 2.0 J. What is the capacitance?
54. A 2.0-μF capacitor is charged to 150 V. It is then connected to an uncharged 1.0-μF capacitor through a 2.2-kΩ resistor, by closing switch S in Fig. 28-63. Find the total energy dissipated in the resistor as the circuit comes to equilibrium. *Hint:* Think about charge conservation.
55. For the circuit of Example 28-9, take $\mathscr{E} = 100$ V, $R_1 = 4.0$ kΩ, and $R_2 = 6.0$ kΩ, and assume the capacitor is

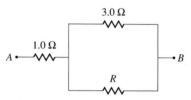

FIGURE 28-63 Problem 54.

initially uncharged. What are the currents in both resistors and the voltage across the capacitor (a) just after the switch is closed and (b) a long time after the switch is closed? Long after the switch is closed it is again opened. What are I_1, I_2, and V_C (c) just after this switch opening and (d) a long time later?

56. In the circuit of Fig. 28-64 the switch is initially open and both capacitors initially uncharged. All resistors have the same value R. Find expressions for the current in R_2 (a) just after the switch is closed and (b) a long time after the switch is closed. (c) Describe qualitatively how you expect the current in R_3 to behave after the switch is closed.

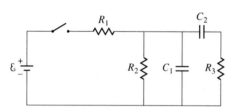

FIGURE 28-64 Problem 56.

57. In the circuit of Fig. 28-65 the switch is initially open and the capacitor is uncharged. Find expressions for the current I supplied by the battery (a) just after the switch is closed and (b) a long time after the switch is closed.

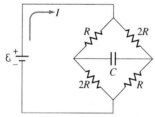

FIGURE 28-65 Problem 57.

58. Obtain an expression for the rate (dV/dt) at which the voltage across a charging capacitor increases. Evaluate your result at time $t = 0$, and show that if the capacitor continued charging steadily at this rate it would be fully charged in exactly one time constant.

Paired Problems

(Both problems in a pair involve the same principles and techniques. If you can get the first problem, you should be able to solve the second one.)

59. A 3.3-kΩ resistor and a 4.7-kΩ resistor are connected in parallel, and the pair is in series with a 1.5-kΩ resistor. What is the resistance of the combination?

60. Find the value of R in Fig. 28-66 that will make the resistance between points A and B equal to R.

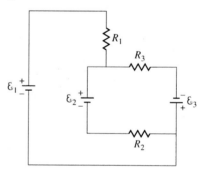

FIGURE 28-66 Problem 60.

61. A battery's voltage is measured with a voltmeter whose resistance is 1000 Ω; the result is 4.36 V. When the measurement is repeated with a 1500-Ω meter the result is 4.41 V. What are (a) the battery voltage and (b) its internal resistance?

62. An ammeter with a resistance of 1.4 Ω is connected momentarily across a battery (not the way to treat an ammeter!) and it reads 9.78 A. When the measurement is repeated with a meter whose resistance is 2.1 Ω the reading is 7.46 A. What are (a) the battery voltage and (b) its internal resistance?

63. In Fig. 28-67, take $\mathscr{E}_1 = 12$ V, $\mathscr{E}_2 = 6.0$ V, $\mathscr{E}_3 = 3.0$ V, $R_1 = 1.0$ Ω, $R_2 = 2.0$ Ω, and $R_3 = 4.0$ Ω. Find the current in R_2 and give its direction.

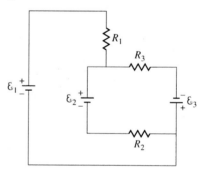

FIGURE 28-67 Problems 63, 64.

64. (a) With all values except $\mathscr{E}_2$ as given in the preceding problem, find $\mathscr{E}_2$ such that there is no current in this battery. (b) What are the currents in R_1 and R_2 under these conditions?

65. In Fig. 28-68 what are the meter readings when (a) an ideal voltmeter or (b) an ideal ammeter is connected between points A and B?

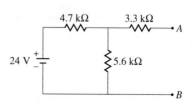

FIGURE 28-68 Problems 65, 66.

66. In Fig. 28-68 what are the meter readings when (a) a voltmeter with 50-kΩ resistance or (b) an ammeter with 150-Ω resistance is connected between points A and B?

67. An initially uncharged capacitor in an RC circuit reaches 75% of its full charge in 22.0 ms. What is the time constant?

68. Find the resistance needed in an RC circuit to bring a 20-μF capacitor from zero charge to 45% of its full charge in 140 ms.

Supplementary Problems

69. Suppose the currents into and out of a circuit node differed by 1 μA. If the node consists of a small metal sphere with diameter 1 mm, how long would it take for the electric field around the node to reach the breakdown field in air (3 MV/m)?

70. A problem on dairy farms is "stray voltage," caused by corroded wiring, poor wiring practices, or ground currents associated with nearby power lines. These conditions can result in several volts of potential difference between metal objects such as watering bowls, feed troughs, or milking equipment, and the ground. Cows feel slight shocks that make them nervous, resulting in reduced milk output. As a result, farmers can face serious financial losses. Figure 28-69 shows a circuit model for a stray voltage situation; the 1.5-kΩ resistor represents the resistance of corroded connections and poor wiring; you can assume the ground has negligible resistance. (a) The resistance from a cow's mouth to hoof is approximately 350Ω. How much current will flow through the cow in the situation shown? (It takes only about 1 mA to affect milk production.) In an effort to diagnose the problem, the farmer moves the cow aside and connects a multimeter between the watering bowl and ground. What will it read if it's set to measure (b) voltage and (c) current?

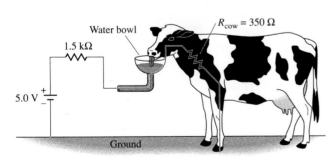

FIGURE 28-69 Stray voltage can bankrupt a dairy farm. (Problem 70)

71. In Fig. 28-70, what is the current in the 4-Ω resistor when each of the following circuit elements is connected between points A and B: (a) an ideal ammeter; (b) an ideal voltmeter; (c) another 4.0-Ω resistor; (d) an uncharged capacitor, right after it's connected; (e) long after the capacitor of part (d) is connected; (f) an ideal 12-V battery, with its positive terminal at A; (g) a capacitor initially charged to 12 V, right after

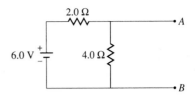

FIGURE 28-70 Problem 71.

it's connected with its positive plate at A; (h) long after the capacitor in part (g) is connected?

72. A resistance R is connected across a battery with internal resistance R_{int}. Show that the maximum power dissipation in R occurs when $R = R_{int}$. *Note:* This is not the way to treat a battery! But it is the basis for matching loads in amplifiers and other devices; for example, a stereo amplifier designed to drive 8-Ω speakers has internal resistance close to 8 Ω.

73. A parallel-plate capacitor is insulated with a material of dielectric constant κ and resistivity ρ. Since the resistivity is finite, the capacitor "leaks" charge and can be modeled as an ideal capacitor in parallel with a resistor. (a) Show that the time constant of the capacitor is independent of its dimensions (provided the spacing is small enough that the usual parallel-plate approximation applies) and is given by $\varepsilon_0 \kappa \rho$. (b) If the insulating material is polystyrene ($\kappa = 2.6$, $\rho = 10^{16}$ $\Omega \cdot$m), how long will it take for the stored energy in the capacitor to decrease by a factor of 2?

74. Of the total energy drawn from a battery in charging an RC circuit, show that only half ends up as stored energy in the capacitor. *Hint:* What happens to the rest of it? You will need to integrate.

75. Write the loop and node laws for the circuit of Fig. 28-71, and show that the time constant for this circuit is $R_1 R_2 C/(R_1 + R_2)$.

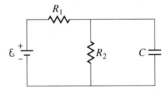

FIGURE 28-71 Problem 75.

76. The circuit in Fig. 28-72 extends forever to the right, and all the resistors have the same value R. Show that the equivalent resistance measured across the two terminals at left is $\frac{1}{2}R(1 + \sqrt{5})$. *Hint:* You don't need to sum an infinite series.

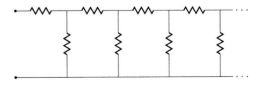

FIGURE 28-72 Problem 76.

29 The Magnetic Field

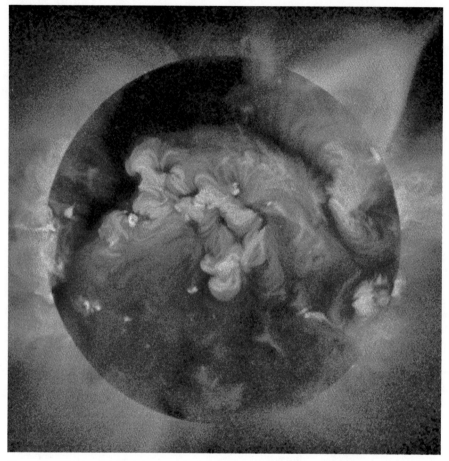

Magnetic fields shape delicate loops and other structures in the Sun's atmosphere, imaged here in X rays by the Japanese satellite Yohkoh.

People are fascinated with magnets. Magnetism—the seemingly mysterious force you feel when you try to push two magnets together in a way they don't want to go—is always intriguing. Some uses of magnets, like holding notes on refrigerators, are mundane. But others—holding gas at a temperature of one hundred million K in a nuclear fusion reactor, or converting electrical into mechanical energy in the motors of a railroad locomotive—are more impressive. And magnetism, like electricity, is at the heart of many natural phenomena and technological devices. Video and audio cassette recorders, electric motors, TV picture tubes, computer disks, and electric power plants would be impossible without magnetism.

Earth's magnetism helps us find our way around, provides historical evidence for the evolution of our planet, and protects us from harmful radiation. Birds, sea turtles, and some bacteria use Earth's magnetism for navigation. Without magnetism we would not even see, for light itself originates in an interaction between magnetism and electricity. As with electricity, we often do not recognize the magnetic character of everyday phenomena.

In this chapter we introduce magnetism, and will find immediately that it's intimately connected with electricity. In subsequent chapters we explore further the deep relation between electricity and magnetism, and will eventually come to see electricity and magnetism as two inseparable aspects of the same underlying phenomenon.

29-1 WHAT IS MAGNETISM?

You know about magnetism because you've played with magnets or used them in everyday tasks such as sticking notes to your refrigerator. You know that magnets exert forces on each other and on certain materials, such as iron and steel. It's convenient to describe that interaction in terms of a **magnetic field** (symbol **B**). We say that one magnet produces a magnetic field, and that a second magnet responds to the field in its immediate vicinity. That way we avoid the awkward "action at a distance" picture, in which one magnet somehow reaches out across empty space to pull on another. We can picture a magnetic field using field lines, just as we did for electric fields, and can trace out magnetic field lines using small iron filings that align themselves with the field (Fig. 29-1).

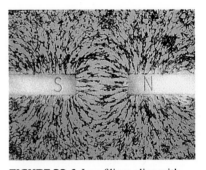

FIGURE 29-1 Iron filings align with the magnetic field, tracing out the field from a pair of bar magnets. The field is strongest near the magnetic poles. We'll see in the next chapter why iron is a special magnetic material.

You may think we're now going to give rules for finding the magnetic field produced by a given magnet, and for the force a magnet experiences in a magnetic field. But we're not. That's because the magnetism you're familiar with—involving magnets and their interaction with specific materials such as iron—is not particularly fundamental. Rather, the magnetism that's familiar to you is a specialized and limited manifestation of a more fundamental and universal phenomenon. Here we'll go straight to the basics of magnetism, and later (in the next chapter) will come back to understand how the magnets you're familiar with fit into the larger picture.

In Chapters 23–28 we studied electrical phenomena, all of which ultimately involve electric charge. We saw how a charge produces an electric field, and how other charges respond to that field. We're now dealing with the magnetic field, so you might expect that we're about to introduce magnetic charge and tell how it gives rise to the magnetic field. But again, no. The fact is that no one has ever found a magnetic charge, an entity that would produce a radially outward magnetic field like the electric field of a point charge. Some theories of elementary particles and the origin of the universe suggest that such magnetic charges—called **magnetic monopoles**—should exist. But they've never been observed, and even if they exist, they play no role in the magnetic phenomena with which we're familiar. We'll have more to say about magnetic monopoles in the next chapter.

So if it's not about magnets or magnetic charge, what *is* magnetism about? Simple: it's about *electric* charge—the same electric charge we've been dealing with since Chapter 23. But whereas the phenomena of electricity involve electric charge, period,

> ▌ **the phenomena of magnetism involve *moving* electric charge.**

In particular, *moving* electric charge is the source of magnetic fields, and *moving* electric charges experience forces from magnetic fields. In this chapter we'll assume we have a magnetic field and will explore the magnetic force on moving electric charges that results from that field. In the next chapter we'll see just how moving electric charges give rise to magnetic fields. That will lead us to understand technological applications such as electromagnets, the magnetic fields of Earth and other astrophysical bodies, and how the familiar magnetism of materials such as iron arises ultimately from the motions of the electrons in those materials.

29-2 THE MAGNETIC FORCE ON A MOVING CHARGE

In Chapter 23 we defined the electric field **E** through the relation $\mathbf{F}_E = q\mathbf{E}$, where $\mathbf{F}_E$ is the electric force on a charge q. We're now going to develop the analogous relation between a *moving* charge q and the force $\mathbf{F}_B$ it experiences in a magnetic field **B**.

Consider a region with no electric field, but in which a magnetic field is present. You could verify the presence of the magnetic field and determine its direction with a compass, which itself is just a small magnet that's free to pivot into alignment with the magnetic field. More fundamentally, you can take our description of the force experienced by a moving charge as defining what it means for there to be a magnetic field present.

Now let's put a point charge q in the magnetic field. If the charge is stationary, we find that it experiences no magnetic force. But suppose the charge is moving. We won't worry about how it got moving—except that, as we'll soon see, magnetic force can't be responsible. Experiment shows that the moving charge experiences a magnetic force such that

1. The magnetic force is always at right angles both to the velocity **v** of the charge and to the magnetic field **B** (Fig. 29-2).
2. The strength of the magnetic force is proportional to the product of the charge q, its speed v, and the magnetic field strength B.
3. The force is greatest if the charged particle is moving at right angles to the magnetic field **B** and is zero if the charge velocity **v** is parallel or antiparallel to the field. In general, the magnetic force is proportional to the sine of the angle between the vectors **v** and **B** (see Fig. 29-2).

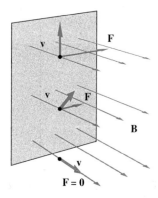

FIGURE 29-2 The magnetic force on a charged particle is perpendicular to the particle's velocity **v** and to the magnetic field **B**. The magnitude of the force depends on the angle between **v** and **B**, and is greatest when **v** and **B** are perpendicular (top). When **v** and **B** are parallel there is no magnetic force (bottom).

Putting these facts together allows us to write the magnetic force compactly in terms of the vector cross product introduced in Chapter 13:

$$\mathbf{F}_B = q\mathbf{v} \times \mathbf{B}, \quad \text{(magnetic force)} \tag{29-1a}$$

where $\mathbf{F}_B$ is the magnetic force on a particle of charge q moving with velocity **v** at a point where the magnetic field is **B**. Recall from Chapter 13 that the cross product $\mathbf{v} \times \mathbf{B}$ is a vector of magnitude $vB\sin\theta$, where θ is the angle between

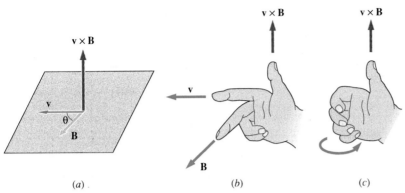

FIGURE 29-3 Ways to apply the right-hand rule. (*a*) Two vectors **v** and **B** and their cross product. The two vectors define a plane, and the cross product is always perpendicular to that plane. (*b*)–(*c*) All the right-hand rule does is distinguish between the two possible directions perpendicular to the plane. In (*b*), the fingers of the right hand point in the directions of the vectors **v** and **B**, and the cross product **v** × **B** in the direction of the thumb; in (*c*) the curved arrow describes a rotation that would take the vector **v** onto the vector **B**.

v and **B**. Thus the magnetic force has magnitude

$$F = qvB\sin\theta. \tag{29-1b}$$

The direction of **v** × **B** is perpendicular to both **v** and **B**, with the choice of the two possible perpendicular directions being made by the right-hand rule (Fig. 29-3). Because the charge q also enters Equation 29-1, the direction of the magnetic force is that of **v** × **B** for a positive charge but opposite **v** × **B** for a negative charge (Fig. 29-4).

We can regard Equation 29-1 as the definition of the magnetic field. If we put a particle of charge q moving with velocity **v** in a region free of other influences (i.e., electric and gravitational fields), then the presence of a force **F** on the particle shows that there is a magnetic field **B** implied by Equation 29-1a. Equations 29-1 show that the SI units of magnetic field are N·s/C·m, a unit given the name **tesla** (T) after the Serbian-American inventor Nikola Tesla (1865–1943). One tesla is a strong magnetic field, and a smaller unit called the gauss (G), equal to 10^{-4} T, is often used. Earth's magnetic field, for example, is a little under 1 G, while the field at the poles of a toy magnet may be 100 G. Strong laboratory magnets (Fig. 29-5) produce fields ranging from several T to

FIGURE 29-5 This superconducting electromagnet is used to steer high-energy beams of heavy atomic nuclei at the Laboratory of High Energies in Dubna, Russia. The Dubna laboratory is one of the world's leading facilities for the production and study of heavy nuclei.

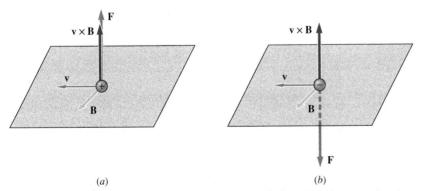

FIGURE 29-4 (*a*) When the charge is positive, the magnetic force is in the same direction as the cross product **v** × **B**. (*b*) When the charge is negative, the force q**v** × **B** is opposite **v** × **B**.

nearly 40 T, while magnetars—incredibly dense, rapidly rotating collapsed stars first identified in 1998—have fields up to 10^{11} T.

Got It!

Figure 29-6 shows a proton in a magnetic field. For which of the three possible proton velocities shown will the magnetic force be greatest? What will be the direction of the magnetic force in each case?

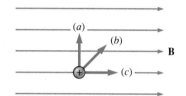

FIGURE 29-6 For which velocity is the magnetic force greatest? (The speed is the same in all three cases.)

EXAMPLE 29-1	*Steering Protons*

A magnetic field of 0.10 T is used to steer charged-particle beams in a nuclear physics experiment. The field points vertically upward. Three protons enter the field region, two moving horizontally and one vertically as shown in Fig. 29-7. All three are moving at 2.0×10^6 m/s. What is the magnetic force on each?

Solution
Proton 2 is moving parallel to the field. For it, $\mathbf{v} \times \mathbf{B} = \mathbf{0}$ and it experiences no magnetic force. Protons 1 and 3 are moving at right angles to the field, so $\sin \theta = 1$ and Equation 29-1b gives

$$F = qvB = (1.6 \times 10^{-19}\ \text{C})(2.0 \times 10^6\ \text{m/s})(0.10\ \text{T})$$

$$= 3.2 \times 10^{-14}\ \text{N}.$$

Since the protons carry positive charge, the direction of the force is that of the product $\mathbf{v} \times \mathbf{B}$. For proton 1, moving to the right, $\mathbf{v} \times \mathbf{B}$ is out of the page. For proton 3, moving to the left, the force is into the page. This example shows that the magnetic field alone does not determine the magnetic force. Identical particles in the same field experience different forces if their velocities are different. Had the particles been electrons the forces would have been in the opposite directions. (Why?)

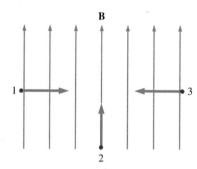

FIGURE 29-7 What is the magnetic force on each proton? (Example 29-1)

EXERCISE A 1.3-T magnetic field points in the x direction. A particle carrying 1.0 μC is moving at 20 m/s in the x-y plane and experiences a magnetic force of 1.4×10^{-5} N. What angle does the particle's velocity make with the x axis?

Answer: 33°

Some problems similar to Example 29-1: 1–11

Although electricity and magnetism are related, the electric field and the magnetic field are distinct. In particular, both may be present simultaneously. In that case, a charged particle experiences both the magnetic force $\mathbf{F}_B$ of Equation 29-1 and also the electric force $q\mathbf{E}$, for a net **electromagnetic force** given by

$$\mathbf{F} = q\mathbf{E} + q\mathbf{v} \times \mathbf{B}. \qquad \text{(electromagnetic force)} \qquad (29\text{-}2)$$

EXAMPLE 29-2	*A Velocity Selector*

A wide range of applications, from manufacturing computer chips to cancer treatment, require charged-particle beams with precise velocities. In other cases—like analyzing charged-particle populations in interplanetary space—scientists need to classify particles by their speeds. Both tasks can be accomplished by a **velocity selector**, a device that uses electric and magnetic fields together to pass only particles with a specific velocity.

Figure 29-8 shows the perpendicular electric and magnetic fields used in a velocity selector; the fields have magnitudes E and B, respectively. A charged particle enters the field region, moving perpendicular to both fields, as shown. What speed must it have if it's to pass through the region undeflected?

Solution

The net force on a particle must be zero if it is to be undeflected. Consider a positively charged particle heading into the page in Fig. 29-8. The electric field points to the right, so the electric force $q\mathbf{E}$ is to the right. Applying the right-hand rule with the velocity vector $\mathbf{v}$ into the page and the magnetic field $\mathbf{B}$ downward gives a magnetic force to the left; since v and B are at right angles, the magnitude of the magnetic force is qvB. So the electric and magnetic forces are in opposite directions; for them to cancel their magnitudes must be equal:

$$qE = qvB,$$

or

$$v = \frac{E}{B}.$$

Particles with any other velocity will be deflected by a nonzero net force, so only those particles emerging undeflected have the precise speed $v = E/B$. Note that this selected speed is independent of the charge—and even of its sign, since the directions of both forces would reverse for a negative charge.

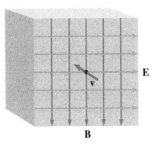

FIGURE 29-8 Crossed electric and magnetic fields give rise to oppositely directed forces on charged particles moving perpendicular to the fields. The magnetic force depends on the particle speed, but the electric force does not; therefore, only those particles with just the right speed can traverse the field region undeflected.

The velocity selector makes use of an important difference between the electric and magnetic forces: the electric force does not depend on a charged particle's velocity, while the magnetic force does. That's what makes possible the velocity selector's cancellation of the two forces at only one specific velocity. You can explore the velocity selector further with ActivPhysics Activity 13.8.

EXERCISE You have a magnet that produces a 0.25-T field. What strength electric field should you apply to make a velocity selector that passes 2.8×10^5 m/s particles undeflected?

Answer: 70 kV/m

Some problems similar to Example 29-2: 12–14

13.8
Velocity Selector

29-3 THE MOTION OF CHARGED PARTICLES IN MAGNETIC FIELDS

Like any force, the magnetic force deflects a particle from the straight-line path that Newton's first law says it would otherwise follow (Fig. 29-9). Use of magnetic forces to "steer" charged particles is the basis of many practical devices, from TV tubes to giant particle accelerators. Magnetic forces shape the trajectories of charged particles in a range of natural situations, especially in astrophysics.

FIGURE 29-9 (*a*) In the absence of a magnetic field, an electron beam moves in a straight line. (*b*) A magnetic field causes the beam to deflect. If the electrons are moving upward in the photo, which way is the field pointing?

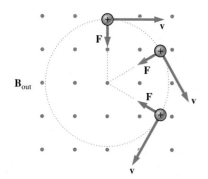

FIGURE 29-10 A positively charged particle moving at right angles to a uniform magnetic field describes a circular path. Note the convention that dots represent magnetic field lines emerging from the page; we designate this field by $\mathbf{B}_{out}$. Crosses, in contrast, would represent field lines going into the page. You can think of the dots as the tips of arrows and crosses as the feathers at the tails.

Unlike most other forces, the magnetic force is necessarily at right angles to the particle velocity. That means force and particle displacement are perpendicular. Since work is the dot product of force with displacement (Equation 7-5; $W = \mathbf{F} \cdot \Delta\mathbf{r}$), and the dot product of perpendicular vectors is zero, we can conclude that

❙ The magnetic force does no work on a charged particle.

Both the kinetic energy and thus the speed of a charged particle subject only to a magnetic force are therefore constant. The magnetic force changes only the direction of the particle's velocity, not its magnitude. What sort of motion results from the magnetic force? Suppose a particle with positive charge q is moving at right angles to a uniform magnetic field $\mathbf{B}$, as shown in Fig. 29-10. At the instant the particle's velocity is to the right, the outward-pointing magnetic field gives a force $q\mathbf{v} \times \mathbf{B}$ that is downward. Since this force is at right angles to the velocity, it changes the direction but not the magnitude of the velocity. The magnetic force on the particle with its new velocity is still perpendicular to the velocity, and since the magnitude of the velocity is unchanged, so is the magnitude of the force. What we've just described—a force of constant magnitude always at right angles to a particle's velocity—is the prescription for uniform circular motion. Thus, a charged particle moving in a plane perpendicular to a uniform magnetic field describes a circular path. The magnetic force acts exactly like the tension in a string when you tie a mass to the string and whirl it around in a circle. The tension is perpendicular to the motion and changes its direction but not its speed.

How big is the circle, and how long does it take to get around? We can answer these questions like we do any questions about the effects of forces—namely, by using Newton's second law. In its circular path, the charged particle undergoes an acceleration v^2/r, directed toward the center of the circle. What causes this acceleration? The magnetic force! With the field and velocity at right angles, the magnitude of the magnetic force is just

$$F = qvB,$$

and the force points toward the center of the circle. Writing Newton's law $\mathbf{F} = m\mathbf{a}$ then gives

$$qvB = m\frac{v^2}{r},$$

so
$$r = \frac{mv}{qB}. \tag{29-3}$$

This result makes sense: the larger the particle's momentum mv, the harder it is for the magnetic force to bend it out of a straight line, so the larger the radius of the orbit. On the other hand, if we make the field or charge larger, then the magnetic force increases, giving a tighter orbit.

This variation of orbital radius is used in the mass spectrometer, a device that sorts ionized atoms and molecules according to their charge-to-mass ratio. Problem 27 and ActivPhysics Activity 13.7 show how the mass spectrometer works. Another practical application is the television picture tube, described in the example below.

13.7
Mass Spectrometer

Got It!

A uniform magnetic field points out of this page. Will an electron circle clockwise or counterclockwise as viewed from above the page?

| **EXAMPLE 29-3** | *A TV Picture Tube* |

In a TV picture tube, deflection of the electron beam that "paints" the TV picture is accomplished using magnetic fields. The geometry of a certain tube requires that the electron beam be bent in a circular arc with a minimum radius of 4.5 cm (Fig. 29-11). If the electrons are accelerated from rest through a 25-kV potential difference before they enter the magnetic field region, what is the magnetic field strength required? In what direction should the field point to accomplish the deflection shown in Fig. 29-11? Assume that the field is uniform over the deflecting region and zero elsewhere.

Solution

Solving Equation 29-3 for the magnetic field strength B gives

$$B = \frac{mv}{er},$$

with e the elementary charge. "Falling" through a potential difference $V = 25$ kV, the electron of charge e acquires a kinetic energy $\frac{1}{2}mv^2 = Ve$, so its speed is

$$v = \sqrt{\frac{2Ve}{m}}.$$

Our expression for the field then becomes

$$B = \frac{m}{er}\sqrt{\frac{2Ve}{m}} = \frac{1}{r}\sqrt{\frac{2mV}{e}}$$

$$= \frac{1}{0.045 \text{ m}}\left(\frac{(2)(9.1\times10^{-31} \text{ kg})(25\times10^3 \text{ V})}{1.6\times10^{-19} \text{ C}}\right)^{1/2}$$

$$= 0.012 \text{ T}.$$

To achieve an initially downward deflection, the force $q\mathbf{v} \times \mathbf{B}$ must be initially downward. But the electron charge is negative, so $\mathbf{v} \times \mathbf{B}$ must be upward. Application of the right-hand rule to the rightward-moving electrons shows that the magnetic field $\mathbf{B}$ must be into the page in Fig. 29-11.

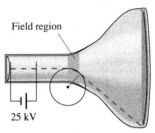

FIGURE 29-11 A TV picture tube requiring a 4.5-cm bending radius (marked with a diagonal line) for maximum deflection of the electron beam. Which way should the magnetic field point to deflect an electron in the direction indicated?

How does deflection of the electron beam result in a TV picture? In conventional TV, the magnetic field is varied so that three electron beams—one for each of the colors red, green, and blue—sweeps across the front of the screen in horizontal lines, starting at the top of the screen and working downward. A scan of the entire screen occurs thirty times each second. The electron current in each beam varies to match the brightness of its color at each point in the picture to be displayed, controlled by varying electric fields in the TV tube that themselves follow the signal coming into the TV from an antenna, cable, or VCR. The screen itself is coated with materials that glow in red, green, or blue when struck by the electrons, so the result is a reconstruction of the image that entered the TV as an electrical signal.

EXERCISE A beam of protons moving at 2.5×10^5 m/s is deflected through a 90° turn by a 10-mT magnetic field oriented perpendicular to the beam's velocity. What is the radius of the turn?

Answer: 26 cm

Some problems similar to Example 29-3: 15, 18, 21

The Cyclotron Frequency

How long does it take a charged particle to complete its circular orbit in a uniform magnetic field? The circumference of the orbit is $2\pi r$, so the period T of the circular motion is

$$T = \frac{2\pi r}{v}.$$

Using Equation 29-3 for the radius r gives

$$T = \frac{2\pi r}{v} = \frac{2\pi}{v}\frac{mv}{qB} = \frac{2\pi m}{qB}. \qquad (29\text{-}4)$$

13.4

Magnetic Force on a Particle

FIGURE 29-12 The Crab Nebula, remnant of a supernova explosion observed nearly 1000 years ago. Intense radio emission occurs as electrons undergo circular motion in the Crab's magnetic field. The frequency of the emission is related to the cyclotron frequency of the electrons' motion, and its measurement therefore allows determination of the magnetic field.

This remarkable result shows that the period of the circular motion is independent of the particle's speed and the size of its orbit. You can see why from Equation 29-3: the larger the speed v the larger the radius r, and therefore the circumference, in direct proportion to the speed. So a faster particle describes a larger circle, and ends up taking the same time to go around. Physically, that's because the magnetic force depends on the particle's speed.

Equivalently, we can describe the particle's circular motion in terms of its frequency, in revolutions per second, which is just the inverse of the period:

$$f = \frac{qB}{2\pi m}. \tag{29-5}$$

This quantity is called the **cyclotron frequency**, since it's the frequency at which charged particles circulate in a cyclotron particle accelerator. Because the cyclotron frequency depends only on the magnetic field and the particle's charge-to-mass ratio, observing cyclotron motion provides astrophysicists a direct measure of magnetic fields in distant astrophysical objects (Fig. 29-12). Conversely, a fixed magnetic field guarantees a specific cyclotron frequency, regardless of the particles' speeds. Microwave ovens exploit this fact, their microwaves generated by electrons circling 2.4 billion times each second in a special tube called a magnetron (see Problem 21).

APPLICATION	*The Cyclotron*

Physicists studying the basic structure of matter need tools that can probe the atomic nucleus and its constituent particles. The only probes sufficiently small are subatomic particles themselves, accelerated to high enough energies that they can disrupt the strong nuclear force. How is this acceleration accomplished? One way is to accelerate particles of charge q through a large potential difference V, giving each particle energy qV. But there are practical problems in the generation and handling of potential differences much over a million volts. To achieve higher energies, devices are used that circumvent the need for a single large potential difference. One of the earliest and most successful such devices is the **cyclotron** (Fig. 29-13). The device consists of an evacuated chamber between the poles of a magnet. At the center of the chamber is a source of the particles to be accelerated, usually protons or light ions. The ions undergo circular motion in the magnetic field.

Also within the evacuated chamber are two hollow conducting structures each shaped like the letter D (Fig. 29-12). A modest potential difference is applied across these two "dees," and this potential difference is made to alternate in polarity with the same frequency as the circular motion of the ions. Recall that this frequency depends only on the magnetic field strength and the charge-to-mass ratio of the ions, but not on their energy. As the ions circle around in the cyclotron, they are accelerated across the gap between the dees by the strong electric field associated with the potential difference. Because each

dee is a hollow, nearly closed conducting structure, there is no electric field within the dees.

Once inside a dee, the ions simply follow a circle in the magnetic field. Halfway round they again cross the gap between dees. If the electric field were steady, the ions would be *decelerated* at this crossing. But the electric field changes direction in step with the ions' circular motion, so each time the ions cross the dee gap they are accelerated and gain more energy. They move faster and in ever larger circles, but always

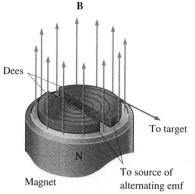

FIGURE 29-13 A cyclotron, showing one magnet pole, dees, and a typical ion trajectory (in red). Not shown are the vacuum chamber surrounding the dees, upper pole, and frame supporting pole pieces and electromagnet windings.

with the same orbital period. Eventually the ion orbits become nearly the size of the machine. At this point an electrostatic field provided by a high-voltage electrode deflects the ions out of the magnetic field and toward a target, where their interactions with target nuclei cause nuclear reactions.

In addition to providing experimental data on nuclear structure, cyclotrons are valuable in producing short-lived radioactive isotopes for a variety of purposes, particularly medical research and diagnosis. A number of large hospitals have their own cyclotrons (Fig. 29-14); in particular, the diagnostic pro-

cedure known as positron emission tomography (PET) requires cyclotron-produced radioisotopes.

At very high energies, the theory of relativity (Chapter 38) comes into play and alters our conclusion that the cyclotron frequency is independent of particle energy. As a result, the cyclotron cannot be used to achieve these relativistic energies. An alternate accelerator design is the **synchrotron**, in which both the magnetic field and frequency of an alternating electric field are varied to account for increasing particle energy, while the orbital radius is held constant (Fig. 29-15).

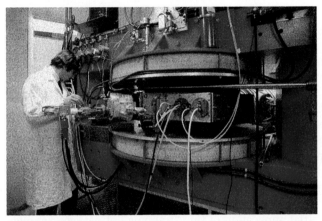

FIGURE 29-14 This cyclotron at Massachusetts General Hospital was used to produce radioisotopes for research leading to the development of the medical diagnostic procedure known as positron emission tomography (PET).

FIGURE 29-15 Aerial view of Fermilab, the Fermi National Accelerator Laboratory at Batavia, Illinois. Large circle is the 2-km diameter Tevatron, a synchrotron that accelerates protons to energies approaching 1 TeV (10^{12} eV).

EXAMPLE 29-4	*Designing a Cyclotron*

A cyclotron is to accelerate protons to a kinetic energy of 5.0 MeV. If the magnetic field in the cyclotron is 2.0 T, what must be the radius of the cyclotron and the frequency at which the dee voltage is alternated?

Solution

The cyclotron frequency is given by Equation 29-5:

$$f = \frac{qB}{2\pi m} = \frac{(1.6\times10^{-19}\,\text{C})(2.0\,\text{T})}{(2\pi)(1.67\times10^{-27}\,\text{kg})} = 3.0\times10^7\,\text{Hz}.$$

This is the frequency required to accelerate protons at each crossing of the dee gap; incidentally, it is about the frequency of a citizens band (CB) radio transmitter.

An energy of 5.0 MeV is equal to

$$(5.0\times10^6\,\text{eV})(1.6\times10^{-19}\,\text{J/eV}) = 8.0\times10^{-13}\,\text{J},$$

so the proton kinetic energy is

$$K = \tfrac{1}{2}mv^2 = 8.0\times10^{-13}\,\text{J}.$$

Solving for the speed v gives

$$v = \sqrt{\frac{2K}{m}} = \sqrt{\frac{(2)(8.0\times10^{-13}\,\text{J})}{1.67\times10^{-27}\,\text{kg}}} = 3.1\times10^7\,\text{m/s}.$$

Equation 29-3 then gives the radius needed to accommodate 5-MeV protons:

$$r = \frac{mv}{qB} = \frac{(1.67\times10^{-27}\,\text{kg})(3.1\times10^7\,\text{m/s})}{(1.6\times10^{-19}\,\text{C})(2.0\,\text{T})} = 0.16\,\text{m}.$$

To ensure a uniform magnetic field over the particle trajectories, the radii of the magnet pole pieces would have to be somewhat larger than this value.

EXERCISE A microwave oven uses 2.4-GHz microwaves, generated by electrons circling at this frequency in the magnetic field of a magnetron tube. (a) What is the magnetic field strength? (b) If the energy associated with an electron's circular motion is 890 eV, what is the radius of its circular path?

Answers: (a) 86 mT; (b) 1.2 mm

Some problems similar to Example 29-4: 17, 25, 26

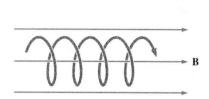

FIGURE 29-16 A particle in a uniform magnetic field describes a spiral path, its motion along the field direction unaffected by the magnetic force.

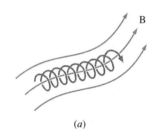

(a)

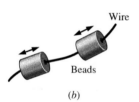

(b)

FIGURE 29-17 (a) Charged particles undergoing spiral motion about the magnetic field direction are "frozen" to the field like (b) beads sliding along a wire.

Particle Trajectories in Three Dimensions

What if a particle's motion is not confined to a plane perpendicular to the magnetic field? Then we can resolve its velocity into two vectors, one perpendicular and the other parallel to the magnetic field. Since the magnetic force is always perpendicular to the field, there is no component of force along the field direction—and therefore the velocity component in this direction is unaffected by the magnetic force. The force acts only on the velocity component perpendicular to the field, and here our previous analysis applies: in the plane perpendicular to the field, the particle's motion is circular with frequency given by Equation 29-5. In the absence of other forces the particle moves uniformly along the field direction while executing circular motion perpendicular to the field. The resulting trajectory is a spiral, as shown in Fig. 29-16.

The absence of magnetic force along the field direction means that particles move readily along the field. But if you try to push them at right angles to the field, they simply move in larger circles about the field direction. As a result, charged particles are often described as being "frozen" to the magnetic field (Fig. 29-17). Nonuniform fields and collisions between particles make this "freezing" of particles and field less than perfect, but in many cases the particle density is low enough that the "frozen" assumption is an excellent approximation. Unlike our relatively cool planet Earth, much of the universe consists of free electrons and protons, not bound into neutral atoms. As a result, magnetic fields are a dominant influence on matter throughout much of the universe (Fig. 29-18).

An important terrestrial application of this "trapping" of particles on magnetic field lines occurs in nuclear fusion reactors. These experimental devices—whose successful development would make 1 gallon of sea water the energy equivalent of more than 300 gallons of gasoline—have to contain ionized gas (plasma) at temperatures around 100 million kelvins. They do so with "magnetic bottles," most commonly toroidal (doughnut-shaped) chambers whose circular magnetic fields never intersect the chamber walls and therefore keep the hot plasma from touching the walls (Fig. 29-19).

FIGURE 29-18 Magnetic fields govern the behavior of matter throughout much of the universe. Here, concentrations of ionized gas trace out magnetic field loops in the Sun's atmosphere.

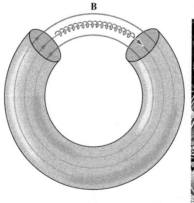

(a)

(b)

FIGURE 29-19 (a) Charged particles spiral about the circular field lines in a simplified fusion reactor. With its toroidal shape, the machine has no "ends" from which magnetic field lines emerge. The field therefore keeps charged particles away from the chamber walls. (b) The Tokamak Fusion Test Reactor at Princeton University. This view, taken during construction, shows clearly the machine's toroidal shape.

| APPLICATION | *The Aurora and Magnetic Mirrors* |

Earth possesses a magnetic field whose origin we'll consider in the next chapter. This field shields Earth's surface from the direct impact of high-energy particles from the Sun and elsewhere in the cosmos. Particles reaching Earth's vicinity are trapped into spiral motion about the magnetic field, so they can't penetrate directly to the surface. This trapping generally occurs on the field lines that intersect Earth in the polar regions (Fig. 29-20a). High-energy particles moving along these field lines slam into the upper atmosphere near the poles, exciting oxygen and nitrogen atoms and thereby producing the spectacular displays we call the aurora (Fig. 29-20b, c). Bursts of solar particles also buffet Earth's magnetic field, causing "magnetic storms" that can severely disrupt communications and electric power transmission.

Fig. 29-21 shows a particle spiraling into a region of stronger magnetic field, like the polar regions in Fig. 29-20a. Note that there is a component of magnetic force opposite to the general direction of motion. This force eventually reverses the particle's forward motion, with the result that the stronger field region acts like a **magnetic mirror**, reflecting particles that attempt to penetrate. This means that particles trapped in Earth's magnetic field bounce back and forth between northern and southern hemispheres, reflected by the magnetic mirrors of higher field strength near the poles. Auroral displays in opposite hemispheres are often strikingly similar since they are caused by the same particle populations mirroring back and forth. Particles that penetrate the upper atmosphere and cause auroral displays combine with atmospheric atoms and are lost to the mirroring particle population, but they're continually replaced with new particles arriving from the Sun.

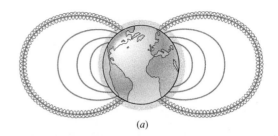

(a)

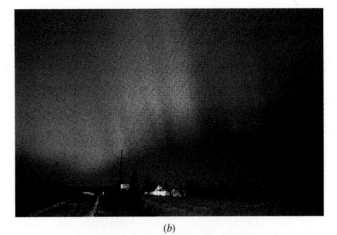

(b)

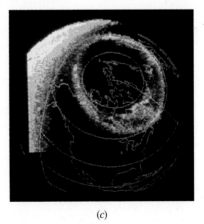

(c)

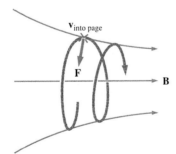

FIGURE 29-21 The magnetic mirror effect. A charged particle is spiraling into a region of stronger magnetic field. At the point shown its velocity is into the page, and the magnetic force—proportional to $\mathbf{v} \times \mathbf{B}$—has a component to the left. This force eventually reverses the rightward motion of the particle.

FIGURE 29-20 The aurora arises from the interaction of high-energy particles trapped in Earth's magnetic field. (*a*) Particles trapped in the magnetic field spiral between the northern and southern polar regions. Diagram is highly simplified; Earth's field is actually more complicated because of interactions with the solar wind, a stream of ionized gas flowing outward from the Sun. (*b*) A colorful aurora viewed from Canada's Prince Edward Island. (*c*) The aurora appears as a circle surrounding Earth's north magnetic pole in this satellite image.

29-4 THE MAGNETIC FORCE ON A CURRENT

So far we've considered the magnetic force on individual charged particles. An electric current is simply a group of charged particles sharing a common motion, so we should expect a current to interact with a magnetic field.

The Force on a Straight Wire

Imagine a long straight wire carrying a current I through a uniform magnetic field **B**, as shown in Fig. 29-22. If each charge carrier has a drift velocity $\mathbf{v}_d$ along the wire, and if each carries charge q, then the magnetic force on each charge carrier is given by Equation 29-1:

$$\mathbf{F}_q = q\mathbf{v}_d \times \mathbf{B}.$$

(Of course the charge carriers also have random thermal velocities. But these average to zero and therefore make no net contribution to the magnetic force.) If the wire has cross-sectional area A and contains n charge carriers per unit volume, then the net force on all the charge carriers in a length ℓ of the wire is

$$\mathbf{F} = nA\ell q\mathbf{v}_d \times \mathbf{B}.$$

The product $nAqv_d$ is just the current I, as we found in deriving Equation 27-2. If we define a vector $\boldsymbol{\ell}$ whose magnitude is the length ℓ of the wire and whose direction is along the current, then we can write

$$\mathbf{F} = I\boldsymbol{\ell} \times \mathbf{B}. \qquad \text{(magnetic force on a current)} \qquad (29\text{-}6)$$

The direction of this force is at right angles to both the current and the magnetic field, or out of the page in Fig. 29-22. For a given direction of the current, the direction of the force does not depend on the sign of the charge carriers. If the current is to the right, then positive charges move to the right and the force on each is out of the page. If the charges are negative, they move to the left and the force is still out of the page because both the sign of the velocity and the sign of the charge are reversed, given the same sign for the force $q\mathbf{v} \times \mathbf{B}$.

Strictly speaking, Equation 29-6 gives the net magnetic force only on the charge carriers in the wire. But the motion of the charge carriers—typically electrons—under the influence of the magnetic force causes charge separation in the wire, and the resulting electric field exerts a force on the fixed charges—typically ions—in the wire (Fig. 29-23). Thus the entire wire experiences the force. Although its origin is not entirely magnetic, we loosely call the force given by Equation 29-6 the magnetic force on the wire.

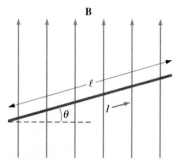

FIGURE 29-22 A straight wire carrying current I through a uniform magnetic field. The charge carriers in the wire experience a magnetic force, in this case out of the page.

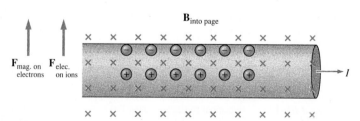

FIGURE 29-23 Electrons moving to the left in a wire are deflected upward by the magnetic force, resulting in charge separation and therefore in an upward electric force on the fixed ions. As a result the entire wire is ultimately influenced by the magnetic force on the moving electrons.

The magnetic force on a current-carrying wire is the basis for many practical devices, including loudspeakers and the electric motors that start cars and run refrigerators, CD players, computer disk drives, subway trains, pumps, food processors, power tools, and myriad other useful instruments of modern society. At the end of this chapter we'll see just how electric motors work.

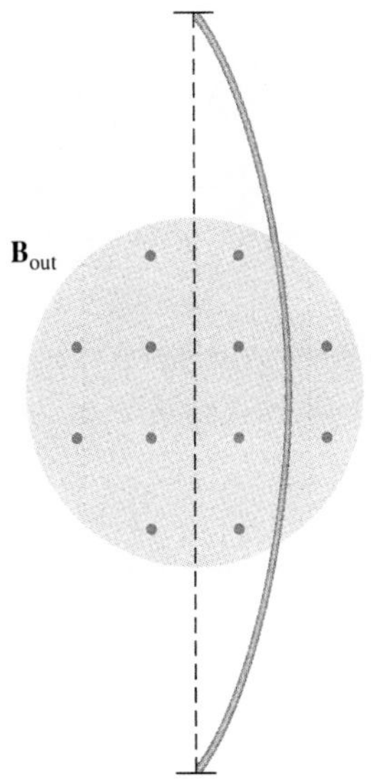

Got It!

Figure 29-24 shows a flexible, current-carrying wire passing through a region where a magnetic field points out of the page. The wire is deflected to the right, as shown in Fig. 29-24. Is the current flowing upward or downward in the wire?

FIGURE 29-24 A flexible wire passes through a region containing a magnetic field pointing out of the page. Which direction is the current in the wire when it's deflected as shown?

EXAMPLE 29-5	*Magnetic Force on a Power Line*

A power line runs along Earth's equator, where Earth's magnetic field points horizontally from south to north and has a strength of about 0.5 G. The current in the power line is 500 A, flowing from west to east. What are the magnitude and direction of the magnetic force on 1 km of the power line?

Solution

Let eastward be the x direction, northward the y direction, and upward the z direction. After we convert gauss to tesla, Equation 29-6 gives

$$\mathbf{F} = I\boldsymbol{\ell} \times \mathbf{B} = (500 \text{ A})(1000\hat{\mathbf{i}} \text{ m}) \times (0.5 \times 10^{-4} \hat{\mathbf{j}} \text{ T})$$
$$= 25\hat{\mathbf{k}} \text{ N}.$$

This 25-N upward force is negligible compared with the weight—on the order of 2×10^4 N—of 1 km of power line.

EXERCISE A 2.0-m-long wire has a mass of 37 g. The wire extends horizontally, at 40° to a horizontal magnetic field of 0.075 T. What current in the wire will result in the magnetic force suspending it against gravity?

Answer: 3.8 A

Some problems similar to Example 29-5: 33, 35, 37

APPLICATION	*Magnetic Levitation and Propulsion*

Engineers throughout the world are at work on transportation systems whose operation results directly from the magnetic force on a straight current-carrying conductor. In so-called maglev vehicles, magnetic forces levitate the vehicle just a few centimeters above a conducting guideway and also provide the horizontal force that propels the vehicle (Fig. 29-25). Such vehicles should be capable of 500-km/h speeds, well above the 300 km/h maximum for high-speed rail systems. Maglev vehicles should prove especially effective for travel between cities in densely populated regions.

A related application is so-called magnetohydrodynamic (MHD) propulsion, a kind of jet propulsion in which a

FIGURE 29-25 A magnetically levitated vehicle under development in Japan.

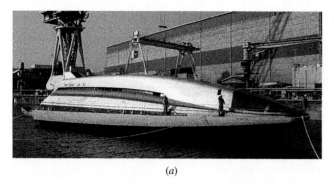

(a)

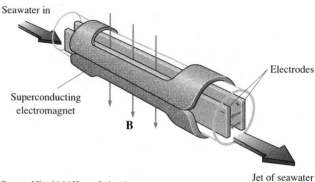

Seawater in

Superconducting
electromagnet

B

Electrodes

Jet of seawater

Source: Mitsubishi Heavy Industries

(b)

conducting fluid is accelerated by the magnetic force. Engineers are currently experimenting with MHD propulsion for ships. Because sea water is a reasonably good electrical conductor, passage of a current through sea water in a magnetic field results in a magnetic force on the water. Figure 29-26 shows the experimental Japanese ship Yamato-1 and its MHD propulsion system.

FIGURE 29-26 (*a*) The Japanese ship Yamato-1 uses MHD propulsion. (*b*) Schematic diagram of the MHD propulsion unit. Superconducting electromagnet produces a magnetic field; current flowing in the sea water between the two electrodes then experiences a magnetic force that ejects a jet of water at right.

APPLICATION	*The Hall Effect*

The force on a current-carrying conductor is independent of the sign of the charge carriers. But there's a subtle difference. Fig. 29-27 shows two conductors, each with the same current *I* to the right and magnetic field **B** pointing into the page. In Fig. 29-27*a* the current is carried by electrons moving to the *left*. The product **v** × **B** is downward, but since electrons are negative the force $q\mathbf{v} \times \mathbf{B}$ is upward. As a result, the upper edge of the conductor is negative with respect to the lower edge. In Fig. 29-27*b* the current is carried by protons moving to the *right*. Again the force $q\mathbf{v} \times \mathbf{B}$ is upward, so now the upper edge of the conductor is positive.

This phenomenon of charge separation is the **Hall effect**. The separated charge gives rise to an electric field and therefore to a measurable potential difference—the **Hall potential**—between opposite edges of the conductor. The sign of the Hall potential depends on the sign of the charge carriers. Charge separation will stop once the electric force on the charge carriers cancels the magnetic force. The electric force has magnitude qE and, with **B** perpendicular to the current, the magnetic force has magnitude qv_dB, with v_d the charge-carrier drift speed. Equating these magnitudes gives $E = v_dB$. In a rectangular conductor this field will be essentially uniform, so the Hall potential becomes

$$V_H = Eh = v_dBh,$$

where *h* is the conductor height shown in Fig. 29-27. But Equation 27-2 gives $I = nAqv_d$, with *n* the number density of charge carriers, *A* the conductor's cross-sectional area, and *q*

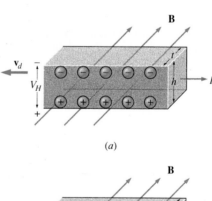

(a)

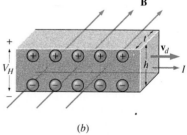

(b)

FIGURE 29-27 The Hall potential V_H arises from the deflection of charge carriers by the magnetic force when a current-carrying conductor is in a magnetic field. Although the magnetic force on the conductor is independent of the sign of the charge carriers, the sign of the Hall potential does depend on the sign of the charge carriers. In both (*a*) and (*b*) the current is to the right, carried in (*a*) by negative charge carriers moving to the left and in (*b*) by positive charge carriers moving to the right.

the charge on each carrier. Solving for v_d and using the result in our expression for V_H gives

$$V_H = \frac{IBh}{nAq},$$

or, since $A = ht$ with t the conductor thickness shown in Fig. 29-27,

$$V_H = \frac{IB}{nqt}. \tag{29-7}$$

The quantity $1/nq$ is the **Hall coefficient**. Measurement of V_H in a sample of known thickness carrying known current in a known magnetic field yields the value of this coefficient and, thus, gives information on the nature and density of the charge carriers. Alternatively, measurement of V_H in a material with known Hall coefficient carrying a known current provides a direct measure of the magnetic field strength (see Problem 45).

Nonuniform Fields and Curved Conductors

Equation 29-6 gives the force, $\mathbf{F} = I\boldsymbol{\ell} \times \mathbf{B}$, on a straight conductor of length ℓ carrying current I in a uniform magnetic field $\mathbf{B}$. We can still use this equation if the conductor bends or the field varies with position, if we apply it only to a very small segment of this conductor—so small that the segment is essentially straight and the field essentially uniform over the segment. Designating this segment by $d\boldsymbol{\ell}$, Equation 29-6 becomes

$$d\mathbf{F} = I \, d\boldsymbol{\ell} \times \mathbf{B}$$

for the small force on the segment (Fig. 29-28). To find the total force on the conductor, we sum the forces on all such segments. In the limit of very small segments, this sum becomes an integral, and we have

$$\mathbf{F} = \int d\mathbf{F} = \int I \, d\boldsymbol{\ell} \times \mathbf{B}. \tag{29-8}$$

The integration is taken over the entire section of conductor on which we are calculating the force.

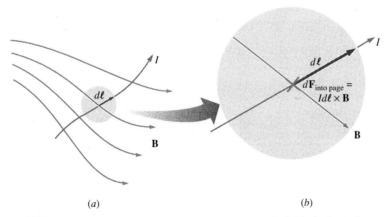

(a)   (b)

FIGURE 29-28 (a) A curved conductor in a nonuniform magnetic field. (b) A small segment $d\boldsymbol{\ell}$ can be treated as a straight wire in a uniform field; the magnetic force on the segment is $d\mathbf{F} = I \, d\boldsymbol{\ell} \times \mathbf{B}$.

EXAMPLE 29-6	*The Force on a Curved Conductor*

A semicircular wire connects two points C and D a horizontal distance $2R$ apart (Fig. 29-29a). The wire carries a current I from C to D and is in a uniform magnetic field **B** pointing upward. Show that the magnetic force on this semicircular wire is the same as the force that a straight wire from C to D would experience if it carried the same current I.

Solution

Since the orientation of the wire relative to the field varies, we use the integral in Equation 29-8 to calculate the force. Figure 29-29a shows an infinitesimal segment $d\ell$ of the wire, and the angle θ that specifies its position on the semicircular arc. This infinitesimal segment subtends an infinitesimal angle $d\theta$, as shown. A blown-up view of the segment (Fig. 29-29b) shows that the angle between the segment $d\ell$ and the magnetic field **B** is also θ. Then the magnitude of the force on the segment is

$$dF = I\,d\ell\,B\sin\theta\,.$$

Application of the right-hand rule shows that the direction of the force element is out of the page for all values of θ on the semicircle—that is, for $0 \le \theta \le \pi$. Therefore, the integral in Equation 29-8 describes a sum of vectors all of which point in the same direction, so the magnitude of the net force is

$$F = \int dF = \int_0^\pi IB\sin\theta\,d\ell\,.$$

But $d\ell$ subtends the angle $d\theta$, so $d\ell = R\,d\theta$ (Fig. 29-30). Then, taking the constants I, B, and R outside the integral, we have

$$F = IBR \int_0^\pi \sin\theta\,d\theta = IBR\,(-\cos\theta)\Big|_0^\pi$$
$$= IBR[-(-1-1)] = IB(2R)\,.$$

This is just the force we would get from Equation 29-6 for a straight wire of length $2R$ carrying current I perpendicular to a magnetic field **B**. You can see why this is: Equation 29-6 shows that the magnetic force depends on the quantity $d\ell \sin\theta$, which is the component of the segment $d\ell$ perpendicular to the field. That component is what you get if you take the straight path from C to D instead of the semicircle. Indeed, the force on any piece of wire carrying the same current from C to D would be the same as long as it stayed in the region of uniform field. A corollary is that the net force on any *closed* loop of current in a uniform magnetic field must be zero (see Problem 43).

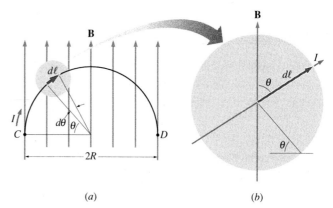

(a)   (b)

FIGURE 29-29 (a) A semicircular wire carries current I between points C and D. (b) Blowup of an infinitesimal segment $d\ell$ of the wire, showing that the segment makes an angle θ with the magnetic field.

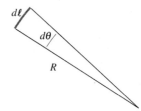

FIGURE 29-30 An angle in radians is defined as the ratio of subtended arc to radius. Here the angle $d\theta$ is so small that the difference between a circular arc and the straight segment $d\ell$ is insignificant. Therefore $d\ell = R\,d\theta$.

EXERCISE A 15-cm-long wire carrying 4.8 A is bent into a quarter circle and oriented like the left half of the semicircular wire in Fig. 29-29a (i.e., from point C to the top of the semicircle). If the magnetic field shown in Fig. 29-29a has magnitude 0.65 T, what is the magnetic force on the wire?

Answer: 0.30 N

Some problems similar to Example 29-6: 40–43

A common application using the force on a current-carrying wire is the loudspeaker, shown in Fig. 29-31. Here an unusually shaped magnet produces a nonuniform magnetic field that results in a net force on a current-carrying coil. The current in the coil alternates direction in accordance with the audio signal

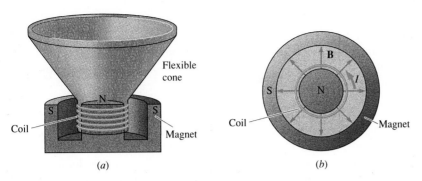

FIGURE 29-31 A loudspeaker uses the magnetic force on a current-carrying coil to convert electrical energy into sound. (*a*) Cutaway view; (*b*) top view of the magnet, showing the nonuniform field and placement of the coil. With the current direction indicated, the net force is into the page. There's a net force on the loop only because the field is nonuniform.

from an amplifier, and this results in an alternating force that moves the coil back and forth. The coil, in turn, is connected to a flexible cone that moves to produce sound waves.

29-5 A CURRENT LOOP IN A MAGNETIC FIELD

Closed loops of current are important in a wide variety of natural and technological systems. Loops of current-carrying wire are at the heart of every electric motor, while miniature current loops associated with charged quarks circulating within the proton are responsible for nuclear magnetic resonance (NMR), widely used to determine the structure of chemical compounds and as the basis of the medical technique called magnetic resonance imaging (MRI). We now show that the magnetic forces on different parts of a current loop result in a torque on the loop; it's that torque that drives electric motors and the motion of protons in NMR.

Consider a rectangular current loop in a uniform magnetic field, with the normal to the loop making an angle θ with the magnetic field, as shown in Fig. 29-32*a*. Since current flows in opposite directions on opposite sides and since the field is uniform, the magnetic forces on opposite sides cancel and there is no net magnetic force on the loop. The right-hand rule shows that the forces on the top and bottom of the loop point directly upward and downward, respectively, and therefore result in no net torque.

The forces on the vertical sections of the loop, however, do produce a torque. Figure 29-32*b* shows a top view of the loop, with the forces resulting from the

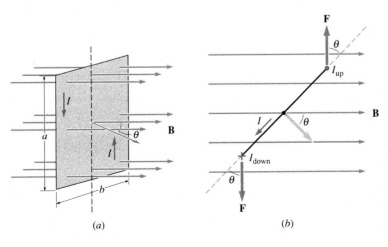

FIGURE 29-32 (*a*) A rectangular current loop in a uniform magnetic field. Shading indicates the plane of the loop. The angle between the loop normal and the magnetic field is θ. (*b*) Top view of the current loop, showing that magnetic forces on the vertical sides result in a net torque. The angles used in the torque calculation are the same as the angle θ between the loop normal and the magnetic field.

upward- and downward-flowing currents in the vertical sides. From the figure, it's clear that these forces give rise to a net torque twisting the loop counterclockwise. Each vertical side is a straight wire of length a carrying current I at right angles to the horizontally directed magnetic field $\mathbf{B}$, so the magnitude of the force on each side is simply

$$F_{\text{side}} = IaB .$$

The distance from the loop's central axis to the sides where this force acts is half the loop width, or $b/2$. The geometry of Fig. 29-32b shows that the angle used in calculating the torque is the same as the angle θ between the loop normal and the magnetic field. Therefore, the torque due to the force on each side is

$$\tau_{\text{side}} = F \frac{b}{2} \sin\theta = Ia \frac{b}{2} B \sin\theta .$$

Accounting for the contributions from both sides gives the magnitude of the net torque on the loop:

$$\tau = IabB \sin\theta .$$

We can express the torque in vector notation if we define a vector $\mathbf{A}$ whose magnitude is the area ab of the loop and which is perpendicular to the loop. We choose the direction of $\mathbf{A}$ by the right-hand rule: wrap your fingers around the loop in the direction of the current and your thumb points in the direction of $\mathbf{A}$. This is the same direction as the loop normal shown in Fig. 29-32. Then we can write

$$\boldsymbol{\tau} = I\mathbf{A} \times \mathbf{B} . \tag{29-9}$$

Although we derived this equation for a rectangular loop, it holds in fact for any current loop. The torque on a current loop depends on the current, the loop area, the magnetic field, and the orientation between loop and field.

Equation 29-9 should remind you of Equation 23-12 for the torque on an electric dipole in an electric field. There we had

$$\boldsymbol{\tau} = \mathbf{p} \times \mathbf{E} ,$$

where $\mathbf{p}$ is the electric dipole moment and $\mathbf{E}$ the electric field. Comparison with Equation 29-9 suggests that a current loop in a magnetic field behaves analogously to an electric dipole in an electric field. As far as its response to magnetic fields is concerned, therefore,

| **A current loop constitutes a magnetic dipole.**

The quantity $I\mathbf{A}$ in Equation 29-9 plays the same role as the electric dipole moment in the equation $\boldsymbol{\tau} = \mathbf{p} \times \mathbf{E}$. We therefore call this quantity the **magnetic dipole moment, $\boldsymbol{\mu}$**:

$$\boldsymbol{\mu} = I\mathbf{A} . \quad \text{(single-turn loop)}$$

The direction of the vector $\boldsymbol{\mu}$ is the same as the direction we defined for $\mathbf{A}$: curl your right fingers in the direction of the loop current, and your thumb points in the direction of $\boldsymbol{\mu}$ (Fig. 29-33). (With ActivPhysics Activity 13.6 you can

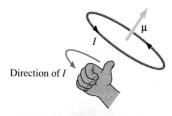

Direction of I

FIGURE 29-33 Using the right-hand rule to find the direction of a current loop's magnetic moment.

graphically resize a current loop to see the effect on magnetic moment and torque.) More generally, a loop may consist of N turns of conducting wire; then each contributes $I\mathbf{A}$ to give the total magnetic moment:

$$\boldsymbol{\mu} = NI\mathbf{A}. \qquad \text{(magnetic dipole moment)} \qquad (29\text{-}10)$$

Clearly the units of magnetic moment are A·m². Using the magnetic moment vector, Equation 29-9 then becomes

$$\boldsymbol{\tau} = \boldsymbol{\mu} \times \mathbf{B}, \qquad \text{(torque on a current loop)} \qquad (29\text{-}11)$$

in analogy with the electric case. The magnetic moment vector of a current loop is perpendicular to the plane of the loop, and the torque given in Equation 29-11 tends to align the magnetic moment with the field (Fig. 29-34). It takes work to twist the loop's magnetic moment vector out of alignment with the field. In exact analogy with the electric-dipole case summarized in Equation 23-10, we express the associated potential energy as

$$U_{\text{magnetic}} = -\boldsymbol{\mu} \cdot \mathbf{B}. \qquad (29\text{-}12)$$

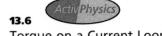

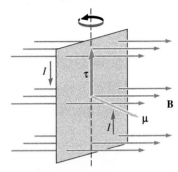

FIGURE 29-34 The torque on a current loop tends to align the loop's magnetic moment vector with the magnetic field.

EXAMPLE 29-7	*Pointing a Satellite*

Some satellites use the magnetic torque on current loops to point themselves in space. Earth itself provides the magnetic field, while electricity from solar panels powers coils that constitute the current loops; unlike rocket-based pointing systems, there's no fuel to run out. Three mutually perpendicular coils allow the satellite to point itself in any direction. One satellite uses 30-cm-diameter circular coils, each with 1000 turns. (a) If the satellite orbits at an altitude where Earth's magnetic field is 0.24 G, and if specifications call for a maximum torque of 1.3 mN·m from each coil, what should be the coil current? (b) How much work is done on the coil to rotate it from its maximum-torque orientation to an angle of 120° to the field?

Solution

(a) The maximum torque occurs when the coil's magnetic moment is perpendicular to the field; Equation 29-11 shows that this maximum torque has magnitude $\tau_{\text{max}} = \mu B$. The magnetic moment of the coil is the product of the number of turns, the current, and the coil area πR^2, as given by Equation 29-10. Thus the maximum torque is

$$\tau_{\text{max}} = NI\pi R^2 B.$$

Solving for the current gives

$$I = \frac{\tau_{\text{max}}}{N\pi R^2 B} = \frac{1.3 \times 10^{-3} \text{ N·m}}{(1000)(\pi)(0.15 \text{ m})^2 (0.24 \times 10^{-4} \text{ T})}$$

$$= 0.766 \text{ A}.$$

(b) The loop's potential energy is given by Equation 29-12: $U = -\boldsymbol{\mu} \cdot \mathbf{B} = -\mu B \cos\theta$. Maximum torque occurs when $\theta = 90°$, so the work in rotating the coil—equal to the difference in its potential energies in the two orientations—is

$$W = U_{120°} - U_{90°} = -\mu B \cos 120° - (-\mu B \cos 90°)$$

$$= (-1.3 \times 10^{-3} \text{ N·m})(\cos 120°)$$

$$= 0.65 \text{ mJ},$$

where we recognized the quantity μB as the maximum torque defined earlier.

EXERCISE An electric motor consists of a 550-turn loop with area 100 cm² in a 0.23-T magnetic field. What loop current is necessary if the motor is to develop a maximum torque of 3.7 N·m?

Answer: 2.9 A

Some problems similar to Example 29-7: 47, 48, 50–52

APPLICATION	*Electric Motors*

Electric motors are so much a part of our lives that we hardly think of them. But CD players, car starters, refrigerators, vacuum cleaners, power saws, subway trains, computer disk drives, food processors, washing machines, fans, hair dryers, water pumps, oil burners, and most industrial machinery would be difficult or impossible to build without electric motors (Fig. 29-35).

At the heart of every electric motor is a current loop in a magnetic field. But instead of a steady current, the loop carries a current that reverses periodically. In direct-current (DC) motors, this reversal is achieved through the electrical contacts

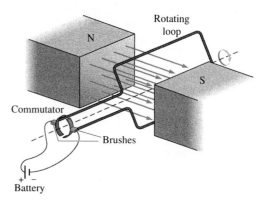

FIGURE 29-36 A simple electric motor. Current flows from the battery through the stationary brushes to the rotating commutator and loop. The direction of the loop current reverses as the two halves of the commutator rotate to contact different brushes.

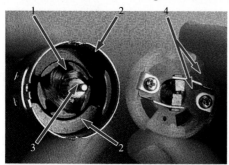

FIGURE 29-35 (*a*) A small electric motor, partially disassembled. At left is the rotating coil (1), surrounded by permanent magnets (2). The commutator (3) is on the forward shaft. At right are the brushes (4), which fit around the commutator to supply current to the rotating coils. (*b*) This electric motor powers General Motors' EV1 electric car.

that provide current to the loop. Figure 29-36 shows a simple motor consisting of a loop in the field of a permanent magnet. Current from an external battery reaches the loop through a set of stationary "brushes," which make contact with a pair of semicircular conductors called the "commutator." The commutator is attached rigidly to the loop, which rotates to align its dipole moment with the field. Just as it reaches alignment, however, the brushes cross the gaps in the commutator. This reverses the connections to the battery, reversing the loop current. This in turn reverses the magnetic moment of the loop, so it's no longer aligned with the field. The loop then rotates another 180° to align its new magnetic moment vector with the field. Just as it reaches alignment, the current again reverses. This process repeats, resulting in continuous rotation of the loop. A rigid shaft through loop and commutator delivers mechanical work to the device powered by the motor. The source of this work is the battery or whatever supplies electrical energy to the motor. The motor itself is a device that converts electrical to mechanical energy; the magnetic field is an intermediary in this conversion.

CHAPTER SYNOPSIS

Summary

1. **Magnetism** is a fundamental interaction described in terms of **magnetic fields**. Magnetic fields interact with **moving electric charges**. A moving charged particle experiences a force that depends on its charge, its velocity, and the magnetic field. The force is at right angles to both velocity and field, and is given by

$$\mathbf{F} = q\mathbf{v} \times \mathbf{B}.$$

Because it's at right angles to the particle's velocity, the magnetic force does no work on a charged particle. In a uniform magnetic field, a particle's trajectory is a circle or spiral, with orbital period independent of the particle's speed.

2. An electric current is made up of moving electric charges, so there is a net magnetic force on an electric current. For a straight wire of length ℓ carrying current I in a magnetic

field **B**, the force is

$$\mathbf{F} = I\boldsymbol{\ell} \times \mathbf{B}.$$

3. A particularly important case of a current in a magnetic field is a closed current loop. Such a loop behaves like a **magnetic dipole** with magnetic dipole moment

$$\boldsymbol{\mu} = NIA,$$

where N is the number of turns in the loop, I the loop current, and **A** a vector perpendicular to the plane of the loop and whose magnitude is the loop area. A current loop in a magnetic field experiences a torque given by $\tau = \boldsymbol{\mu} \times \mathbf{B}$, and the associated potential energy is $U_B = -\boldsymbol{\mu} \cdot \mathbf{B}$.

Terms You Should Understand

(Pairs are closely related terms whose distinction is important; number in parentheses is chapter section where term first appears.)

magnetic field (29-1, 29-2)
magnetic force, electromagnetic force (29-2)
tesla, gauss (29-2)
cyclotron frequency (29-3)
cyclotron, synchrotron (29-3)
magnetic mirror (29-3)
Hall effect, Hall potential (29-4)
current loop (29-5)

magnetic dipole moment (29-5)
electric motor (29-5)

Symbols You Should Recognize

B (29-1, 29-2)
T (29-2)
$\boldsymbol{\mu}$ (29-5)

Problems You Should Be Able to Solve

calculating magnetic force vectors given charge, velocity, and magnetic field (29-2)
analyzing charged-particle trajectories in uniform magnetic fields (29-3)
finding magnetic forces on straight conductors in uniform fields (29-4)
using integration to determine magnetic forces with curved conductors and/or nonuniform fields (29-4)
determining magnetic dipole moments of current loops (29-5)
evaluating torque and potential energy for current loops in magnetic fields (29-5)

Limitations to Keep in Mind

Magnetic forces arise only when charges are *moving*.
The cyclotron frequency is independent of particle energy only for speeds much less than the speed of light.

QUESTIONS

1. A charged particle moves through a region containing only a magnetic field. Under what condition will the particle experience no force?
2. An electron moving with velocity **v** through a magnetic field **B** experiences a magnetic force **F**. Which of the vectors **F**, **v**, and **B** must be at right angles?
3. In Fig. 29-37 a high-energy gamma ray has decayed into an electron and its positively charged antiparticle, a

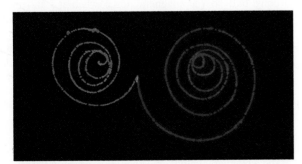

FIGURE 29-37 Creation of an electron-positron pair in the decay of a gamma ray incident from the top of the figure. Both particles come into existence moving essentially downward in the photo, at the point where the two trajectories diverge. (Question 3)

positron. A magnetic field points out of the plane of the photograph, and the electron and positron spiral in this field. Which path belongs to which particle?
4. A magnetic field points out of this page. Will a positively charged particle moving in the plane of the page circle clockwise or counterclockwise as viewed from above?
5. An electron moves through a region in a straight line at constant speed. Can you conclude that there is no magnetic field in the region? Could you so conclude if you knew that there were no electric or gravitational forces on the electron? Explain.
6. High-resolution color TV monitors sometimes have a built-in circuit that compensates for changes in the orientation of Earth's magnetic field relative to the TV picture tube as the monitor is moved from one place to another. Why is this necessary?
7. What is meant by the statement that charged particles can be "trapped" by magnetic fields?
8. An electron beam comes straight to the center of a TV screen, where it makes a spot of light. If you hold the north pole of a bar magnet on the left side of the picture tube, which way will the spot move? (Magnetic field lines emerge from the north pole of a magnet.)

9. Do particles in a cyclotron gain energy from the electric field, the magnetic field, or both? Explain.

10. A cyclotron is designed to accelerate either hydrogen or deuterium nuclei. If the magnetic field is unchanged, how must the frequency of the alternating dee voltage be changed in order to switch from hydrogen to deuterium?

11. An electron and a proton moving at the same speed enter a region containing a uniform magnetic field. Which is deflected more from its original path?

12. An electron and a proton with the same kinetic energy enter a region containing a uniform magnetic field. Which is deflected more from its original path?

13. For what orientation of electric and magnetic fields could the net force on a particle be zero?

14. Will the velocity selector of Example 29-2 work for particles coming out of the page in Fig. 29-8? Why or why not?

15. What does magnetism have to do with the fact that auroras are seen near Earth's poles?

16. In a certain region uniform electric and magnetic fields are at right angles to one another. A positively charged particle is released from rest in this region. Describe qualitatively its subsequent motion.

17. How do the period and radius of an electron's orbit in a magnetic field depend on its velocity?

18. Current in a certain ionic solution is carried equally by positive and negative ions. Would you expect the Hall effect to occur in this solution?

19. Two identical particles carrying equal charge are moving in opposite directions along a magnetic field, when they collide elastically head-on. Describe their subsequent motion.

20. Repeat the above question for the case when the two particles are moving instantaneously perpendicular to the field when they collide.

21. Under what conditions will a current loop in a magnetic field experience zero torque?

22. What would happen to a motor with no commutator?

PROBLEMS

ActivPhysics can help with these problems:
Activities 13.4, 13.6, 13.7, 13.8

Section 29-2 The Magnetic Force on a Moving Charge

1. (a) What is the minimum magnetic field needed to exert a 5.4×10^{-15}-N force on an electron moving at 2.1×10^7 m/s? (b) What magnetic field strength would be required if the field were at 45° to the electron's velocity?

2. An electron moving at right angles to a 0.10-T magnetic field experiences an acceleration of 6.0×10^{15} m/s². (a) What is the electron's speed? (b) By how much does its *speed* change in 1 ns ($= 10^{-9}$ s)?

3. What is the magnitude of the magnetic force on a proton moving at 2.5×10^5 m/s (a) at right angles; (b) at 30°; (c) parallel to a magnetic field of 0.50 T?

4. A magnetic field of 0.10 T points in the x direction. A charged particle carrying 1.0 μC enters the field region moving at 20 m/s. What are the magnitude and direction of the force on the particle when it first enters the field region if it does so moving (a) along the x axis; (b) along the y axis; (c) along the z axis; (d) at 45° to both x and y axes?

5. A particle carrying a 50-μC charge moves with velocity $\mathbf{v} = 5.0\mathbf{\hat{i}} + 3.2\mathbf{\hat{k}}$ m/s through a uniform magnetic field $\mathbf{B} = 9.4\mathbf{\hat{i}} + 6.7\mathbf{\hat{j}}$ T. (a) What is the force on the particle? (b) Form the dot products $\mathbf{F} \cdot \mathbf{v}$ and $\mathbf{F} \cdot \mathbf{B}$ to show explicitly that the force is perpendicular to both $\mathbf{v}$ and $\mathbf{B}$.

6. Moving in the x direction, a particle carrying 1.0 μC experiences no force. Moving with speed v at 30° to the x axis, the particle experiences a magnetic force of 2.0 N. What magnetic force would it experience if it moved along the y axis with speed v?

7. A proton moving with velocity $\mathbf{v}_1 = 3.6 \times 10^4\,\mathbf{\hat{j}}$ m/s experiences a magnetic force of $7.4 \times 10^{-16}\,\mathbf{\hat{i}}$ N. A second proton moving on the x axis experiences a magnetic force of $2.8 \times 10^{-16}\,\mathbf{\hat{j}}$ N. Find the magnitude and direction of the magnetic field, and the velocity of the second proton.

8. The magnitude of Earth's magnetic field is a little less than 1 G near Earth's surface. What is the maximum possible magnetic force on an electron with kinetic energy of 1 keV? Compare with the gravitational force on the same electron.

9. An alpha particle (2 protons, 2 neutrons) is moving with velocity $\mathbf{v} = 150\mathbf{\hat{i}} + 320\mathbf{\hat{j}} - 190\mathbf{\hat{k}}$ km/s in a magnetic field $\mathbf{B} = 0.66\mathbf{\hat{i}} - 0.41\mathbf{\hat{j}}$ T. Find the magnetic force on the particle.

10. How much charge would you need to put on a 2.7-g ping-pong ball so the magnetic force when it's moving at 6.0 m/s at right angles to Earth's 44-μT magnetic field is equal to its weight? Is this realistic?

11. A 1.4-μC charge moving at 185 m/s experiences a magnetic force $\mathbf{F}_B = 2.5\mathbf{\hat{i}} + 7.0\mathbf{\hat{j}}$ μN in a magnetic field $\mathbf{B} = 42\mathbf{\hat{i}} - 15\mathbf{\hat{j}}$ mT. What is the angle between the particle's velocity and the magnetic field?

12. A velocity selector uses a 60-mT magnetic field and a 24 kN/C electric field. At what speed will charged particles pass through the selector undeflected?

13. A region contains an electric field $\mathbf{E} = 7.4\mathbf{\hat{i}} + 2.8\mathbf{\hat{j}}$ kN/C and a magnetic field $\mathbf{B} = 15\mathbf{\hat{j}} + 36\mathbf{\hat{k}}$ mT. Find the electromagnetic force on (a) a stationary proton, (b) an electron moving with velocity $\mathbf{v} = 6.1\mathbf{\hat{i}}$ Mm/s.

14. A charged particle is moving at right angles to both a 1.1 kN/C electric field and a 0.75-T magnetic field. If the magnitude of the electric force on the particle is twice that of the magnetic force, what is the particle's speed?

Section 29-3 The Motion of Charged Particles in Magnetic Fields

15. What is the radius of the circular path described by a proton moving at 15 km/s in a plane perpendicular to a 400-G magnetic field?
16. How long does it take an electron to complete a circular orbit at right angles to a 1.0-G magnetic field?
17. Radio astronomers detect electromagnetic radiation at a frequency of 42 MHz from an interstellar gas cloud. If this radiation is caused by electrons spiraling in a magnetic field, what is the field strength in the gas cloud?
18. A beam of electrons moving in the x direction at 8.7×10^6 m/s enters a region where a uniform magnetic field of 180 G points in the y direction. How far into the field region does the beam penetrate?
19. Electrons and protons with the same kinetic energy are moving at right angles to a uniform magnetic field. How do their orbital radii compare?
20. The Van Allen belts are regions in space where high-energy charged particles are trapped in Earth's magnetic field. If the field strength at the Van Allen belts is 0.10 G, what are the period and radius of the spiral path described (a) by a proton with a 1.0-MeV kinetic energy? (b) by a 10-MeV proton?
21. Microwaves in a microwave oven are produced by electrons circling in a magnetic field at a frequency of 2.4 GHz. (a) What is the magnetic field strength? (b) The electrons' motion takes place inside a special tube called a magnetron. If the magnetron can accommodate electron orbits with a maximum diameter of 2.5 mm, what is the maximum electron energy?
22. Show that the orbital radius of a charged particle moving at right angles to a magnetic field B can be written

$$r = \frac{\sqrt{2Km}}{qB},$$

where K is the kinetic energy in joules, m the particle mass, and q its charge.
23. Two protons, moving in a plane perpendicular to a uniform magnetic field of 500 G, undergo an elastic head-on collision. How much time elapses before they collide again? *Hint:* Draw a picture.
24. Repeat the preceding problem for the case of a proton and an antiproton colliding head-on (a) if they have the same speed and (b) if they have different speeds. (An antiproton has the same mass as a proton, but carries the opposite charge.)
25. A cyclotron is designed to accelerate deuterium nuclei. (Deuterium has one proton and one neutron in its nucleus.)

(a) If the cyclotron uses a 2.0-T magnetic field, at what frequency should the dee voltage be alternated? (b) If the vacuum chamber has a diameter of 0.90 m, what is the maximum kinetic energy of the deuterons? (c) If the magnitude of the potential difference between the dees is 1500 V, how many orbits do the deuterons complete before achieving the energy of part (b)?
26. Without changing the magnetic field, how could the cyclotron of the preceding problem be modified to accelerate (a) protons and (b) alpha particles (two protons and two neutrons)? What would be the maximum energy achievable with (c) protons and (d) alpha particles?
27. Figure 29-38 shows a simple mass spectrometer, designed to analyze and separate atomic and molecular ions with different charge-to-mass ratios. In the design shown, ions are accelerated through a potential difference V, after which they enter a region containing a uniform magnetic field. They describe semicircular paths in the magnetic field, and land on a detector a lateral distance x from where they entered the field region, as shown. Show that x is given by

$$x = \frac{2}{B}\sqrt{\frac{2V}{(q/m)}},$$

where B is the magnetic field strength, V the accelerating potential, and q/m the charge-to-mass ratio of the ion. By counting the number of ions accumulated at different positions x, one can determine the relative abundances of different atomic or molecular species in a sample.

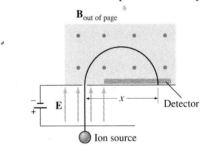

FIGURE 29-38 A mass spectrometer (Problem 27).

28. A mass spectrometer like that of the preceding problem has $V = 2000$ V and $B = 1000$ G. It is used to analyze a gas sample suspected of containing Ne, O_2, CO, SO_2, and NO_2. Ions are detected at distances of 58 cm, 68 cm, and 87 cm from the entrance to the field region. Which gases are actually present? Assume that all molecules are singly ionized.
29. A mass spectrometer is used to separate the fissionable uranium isotope U-235 from the much more abundant isotope U-238. To within what percentage must the magnetic field be held constant if there is to be no overlap of these two isotopes? Both isotopes appear as constituents of uranium hexafluoride gas (UF_6), and the gas molecules are all singly ionized.

30. An electron is moving in a uniform magnetic field of 0.25 T; its velocity components parallel and perpendicular to the field are both equal to 3.1×10^6 m/s. (a) What is the radius of the electron's spiral path? (b) How far does it move along the field direction in the time it takes to complete a full orbit about the field direction?

31. An electron moving at 3.8×10^6 m/s enters a region containing a uniform magnetic field $\mathbf{B} = 18\hat{\mathbf{k}}$ mT. The electron is moving at 70° to the field direction, as shown in Fig. 29-39. Find the radius r and pitch p of its spiral path, as indicated in the figure.

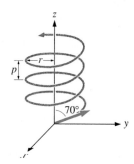

FIGURE 29-39 Problems 31, 32.

32. A proton in interstellar space describes a spiral path about a 15-mG magnetic field, with velocity component 40 km/s perpendicular to the field. If the pitch of the helix (see Fig. 29-39) is 8.7 km, what is the proton's velocity component parallel to the field?

Section 29-4 The Magnetic Force on a Current

33. What is the magnitude of the force on a 50-cm-long wire carrying 15 A at right angles to a 500-G magnetic field?

34. A wire coincides with the x axis, carrying 2.4 A in the $+x$ direction. The wire passes through a region containing a uniform magnetic field $\mathbf{B} = 0.17\hat{\mathbf{i}} + 0.32\hat{\mathbf{j}} - 0.21\hat{\mathbf{k}}$ T. Find a vector expression for the force per unit length on the wire in the magnetic field region.

35. A wire carrying 15 A makes a 25° angle with a uniform magnetic field. The magnetic force per unit length of wire is 0.31 N/m. (a) What is the magnetic field strength? (b) What is the maximum force per unit length that could be achieved by reorienting the wire in this field?

36. A wire of negligible resistance is bent into a rectangle as shown in Fig. 29-40, and a battery and resistor are connected as shown. The right-hand side of the circuit extends

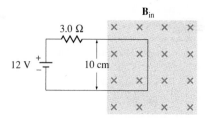

FIGURE 29-40 Problem 36.

into a region containing a uniform magnetic field of 38 mT pointing into the page. Find the magnitude and direction of the net force on the circuit.

37. In a high-magnetic-field experiment, a conducting bar carrying 7.5 kA passes through a 30-cm-long region containing a 22-T magnetic field. If the bar makes a 60° angle with the field direction, what force is necessary to hold it in place?

38. A 20-cm-long conducting rod with mass 18 g is suspended by wires of negligible mass, as shown in Fig. 29-41. The rod is in a region containing a uniform magnetic field of 0.15 T pointing horizontally into the page, as shown. An external circuit supplies current between the support points A and B. (a) What is the minimum current necessary to move the bar to the upper position shown? (b) Which direction should the current flow?

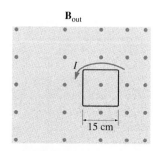

FIGURE 29-41 Problem 38.

39. A piece of wire with mass per unit length 75 g/m runs horizontally at right angles to a horizontal magnetic field. A 6.2-A current in the wire results in its being suspended against gravity. What is the magnetic field strength?

40. A nonuniform magnetic field points out of the page, as shown in Fig. 29-42. The field strength increases at the rate of 2.0 mT/cm as you move to the right. A square wire loop 15 cm on a side lies in a plane perpendicular to the field, and a 2.5-A current circles the loop in the counterclockwise direction. What are the magnitude and direction of the net magnetic force on the loop?

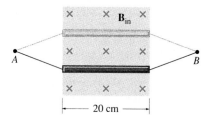

FIGURE 29-42 Problem 40.

41. A wire carrying 1.5 A passes through a region containing a 48-mT magnetic field. The wire is perpendicular to the field and makes a quarter-circle turn of radius 21 cm as it passes through the field region, as shown in Fig. 29-43. Find the magnitude and direction of the magnetic force on this section of wire

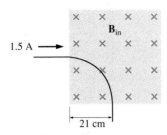

FIGURE 29-43 Problem 41.

42. A wire coincides with the x axis, and carries a current $I = 2.0$ A in the $+x$ direction. A nonuniform magnetic field points in the y direction, given by $\mathbf{B} = B_0(x/x_0)^2\hat{\mathbf{j}}$, where $B_0 = 0.22$ T, $x_0 = 1.0$ m, and x is the x coordinate. Find the force on the section of wire between $x = 1.0$ m and $x = 3.5$ m.

43. Apply Equation 29-8 to a closed current loop of arbitrary shape in a *uniform* magnetic field, and show that the net force on the loop is zero. *Hint:* Both I and B are constant as you go around the loop, so you can take them out of the integral. What is the remaining vector integral?

44. A rectangular copper strip measures 1.0 mm in the direction of a uniform 2.4-T magnetic field. When the strip carries a 6.8-A current at right angles to the field, the Hall voltage across the strip is 1.2 μV. Find the number density of free electrons in the copper.

45. The probe in a Hall-effect magnetometer uses a semiconductor doped to a charge-carrier density of 7.5×10^{20} m^{-3}. The probe measures 0.35 mm thick in the direction of the magnetic field being measured, and carries a 2.5-mA current perpendicular to the field. If its Hall potential is 4.5 mV, what is the magnetic field strength?

Section 29-5 A Current Loop in a Magnetic Field

46. Earth has a magnetic dipole moment associated with currents flowing in the planet's liquid outer core. Suppose that current flowed in a single loop at the outer edge of the liquid core (radius 3000 km). What current would be needed to give the observed dipole moment of 8.0×10^{22} A·m^2? (The actual current structure is more complex than a single loop.)

47. A single-turn square wire loop 5.0 cm on a side carries a 450-mA current. (a) What is the magnetic moment of the loop? (b) If the loop is in a uniform 1.4-T magnetic field with its dipole moment vector at 40° to the field direction, what is the magnitude of the torque it experiences?

48. An electric motor contains a 250-turn circular coil 6.2 cm in diameter. If it is to develop a maximum torque of 1.2 N·m at a current of 3.3 A, what should be the magnetic field strength?

49. A bar magnet experiences a 12-mN·m torque when it is oriented at 55° to a 100-mT magnetic field. What is the magnitude of its magnetic dipole moment?

50. A single-turn wire loop 10 cm in diameter carries a 12-A current. It experiences a torque of 0.015 N·m when the normal to the loop plane makes a 25° angle with a uniform magnetic field. What is the magnetic field strength?

51. A simple electric motor like that of Fig. 29-36 consists of a 100-turn coil 3.0 cm in diameter, mounted between the poles of a magnet that produces a 0.12-T field. When a 5.0-A current flows in the coil, what are (a) its magnetic dipole moment and (b) the maximum torque developed by the motor?

52. A satellite with rotational inertia 20 kg·m^2 is in orbit at a height where Earth's magnetic field strength is 0.18 G. It has a magnetic torquing system, as described in Example 29-7, that uses a 1000-turn coil 30 cm in diameter. What should be the current in the coil if the magnetic torque is to give the satellite a maximum angular acceleration of 0.0015 s^{-2}?

53. Nuclear magnetic resonance (NMR) is a technique for analyzing chemical structures and is also the basis of magnetic resonance imaging used for medical diagnosis. The NMR technique relies on sensitive measurements of the energy needed to flip atomic nuclei upside-down in a given magnetic field. In an NMR apparatus with a 7.0-T magnetic field, how much energy is needed to flip a proton ($\mu = 1.41 \times 10^{-26}$ A·m^2) from parallel to antiparallel to the field?

54. A wire of length ℓ carries a current I. (a) Find an expression for the magnetic dipole moment that results when the wire is wound into an N-turn circular coil. (b) For what integer value of N is this moment a maximum?

Paired Problems

(Both problems in a pair involve the same principles and techniques. If you can get the first problem, you should be able to solve the second one.)

55. Find the magnetic force on an electron moving with velocity $\mathbf{v} = 8.6 \times 10^5 \hat{\mathbf{i}} - 4.1 \times 10^5 \hat{\mathbf{j}}$ m/s in a magnetic field $\mathbf{B} = 0.18\hat{\mathbf{j}} + 0.64\hat{\mathbf{k}}$ T.

56. A proton moving with velocity $\mathbf{v} = 2.0 \times 10^5 \hat{\mathbf{i}} + 4.0 \times 10^5 \hat{\mathbf{j}}$ m/s experiences a magnetic force $\mathbf{F} = 10\hat{\mathbf{i}} - 5.0\hat{\mathbf{j}} + 21\hat{\mathbf{k}}$ fN. What is the z component of the magnetic field?

57. Proponents of space-based particle-beam weapons have to confront the effect of Earth's magnetic field on their beams. If a beam of protons with kinetic energy 100 MeV is aimed in a straight line perpendicular to Earth's magnetic field in a region where the field strength is 48 μT, what will be the radius of the protons' circular path?

58. Electrons are accelerated through a 30-kV potential difference at the rear of a TV tube. The electron beam is initially headed straight toward the center of the tube. The TV is oriented so the beam is perpendicular to Earth's magnetic field, in a location where the field strength is 62 μT. What will be the radius of the electron beam's curved path?

59. A 170-mT magnetic field points into the page, confined to a square region as shown in Fig. 29-44. A square conducting loop 32 cm on a side carrying a 5.0-A current in the

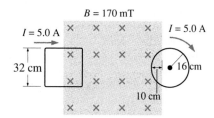

FIGURE 29-44 Problems 59, 60.

clockwise sense extends partly into the field region, as shown. Find the magnetic force on the loop.

60. Find the force on the circular current loop shown at the right of Fig. 29-44. The loop carries 5.0 A clockwise, has radius 16 cm, and extends 10 cm into the field region.

61. An old-fashioned analog meter uses a wire coil in a magnetic field to deflect the meter needle. If the coil is 2.0 cm in diameter and consists of 500 turns of wire, what should be the magnetic field strength if the maximum torque is to be 1.6 μN·m when the current in the coil is 1.0 mA?

62. A circular wire coil 15 cm in diameter carries a 460-mA current and experiences a 0.020-N·m torque when the normal to the coil makes a 27° angle with a 42-mT magnetic field. How many turns are in the coil?

Supplementary Problems

63. Electrons in a TV picture tube are accelerated through a 30-kV potential difference and head straight for the center of the tube, 40 cm away. If the electrons are moving at right angles to Earth's 0.50-G magnetic field, by how much do they miss the screen's exact center?

64. The coil in the loudspeaker of Fig. 29-31 consists of 100 turns of wire, 3.5 cm in diameter. The magnetic field strength at the coil is 0.64 T. Find the magnitude of the force on the speaker coil when the current in the coil is 2.1 A.

65. A conducting bar with mass 15.0 g and length 22.0 cm is suspended from a spring in a region where a 0.350-T magnetic field points into the page, as shown in Fig. 29-45. With no current in the bar, the spring length is 26.0 cm. The bar is supplied with current from outside the field

region, using wires of negligible mass. When a 2.00-A current flows from left to right in the bar, it rises 1.2 cm from its equilibrium position. Find (a) the spring constant and (b) the unstretched length of the spring.

66. In 2.0 μs, an electron moves 15 cm in the direction of a 0.10-T magnetic field. If the electron's velocity components perpendicular and parallel to the field are equal, (a) what is the length of its actual spiral trajectory and (b) how many orbits about the field direction does it complete?

67. A solid disk of mass M and thickness d sits on an incline, as shown in Fig. 29-46. A loop of wire is wrapped around the disk, running along a diameter and oriented so the loop is parallel to the incline. A uniform magnetic field $\mathbf{B}$ points vertically upward. Find an expression for the current I in the loop that will keep it from rolling down the incline.

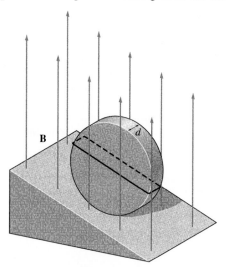

FIGURE 29-46 Problem 67.

68. A disk of radius R carries a uniform surface charge density σ and is rotating with angular frequency ω. Show that its magnetic dipole moment is $\frac{1}{4}\pi\sigma\omega R^4$. *Hint:* Divide the disk into concentric rings. Treat each as a loop carrying an infinitesimal current, and integrate over all the loops.

69. A 10-turn wire loop measuring 8.0 cm by 16 cm carrying 2.0 A lies in a horizontal plane but is free to rotate about the axis shown in Fig. 29-47. A 50-g mass hangs from one

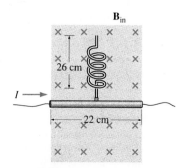

FIGURE 29-45 Problem 65.

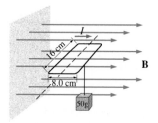

FIGURE 29-47 Problem 69.

side of the loop, and a uniform magnetic field points horizontally, as shown. What magnetic field strength is required to hold the loop in its horizontal position?

70. A closed current loop is made from two semicircular wire arcs of radius R, joined at right angles as shown in Fig. 29-48. The loop carries a current I and is oriented with the plane of one semicircle perpendicular to a uniform magnetic field **B**, as shown. Find (a) the magnetic moment of this nonplanar loop and (b) the torque on the loop. *Hint:* You can think of the loop as a superposition of two semicircular loops, each closed along the dashed line shown (why?).

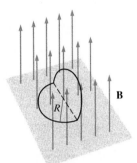

FIGURE 29-48 Problem 70.

71. A circular wire loop of mass m and radius R carries a current I. The loop is hanging horizontally below a cylindrical bar magnet, suspended by the magnetic force, as shown in Fig. 29-49. If the field lines crossing the loop make an angle θ with the vertical, show that the strength of the magnet's field at the loop's position is $B = mg/2\pi RI\sin\theta$.

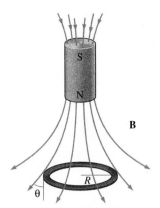

FIGURE 29-49 Problem 71.

72. A square wire loop of mass m carries a current I. It is initially in equilibrium, with its magnetic moment vector aligned with a uniform magnetic field **B**. The loop is rotated slightly out of equilibrium about an axis through the centers of two opposite sides and then released. Show that it executes simple harmonic motion with period given by $T = 2\pi\sqrt{m/6IB}$.

73. Early models pictured the electron in a hydrogen atom as being in a circular orbit of radius 5.29×10^{-11} m about the stationary proton, held in orbit by the electric force. Find the magnetic dipole moment of such an atom. This quantity is called the *Bohr magneton* and is typical of atomic-sized magnetic moments. *Hint:* The full electron charge passes any given point in the orbit once per orbital period. Use this fact to calculate the average current.

30 Sources of the Magnetic Field

Moving electric charge produces magnetic fields. Here a large electromagnet lifts scrap metal in a recycling operation. When the current through the electromagnet is switched off, it will drop the metal.

The preceding chapter introduced the magnetic field and its effect on matter. Here we consider the opposite question: How does matter produce magnetic fields in the first place? We've seen that magnetic fields exert forces on moving electric charges—a fact that implies a deep relation between electricity and magnetism. That relation in fact goes two ways: Not only do magnetic fields affect moving electric charges, but moving charges themselves produce magnetic fields.

30-1 THE BIOT-SAVART LAW

The first inkling of a relation between electricity and magnetism came in 1820 when the Danish scientist Hans Christian Oersted discovered that a compass needle is deflected by an electric current (Fig. 30-1). A mere month after Oersted's discovery became known in Paris, the French scientists Jean Baptiste Biot and Félix Savart had experimentally determined the form of the magnetic field arising from a steady current. Biot and Savart's result gives the contribution $d\mathbf{B}$ to the magnetic field at some point P due to a small element of current, just as Coulomb's law in the form of Equation 23-9a gives the contribution $d\mathbf{E}$ to the electric field from a small charge element dq:

$$d\mathbf{E} = \frac{k\, dq}{r^2}\hat{\mathbf{r}}$$

(see Fig. 30-2a). In this expression the field $d\mathbf{E}$ depends directly on the charge element dq, inversely on the square of the distance r, and on a universal constant, k (or, equivalently, $1/4\pi\varepsilon_0$). The direction of $d\mathbf{E}$ is determined by the unit vector $\hat{\mathbf{r}}$ from the charge element toward the field point P.

Biot and Savart found similar results for the magnetic field, as described in Fig. 30-2b. Here a steady current I is flowing, and we consider the contribution $d\mathbf{B}$ that a small length $d\ell$ of this current makes to the magnetic field at point P. The product $I\, d\ell$ plays the same role as does dq in Coulomb's law. Both dq and $I\, d\ell$ describe sources of the fields, charge for the electric field, and moving charge for the magnetic field. The quantity $I\, d\ell$ has the units of charge multiplied by velocity—showing that *moving* charge is at the heart of magnetism. Furthermore, the magnetic field due to the current element $I\, d\ell$ falls off inversely as the square of the distance, just like the electric field of a charge element dq.

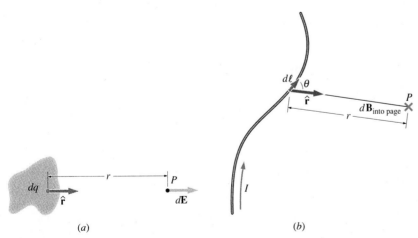

FIGURE 30-2 (a) Coulomb's law gives the electric field $d\mathbf{E}$ at point P due to an infinitesimal charge element dq. (b) The Biot-Savart law gives the magnetic field $d\mathbf{B}$ at point P arising from the current I flowing along the infinitesimal vector $d\ell$. The unit vector $\hat{\mathbf{r}}$ points from the current element $I\, d\ell$ toward the field point P.

But there are also important differences. The source of the electric field—charge—is a scalar quantity, whereas the source of the magnetic field is *moving* charge, and movement has direction. We can account for the direction of the current in Fig. 30-2*b* by defining a vector $d\ell$ whose magnitude is the length $d\ell$ and which points in the direction of the current. Biot and Savart found that the magnetic field $d\mathbf{B}$ depends on sine of the angle θ between this vector $d\ell$ and the unit vector $\hat{\mathbf{r}}$ from the current element $I\,d\ell$ toward the field point P, and that the direction of $d\mathbf{B}$ is perpendicular to both vectors. Mathematically, the $\sin\theta$ dependence and perpendicular direction together are described by a cross product. Thus our results for the magnetic field $d\mathbf{B}$ can be summarized in a compact vector equation, called the **Biot-Savart law**:

$$d\mathbf{B} = \frac{\mu_0}{4\pi}\frac{I\,d\ell \times \hat{\mathbf{r}}}{r^2}, \quad \text{(Biot-Savart law)} \qquad (30\text{-}1)$$

where μ_0 is a constant called the permeability constant, which has the exact value $4\pi \times 10^{-7}$ N/A^2.

Besides the more complicated directionality evidenced by the cross product in the Biot-Savart law, there's another distinction between the Biot-Savart law and Coulomb's law. Both describe the fields of localized structures—current elements and point charges—that are sources of the fields. It makes sense to talk about the electric field of an isolated point charge. But can we have an isolated current element? Not in a steady-state situation, where the current flowing into a current element must be the same as the current flowing out. Thus any Biot-Savart calculation necessarily involves the fields produced by many small current elements from an entire circuit. Experimentally, we find that the magnetic field obeys the superposition principle, so the net field at any point is the vector sum—or integral—of the fields of individual current elements:

$$\mathbf{B} = \int d\mathbf{B} = \int \frac{\mu_0}{4\pi}\frac{I\,d\ell \times \hat{\mathbf{r}}}{r^2}, \qquad (30\text{-}2)$$

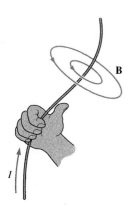

FIGURE 30-3 Magnetic field lines generally encircle a current. The field direction is given by the right-hand rule: Point your right thumb in the direction of the current, and your fingers curl in the direction of the field.

where the integration is taken over the entire circuit in which the current I flows. The field given by Equation 30-2 depends on the details of the current configuration, but the directionality associated with the cross product means that, quite generally, magnetic field lines encircle the current that is their source (Fig. 30-3).

EXAMPLE 30-1	*The Field of a Current Loop*

Solution

Find the magnetic field at an arbitrary point P on the axis of a circular loop of radius a carrying current I.

Let the loop axis be the x axis, with the origin at the loop center. Figure 30-4*a* shows the field contribution $d\mathbf{B}$ at P arising from a current element $I\,d\ell$ at the top of the loop, with its direction given by the cross product $d\ell \times \hat{\mathbf{r}}$. The symmetry of the situa-

tion shows that all points on the loop produce similar field elements $d\mathbf{B}$, each making the same angle θ with the axis, giving a net field that points along the axis (Fig. 30-4*b*). To find that net field we therefore need sum only the x components of the field contributions from around the loop.

Figure 30-4*a* also shows that the vectors $d\ell$ and $\hat{\mathbf{r}}$ are perpendicular; therefore, the product $d\ell \times \hat{\mathbf{r}}$ has magnitude $|d\ell||\hat{\mathbf{r}}|\sin 90° = d\ell$ since $\hat{\mathbf{r}}$ is a unit vector. Then the

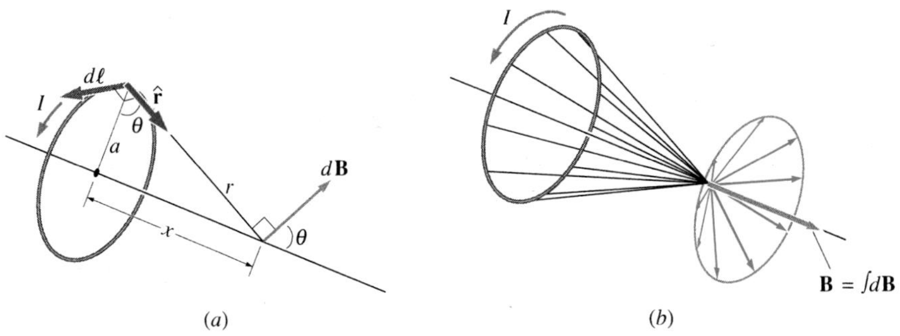

FIGURE 30-4 A current loop whose axis is the x axis. (a) The magnetic field $d\mathbf{B}$ arising from a current element of length $d\ell$ on the loop is perpendicular to the vectors $d\ell$ and $\hat{\mathbf{r}}$, and thus makes the angle θ with the loop axis. (b) Current elements all around the loop produce similar field elements $d\mathbf{B}$, with the result that the net field $\mathbf{B}$ points along the axis.

(a)

(b)

$\mathbf{B} = \int d\mathbf{B}$

magnitude of the field contribution $d\mathbf{B}$, as given by the Biot-Savart law, is

$$dB = \frac{\mu_0 I}{4\pi} \frac{|d\boldsymbol{\ell} \times \hat{\mathbf{r}}|}{r^2} = \frac{\mu_0 I}{4\pi} \frac{d\ell}{x^2 + a^2}.$$

To find the net field, we need to sum the x components $dB_x = dB \cos\theta$, which are the same for all current elements around the loop. Figure 30-4a shows that $\cos\theta = a/r = a/\sqrt{x^2 + a^2}$, so the net field becomes

$$B = \int_{\text{loop}} dB \cos\theta$$

$$= \int_{\text{loop}} \left(\frac{\mu_0 I}{4\pi} \frac{d\ell}{x^2 + a^2}\right)\left(\frac{a}{\sqrt{x^2 + a^2}}\right)$$

$$= \frac{\mu_0 I a}{4\pi(x^2 + a^2)^{3/2}} \int_{\text{loop}} d\ell,$$

where the integral reduces to such a simple form because the distance x is the same for all points on the loop. The remaining integral just means the sum of all the infinitesimal segments $d\ell$

around the loop—or the loop circumference $2\pi a$. Thus, the magnitude of the magnetic field on the loop axis becomes

$$B = \frac{\mu_0 I a^2}{2(x^2 + a^2)^{3/2}}. \tag{30-3}$$

ActivPhysics Activity 13.2 shows you the entire field of this current loop.

EXERCISE Earth's magnetic field at temperate latitudes is about 50 μT. You're experimenting with the effect of magnetic fields on living cells and need a control point where the magnetic field is zero. To get such a point, you orient a 12-cm-diameter wire loop so the field at its center just cancels Earth's field. What loop current is required?

Answer: 4.8 A

Some problems similar to Example 30-1: 1–3, 5, 15, 17

13.2
Magnetic Field of a Loop

We found in the preceding chapter that a current loop behaves like a magnetic dipole when it's in an external magnetic field. Does the loop also produce a dipole-like field? At points far from the loop ($x \gg a$), we can neglect a^2 compared with x^2 in the denominator of Equation 30-3, which then becomes

$$B = \frac{\mu_0 I a^2}{2x^3} = \frac{\mu_0}{2\pi} \frac{\mu}{x^3}, \qquad (x \gg a) \tag{30-4}$$

where the second equality follows by introducing the loop's magnetic dipole moment $\mu = I\pi a^2$ as defined in Equation 29-10. Equation 30-4 shows the inverse-cube behavior we found earlier for the field of an *electric* dipole. Although we derived it for a circular loop, Equation 30-4 in fact holds at large distances from a current loop of *any* shape, suggesting that the field is essentially that of a magnetic dipole. A much more difficult calculation would confirm that the distant field off the axis also shows an inverse-cube dependence and exhibits the angular dependence typical of a dipole. We conclude that, in both its response to magnetic fields and its production of magnetic fields:

▌ **A current loop constitutes a magnetic dipole.**

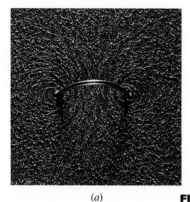

(a)

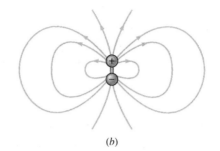

(b)   (c)

FIGURE 30-5 (a) The magnetic field of a current loop, as traced by iron filings. Note that field lines encircle the current-carrying wire. (b) The electric field of an electric dipole and (c) the magnetic field of a current loop. Far from their sources, the field patterns are identical, and exhibit the $1/r^3$ dependence of the dipole field.

Figure 30-5a shows the field of a current loop as traced by iron filings, while Figs. 30-5b, c compare the fields of an electric dipole and a magnetic dipole. It's the similarity of the overall field patterns—becoming mathematically identical at large distances, including the $1/r^3$ dependence—that leads us to identify the current loop as a magnetic dipole. Physically, a current-loop dipole doesn't look anything like its electric analog, a pair of opposite electric charges. But its behavior, both in response to magnetic fields and in producing magnetic fields, is completely analogous to that of an electric dipole with respect to electric fields. We'll see later that the familiar bar magnet is nothing but a collection of current-loop magnetic dipoles; what we call the north pole isn't a pole at all but just the end where magnetic field lines emerge from the current loops. The current loop in Fig. 30-5c acts essentially like a very short bar magnet, with its north end upward and south end downward. In fact, the electromagnet shown in the opening photo for this chapter is nothing but a current loop (actually many turns of wire), which produces a strong magnetic field when the current is on. We'll take a deeper look at electric and magnetic dipoles, and magnets, at the end of this chapter.

APPLICATION	*Magnetic Fields of Earth and Sun*

Earth, Sun, and many other astronomical objects possess magnetic fields. Reasonably close to Earth, the field approximates that of a magnetic dipole of dipole moment $\mu = 8.0 \times 10^{22}$ A·m^2 (Fig. 30-6). The direction of the dipole moment vector differs by about 11° from that of Earth's rotation axis, and this accounts for the difference between magnetic and true north. Locally, the field often deviates significantly from a pure dipole form, and these deviations provide geologists with

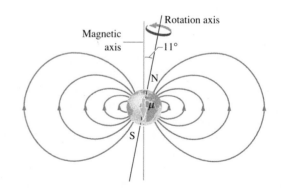

FIGURE 30-6 Earth's magnetic field approximates that of a magnetic dipole located near the center of the Earth and inclined at 11° to the rotation axis. Note from the field direction that Earth's "north" pole is really a magnetic south pole.

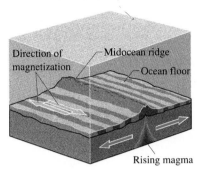

FIGURE 30-7 Magma emerges at the midocean ridges, pushing older portions of the ocean floor farther apart. As the magma solidifies, it becomes magnetized in the direction of Earth's magnetic field. (This occurs as atomic-scale current loops in magnetic materials such as iron align with the field and then retain permanently their magnetization, as we'll see later in the chapter.) Analysis of the ocean floor reveals bands of alternating magnetic polarity, showing that Earth's magnetic field reverses on a time scale of 10^5 to 10^6 years. Dark bands represent regions with Earth's present magnetic polarity.

clues to the detailed structure of the planet. The field is not constant; locally, its direction varies significantly over times as short as a few years, and the overall field reverses about every half million years or so (Fig. 30-7). At substantial distances from Earth the field is distorted from its dipole form by the solar wind, a flow of high-speed particles from the Sun (see Fig. 30-57, with Problem 30).

What causes Earth's magnetic field? We know that electric currents produce magnetic fields. Deep inside Earth are a solid inner core and a liquid outer core, both rich in iron. Through an interaction not yet fully understood, the planet's rotation combined with convective motions due to internal heating produces electric currents in the liquid core. For reasons even less well understood, those currents and the resulting magnetic field undergo reversals on a time scale of approximately a million years. Problems 5 and 6 deal with Earth's magnetic field and its origin.

Earth's magnetic field is crucial to our well-being. As we saw in the preceding chapter, high-energy particles from the Sun and elsewhere are trapped in the magnetic field and have difficulty reaching Earth's surface. Thus the field protects us from harmful particulate radiation. During the field reversals, which last about 10,000 years, the magnetic field is significantly reduced and surface exposure to high-energy particulate radiation is accordingly increased. Some scientists speculate that evolutionary changes due to radiation-induced mutations may accelerate at these times.

The Sun's magnetic field probably arises in the same way as does Earth's, although the gaseous nature of the star and the intense energy flow resulting from nuclear fusion in the Sun's core make its magnetic field much more dynamic. The Sun's field reverses every 11 years, giving rise to the solar activity cycle whose best-known indicator is the count of sunspots—regions of intense magnetic field at the solar surface (Fig. 30-8).

The complex behavior of astrophysical magnetic fields is governed entirely by Newton's laws and the laws of electromagnetism. That we do not yet fully understand these magnetic fields is testimony to the rich variety of phenomena subsumed under those laws.

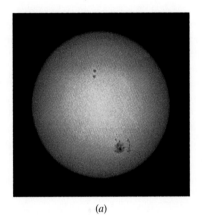

(a)

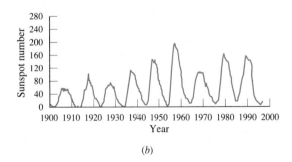

(b)

FIGURE 30-8 (a) Sunspots are regions of intense magnetic field at the Sun's surface. (b) The solar magnetic activity cycle is clearly evident in this plot of the number of sunspots.

Any steady current ultimately flows in a complete, closed circuit, and therefore at great distances its magnetic field is dipolar. But closer in the field configuration depends on the details of the current. An important case is the field near a straight stretch of current. We can approximate this field as that of an infinite line of current, which we calculate in Example 30-2.

| EXAMPLE 30-2 | *The Field of a Straight Wire* |

What is the magnetic field produced by an infinitely long straight wire carrying a steady current I?

Solution

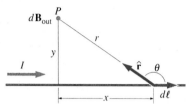

FIGURE 30-9 Geometry for calculating the field at P due to an infinite straight wire carrying a steady current I along the x axis. All current elements along the wire contribute fields at P that point out of the page.

Let the wire coincide with the x axis, and consider an arbitrary point P on the y axis. Figure 30-9 shows a current element $I\,d\ell$ on the wire. At point P the field $d\mathbf{B}$ of this element is perpendicular to both the wire and the vector $\hat{\mathbf{r}}$—that is, $d\mathbf{B}$ points out of the page. Clearly this is true for all current elements along the wire, so we can find the net field by integrating the field contributions dB without needing a vector integration. Using the Biot-Savart law, we have

$$dB = \frac{\mu_0 I}{4\pi} \frac{|d\ell \times \hat{\mathbf{r}}|}{r^2} = \frac{\mu_0 I}{4\pi} \frac{d\ell\,\sin\theta}{r^2},$$

where we used the fact that $\hat{\mathbf{r}}$ is a unit vector making an angle θ with $d\ell$. Figure 30-9 shows that $r^2 = x^2 + y^2$ and $\sin\theta = y/r = y/\sqrt{x^2 + y^2}$. And, since the segment $d\ell$ lies along the x axis, $d\ell = dx$. Making these substitutions and integrating over the entire wire (from $x = -\infty$ to $x = +\infty$) gives the net field at point P:

$$B = \int dB = \int_{-\infty}^{\infty} \frac{\mu_0 I}{4\pi} \frac{y\,dx}{(x^2 + y^2)^{3/2}}$$

$$= \frac{\mu_0 I y}{4\pi} \frac{x}{y^2 \sqrt{x^2 + y^2}}\bigg|_{-\infty}^{\infty},$$

where we found the integral in the table of integrals in Appendix A. (See Problem 71 for another approach.) At the limits $x = \pm\infty$ the expression $x/\sqrt{x^2 + y^2}$ takes on the values ± 1, so we have

$$B = \frac{\mu_0 I}{4\pi y}[1 - (-1)] = \frac{\mu_0 I}{2\pi y}. \tag{30-5}$$

Since the wire has cylindrical symmetry this result must hold anywhere, and the result is circular field lines encircling the wire, as shown in Fig. 30-10 and explored further in Activ-Physics Activity 13.1.

The field given by Equation 30-5 falls as the inverse of the distance from the wire. This should not be surprising: we found

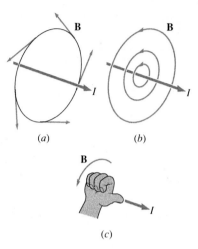

FIGURE 30-10 (*a*) Some magnetic field vectors associated with a straight wire carrying a steady current. (*b*) The corresponding magnetic field lines are circles, concentric with the wire. (*c*) The right-hand rule gives their direction.

the same dependence on distance for the *electric* field of an infinitely long charged line. The field patterns differ, though, in that the electric field points radially from the charged line while the magnetic field encircles the current-carrying wire. Although Equation 30-5 applies strictly only to an infinitely long wire, it is a good approximation for a finite wire at distances small compared with the wire length (Fig. 30-11).

EXERCISE A power line carries 450 A. How close would you have to be to the line for its magnetic field to equal Earth's 50-μT field?

Answer: 1.8 m

Some problems similar to Example 30-2: 4, 11, 57, 58

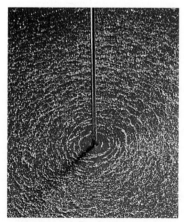

FIGURE 30-11 Iron filings trace out the circular magnetic field surrounding a current-carrying wire.

13.1
Magnetic Field of a Wire

Got It!

Figure 30-12 shows two wire loops bent into shapes consisting of straight and semicircular sections. Both loops carry the same steady current in the direction shown. (a) What will be the directions of the magnetic fields at the points P and Q? (b) At which point will the field be stronger?

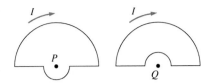

FIGURE 30-12 Think about the magnetic fields at points P and Q.

30-2 THE MAGNETIC FORCE BETWEEN TWO CONDUCTORS

In the preceding chapter we found the force on a straight wire of length ℓ carrying a current I through a magnetic field **B**:

$$\mathbf{F} = I\boldsymbol{\ell} \times \mathbf{B},$$

where the vector $\boldsymbol{\ell}$ is in the direction of the current flow. Through Equation 30-5 we now know the magnetic field produced by a long wire. If two long, parallel wires carry current in the same direction, as shown in Fig. 30-13, then each will experience a force arising from the other's field. We now determine that force.

If d is the distance between the wires, then at wire 2 the field magnitude B_1 due to the current I_1 is, from Equation 30-5,

$$B_1 = \frac{\mu_0 I_1}{2\pi d}.$$

The field is perpendicular to wire 2, so the magnitude of the force on a length ℓ of wire 2 is

$$F_2 = I_2 \ell B_1 = \frac{\mu_0 I_1 I_2 \ell}{2\pi d}. \tag{30-6}$$

Calculating the force on a length ℓ of wire 1 would amount to interchanging the subscripts 1 and 2, giving a force of the same magnitude.

What is the direction of the force? Evaluating the cross product of $\boldsymbol{\ell}$ and **B** in Fig. 30-13 shows that the force on wire 2 is toward wire 1, and vice versa. By using the right-hand rule, you can convince yourself that reversing one of the currents would reverse the directions of both forces. So we conclude that currents in the same direction experience an attractive magnetic force, while currents in the opposite direction experience a magnetic repulsion.

The force between nearby conductors must be considered in the construction of electrical devices carrying large currents. In electromagnets—coils of wire designed to produce large magnetic fields that can be turned on or off with the current in the coils—nearby conductors must have enough physical support that magnetic forces do not destroy the device (Fig. 30-14).

The hum you often hear around electrical equipment comes from the mechanical vibration of tightly wound conductors in transformers and other electrical components. This vibration results from the changing magnetic force associated with the 60-Hz alternating current.

The magnetic force between conductors is the basis for the definition of the ampere and, consequently, the coulomb. One ampere is defined as the current flowing in two long, parallel conductors 1 m apart when they carry equal currents and experience a magnetic force of 2×10^{-7} N on each meter of their length. It then follows that 1 coulomb is the amount of charge passing in 1 s through a wire carrying 1 A.

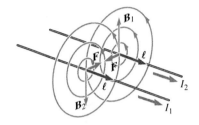

FIGURE 30-13 The magnetic force between two parallel wires carrying current in the same direction is attractive.

13.5
Magnetic Force on a Wire

FIGURE 30-14 This superconducting electromagnet was torn apart by the magnetic forces from a current of 50 kA flowing in its coils. The magnetic field reached 55 T—over one million times Earth's field. Coils were made from copper/niobium composite with the strength of steel and were reinforced with Kevlar and a steel casing. The coils originally encircled the channel where a pencil has been placed to show the scale.

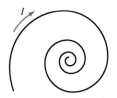

FIGURE 30-15 Will the spiral tighten or loosen when current flows as shown?

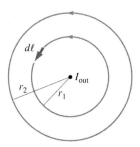

FIGURE 30-16 Two magnetic field lines surrounding a wire carrying current out of the page. The vector $d\ell$ denotes an infinitesimal portion of a circular path that coincides with the inner field line.

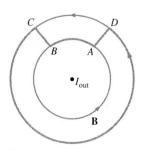

FIGURE 30-17 A closed loop that does not coincide with a single field line. The line integral of the magnetic field around this loop has the same value— $\mu_0 I$—that it has around a circular loop coinciding with a field line.

Got It!

A piece of wire is wound into a flat spiral as shown in Fig. 30-15. If a current is passed through the coil (supplied by flexible wires that aren't shown), will the coil tighten up or become looser? Will your answer change if the current direction reverses?

30-3 AMPÈRE'S LAW

In Chapter 23 we did several relatively cumbersome electric field calculations using Coulomb's law. For example, we found the field of an infinite line charge by integrating over all the charge elements along the line. Then in Chapter 24 we introduced Gauss's law and showed how it made electric field calculations much easier in situations with sufficient symmetry.

Can we make a statement that would enable us to calculate magnetic fields with comparable ease? Figure 30-16 shows two of the circular magnetic field lines surrounding a long wire carrying current I out of the page. Imagine moving around the inner circle. As you move a short way, form the product of the distance $d\ell$ that you travel with the component of the magnetic field in the direction you're going. Here the field is entirely in the direction of your path, so that product is simply $B\,d\ell$, where B is the field magnitude; more generally, it would be the dot product $\mathbf{B} \cdot d\ell$ to account for an arbitrary angle between the field and your path. Now consider adding up all these products as you go around a complete circle. Formally, the result is the line integral $\oint \mathbf{B} \cdot d\ell$, or, in this case where the directions of the path and field coincide, just $\oint B\,d\ell$. Here the circle indicates that the integration is done around a *closed* path. The magnitude of $\mathbf{B}$ is given by Equation 30-5: $B = \dfrac{\mu_0 I}{2\pi r_1}$, where we've replaced y by the radius r_1. Evaluating $\oint \mathbf{B} \cdot d\ell$ then gives

$$\oint \mathbf{B} \cdot d\ell = \frac{\mu_0 I}{2\pi r_1} \oint d\ell = \frac{\mu_0 I}{2\pi r_1}(2\pi r_1) = \mu_0 I,$$

where we took $B = \mu_0 I/2\pi r_1$ outside the integral because r_1 is the constant radius of the circular field line. What remains of the integral, $\oint d\ell$, is just the circumference, $2\pi r_1$. Our final answer, $\mu_0 I$, is thus independent of the radius r_1. We would get the same answer going around the outer circle, or indeed any circular path. On a larger path the distance is greater, but the field—dropping as $1/r$—is correspondingly weaker, making the value of $\oint \mathbf{B} \cdot d\ell$ the same. Thus the line integral $\oint \mathbf{B} \cdot d\ell$ does not depend on the radius of the circular path, but only on the current I encircled by that path.

We'll get the same result even if the path doesn't correspond to a field line. Figure 30-17 shows why for a path consisting of two circular arcs and radial lines joining them. The radial segments DA and BC contribute nothing to the quanity $\oint \mathbf{B} \cdot d\ell$ because the field is perpendicular to the path, and the large arc CD gives the same contribution as would the smaller arc BA because the field is weaker by just the right amount to compensate for arc CD's greater length. So going around the path shown in Fig. 30-17 gives the same value for the line integral—namely, $\mu_0 I$—as would going around a purely circular path. We can generalize this result to an arbitrary path by approximating the path as a series

FIGURE 30-18 Approximating an irregular loop as a series of arcs and radial segments shows that the line integral of the magnetic field is $\mu_0 I$ for *any* closed loop.

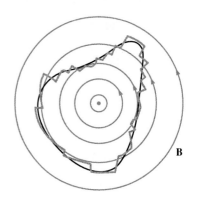

of circular arcs and radial segments (Fig. 30-18). Thus the quantity $\oint \mathbf{B} \cdot d\boldsymbol{\ell}$ has the same value, $\mu_0 I$, around *any* path surrounding a line current I. And because the superposition principle holds for magnetic fields, the result must be true for *any* distribution of current, not just the single line current we considered here. This result is in fact a universal statement about the relation between current and magnetic field:

> The value of the line integral $\oint \mathbf{B} \cdot d\boldsymbol{\ell}$ around any closed loop is proportional to the current encircled by that loop. Mathematically,

$$\oint \mathbf{B} \cdot d\boldsymbol{\ell} = \mu_0 I_{\text{encircled}} . \quad \text{(Ampère's law, steady currents)} \qquad (30\text{-}7)$$

This statement is a form of **Ampère's law**, one of the four fundamental laws of electromagnetism. Ampère's law says that whatever arrangement of currents we might have, and however complicated the resulting magnetic field, that field is such that the line integral $\oint \mathbf{B} \cdot d\boldsymbol{\ell}$ around any closed loop will have the value $\mu_0 I$, where I is the net current *encircled* by that loop. Compare this with Gauss's law, which says that whatever arrangement of electric charges we might have, the resulting electric field is such that the surface integral $\oint \mathbf{E} \cdot d\mathbf{A}$ has the value q/ε_0, where q is the *enclosed* charge.

There's one important restriction on Ampère's law as expressed in Equation 30-7: it's exactly correct only for *steady* currents—that is, currents that don't change with time. We'll show in Chapter 34 how to relax that restriction—with profound implications. Until then, we restrict ourselves to steady currents for which Equation 30-7 holds, or to currents that change only slowly, for which it's a good approximation.

With the restriction to steady currents, our statement of Ampère's law is true for *any* closed loop whatsoever, no matter what its shape or orientation: for any loop, the line integral of the magnetic field around the loop is proportional to the encircled current. It doesn't matter whether the current is in a single wire or in a number of wires or distributed throughout space; in any case, we simply add the currents to obtain the net current encircled by the loop. If there are currents flowing in opposite directions we add them with appropriate algebraic signs. A current counts as positive if, when you curl the fingers of your right hand in the direction of the loop, your right thumb points in the general direction of the current.

Although Ampère's law describes the relation between the magnetic field on a loop and the current *encircled* by that loop, we emphasize that the field $\mathbf{B}$ in Ampère's law is the *net field* from all currents, whether inside the loop or not. We found the same thing with Gauss's law, which relates the electric field $\mathbf{E}$ on a closed surface to the enclosed charge; $\mathbf{E}$ itself, however, is the *net field* arising from all sources, whether enclosed or not.

Ampère's law, like Gauss's, is a truly universal statement describing the relation between magnetic field and electric current. It holds in the electromagnetic devices we build, in atomic and molecular systems, in the interaction of fluid motion and electric charge that gives rise to Earth's magnetic field, and in distant astrophysical objects (Fig. 30-19). Although it is difficult to show mathematically, the Biot-Savart law follows logically from Ampère's law in the same sense that Coulomb's law follows from Gauss's.

(a)

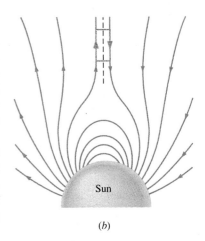

(b)

FIGURE 30-19 (*a*) A coronal streamer in the Sun's outer atmosphere contains oppositely directed magnetic fields in close proximity. (*b*) A model calculation of the coronal magnetic field. Since $\oint \mathbf{B} \cdot d\boldsymbol{\ell}$ is clearly nonzero around the loop shown, there must be current in the region encircled by the loop.

| **EXAMPLE 30-3** | *Solar Currents* |

The long dimension of the rectangular loop in Fig. 30-19*b* is 4×10^8 m, and the magnetic field strength in the vicinity of the loop is essentially constant at 2 mT. Find the total current encircled by the rectangle. In what direction is this current flowing?

Solution

We can't insert an ammeter into the Sun's atmosphere, but we can determine the current using Ampère's law. The short ends of the rectangle in Fig. 30-19*b* are perpendicular to the field, so here $\mathbf{B} \cdot d\boldsymbol{\ell} = 0$ and there is no contribution to the line integral around the loop. Moving around the loop in the direction shown means going *with* the field along both long dimensions (note that this is because the field direction reverses across the dashed line). Since the field is uniform, the contribution to the line integral from each side is just $B\ell$. Thus $\oint \mathbf{B} \cdot d\boldsymbol{\ell} = 2B\ell$. Ampère's law tells us that the line integral of the magnetic field around a closed loop has the value $\mu_0 I$, so

$$2B\ell = \mu_0 I,$$

or

$$I = \frac{2B\ell}{\mu_0} = \frac{(2)(2 \times 10^{-3} \text{ T})(4 \times 10^8 \text{ m})}{4\pi \times 10^{-7} \text{ N/A}^2} = 1 \times 10^{12} \text{ A}.$$

This is a colossal current by terrestrial standards, but is typical of large-scale currents on the Sun.

Since the line integral is positive, we curl our right fingers around the loop in the direction shown by the arrows and our thumb must point in the direction of the current—that is, into the page in Fig. 30-19. In three dimensions this current flows around the Sun in approximately the equatorial plane.

Tip

Amperian Loops The loop used with Ampère's law is truly arbitrary. It need not coincide with a field line, as Fig. 30-18 showed. Example 30-3 showed this, too; here, the rectangular loop coincided with the straight field lines over its long sides but not along its shorter ends. The loop used with Ampère's law is called an **amperian loop**. Don't confuse amperian loops with field lines!

EXERCISE Figure 30-20 shows a cross-sectional view of three wires carrying current perpendicular to the plane of the page. Wire *A* carries 20 A out of the page. $\oint \mathbf{B} \cdot d\boldsymbol{\ell}$ around loop 1 in the direction shown has the value 1.26×10^{-5} T·m, and the line integral around loop 2 has the value -6.28×10^{-6} T·m. Find the currents in wires *B* and *C*, and the directions of those currents.

Answers: *B*: 10 A into page; *C*: 5 A out of page

Some problems similar to Example 30-3: 28–30

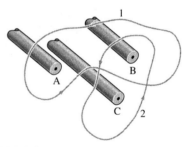

FIGURE 30-20 What are the currents in wires *B* and *C*?

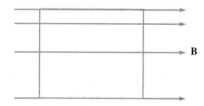

FIGURE 30-21 Which way is the current in this region? Gray rectangle is an amperian loop.

Got It!

Figure 30-21 shows a magnetic field that points to the right but increases in strength as you move up the page. A rectangular amperian loop is also shown. Use Ampère's law to argue that there must be current flowing in this region, and find its direction.

30-4 USING AMPÈRE'S LAW

For charge distributions with sufficient symmetry we used Gauss's law to solve for the electric field in a simple and elegant way. Similarly, for current distributions with sufficient symmetry we can use Ampère's law to solve for the magnetic field. Doing so requires finding suitable amperian loops over which we can evaluate the line integral of the magnetic field.

The Field of a Straight Wire

Here we use Ampère's law to determine the field of an infinite straight wire. This is the same calculation we did in Example 30-2 using the Biot-Savart law.

Figure 30-22 shows the wire, which carries current I. We know that magnetic field lines generally encircle the currents that are their sources. Here cylindrical symmetry requires that those field lines be circles centered on the wire and that the magnetic field strength cannot depend on angular position around the wire. Thus B must be constant on a field line. Applying the right-hand rule—thumb along the current, curling the fingers of the right hand—shows that the magnetic field circles counterclockwise around the wire. And since the wire is infinitely long, Fig. 30-22 represents the field anywhere along the wire.

Given the symmetry, an appropriate amperian loop for evaluating the line integral is itself a circle, also shown in Fig. 30-22. The magnetic field everywhere on this amperian loop is in the same direction as the loop, so the dot product $\mathbf{B} \cdot d\boldsymbol{\ell}$ becomes simply $B\,d\ell$. Then the line integral around the loop is

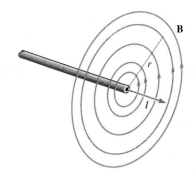

FIGURE 30-22 Circular field lines surrounding an infinitely long wire. Gray circle is an amperian loop for evaluating the line integral of the magnetic field. Although we've drawn only four field lines, the field exists everywhere, including on the amperian loop.

$$\oint_{\text{loop}} \mathbf{B} \cdot d\boldsymbol{\ell} = \oint_{\text{loop}} B\,d\ell = B\oint_{\text{loop}} d\ell = 2\pi r B.$$

Here we can take the field magnitude B outside the integral because it's constant on the circular amperian loop; the remaining integral is then the loop circumference $2\pi r$. Ampère's law equates this line integral to μ_0 times the encircled current, so

$$2\pi r B = \mu_0 I,$$

or

$$B = \frac{\mu_0 I}{2\pi r}. \tag{30-8}$$

This result is the same as Equation 30-5, but here we derived it in a much simpler way.

> **Tip**
>
> *Symmetry Is Crucial* Our use of Ampère's law to derive the field of a long wire depends crucially on symmetry. We cannot arbitrarily pull B outside the integral unless we know—as we do here from symmetry—that it is constant in magnitude and in direction relative to our amperian loop.

Our calculation made no assumptions about the diameter of the wire. Therefore Equation 30-8 holds for any long cylindrical wire, thick or thin, as long as we restrict ourselves to points *outside* the wire so that our amperian loop encircles the *entire* current. In fact, you can easily convince yourself that Equation 30-8 must hold *outside* any current distribution with cylindrical symmetry. To calculate the field *inside* a current distribution, however, we must be careful to use only the actual current encircled by our amperian loop. Example 30-4 illustrates this point.

EXAMPLE 30-4	*Inside a Wire*

A long, straight wire of radius R carries a current I uniformly distributed over its cross-sectional area. What is the magnetic field as a function of position within the wire?

Solution

All the symmetry arguments we used to find the field outside a wire still apply here, so the line integral around a circular amperian loop of radius r is still $2\pi r B$. What's different is that an amperian loop within the wire no longer encircles the entire current (Fig. 30-23). How much current is encircled? The current is distributed uniformly, giving a current density (current per unit area) $J = I/A = I/\pi R^2$. The encircled current is then the current density times the loop area, or

$$I_{encircled} = \left(\frac{I}{\pi R^2}\right)(\pi r^2) = I\frac{r^2}{R^2}.$$

Equating the line integral $2\pi r B$ to μ_0 times this encircled current gives

$$2\pi r B = \mu_0 I \frac{r^2}{R^2},$$

or

$$B = \frac{\mu_0 I r}{2\pi R^2}. \tag{30-9}$$

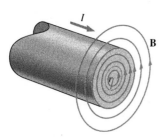

FIGURE 30-23 Cross section of a long cylindrical wire carrying current out of the page. Symmetry requires that the magnetic field be circular inside as well as outside the wire. Current is distributed uniformly over the wire; in applying Ampère's law to the amperian loop shown in gray we need the fraction of the total current encircled by the loop.

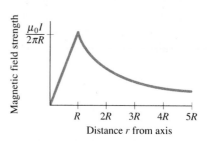

FIGURE 30-24 The magnetic field inside a wire is zero at the wire's axis and increases linearly with radial distance, while beyond the wire radius R it drops as $1/r$.

Does this result make sense? The field increases linearly with distance from the axis—just as we found for the *electric* field *inside* a uniformly charged cylinder. Here the increase occurs because we encircle more and more current—with $I_{encircled}$ growing as r^2—as long as we're inside the wire. Once we reach the surface, of course, the encircled current remains constant and the field begins to decrease inversely with distance, as described in Equation 30-8. Figure 30-24 plots the field strengths both inside and outside the wire.

This example is not merely academic; in superconducting wires, for example, strong magnetic fields can destroy superconductivity, so it's important to know the field throughout the wire.

EXERCISE A power line 4.0 cm in diameter carries 1.5 kA. Find the magnetic field (a) 1.0 cm from the axis of the wire and (b) 10 cm from the axis.

Answers: (a) 7.5 mT; (b) 3.0 mT

Some problems similar to Example 30-4: 32, 33, 37, 65

Got It!

A coaxial cable consists of an inner wire carrying current I in one direction, and an outer cylindrical conductor carrying the same current in the opposite direction; the current is distributed symmetrically in the outer conductor. (See Fig. 30-60 if the configuration isn't clear). If the current in the outer conductor only is doubled, will the magnetic field change (a) in between the two conductors or (b) outside the outer conductor?

<table>
<tr><td>**EXAMPLE 30-5**</td><td>*A Current Sheet*</td></tr>
</table>

An infinite flat sheet carries a current out of the page, as shown in Fig. 30-25. The current is distributed uniformly along the sheet, with the current per unit width along the sheet given by J_s. Find the magnetic field of this sheet.

Solution

What might the field of this sheet look like? Figure 30-26 suggests that we can consider the sheet to be made of many parallel wires. The vector sum of the fields of these wires gives a net field to the left above and to the right below the sheet. We can also argue from symmetry that the fields must point horizontally and with magnitude that is independent of position parallel to the sheet; since the sheet extends infinitely to the right and left, there's nothing to favor an upward or downward deflection of the field lines or any variation in field magnitude

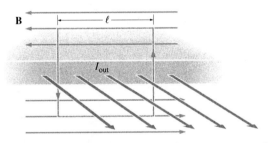

FIGURE 30-25 A current sheet (gray) extends infinitely to the left and right, as well as in and out of the page. Field lines and a rectangular amperian loop are also shown.

parallel to the sheet. We've drawn these horizontal field lines, and an appropriate amperian loop, in Fig. 30-25.

We already evaluated $\oint \mathbf{B} \cdot d\boldsymbol{\ell}$ for a similar geometry in Example 30-3; the result is simply $2B\ell$, with ℓ the width of the amperian rectangle. The current per unit width of the sheet is J_s, so our rectangular loop of width ℓ encircles a current $I = J_s\ell$. Equating μ_0 times this encircled current to the line integral $\oint \mathbf{B} \cdot d\boldsymbol{\ell} = 2B\ell$ gives

$$2B\ell = \mu_0 J_s \ell,$$

or
$$B = \tfrac{1}{2}\mu_0 J_s. \qquad (30\text{-}10)$$

Thus the magnetic field of an infinite current sheet is independent of distance from the sheet. We found the same result for the electric field of an infinite charged plane. Although the infinite sheet is an idealization, Equation 30-10 is a good approximation to the field near long, wide, flat conductors. Thin current sheets also form in conducting plasmas like those in fusion reactors and in the Sun's atmosphere, where they can lead to sudden dissipation of energy.

EXERCISE Current in a printed circuit board is carried in a long copper strip 2.1 mm wide and much thinner than its width. If the current in the strip is 35 mA, spread uniformly over its cross section, find the magnetic field strength near the strip's surface.

Answer: 10 μT

Some problems similar to Example 30-5: 38, 39, 42

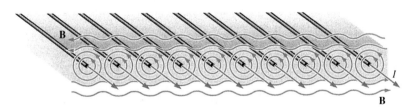

FIGURE 30-26 A current sheet approximated by closely spaced parallel wires. The magnetic field of the sheet is the vector superposition of the fields of the individual wires. In the limit of infinitesimally spaced wires, the field lines become straight and strictly horizontal.

Fields of Simple Current Distributions

We've just used Ampère's law to calculate the magnetic fields of two simple, symmetric current distributions. Although those magnetic fields may look quite different from the electric fields of correspondingly symmetric charge distributions, they exhibit the same dependences on distance. Table 30-1 summarizes the electric and magnetic fields of several simple charge and current distributions. Real distributions are usually more complicated, but often they can be approximated by these simple cases. Far from any current loop, for example, the magnetic field is that of a dipole. Very near *any* wire, its magnetic field is essentially that

TABLE 30-1 *Fields of Some Simple Charge and Current Distributions*

DISTRIBUTION	FIELD DEPENDENCE ON DISTANCE*	ELECTRIC OR MAGNETIC FIELD
Electric dipole	$\dfrac{1}{r^3}$	
Magnetic dipole	$\dfrac{1}{r^3}$	
Spherically symmetric charge distribution	$\dfrac{1}{r^2}$	
Spherically symmetric current distribution	Impossible for steady current	
Charge distribution with line symmetry	$\dfrac{1}{r}$	
Current distribution with line symmetry	$\dfrac{1}{r}$	
Infinite flat sheet of change	Uniform field; no variation	
Current sheet	Uniform field; no variation	

* For field *outside* distribution.

of a long straight wire. For situations that lack symmetry and in which approximations are not adequately accurate, we can always calculate the magnetic field of
a steady current distribution from the Biot-Savart law, just as we can always
calculate the electric field of an arbitrary charge distribution from Coulomb's law.

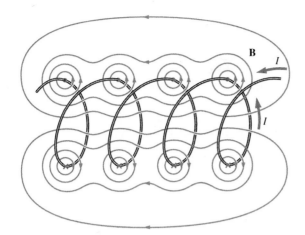

FIGURE 30-27 The magnetic field arising from the current in a loosely wound coil of wire is strongest within the coil and weaker outside. Field is shown only in the plane of the page; dots show current emerging from the page and crosses mark current going into the page.

30-5 SOLENOIDS AND TOROIDS

We found in Chapter 26 that we can produce a uniform electric field between the two closely spaced, charged conducting plates of a capacitor. Is there an analogous device that will produce a uniform magnetic field?

Figure 30-27 shows a coil of wire carrying current I. Close to the wire are magnetic field lines encircling the wire. We show these field lines in Fig. 30-27 at the top and bottom of the coil, where they cross the plane of the page. The net field anywhere is, of course, just the vector sum of the field contributions from all parts of the coil. You can see that inside the coil, the fields from current elements at the top and bottom all have a component to the right and so tend to reinforce. Outside the coil, though, field components from top and bottom are in opposite directions and thus reduce the net field, which points to the left as shown in the figure.*

Imagine making the coil longer and winding it more tightly. Such a long, tightly wound coil is a **solenoid**. Figure 30-28 shows what happens as the solenoid gets longer: the interior field stays essentially the same, but exterior field lines spread into more distant regions before closing back on themselves. Therefore, the field strength outside the solenoid—as evidenced by the density of field lines— decreases. In the limit of an infinitely long solenoid, the interior field becomes perfectly straight and the exterior field goes to zero. A real solenoid approaches this ideal limit when its length is much greater than its diameter. Figure 30-29 shows the field of a solenoid as traced by iron filings. Incidentally, the solenoid fields of Figs. 30-28 and 30-29 might remind you of the field of a bar magnet. They should: we'll soon see that a bar magnet and a solenoid, although superficially very different things, are magnetically very similar.

* Because the coil carries a net current from right to left, there is also a weak field component outside that encircles the coil. This component plays no role in the discussion that follows, and we ignore it.

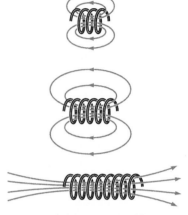

FIGURE 30-28 As a solenoid gets longer, the interior field stays nearly constant but the exterior field weakens as the field lines spread ever farther apart.

13.3
Magnetic Field of a Solenoid

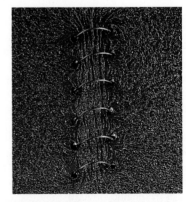

FIGURE 30-29 Iron filings trace the magnetic field of a solenoid. Note that the field is strong inside the solenoid, causing the filings to align strongly, and relatively weak outside, except near the ends. (With ActivPhysics Activity 13.3 you can simulate the pattern of iron filings around a solenoid.)

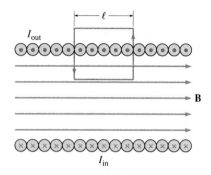

FIGURE 30-30 Cross section of a long solenoid, showing a rectangular amperian loop straddling the region where the solenoid coils emerge from the plane of the page.

In the long-solenoid limit, we can use Ampère's law to find the field in the solenoid. Figure 30-30 shows a cross section through a long solenoid, with a rectangular amperian loop. Since the exterior field is zero, there's no contribution to the line integral $\oint \mathbf{B} \cdot d\boldsymbol{\ell}$ from the top of the amperian loop. The loop's vertical sides are at right angles to the field, so they, too, contribute nothing to the line integral. The only contribution is from the bottom of the loop. Going counterclockwise around the loop, we move with the field on this segment. Since the field cannot vary with position along the infinite solenoid, the contribution to the line integral is just $B\ell$; since the other three sides contribute nothing, this is the value of $\oint \mathbf{B} \cdot d\boldsymbol{\ell}$.

To apply Ampère's law we need the encircled current. If there are n turns per unit length of solenoid, the amperian loop encircles $n\ell$ turns. The same current I flows in each turn, so the encircled current is $n\ell I$. Applying Ampère's law then gives

$$B\ell = \mu_0 n \ell I,$$

or

$$B = \mu_0 nI. \quad \text{(solenoid)} \tag{30-11}$$

Since the vertical dimension of the amperian rectangle never entered our calculation, this field magnitude is the same anywhere inside the solenoid. The magnetic field in the solenoid is therefore uniform. Although it looks very different, the long solenoid with its uniform magnetic field is the magnetic analog of a closely spaced parallel-plate capacitor, which produces a uniform electric field.

Although Figs. 30-27 and 30-28 depict circular coils, the derivation of Equation 30-11 is based only on Fig. 30-30, which could represent a solenoid whose coils are circular, square, or any other shape.

APPLICATION	*Everyday Solenoids, Medical Solenoids*

Solenoids of all sizes are used in a wide variety of experimental and practical devices. Because a solenoid is hollow, magnetic materials such as iron will be pulled into the solenoid by the nonuniform magnetic field near its ends, and solenoids are therefore used to produce straight-line motion in mechanical devices. For example, turning the key to start your car sends current through a solenoid in the car's starter motor. A magnetic field develops in the solenoid, pulling in a steel plunger. Movement of the plunger joins a set of electrical contacts allowing current to flow to the starter motor. At the same time, the rod moves a small gear to the end of the motor shaft, engaging a gear on the engine's flywheel so that the starter motor can turn the engine (Fig. 30-31).

Running a dishwasher or washing machine also involves solenoids. The valves that control the flow of water in these machines are solenoid valves, opened and closed as a steel rod moves in or out of a solenoid.

Finally, huge solenoids with human-size interiors are used to produce the strong, uniform magnetic fields needed for magnetic resonance imaging (MRI). This high-tech medical

FIGURE 30-31 Cross section of a car starter motor, showing the workings of the solenoid. Turning the key to start the car sends current through the solenoid coils, creating a magnetic field that pulls the steel plunger into the solenoid. The lever attached to the plunger then pushes the gear outward on the shaft, engaging a larger gear on the gasoline engine. The electric starter motor turns to start the engine. Armature of the motor is the coil that forms the heart of the motor (recall Figs. 29-35 and 29-36).

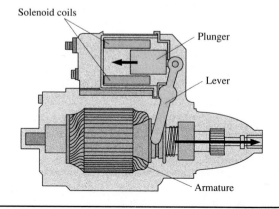

technique images the body's interior without the need for X rays or other radiation (Fig. 30-32). The MRI solenoids use superconducting wire cooled with liquid helium to achieve high currents and correspondingly high magnetic fields.

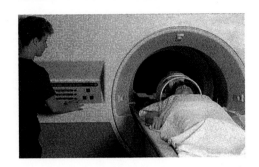

FIGURE 30-32 Patient being inserted into a superconducting solenoid used for magnetic resonance imaging (MRI), a powerful and relatively new medical diagnostic technique.

EXAMPLE 30-6	*An MRI Solenoid*

A solenoid used in magnetic resonance imaging is 2.4 m long and 95 cm in diameter. It is wound from a niobium-titanium superconducting wire 2.0 mm in diameter, with adjacent turns separated by an insulating layer of negligible thickness. What current is necessary to produce a 1.5-T magnetic field inside the solenoid?

Solution

The magnetic field is given by Equation 30-12, $B = \mu_0 n I$, so if we know n—the number of turns per unit length—we can solve for I. Since the wire has diameter $d = 2.0$ mm, 5 turns will occupy 1 cm and therefore $n = 500$ turns/meter. Solving

Equation 30-11 for I then gives

$$I = \frac{B}{\mu_0 n} = \frac{(1.5 \text{ T})}{(4\pi \times 10^{-7})(500 \text{ m}^{-1})} = 2.4 \text{ kA}.$$

This is a large current, but readily handled by the niobium-titanium superconductor.

EXERCISE Copper wire 0.40 mm in diameter is tightly wound into a long solenoid, and a 3.6-A current passed through it. What is the magnetic field in the solenoid?

Answer: 11 mT

Some problems similar to Example 30-6: 43–45, 48

Toroids

A **toroid** is a solenoid bent into a doughnut shape (Fig. 30-33). Toroidal geometry is widely used in fusion reactors, as discussed in the preceding chapter, and toroidal coils help produce the magnetic field that confines the fusion plasma.

Symmetry requires that the toroid's field lines be circular, with constant magnitude on any line. We can readily calculate the line integral of this magnetic field around a circular amperian loop, like that shown in Fig. 30-34. This loop coincides with a field line, and symmetry ensures that the magnetic field has the same magnitude over the loop. Therefore the line integral becomes

$$\oint_{\text{loop}} \mathbf{B} \cdot d\ell = \oint_{\text{loop}} B \, d\ell = B \oint_{\text{loop}} d\ell = 2\pi r B.$$

To apply Ampère's law we equate this quantity to μ_0 times the encircled current. If the toroid consists of N turns and carries a current I, then an amperian loop inside the toroid encircles a total current NI. Then Ampère's law becomes

$$2\pi r B = \mu_0 N I,$$

or

$$B = \frac{\mu_0 N I}{2\pi r}. \qquad \text{(toroid)} \qquad (30\text{-}12)$$

FIGURE 30-33 A toroidal coil.

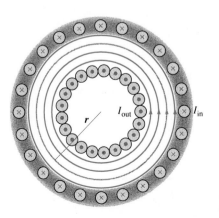

FIGURE 30-34 Cross section of a toroid showing current emerging at inner edge of coils and descending into plane of page at outer edge. Also shown are circular field lines and an amperian loop of radius r (gray) for use in calculating the field. You can confirm the field direction using the right-hand rule.

This result holds when the amperian loop is within the toroid itself. But if it's inside the inner edge (inside the "doughnut's hole"), there's no encircled current and, therefore, no magnetic field. And beyond the outer edge, the amperian loop encircles equal but opposite currents, giving zero net current and again no magnetic field. As with a solenoid, the individual turns of a toroid need not be circular.

The toroidal field of Equation 30-12 is not uniform but exhibits a $1/r$ decrease. This nonuniformity causes problems with plasma confinement in fusion reactors, where it causes a drift of particles perpendicular to the field and therefore toward the walls of the machine.

30-6 MAGNETIC MATTER

FIGURE 30-35 In the classical model of the atom, the circling electron constitutes a miniature current loop. The atom is therefore a magnetic dipole. Here the current—carried by the *negative* electron and therefore opposite the electron's motion—is counterclockwise when viewed from above, so the magnetic moment points upward.

We began our study of magnetism in Chapter 29 with a discussion of magnets. But we quickly moved on to concentrate on the behavior of electric charges in magnetic fields. In this chapter we've further developed the relation between magnetism and electric charge, as we've seen that moving electric charge is the source of magnetic fields. What does electric charge have to do with the familiar magnets we used to introduce magnetism?

In fact the two are one and the same phenomenon. When an electron orbits an atomic nucleus, its circular motion and charge make a miniature current loop, and it therefore constitutes a magnetic dipole (Fig. 30-35); if you worked Problem 73 in the preceding chapter then you've calculated the dipole moment for a simple atomic model. In addition the electron possesses an intrinsic magnetic dipole moment associated with an intrinsic angular momentum called "spin." Interactions among these magnetic dipole moments determine the magnetic properties of individual atoms and of bulk matter. Although an accurate description of magnetism in matter necessarily involves quantum mechanics, we can nevertheless use our knowledge of magnetic dipoles to gain a qualitative understanding of magnetic matter.

Ferromagnetism

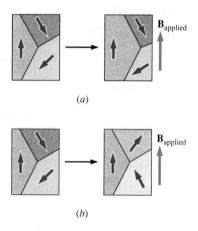

FIGURE 30-36 Domain changes in a ferromagnetic material occur through (a) domain growth and (b) domain realignment. These changes occur when a magnetic field is applied, and result in the material acquiring a net magnetic moment.

Experiment reveals three types of magnetic behavior in bulk matter. **Ferromagnetism**, the most familiar, is actually limited to a few substances, notably the elements iron, nickel, and cobalt, and some compounds. In a ferromagnetic material, a quantum-mechanical interaction among nearby atomic magnetic moments results in regions—called **magnetic domains**—in which all the atomic magnetic moments point in the same direction. A typical domain contains 10^{17} to 10^{21} atoms and occupies a volume on the order of 10^{-12} to 10^{-8} m³. The magnetic moment of a single domain can be large since it's the sum of many atomic magnetic moment vectors all pointing in the same direction. A typical piece of ferromagnetic material, however, contains many domains with their moments in random directions and, therefore, exhibits no net magnetic moment. But when an external magnetic field is applied, a net magnetic moment develops. This occurs because domains that already happen to be aligned with the field can grow by realignment of individual atomic moments in adjacent domains (Fig. 30-36a). In addition, the magnetic moments of entire domains can rotate (Fig. 30-36b).

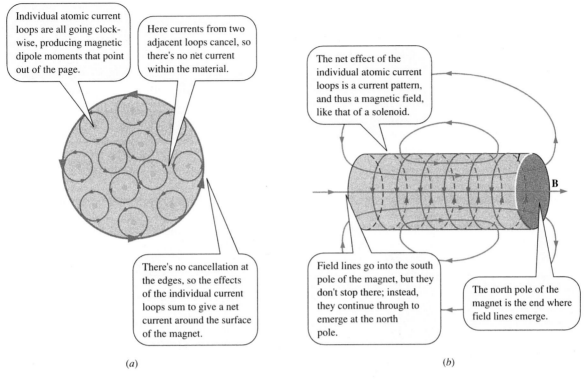

FIGURE 30-37 (*a*) Cross section of a bar magnet, showing individual atomic current loops all aligned the same way (dots represent the magnetic moment vectors). *Within* the material, adjacent atomic currents cancel. But they don't cancel at the edges, leaving a net current encircling the magnet. (*b*) Side view shows that this magnetization current is similar to the current in the coils of a solenoid. The bar magnet's field is therefore similar to that of a solenoid.

Since any dipole experiences a force in a nonuniform field, a piece of ferromagnetic material in such a field experiences a net force; this is why iron and other ferromagnetic materials are attracted to magnets even though they themselves are not magnets.

Some ferromagnetic materials retain significant magnetization even after the applied field has been removed. These so-called *hard* ferromagnetic materials make permanent magnets. A common bar magnet is a piece of hard ferromagnetic material that's been magnetized with its internal magnetic dipoles aligned along its long dimension. We suggested earlier that a bar magnet is magnetically similar to a solenoid, and Fig. 30-37 shows why: the internal atomic current loops give a net current flowing around the magnet, just like the current in a solenoid. This so-called magnetization current, however, arises not from the steady flow of charge in the material, but as the sum of the individual atomic current loops.

Permanent magnetization persists unless a strong magnetic field is applied that changes its direction or strength. Computer disks, credit cards, and audio- and videotapes (Fig. 30-38) make use of hard ferromagnetic materials that

FIGURE 30-38 Videotapes, credit cards, and computer disks all store information using hard ferromagnetic materials.

retain information as patterns of permanent magnetization; these magnetic media can be "rewritten" by applying a magnetic field strong enough to alter the magnetization and thus the stored information. We'll take a closer look at magnetic recording in the next chapter.

Permanent magnetization in so-called "soft" ferromagnetic materials, in contrast, is negligible. Such materials are used in applications that require magnetization to be turned on and off rapidly; these include the "heads" that read and write information on computer disks and audio- and videotapes, as well as electromagnets such as the one shown at the beginning of this chapter.

Random thermal motions tend to disrupt the alignment of individual magnetic moments. Thus ferromagnetic effects weaken with increasing temperature. Above the so-called **Curie temperature**, ferromagnetism ceases altogether. Curie temperatures for the common ferromagnetic elements nickel, iron, and cobalt are 631, 1043, and 1395 K, respectively. The rarer ferromagnetic elements dysprosium and gadolinium have much lower Curie temperatures of 85 and 289 K, respectively. The disappearance of ferromagnetism at the Curie temperature is an example of a phase transition, analogous to the solid/liquid/gas transitions we studied in Chapter 20.

Paramagnetism

Many substances that are not ferromagnetic nevertheless consist of atoms or molecules with permanent magnetic dipole moments. What distinguishes these **paramagnetic** materials from ferromagnetic substances is the absence of a strong interaction that tends to align nearby moments. As a result, individual atomic moments are not organized into domains, but point in random directions. An applied magnetic field still brings the atomic magnetic moments into some degree of alignment, but at all but the coldest temperatures this alignment is far less complete than in a ferromagnetic material. Therefore paramagnetic materials are attracted only weakly to magnets (Fig. 30-39), and paramagnetism decreases with increasing temperature. Unlike ferromagnetism, paramagnetism is not a strong enough effect to have many technological applications, but it does provide an important way of probing the structure of materials and can also be exploited to help achieve very low temperatures.

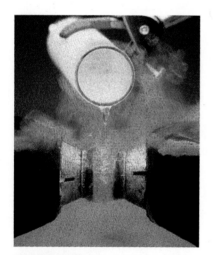

FIGURE 30-39 Liquid oxygen (O_2) is one of the more strongly paramagnetic materials. Here liquid oxygen is suspended between the poles of a magnet.

Diamagnetism

Even materials with no intrinsic magnetic moments can have magnetic moments induced when a magnet approaches or when an applied magnetic field otherwise changes. Such materials are termed **diamagnetic**. In contrast to paramagnetic and ferromagnetic materials, diamagnetic materials are repelled by magnets. We will explore the origins of diamagnetism in the next chapter.

Magnetic Susceptibility

We can characterize the effect of atomic magnetic dipoles on bulk matter just as we did in Chapter 23 for electric dipoles in dielectrics. There we found that atomic electric dipoles align with an electric field to reduce the field within the material, and we introduced the dielectric constant κ as the factor quantifying that reduction.

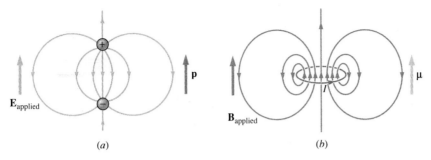

$E_{applied}$

p

$B_{applied}$

μ

(a)   *(b)*

FIGURE 30-40 Although the electric fields far from electric and magnetic dipoles have the same form, the fields *within* the atomic structure giving rise to the different dipole moments have opposite directions. This is because electric dipoles consist of separated point charges, while magnetic dipoles are current loops. When external electric and magnetic fields are applied, respectively, to these two structures, the result is a reduction in the net electric field but an increase in the net magnetic field.

In a magnetic material, alignment of atomic magnetic dipoles has the opposite effect: the field in the material is increased. Figure 30-40 shows why. An electric dipole consists of two separated point charges. The strongest field associated with this dipole is the internal field pointing straight from the positive to the negative charge. When the dipole aligns with an applied electric field, this internal field is *opposite* the applied field and, therefore, *reduces* the net electric field (Fig. 30-40*a*). But, as we've seen, magnetic field lines always *encircle* a current. As Fig. 30-40*b* shows, the field inside the current loop therefore points in the *same* direction as the applied field and, therefore, *increases* the net magnetic field.

Because of the very strong alignment of atomic dipoles that occurs in ferromagnetic materials, these materials greatly increase an applied magnetic field. For that reason the coils of electromagnets, including the heads of computer disk drives and VCRs, are usually wound on a ferromagnetic core to give a much stronger field than would be provided by the coil current alone.

In analogy with the dielectric constant, we introduce the quantity κ_M, called the **relative permeability**, as the factor by which the magnetic field within a material increases as a result of the alignment of atomic magnetic dipoles. For paramagnetic materials, κ_M is slightly greater than 1; for ferromagnetic materials it is much greater than 1. In diamagnetic materials the dipoles align antiparallel to the field; this makes $\kappa_M < 1$ for these materials. Because the relative permeabilities of paramagnetic and diamagnetic materials are very close to 1, it's more convenient to work with the **magnetic susceptibility** χ_M, defined by

$$\chi_M = \kappa_M - 1.$$

The internal field in the material is then given by

$$B_{int} = \kappa_M B_{applied} = (\chi_M + 1)B_{applied}. \tag{30-13}$$

Equation 30-13 is most useful for paramagnetic and diamagnetic materials. In a ferromagnetic material, the internal and external fields are not proportional, and the internal field depends on the past history of the material's exposure to magnetic fields. This phenomenon, called **hysteresis**, is what makes possible

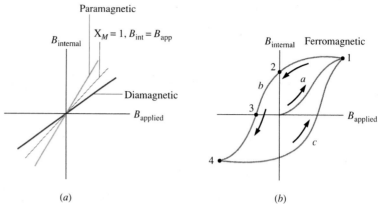

FIGURE 30-41 Internal versus applied magnetic field for different types of magnetic materials. (*a*) In diamagnetic and paramagnetic materials the relationship is linear; paramagnetic materials strengthen the applied field slightly, while diamagnetic materials weaken it slightly. (*b*) In ferromagnetic materials, the relationship depends on the strength of the applied field and on the past history of the material. As the applied field is increased, an initially unmagnetized ferromagnetic material responds by developing an increasing internal field (curve *a*). Eventually the field saturates (point 1) at its maximum possible value. Decreasing the applied field to zero leaves the material with a permanent magnetization (point 2); only a strong field in the opposite direction can eliminate (point 3) and eventually reverse the magnetization (point 4). Curve is for a "hard" ferromagnetic material that retains strong permanent magnetization; curve for a "soft" material would be much narrower, with a much smaller internal field at point 2. Axes are not to scale; field strengths on the vertical axis are much larger, reflecting the high magnetic susceptibility of a ferromagnetic material. Arrows indicate that the applied field is increased (curve *a*), decreased (curve *b*), and increased again (curve *c*).

permanent magnets. Figure 30-41 shows a ferromagnetic material's response to an externally applied magnetic field. If the material is initially unmagnetized, its internal field first increases with increasing applied field (curve *a* in Fig. 30-41). Eventually, though, increasing the applied field leads to little or no increase in the internal field; the material is then **saturated**, and no higher internal field is possible. Saturation occurs when essentially all the magnetic domains in the material are aligned, so there's no way to increase the internal field further. If the applied field is then reduced, the internal field also falls, but not as quickly. Even at zero applied field, there can remain a strong internal field due to the permanent magnetization we discussed earlier (point 2 in Fig. 30-41). Finally, a sufficiently strong field in the opposite direction results in saturation with the opposite magnetization direction.

Table 30-2 lists some magnetic susceptibilities for all three types of magnetic materials. That the ferromagnetic materials listed have susceptibilities many orders of magnitude higher than others shows why we normally think of magnetism only in the context of these special materials. The highest susceptibilities are achieved with special alloys such as permalloy and supermalloy; these are used in making high-field permanent magnets for a variety of applications. The material called "mu metal" is used for magnetic shielding—for example, to prevent distortion by external fields in TV picture tubes and computer monitors, or to shield the magnets used in loudspeakers (recall Fig. 29-31) so they can be placed near videotapes or TV sets without causing damage or distortion. Of the paramagnetic materials listed, liquid oxygen has by far the highest susceptibility, showing again the effect of temperature on paramagnetism. Finally, note the entry for superconductors, which are perfectly diamagnetic. Their susceptibility of -1 implies that $\kappa_M = 0$, showing that they completely exclude magnetic fields. We will explore the reasons for this in the next chapter.

TABLE 30-2 *Magnetic Susceptibilities**

MATERIAL	MAGNETIC SUSCEPTIBILITY, χ_M
Diamagnetic materials	
Copper	-9.6×10^{-6}
Lead	-1.6×10^{-5}
Mercury	-2.8×10^{-5}
Nitrogen (gas, 293 K)	-6.7×10^{-9}
Sodium chloride	-1.4×10^{-5}
Any superconductor	-1
Water	-9.1×10^{-6}
Paramagnetic materials	
Aluminum	2.1×10^{-5}
Chromium	3.1×10^{-4}
Oxygen (gas, 293 K)	1.9×10^{-6}
Oxygen (liquid, 90 K)	3.5×10^{-3}
Sodium	8.5×10^{-6}
Ferromagnetic materials (field and history dependent; maximum value listed)	
Iron (annealed)	5.5×10^{3}
Permalloy (55% Fe, 45% Ni)	2.5×10^{4}
Supermalloy (15.7% Fe, 79% Ni, 5.0% Mo; 0.30% Mn)	8.0×10^{5}
μ-metal (77% Ni, 16% Fe, 5% Cu, 2% Cr)	1.0×10^{5}

*At 300 K unless noted.

30-7 MAGNETIC MONOPOLES AND GAUSS'S LAW

Electric and magnetic fields, at least as we've studied them so far, have very different configurations. Electric fields begin and end on their sources—namely electric charges. Magnetic fields, in contrast, encircle their sources—namely *moving* electric charges. Magnetic fields generally form closed loops, while the electric fields we've encountered so far do not (Fig. 30-42).

Are there particles analogous to electric charges, from which magnetic field lines might originate? There might be. Symmetry arguments based on the existence of electric charge and the many similarities between electricity and magnetism have long suggested to physicists that such **magnetic monopoles**—isolated magnetic north or south poles—might exist. Furthermore, theories of elementary particles suggest that magnetic monopoles should have been created in the Big Bang event that began our universe. However, recent versions of the

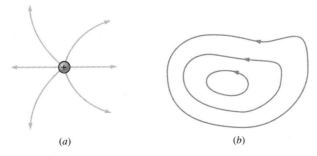

(a)   *(b)*

FIGURE 30-42 At this point in our study of electromagnetism, electric and magnetic field configurations are clearly distinguished. Electric fields (a) begin and end on electric charges, while magnetic fields (b) generally form closed loops.

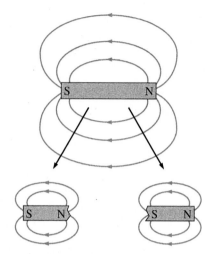

FIGURE 30-43 You can't separate the north and south poles of a bar magnet by cutting it in half; that only produces smaller bar magnets, each with a north and a south pole and thus each a magnetic dipole. That's because the field of a bar magnet arises from atomic current loops (recall Fig. 30-37), not from separate magnetic north and south poles, or monopoles.

Big Bang theory suggest that monopoles should be spread so thinly as to make the chance of detecting one completely negligible.

If they existed, magnetic monopoles would be to the magnetic field what electric charges are to the electric field. Isolated monopoles would give rise to radial magnetic fields like the electric fields of point charges. Monopoles would experience forces in magnetic fields, forces given simply by the product of the monopole's "magnetic charge" and the magnetic field. And *moving* magnetic monopoles would produce electric fields—just as moving electric charges produce magnetic fields.

No one has yet found a magnetic monopole, however, although serious experimental searches continue. Every magnetic field we've ever seen has its origin in moving electric charge, not in separate magnetic north and south poles. That's why you can't make an isolated magnetic north pole by chopping a bar magnet in half (Fig. 30-43). The observed absence of magnetic monopoles means that the most fundamental magnetic field configuration is that of the dipole—in contrast to the simpler electric case, where the spherically symmetric point-charge field is possible. That's why Table 30-1 contains no magnetic entry under spherical geometry.

In the absence of magnetic monopoles, there is no place where magnetic field lines begin or end. That means there is no closed surface through which a nonzero net number of magnetic field lines emerges. In complete analogy with our discussion of Gauss's law in Chapter 24, we can say that the **magnetic flux**—mathematically, the surface integral $\oint \mathbf{B} \cdot d\mathbf{A}$—is zero for every closed surface. This statement is **Gauss's Law for magnetism**:

$$\oint \mathbf{B} \cdot d\mathbf{A} = 0. \tag{30-14}$$

Equation 30-14 is another of the four fundamental laws of electromagnetism. We've now seen three of them: Gauss's law for electricity, Ampère's law (still incomplete because of its restriction to *steady* currents), and Gauss's law for magnetism. In the next chapter we'll encounter the fourth of these fundamental laws.

Although Gauss's law for magnetism has zero on its right-hand side, the law is far from being devoid of content. It says what we've already found to be the case: that magnetic fields must configure themselves so they have no beginnings or endings.

CHAPTER SYNOPSIS

Summary

1. Magnetic fields arise from **moving electric charges**. The field at some point P arising from a steady electric current is described by the **Biot-Savart law**:

$$d\mathbf{B} = \frac{\mu_0}{4\pi} \frac{I \, d\boldsymbol{\ell} \times \hat{\mathbf{r}}}{r^2},$$

where $d\mathbf{B}$ is the contribution to the field from a current element flowing along the infinitesimal vector $d\boldsymbol{\ell}$ a distance r from the point P, and $\hat{\mathbf{r}}$ is a unit vector from the current element toward P. The field at P of an entire current distribution is found by integrating all its contributions $d\mathbf{B}$.

Important special cases include a current loop, which at large distances produces a dipole field, and an infinite straight current, whose field encircles the current and decreases as $1/r$.

2. The field arising from a current exerts a magnetic force on nearby currents; as a result, parallel currents in the same direction attract and those in opposite directions repel.

3. **Ampère's law** relates the line integral of the magnetic field around an arbitrary closed loop to the current encircled by that loop:

$$\oint_{\text{loop}} \mathbf{B} \cdot d\boldsymbol{\ell} = \mu_0 I_{\text{encircled}}.$$

This form holds for all steady currents. It may be used to calculate magnetic fields in cases with sufficient symmetry, including line symmetry (straight wires), plane symmetry (current sheets), solenoids, and toroids.

4. Individual elementary particles and orbiting atomic electrons constitute miniature current loops, which are responsible for magnetic effects in bulk matter. The **relative permeability**, κ_M, gives the ratio of the internal magnetic field in a material to the applied field; this relation is also described by the **magnetic susceptibility**, $\chi_M = \kappa_M - 1$.

   a. In **ferromagnetic** materials, atomic magnetic moments group into domains with net magnetic moments. These align with an applied field, greatly increasing the field within the material. Ferromagnetic materials retain magnetization even after the applied field is removed; this phenomenon of **hysteresis** accounts for permanent magnets. $\kappa_M \gg 1$ for ferromagnetic materials, although the internal field depends on both the applied field and the material's history.

   b. In **paramagnetic** materials, individual atomic magnetic moments become partially aligned with an applied field, but there is no cooperative interaction among the individual moments. $\kappa_M > 1$ for paramagnetic materials.

   c. Diamagnetic materials have no intrinsic magnetic moments. They have $\kappa_M < 1$ and are weakly repelled from magnets.

5. No **magnetic monopoles**, or magnetic analogs of electric charge, have ever been found. Magnetic fields—originating from moving electric charge—therefore form closed loops without beginnings or ends. In the absence of magnetic monopoles, **Gauss's law for magnetism** says that the flux of the magnetic field through any closed surface is zero:

$$\oint \mathbf{B} \cdot d\mathbf{A} = 0.$$

Terms You Should Understand

(Pairs are closely related terms whose distinction is important; number in parentheses is chapter section where term first appears.)

Biot-Savart law (30-1)
Ampère's law (30-3)
solenoid, toroid (30-5)
ferromagnetism, paramagnetism, diamagnetism (30-6)
permeability, susceptibility (30-6)
magnetic monopole (30-7)
Gauss's law for magnetism (30-7)

Symbols You Should Recognize

μ_0 (30-1)

$\oint \mathbf{B} \cdot d\boldsymbol{\ell}$ (30-3)

κ_M, χ_M (30-6)

Problems You Should Be Able to Solve

calculating magnetic fields of simple current distributions by integration using the Biot-Savart law (30-1)
evaluating forces between adjacent conductors (30-2)
evaluating magnetic fields using Ampère's law in situations with sufficient symmetry (30-4)
applying results derived in the text for the fields of straight wires, current loops, solenoids, and toroids (30-1–30-5)
relating internal and applied magnetic fields given magnetic susceptibility (30-6)

Limitations to Keep in Mind

The Biot-Savart law, and Ampère's law as expressed in this chapter, are exactly valid only for *steady* currents—those that never change with time.

QUESTIONS

1. In what two senses does a current loop behave like a magnetic dipole?

2. The electric field far from a pair of equal but opposite charges has the same configuration as the magnetic field far from a current loop. Yet inside the structure giving rise to the fields, the two point in opposite directions. Why?

3. The Biot-Savart law shows that the magnetic field of a current element decreases as $1/r^2$. Could you put together a complete circuit whose field exhibits this $1/r^2$ decrease? Why or why not?

4. Do currents in the same direction attract or repel? Explain.

5. If a current is passed through an unstretched spring, will the spring contract or expand? Explain.

6. Why is it advantageous to define the ampere in terms of magnetic force rather than a standard ammeter?

7. An intense beam of electrons or other charged particles tends to "pinch" or compress to a smaller diameter. Explain the origin of this "pinch effect" in terms of magnetic forces.

8. The field of a long, straight wire consists of circular field lines. Does Ampère's law hold for a square loop surrounding the wire? For a circular loop not concentric with the wire? See Fig. 30-44.

9. If the line integral around a closed loop is zero, does that mean the magnetic field on the loop is zero?

10. Must the integration path in Ampère's law coincide with a field line?

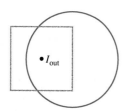

FIGURE 30-44 Question 8.

11. What must be going on inside Earth in order that it have a magnetic field?

12. Figure 30-45 shows some magnetic field lines associated with two parallel wires carrying equal currents perpendicular to the page. Are the currents in the same or opposite directions? How can you tell?

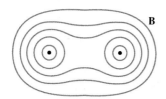

FIGURE 30-45 Question 12.

13. A solid cylinder and a hollow pipe of the same outer diameter carry the same current along their long dimensions, with the current distributed symmetrically about their axes. How do the magnetic fields at their surfaces compare?

14. Why is a piece of iron attracted into a solenoid?

15. Would there be a net magnetic force on a piece of iron deep inside a long solenoid? Explain.

16. In what sense is a long solenoid the magnetic analog of a parallel-plate capacitor?

17. What would happen to the magnetic field inside a solenoid if you (a) doubled the solenoid length without changing the number of turns per unit length or (b) doubled the length without changing the total number of turns?

18. Identify *three* regions in the magnetic field of Fig. 30-46 where there *must* be a current. Which way is the current flowing in each region?

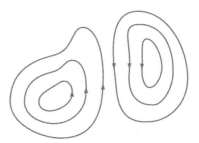

FIGURE 30-46 Question 18.

19. An unmagnetized piece of iron has no net magnetic dipole moment. Yet it is attracted to either pole of a bar magnet. Why?

20. How would you determine experimentally whether a substance was paramagnetic or diamagnetic?

21. Would permanent magnets be possible if the relative permeability of ferromagnetic materials were strictly constant? Explain.

22. Why do paramagnetic and ferromagnetic effects weaken with increasing temperature?

23. If magnetic monopoles existed, then a net motion of monopoles would constitute a "magnetic current." What sort of field should arise from such a "current?"

24. In the absence of magnetic monopoles, why do we even bother to write Gauss's law for magnetism? Does the law have any physical significance?

PROBLEMS

ActivPhysics can help with these problems:
Activities 13.1–13.3, 13.5

Section 30-1 The Biot-Savart Law

1. A wire carries 15 A. You form the wire into a single-turn circular loop with magnetic field 80 μT at the loop center. What is the loop radius?

2. A single-turn wire loop is 2.0 cm in diameter and carries a 650-mA current. Find the magnetic field strength (a) at the loop center and (b) on the loop axis, 20 cm from the center.

3. A 2.2-m-long wire carrying 3.5 A is wound into a tight, loop-shaped coil 5.0 cm in diameter. What is the magnetic field at its center?

4. What is the current in a long wire if the magnetic field strength 1.2 cm from the wire's axis is 67 μT?

5. Suppose Earth's magnetic field arose from a single loop of current at the outer edge of the planet's liquid core (core radius 3000 km), concentric with Earth's center. What current would be necessary to give the observed field strength of 62 μT at the north pole? (The currents responsible for Earth's field are more complicated than this problem suggests.)

6. Earth's magnetic dipole moment is 8.0×10^{22} A·m². What is the magnetic field strength on Earth's surface at either pole?

7. A single-turn current loop carrying 25 A produces a magnetic field of 3.5 nT at a point on its axis 50 cm from the loop

center. What is the loop area, assuming the loop diameter is much less than 50 cm?

8. Two identical current loops are 10 cm in diameter and carry 20-A currents. They are placed 1.0 cm apart, as shown in Fig. 30-47. Find the magnetic field strength at the center of either loop when their currents are in (a) the same and (b) opposite directions.

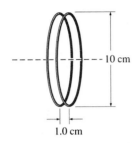

FIGURE 30-47 Problem 8.

9. You have a spool of thin wire that can handle a maximum current of 0.50 A. If you wind the wire into a looplike coil 20 cm in diameter, how many turns should the coil have if the magnetic field at its center is to be 2.3 mT at this maximum current?

10. A single piece of wire is bent so that it includes a circular loop of radius a, as shown in Fig. 30-48. A current I flows in the direction shown. Find an expression for the magnetic field at the center of the loop.

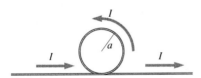

FIGURE 30-48 Problem 10.

11. Two long, parallel wires are 6.0 cm apart. One carries 5.0 A and the other 10 A, with both currents in the same direction. Where on a line perpendicular to both wires is the magnetic field zero?

12. Four long, parallel wires are located at the corners of a square 15 cm on a side. Each carries a current of 2.5 A, with the top two currents into the page in Fig. 30-49 and the bottom two out of the page. Find the magnetic field at the center of the square.

13. A power line carries a 500-A current toward magnetic north and is suspended 10 m above the ground. The horizontal component of Earth's magnetic field at the power line's latitude is 0.24 G. If a magnetic compass is placed on the ground directly below the power line, in what direction will it point?

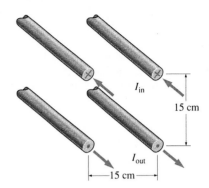

FIGURE 30-49 Problems 12, 23.

14. An electron is moving at 3.1×10^6 m/s parallel to a 1.0-mm-diameter wire carrying 20 A. If the electron is 2.0 mm from the center of the wire, with its velocity in the same direction as the current, what are the magnitude and direction of the force it experiences?

15. Part of a long wire is bent into a semicircle of radius a, as shown in Fig. 30-50. A current I flows in the direction shown. Use the Biot-Savart law to find the magnetic field at the center of the semicircle (point P).

FIGURE 30-50 Problem 15.

16. Use the result given in Problem 57 to find the magnetic field strength at the center of a square loop of side a carrying current I.

17. Figure 30-51 shows a conducting loop formed from concentric semicircles of radii a and b. If the loop carries a current I as shown, find the magnetic field at point P, the common center.

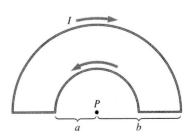

FIGURE 30-51 Problem 17.

Section 30-2 The Magnetic Force between Two Conductors

18. In standard household wiring, parallel wires about 1 cm apart carry currents around 15 A. What is the magnitude of the force per unit length between such wires?

19. It would take a rather large apparatus to implement the definition of the ampere given at the end of Section 30-2. Suppose you wanted to use a smaller apparatus, with wires 50 cm long separated by 2.0 cm. What force would correspond to a current of 1 A?

20. Two parallel copper rods supply power to a high-energy experiment, carrying the same current in opposite directions. The rods are held 8.0 cm apart by insulating blocks mounted every 1.5 m. If each block can tolerate a maximum tension force of 200 N, what is the maximum allowable current?

21. The structure shown in Fig. 30-52 is made from conducting rods. The upper horizontal rod is free to slide vertically on the uprights, while maintaining electrical contact with them. The upper rod has mass 22 g and length 95 cm. A battery connected across the insulating gap at the bottom of the left-hand upright drives a 66-A current through the structure. At what height h will the upper wire be in equilibrium?

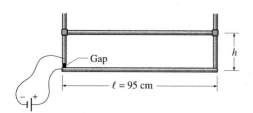

FIGURE 30-52 Problem 21.

22. Three parallel wires 4.6 m long each carry 20 A in the same direction. They are spaced at the vertices of an equilateral triangle 3.5 cm on a side. Find the magnitude of the force on each wire.

23. The wires in Fig. 30-49 carry 2.5-A currents in the directions indicated. Find the net force per unit length on the wire at lower left.

24. A long, straight wire carries 20 A. A 5.0-cm by 10-cm rectangular wire loop carrying 500 mA is located 2.0 cm from the wire, as shown in Fig. 30-53. Find the net magnetic force on the loop.

25. A solenoid 10 cm in diameter is made with 2.1-mm-diameter copper wire wound so tightly that adjacent turns touch, separated only by enamel insulation of negligible thickness. The solenoid carries a 28-A current. In the long, straight wire approximation, what is the net force between two adjacent turns of the solenoid?

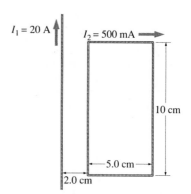

FIGURE 30-53 Problem 24.

26. A long, flat conducting ribbon of width w is parallel to a long straight wire, with its near edge a distance a from the wire (Fig. 30-54). Wire and ribbon carry the same current I; this current is distributed uniformly over the ribbon. Use integration to show that the force per unit length between the two has magnitude $\dfrac{\mu_0 I^2}{2\pi w}\ln\left(\dfrac{a+w}{a}\right)$.

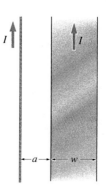

FIGURE 30-54 Problem 26.

Section 30-3 Ampère's Law

27. The line integral of the magnetic field on a closed path surrounding a wire has the value 8.8 μT·m. What is the current in the wire?

28. In Fig. 30-55, $I_1 = 2$ A flowing out of the page; $I_2 = 1$ A, also out of the page, and $I_3 = 2$ A, into the page. What is the line integral of the magnetic field taken counterclockwise around each loop shown?

29. The magnetic field shown in Fig. 30-56 has uniform magnitude 75 μT, but its direction reverses abruptly. How much current is encircled by the rectangular loop shown?

30. The solar wind drags Earth's magnetic field out into a long "magnetotail," where the field reverses direction abruptly

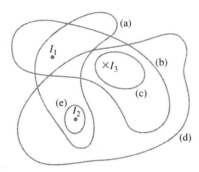

FIGURE 30-55 Problem 28.

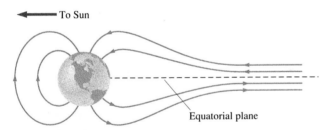

FIGURE 30-56 Problem 29.

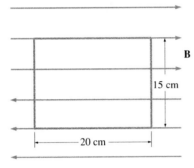

FIGURE 30-57 A simplified view of Earth's magnetic field, showing the long "magnetotail" on the nighttime side, caused by the solar wind dragging Earth's field lines with it. What's the current in the region to the right, where the field lines are essentially straight? (Problem 30)

across the equatorial plane (Fig. 30-57). (a) If the field strength in a section of the magnetotail is 20 nT, what is the current per unit length flowing in the magnetotail? (b) What is the direction of this current in Fig. 30-57?

31. Figure 30-58 shows a magnetic field pointing in the x direction. Its strength, however, varies with position in the y direction. At the top and bottom of the rectangular loop shown the field strengths are 3.4 μT and 1.2 μT, respectively. How much current flows through the area encircled by the loop?

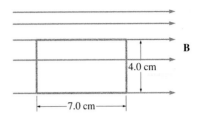

FIGURE 30-58 Problems 31, 66.

Section 30-4 Using Ampère's Law

32. (a) What is the magnetic field strength 0.10 mm from the axis of a 1.0-mm-diameter wire carrying 5.0 A distributed uniformly over its cross section? (b) What is the field strength at the surface of the wire?

33. A solid wire 2.1 mm in diameter carries a 10-A current with uniform current density. What is the magnetic field strength (a) at the axis of the wire, (b) 0.20 mm from the axis, (c) at the surface of the wire, and (d) 4.0 mm from the wire axis?

34. Show that Equations 30-8 and 30-9 give the same results when evaluated at the surface of the wire.

35. A long conducting rod of radius R carries a nonuniform current density given by $J = J_0 r/R$, where J_0 is a constant and r is the radial distance from the rod's axis. Find expressions for the magnetic field strength (a) inside and (b) outside the rod.

36. A long, hollow conducting pipe of radius R carries a uniform current I along the pipe, as shown in Fig. 30-59. Use Ampère's law to find the magnetic field strength (a) inside and (b) outside the pipe.

FIGURE 30-59 Problem 36.

37. Typically, cylindrical wires made from yttrium-barium-copper-oxide superconductor can carry a maximum current density of 6.0 MA/m² at a temperature of 77 K, as long as magnetic field at the conductor surface does not exceed 10 mT. Suppose such a wire is to carry the maximum current density. (a) At what wire diameter would the surface magnetic field equal the 10-mT limit? (b) Is this a maximum or minimum value for the diameter if the field is not to exceed the limit? (c) What current would a wire with this diameter carry?

38. A copper ribbon 1.0 cm wide and 0.15 mm thick is rated for a maximum safe current density of 8.8×10^6 A/m².

What is the maximum magnetic field strength achievable at the surface of this ribbon?

39. Two large, flat conducting plates lie parallel to the x-y plane. They carry equal currents, one in the $+x$ and the other in the $-x$ direction. In each plate the current per meter of width in the y direction is J_s. Find the magnetic field strength (a) between and (b) outside the plates.

40. The coaxial cable shown in Fig. 30-60 consists of a solid inner conductor of radius a and a hollow outer conductor of inner radius b and thickness c. The two carry equal but opposite currents I, uniformly distributed. Find expressions for the magnetic field strength as a function of radial position r (a) within the inner conductor, (b) between the inner and outer conductors, and (c) beyond the outer conductor.

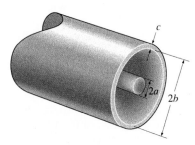

FIGURE 30-60 Problems 40, 61.

41. A hollow conducting pipe of inner radius a and outer radius b carries a current I parallel to its axis and distributed uniformly through the pipe material (Fig. 30-61). Find expressions for the magnetic field for (a) $r < a$, (b) $a < r < b$, and (c) $r > b$, where r is the radial distance from the pipe axis.

FIGURE 30-61 Problem 41.

42. A conducting slab extends infinitely in the x and y directions and has thickness h in the z direction. It carries a uniform current density $\mathbf{J} = J\hat{\mathbf{i}}$. Find the magnetic field strength (a) inside and (b) outside the slab, as functions of the distance z from the center plane of the slab.

Section 30-5 Solenoids and Toroids

43. A superconducting solenoid has 3300 turns per meter and can carry a maximum current of 4.1 kA. What is the magnetic field strength in the solenoid?

44. A solenoid used in a plasma physics experiment is 10 cm in diameter, 1.0 m long, and carries a 35-A current to produce a 100-mT magnetic field. (a) How many turns are in the solenoid? (b) If the solenoid resistance is 2.7 Ω, how much power does it dissipate?

45. You have 10 m of 0.50-mm-diameter copper wire and a battery capable of passing 15 A through the wire. What magnetic field strengths could you obtain (a) inside a 2.0-cm-diameter solenoid wound with the wire as closely spaced as possible and (b) at the center of a single circular loop made from the wire?

46. A toroidal coil of inner radius 15 cm and outer radius 17 cm is wound from 1200 turns of wire. What are (a) the minimum and (b) the maximum magnetic field strengths within the toroid when it carries a 10-A current?

47. A toroidal fusion reactor requires a magnetic field that varies by no more than 10% from its central value of 1.5 T. If the minor radius of the toroidal coil producing this field is 30 cm, what is the minimum value for the major radius of the device?

48. A long solenoid with n turns per unit length carries a current I. The current returns to its driving battery along a wire of radius R that passes through the solenoid, along its axis. Find expressions for (a) the magnetic field strength at the surface of the wire and (b) the angle the field at the wire surface makes with the solenoid axis.

49. We noted that there is a nonzero magnetic field component outside a solenoid, encircling the device, associated with the component of current flow parallel to the solenoid axis. For a long solenoid of radius R, find an expression for the ratio of this external encircling field just outside the solenoid to the field inside, and show explicitly that this ratio tends to zero as the number of turns per unit length becomes large.

50. Derive Equation 30-11 for the field of a solenoid by considering the solenoid to be made of a large number of adjacent current loops. Use Equation 30-3 for the field of a current loop, and integrate over all loops.

Section 30-6 Magnetic Matter

51. When a sample of a certain substance is placed in a 250.0-mT magnetic field, the field inside the sample is 249.6 mT. Find the magnetic susceptibility of the substance. Is it ferromagnetic, paramagnetic, or diamagnetic?

52. A container of liquid oxygen at 90 K is placed in a 500.0-G magnetic field. What is the field strength within the liquid oxygen?

53. A ferromagnetic material is placed in a 2.5-G magnetic field and the field within the material is determined to be 1.8 T. What is the magnetic susceptibility of this material?

54. Figure 30-62 shows the hysteresis curve for the ferromagnetic alloy Alnico V, commonly used in permanent magnets. Use the graph to find approximate values for the maximum field strength obtainable inside this material, (a) in the absence and (b) in the presence of an externally applied field.

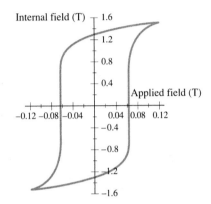

FIGURE 30-62 Problem 54.

Paired Problems

(Both problems in a pair involve the same principles and techniques. If you can get the first problem, you should be able to solve the second one.)

55. Two concentric, coplanar circular current loops have radii a and $2a$. If the magnetic field is zero at their common center, how does the current in the outer loop compare with that in the inner loop?

56. A thin conducting washer of inner radius a and outer radius $2a$ carries a current I distributed uniformly with radial position, as suggested in Fig. 30-63. Find an expression for the magnetic field strength at its center.

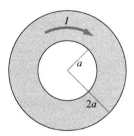

FIGURE 30-63 Problem 56.

57. Figure 30-64 shows a wire of length ℓ carrying current fed by other wires that are not shown. Point A lies on the perpendicular bisector, a distance y from the wire. Adapt the calculation of Example 30-2 to show that the magnetic field at A due to the straight wire alone has magnitude $\dfrac{\mu_0 I \ell}{2\pi y \sqrt{\ell^2 + 4y^2}}$. What is the field direction?

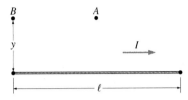

FIGURE 30-64 Problems 57, 58.

58. Point B in Fig. 30-64 lies a distance y perpendicular to the end of the wire. Show that the magnetic field at B has magnitude $\dfrac{\mu_0 I \ell}{4\pi y \sqrt{\ell^2 + y^2}}$. What is the field direction?

59. The largest lightning strikes have peak currents around 250 kA, flowing in essentially cylindrical channels of ionized air. How far from such a flash would the resulting magnetic field be equal to Earth's magnetic field strength, about 50 μT?

60. A particle-beam weapon being tested for ballistic missile defense delivers a 2.5-cm-diameter electron beam carrying a current of 10 kA at an altitude where Earth's magnetic field is 30 μT. How close to the beam would an adversary's surveillance apparatus need to be in order to detect the beam by observing a 1% change in the local magnetic field strength? Assume the beam's magnetic field is parallel to Earth's at the point of detection.

61. A coaxial cable like that shown in Fig. 30-60 consists of a 1.0-mm-diameter inner conductor and an outer conductor of inner diameter 1.0 cm and 0.20 mm thickness. A 100-mA current flows down the center conductor and back along the outer conductor. Find the magnetic field strength (a) 0.10 mm, (b) 5.0 mm, and (c) 2.0 cm from the cable axis.

62. Repeat the preceding problem if the current in the outer conductor only is increased to 200 mA.

Supplementary Problems

63. A circular wire loop of radius 15 cm and negligible thickness carries a 2.0-A current. Use suitable approximations to find the magnetic field of this loop (a) in the loop plane, 1.0 mm outside the loop, and (b) on the loop axis, 3.0 m from the loop center.

64. A long, flat conducting bar of width w carries a total current I distributed uniformly, as shown in Fig. 30-65. Use suitable approximations to write expressions for the

magnetic field strength (a) near the conductor surface ($r \ll w$) and (b) very far from the conductor ($r \gg w$).

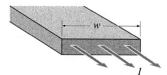

FIGURE 30-65 Problem 64.

65. A long, hollow conducting pipe of radius R and length ℓ carries a uniform current I flowing around the pipe, as shown in Fig. 30-66. Find expressions for the magnetic field (a) inside and (b) outside the pipe. *Hint:* What configuration does this pipe resemble?

FIGURE 30-66 Problem 65.

66. The magnetic field in Fig. 30-58 is given by $\mathbf{B} = by\hat{\imath}$, where $b = 55$ μT/m and y is the vertical coordinate in Fig. 30-58, measured in meters. Find the current density in the region.

67. A wide, flat conducting spring of spring constant $k = 20$ N/m and negligible mass consists of two 6.0-cm-diameter turns, as shown in Fig. 30-67. In its unstretched configuration the coils are nearly touching. A 10-g mass is hung from the spring, and at the same time a current I is passed through it. The spring stretches 2.0 mm. Find I, assuming the coils remain close enough to be treated as parallel wires.

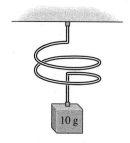

FIGURE 30-67 Problem 67.

68. A solid conducting wire of radius R runs parallel to the z axis and carries a current density given by $\mathbf{J} = J_0(1 - r/R)\hat{\mathbf{k}}$, where J_0 is a constant and r the radial distance from the wire axis. Find expressions for (a) the total current in the wire, (b) the magnetic field strength for $r > R$, and (c) the magnetic field strength for $r < R$.

69. A disk of radius a carries a uniform surface charge density σ, and is rotating with angular speed ω about the central axis perpendicular to the disk. Show that the magnetic field at the disk's center is $\frac{1}{2}\mu_0\sigma\omega a$.

70. Calculate the magnetic field of an infinite current sheet by considering the sheet to be made up of infinitesimal line currents, as suggested in Fig. 30-26, and integrating the fields of these line currents.

71. Work Example 30-2 by expressing all variables in terms of the angle θ and integrating over the appropriate range in θ.

Electromagnetic Induction 31

These wind-driven electric generators use electromagnetic induction to convert the mechanical energy of wind into electrical energy. Underground cables combine the electric power produced by all the generators and the power is then fed into the utility company's power grid. Most of the world's electrical energy is produced by generators driven by steam from burning fossil fuels or from nuclear fission—and all such generators use electromagnetic induction. So do videotapes, computer disks, credit cards, and other magnetic information storage systems.

All the electric and magnetic fields we encountered in the previous chapters had their ultimate origins in electric charge, either stationary or moving. We stressed a relation between electricity and magnetism, whereby electric charge gives rise to and interacts with both the electric field and the magnetic field. The remainder of our study of electromagnetism is devoted to a much more intimate relation between electricity and magnetism, a relation in which the fields themselves interact directly. This interaction forms the basis of new electromagnetic technologies, leads toward an understanding of the nature of light, and points the way to the theory of relativity.

31-1 INDUCED CURRENTS

In 1831, the English scientist Michael Faraday and the American Joseph Henry independently carried out experiments in which electric currents arose in circuits subjected to changing magnetic fields. We now describe four simple experiments that illustrate this phenomenon:

Experiment 1 (Fig. 31-1): A bar magnet is moved in the presence of a circuit consisting of a coil of wire connected to an ammeter. There's no battery or other obvious source of emf in the circuit. As long as the magnet is stationary, there's no current. But when the magnet moves, the ammeter registers a current—which we call an **induced current**, because it's been somehow induced by the movement of the magnet. If we move the magnet faster, the induced current increases. If we reverse the direction of the magnet's motion, the current reverses.

Experiment 2 (Fig. 31-2): A coil is moved in the presence of a stationary magnet. An induced current results that behaves exactly like the current in Experiment 1. So we get the same results whether we move the magnet or the circuit; all that matters is the relative motion between magnet and circuit.

Experiment 3 (Fig. 31-3): Replace the bar magnet with an electromagnet made from a coil of wire carrying a steady current driven by a battery. The new coil creates a magnetic field like that of the bar magnet, and, not surprisingly given the results of Experiments 1 and 2, we get an induced current that depends on the relative motion of the two coils.

Experiment 4 (Fig. 31-4): Hold both coils stationary; then there's no induced current, just as there was none in Experiments 1 and 2 when the magnet and coil were not in relative motion. But now open the switch connecting the battery to the left-hand coil. The current drops quickly to zero, and during the brief interval while it's doing so, the ammeter registers a current in the right-hand coil. Then the induced current ceases as the current in the left-hand coil remains at zero. Now close the switch again: as the current briefly builds up in the left-hand coil, the ammeter registers an induced current in the right-hand coil—and its direction is opposite what it was when the switch was opened. Once the current reaches a steady value, the induced current again ceases.

The common feature in these experiments is a *changing magnetic field*. It does not matter whether the field changes because a magnet is moved, or because a circuit is moved near a magnet, or because the current giving rise to the

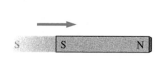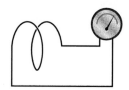

FIGURE 31-1 When a magnet is moved near a closed circuit, current flows in the circuit.

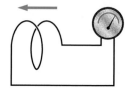

FIGURE 31-2 We get the same results if we move the coil instead of the magnet.

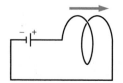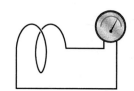

FIGURE 31-3 An induced current also arises when the magnet is replaced by a current-carrying circuit.

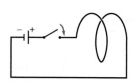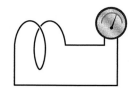

FIGURE 31-4 A current is also induced—even in the absence of any motion—when the current in an adjacent circuit changes.

field changes. In each case, an induced current appears in a circuit subjected to a changing magnetic field. We are observing here a new phenomenon—**electromagnetic induction**—whereby electrical effects arise from *changing* magnetic fields.

31-2 FARADAY'S LAW

We know from Chapter 27 that a source of electromotive force—such as a battery that supplies energy to electric charges—is needed to establish a current in a circuit. When an induced current flows in a circuit, even though there's no battery present, there must still be an emf. This so-called **induced emf** is usually not localized at one point in the circuit, as in a battery, but may be spread throughout the conductors making up the circuit.

Experimentally, we find that the induced emf in a circuit depends on the rate of change of **magnetic flux** through the circuit. Before quantifying this relationship, we show how to calculate magnetic flux.

Magnetic Flux

We introduced magnetic flux at the end of the preceding chapter, and showed that the magnetic flux through any *closed* surface is zero. Here we're interested in the flux through *open* surfaces, which need not be zero (Fig. 31-5). Like the electric flux defined in Chapter 24, magnetic flux is the integral of the magnetic field over a surface:

$$\phi_B = \int \mathbf{B} \cdot d\mathbf{A}. \tag{31-1}$$

As with electric flux, magnetic flux is proportional to the number of field lines passing through the surface. With electromagnetic induction, we're interested in the flux through a surface bounded by the circuit in question. For a circular loop such as the one in Fig. 31-5, that surface can be the circular disk whose circumference is the loop. More generally, the surface can be *any* surface bounded by the loop.

For a flat surface perpendicular to a uniform magnetic field, as in the example below, Equation 31-1 reduces to the simple expression $\phi_B = BA$. Note that the units of magnetic flux are T·m².

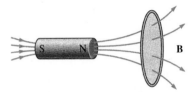

FIGURE 31-5 A circular wire loop in the magnetic field of a bar magnet. The flux ϕ_B is proportional to the number of field lines crossing the circular surface bounded by the loop. If the magnet moves closer to the loop, the number of field lines—and hence the flux— increases.

EXAMPLE 31-1	*The Magnetic Flux through a Solenoid*

A solenoid of circular cross section has radius R, consists of n turns per unit length, and carries a current I. What is the magnetic flux through each turn of the solenoid?

Solution
The field of a solenoid is uniform and parallel to the solenoid axis, as we found in deriving Equation 30-11:

$$B = \mu_0 nI.$$

A flat surface bounded by one turn of the solenoid lies at right angles to this uniform field, so the flux is simply the product of the magnetic field and the area:

$$\phi_B = \int \mathbf{B} \cdot d\mathbf{A} = BA = \mu_0 nI\pi R^2.$$

We're being a little loose here in thinking of a single turn of the solenoid as a closed loop, but if the solenoid is tightly wound this is an excellent approximation. We will be concerned frequently with the flux through a multiturn coil, and in calculating this flux it's convenient to view each turn as an individual loop. The flux through an N-turn coil in a uniform magnetic field is just N times the flux through each turn.

EXERCISE A rectangular wire loop measuring 10 cm by 15 cm is oriented so the normal to the loop makes a 30° angle with a uniform 50-mT magnetic field. Find the magnetic flux through the loop.

Answer: 6.5×10^{-4} T·m²

Some problems similar to Example 31-1: 3, 4

| **EXAMPLE 31-2** | *Magnetic Flux in a Nonuniform Field* |

A long, straight wire carries a current I. A rectangular wire loop of dimensions ℓ by w lies with its closest edge a distance a from the wire, as shown in Fig. 31-6. What is the magnetic flux through the loop?

Solution

The magnetic field of the wire is given by Equation 30-8:

$$B = \frac{\mu_0 I}{2\pi r},$$

where r is the distance from the wire. At the site of the loop, this field points straight into the page, perpendicular to the plane of the loop. However, the field varies with distance from the straight wire, so we can't simply multiply the field by the loop area to get the flux. Instead, we divide the loop into thin strips of width dr and area $dA = \ell\, dr$, as shown in Fig. 31-6. With the field at right angles to each strip, $\mathbf{B} \cdot d\mathbf{A} = B\, dA$, and the flux through any strip is

$$d\phi_B = B\, dA = B\ell\, dr = \frac{\mu_0 I}{2\pi r}\ell\, dr.$$

Then the total flux through the loop is the integral over all such strips contained within the loop, that is, over all strips between $r = a$ and $r = a + w$:

$$\phi_B = \int_a^{a+w} \frac{\mu_0 I}{2\pi r}\ell\, dr = \frac{\mu_0 I\ell}{2\pi}\int_a^{a+w}\frac{dr}{r} = \frac{\mu_0 I\ell}{2\pi}\ln r\,\Big|_a^{a+w}$$

$$= \frac{\mu_0 I\ell}{2\pi}\ln\left(\frac{a+w}{a}\right).$$

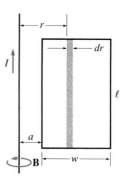

FIGURE 31-6 A rectangular loop in the magnetic field of a long wire. The field to the right of the wire points into the plane of the page, and its magnitude drops inversely with distance from the wire. Area elements for the flux calculation are strips of length ℓ and infinitesimal width dr.

EXERCISE A square wire loop 45 cm on a side lies in the plane of this page, taken to be the x-y plane. The left edge of the loop coincides with the y axis. A magnetic field points into the page; its magnitude varies with position, being given by $B = ax$, where $a = 2.0$ T/m and x is position in meters. Find the flux through this loop.

Answer: 91 mT·m^2

Some problems similar to Example 31-2: 43, 44

Flux and Induced EMF

Having quantified the notion of magnetic flux, we are now ready to state rigorously the experimental fact that changing magnetic flux induces an emf in a circuit. Our statement is a special case of **Faraday's law of induction**, which constitutes another of the four basic laws of electromagnetism:

> The induced emf in a circuit is proportional to the rate of change of magnetic flux through any surface bounded by that circuit.

This statement is a special case of Faraday's law that describes electromagnetic induction specifically in circuits; later we'll present a more general form that applies even when no circuit is present. The induced emf tends to oppose the change in flux—a crucial point to which we'll devote all of Section 31-3—and so in SI units the proportionality between emf and rate of change of flux is just -1. Thus Faraday's law is

$$\mathcal{E} = -\frac{d\phi_B}{dt}, \tag{31-2}$$

where $\mathcal{E}$ is the emf induced in a circuit and ϕ_B the magnetic flux through any surface bounded by that circuit. Problem 1 will help convince you that the units of the rate of change of magnetic flux are indeed volts, the same as the units of emf.

Faraday's law relates the induced emf to the *change* in flux. It isn't magnetic flux or magnetic field that causes an induced emf—it's the *change* in flux. The relation between emf and flux is like the relation between acceleration and velocity, where the acceleration depends not on the actual value of the velocity, but on its *rate of change*. In Fig. 31-1 we changed the flux by moving a magnet near a coil, increasing the flux as more field lines went through the area bounded by the coil. In Fig. 31-4 we changed the current in an adjacent coil, changing the magnetic field and thus the flux. More generally, since the flux $\mathbf{B} \cdot \mathbf{A} = BA\cos\theta$, we can change flux by changing the field strength B, the area A, or the orientation of the surface to the field (i.e., the angle θ between the field and the normal to the surface). The following examples explore these different ways of changing magnetic flux.

13.9
Electromagnetic Induction

EXAMPLE 31-3	*Changing Magnetic Field*

A wire loop of radius 10 cm has a resistance of 2.0 Ω. The loop is at right angles to a uniform magnetic field **B**, as shown in Fig. 31-7. The field strength is increasing at 0.10 tesla/second. What is the magnitude of the induced current in the loop?

Solution

To find the induced current, we need to know the induced emf. Faraday's law tells us that the induced emf is related to the rate of change of magnetic flux through the circuit. Here the field is uniform and at right angles to the loop, so the flux is just the product of the field with the loop area:

$$\phi_B = \int \mathbf{B} \cdot d\mathbf{A} = \pi r^2 B .$$

Why could we take B outside the integral when the field is changing? Because it's changing with *time,* and the integral is over *space.* At any given instant the field is *uniform* in space, and that's all we need to reduce the flux integral to a simple product.

We don't know B, but this doesn't matter because we are really interested in the *rate of change* of the flux, not in the flux itself. With the loop area constant, the rate of change of flux is

$$\frac{d\phi_B}{dt} = \pi r^2 \frac{dB}{dt} = (\pi)(0.10 \text{ m})^2(0.10 \text{ T/s}) = 3.14 \times 10^{-3} \text{ V} .$$

By Faraday's law, this is the magnitude of the induced emf. We then calculate the current using Ohm's law, as we would for any emf:

$$I = \frac{\mathcal{E}}{R} = \frac{3.14 \times 10^{-3} \text{ V}}{2.0 \ \Omega} = 1.6 \times 10^{-3} \text{ A} = 1.6 \text{ mA} .$$

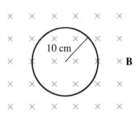

FIGURE 31-7 A circular conducting loop at right angles to a uniform magnetic field.

Tip

It's the Change That Counts Faraday's law relates induced emf to the *rate of change* of magnetic flux. The actual value of the flux—or of the magnetic field if that is what's changing—doesn't matter. You may be troubled by induction problems where the value of the field is not given. You don't need it; what you do need or may be asked to find is the *rate of change* of the field.

EXERCISE A square conducting loop 25 cm on a side lies at right angles to a uniform magnetic field. The loop's resistance is 8.0 Ω, and it carries a current of 14 mA. At what rate is the magnetic field changing?

Answer: 1.8 T/s

Some problems similar to Example 31-3: 4–8

EXAMPLE 31-4	*Changing Area*

A circuit consists of two parallel conducting rails a distance ℓ apart connected at one end by a resistance R. A conducting bar completes the circuit, joining the two rails electrically but being free to slide along them. The whole circuit is in a constant, uniform magnetic field $\mathbf{B}$ at right angles to the plane of the circuit, as shown in Fig. 31-8. The bar is pulled to the right with constant speed v, increasing the area of the circuit as it moves. What is the current in the circuit? Assume the bar and rails are ideal conductors, so the total circuit resistance is R.

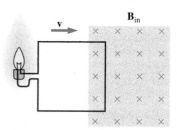

FIGURE 31-8 Pulling the bar to the right increases the circuit area, thereby increasing the magnetic flux and inducing an emf that drives a current.

Solution

Here the current is driven by an induced emf arising from the change in magnetic flux that occurs as the circuit area increases. We determine the emf using Faraday's law, $\mathcal{E} = -d\phi_B/dt$. The circuit area is the rail spacing ℓ times the distance x from resistor to bar. With a uniform field perpendicular to the circuit, the flux integral $\int \mathbf{B} \cdot d\mathbf{A}$ reduces to the product of field strength with the area:

$$\phi_B = \int \mathbf{B} \cdot d\mathbf{A} = BA = B\ell x.$$

Never mind that we don't know x—we do know its rate of change and that's all we need. With the field and the rail spacing constant, the rate of change of flux is

$$\frac{d\phi_B}{dt} = B\ell \frac{dx}{dt} = B\ell v,$$

since dx/dt is just the bar velocity v. Faraday's law tells us that the magnitude of the induced emf is equal to the rate of change of flux, so

$$|\mathcal{E}| = B\ell v.$$

This emf drives a current I around the circuit:

$$|I| = \frac{|\mathcal{E}|}{R} = \frac{B\ell v}{R}.$$

ActivPhysics Activity 13.10 provides a simulation of this example.

EXERCISE A square wire loop 25 cm on a side is moving into a region containing a uniform 1.2-T magnetic field oriented at right angles to the loop, as shown in Fig. 31-9. The loop wire is essentially resistanceless, but inserted in the loop is a 3-V flashlight bulb. How fast must the loop move to keep the bulb lit at its normal brightness?

Answer: 10 m/s

Some problems similar to Example 31-4: 9, 10, 16, 27, 35

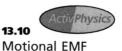

FIGURE 31-9 How fast must the loop move to light the 3-V bulb?

13.10 *ActivPhysics*
Motional EMF

EXAMPLE 31-5	*Changing Orientation: An Electric Generator*

A circular wire loop of radius a and resistance R is initially perpendicular to a constant, uniform magnetic field B. The loop rotates with angular velocity ω about an axis through a diameter, as shown in Fig. 31-10. What is the current in the loop?

FIGURE 31-10 A wire loop rotating in a uniform magnetic field. The flux changes because of the changing orientation of the loop relative to the field, thereby inducing an emf that drives a current around the loop.

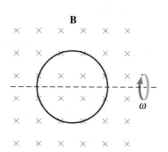

Solution

Again, we must find the rate of change of magnetic flux, from which we can get the induced emf and then the current. Here the field is uniform over the area, but the orientation of the field relative to the area is changing. The definition of magnetic flux contains a dot product to account for this orientation. Evaluating the flux, we have

$$\phi_B = \int \mathbf{B} \cdot d\mathbf{A} = \int B \, dA \cos\theta = B\cos\theta \int dA$$

$$= \pi a^2 B \cos\theta,$$

where θ is the angle between the field and a perpendicular to the loop area. Here we could take the field magnitude B outside the integral because the field is uniform over the loop. And even though the orientation between loop and field changes with *time,* it does not change with *position* at a given instant, so we could also take $\cos\theta$ outside the integral.

The changing orientation is described by giving θ as a function of time. Since the loop rotates with constant angular velocity ω, we can write simply $\theta = \omega t$, where we take the zero of time when $\theta = 0$. Then the flux is

$$\phi_B = \pi a^2 B \cos\omega t,$$

so

$$\frac{d\phi_B}{dt} = \pi a^2 B \frac{d}{dt}(\cos\omega t) = -\pi a^2 B\omega \sin\omega t.$$

By Faraday's law, the emf is then

$$\mathcal{E} = -\frac{d\phi_B}{dt} = \pi a^2 B\omega \sin\omega t,$$

giving a current

$$I = \frac{\mathcal{E}}{R} = \frac{\pi a^2 B\omega}{R} \sin\omega t.$$

(Check the units!)

Unlike the current in the previous two examples, this one changes with time. Its sinusoidal time dependence is in fact just like that of standard alternating current used for electric power—and with good reason: our rotating loop constitutes a simple alternating-current generator. Sinusoidally varying emf's and currents occur whenever conducting loops rotate in uniform magnetic fields.

> ### Tip
>
> *Peak Values* You'll often be asked for the peak value of voltage or current when either quantity is changing with time (more on this in Chapter 33). You've derived a formula like $\mathcal{E} = \pi a^2 B\omega \sin\omega t$ in Example 31-5, but you don't have a value for the time t. It doesn't matter! The peak value occurs when $\sin\omega t = 1$, so just replace $\sin\omega t$ by 1. In Example 31-5, for example, the peak emf is just $\mathcal{E}_p = \pi a^2 B\omega$.

EXERCISE Take the radius $a = 11$ cm in Example 31-5 and the magnetic field strength $B = 0.63$ T. With what angular speed ω must the loop rotate in order to produce a peak emf of 6.0 V?

Answer: 250 s^{-1}

Some problems similar to Example 31-5: 12, 24, 58, 63

You might wonder about the direction of the induced emf and current in these examples since we were concerned only with magnitudes. Formally, that direction follows mathematically from the minus sign in Faraday's law. But in the next section we'll provide a physical justification for the minus sign that makes it much clearer how to determine the direction of induced emf's and currents.

31-3 INDUCTION AND THE CONSERVATION OF ENERGY

Move a bar magnet toward a wire loop, as shown in Fig. 31-11. Without the loop present, it would take no work to move the magnet horizontally at constant

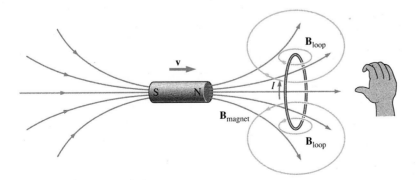

FIGURE 31-11 As the bar magnet moves toward the conducting loop, the changing magnetic flux through the loop induces an emf that drives a current around the loop. Conservation of energy requires that the magnetic field produced by this current *oppose* the motion of the magnet, so the agent moving the magnet does work that ends up heating the loop.

velocity. But with the loop present, moving the magnet induces a current in the loop. Electrical energy is dissipated in the loop's resistance, heating the loop. Where does the energy come from?

There's only one source for the energy—the agent moving the magnet. As you move the magnet, you must be doing positive work. Otherwise you would be getting energy—ultimately heating the loop—for nothing. So you must have to push the magnet against some force. What force? A magnetic force, caused by the interaction of the magnet with the magnetic field produced by the induced current. Think about this! The induced current, like any current, produces a magnetic field. The magnet experiences a force in this field, and you must do work to move the magnet through that field. With the magnetic field as intermediary, the work you do ultimately ends up heating the loop.

As you push the magnet toward the loop, the force the loop's field exerts on the magnet must be repulsive in order that you do positive work on the magnet. In Fig. 31-11 the bar magnet's north pole is toward the loop. To provide a repulsive force the loop must therefore present a north pole to the approaching magnet; that is, field lines must emerge from the loop's interior pointing to the left. What current direction will provide such a field? Application of the right-hand rule gives the answer: Wrap the fingers of your right hand around the loop in the direction of the current, and your right thumb points in the direction of the field in the loop's interior. Thus the current direction is as shown in Fig. 31-11.

This analysis leading to the direction of the induced current was based on conservation of energy, a fundamental principle that we believe applies universally. For electromagnetic induction, we've just seen that conservation of energy requires the following:

The direction of the induced emf and current is such that the magnetic field created by the induced current opposes the change in magnetic flux.

This statement, called **Lenz's law**, is represented mathematically in the minus sign on the right-hand side of Faraday's law (Equation 31-2).

What happens, for example, if you pull the bar magnet away from the loop in Fig. 31-11? Now the loop must present a south pole to the receding magnet, creating an attractive force opposing the magnet's withdrawal (Fig. 31-12). The loop current must be opposite its direction in Fig. 31-11, as again you do work to overcome the magnetic force.

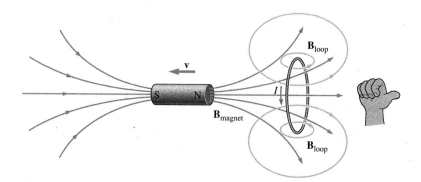

FIGURE 31-12 When the bar magnet is pulled away from the loop, the direction of the induced current is such that the magnetic force opposes the magnet's withdrawal.

Got It!

You push a bar magnet toward a loop, with the north pole toward the loop as in Fig. 31-11. If you keep pushing the magnet straight through the loop, what will be the direction of the current as you pull it out the other side? Will you need to do work, or will work be done on you?

Motional EMF and Lenz's Law

When a conductor moves through a magnetic field, we can understand the origin of the induced emf in terms of the magnetic force on charge carriers in the wire; this emf is called **motional emf**. In the case of motional emf we can show explicitly that Lenz's law requires energy conservation.

Consider a square conducting loop of side ℓ and resistance R being pulled with constant speed v out of a uniform magnetic field **B**, as shown in Fig. 31-13. Since the magnetic flux through the loop is changing, there's an induced emf, and that emf drives a current. Energy is dissipated as heat because of the loop's resistance, and so, as we've just argued, the agent pulling the loop must do work. We'll now demonstrate quantitatively that energy is conserved, by showing that rate of heating in the loop is exactly equal to the rate at which the agent pulling the loop does work.

In Chapter 29 we found that the magnetic force on a charge is given by **F** = q**v** × **B**. Pulling the loop to the right moves its free electrons through the magnetic field; the magnetic force q**v** × **B** on these electrons is downward in Fig. 31-13 (opposite **v** × **B** since electrons are negative). The resulting downward motion of the negative electrons in the left-hand side of the loop constitutes an upward current. This current continues clockwise around the loop, driven by an electric field associated with the separation of charge in the loop's left side.

Now we have a current I in the loop. We found in Chapter 29 that the magnetic force on a current-carrying conductor of length ℓ is **F** = I**ℓ** × **B**. Applying this expression to the conducting loop in Fig. 31-13 shows that there is no magnetic force on the right-hand side (since **B** = **0** there) and that the forces on top and bottom cancel (Fig. 31-14). So the total magnetic force on the loop is that on the left side alone; since the current is upward while the magnetic field is into the page, the magnitude of this force is $I\ell B$, and the right-hand rule shows that it points to the left. This leftward magnetic force has just the direction needed to cancel the rightward applied force, giving the zero net force that Newton's law requires for the loop to move with constant velocity.

We could equally well determine the current direction from magnetic flux considerations. As the loop leaves the field region, the flux through it decreases. The direction of the induced current is such as to oppose this decrease in flux. Therefore the magnetic field of the induced current points into the page, as the induced current tries to maintain the flux. By the right-hand rule, a field within the loop and into the page requires that the induced current flow clockwise.

To calculate the current, we must find the induced emf, which in turn is related to the rate of change of magnetic flux through the loop. With the field and

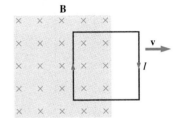

FIGURE 31-13 A conducting loop being withdrawn from a magnetic field. The magnetic force q**v** × **B** on charge carriers in the left side of the loop drives a current clockwise around the loop. The current direction also follows from Lenz's law: The magnetic field produced by the loop current acts to oppose the *decrease* in flux through the loop, and therefore points in the *same* direction as the original field. This requires a clockwise loop current.

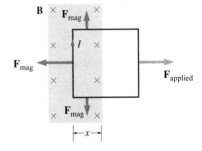

FIGURE 31-14 Forces on the loop. The total magnetic force is that on the left side alone, and the agent pulling the loop must exert an equal but opposite force to maintain constant velocity.

loop perpendicular, and with the field uniform in the region where it is nonzero, the magnetic flux is the product of the magnetic field strength and the loop area that lies within the field:

$$\phi_B = B\ell x,$$

where x is the distance between the left edge of the loop and the right edge of the magnetic field region. The magnetic field remains constant, but as the loop moves the distance x decreases at the rate $dx/dt = -v$ (the minus sign indicates a decrease). Then the rate of change of flux is

$$\frac{d\phi_B}{dt} = \frac{d(B\ell x)}{dt} = B\ell \frac{dx}{dt} = -B\ell v,$$

so Faraday's law gives
$$\mathcal{E} = -\frac{d\phi_B}{dt} = B\ell v.$$

This induced emf drives a current I around the loop, where

$$I = \frac{\mathcal{E}}{R} = \frac{B\ell v}{R}.$$

The rate of energy dissipation in the loop is the product of the emf and the current (Equation 27-8):

$$P = I\mathcal{E} = \frac{B\ell v}{R} B\ell v = \frac{B^2 \ell^2 v^2}{R}. \qquad \left(\begin{array}{c} \text{power dissipated} \\ \text{in loop} \end{array} \right)$$

We've found that the magnetic force on the loop has magnitude $I\ell B$; since the loop is moving with constant velocity, this is also the magnitude of the applied force. Equation 7-21 shows that the rate at which work is done by a force **F** acting on an object moving with velocity **v** is $P = \mathbf{F} \cdot \mathbf{v}$; here, with the applied force and velocity in the same direction, we have

$$P = Fv = I\ell Bv = \frac{B\ell v}{R} \ell Bv = \frac{B^2 \ell^2 v^2}{R}, \qquad \left(\begin{array}{c} \text{power supplied} \\ \text{to pull loop} \end{array} \right)$$

in agreement with our expression for the electric power dissipated in the loop. Thus, all the work done by the agent pulling the loop ends up heating the resistor, showing explicitly that energy is indeed conserved.

Got It!

What will be the direction of the current when the loop in Fig. 31-13 first enters the field, coming in from the left side?

Electromagnetic induction is the principle behind many important technologies, from information storage on computer disks and credit cards to electric power generation. Induction also gives us the flexibility to transform voltage levels in electric power systems, and to provide wireless charging systems for devices ranging from electric cars to toothbrushes. The applications that follow explore some uses of induction.

| APPLICATION | *Electric Generators* |

Probably the most important technological application of induction is the electric generator. The world currently uses electrical energy at the phenomenal rate of about 10^{13} watts—roughly equal to the power output of 100 billion human bodies—and virtually all this power comes from generators. A generator is just a system of conductors in a magnetic field (Fig. 31-15). Mechanical energy is supplied to rotate the conductors, resulting in a changing magnetic flux. An emf is induced and current flows through the generator and on to whatever electrical loads are connected to it. Because the changing flux results from a change in the orientation of the loop relative to the field—i.e., a change in θ in the expression $\phi_B = BA \cos \theta$—a generator such as that of Fig. 31-15 produces an alternating emf that varies sinusoidally with time (Fig. 31-16), as we saw in Example 31-5.

Any source of mechanical energy can power the generator, but the most common is steam from burning fossil fuels or from nuclear fission (Fig. 31-17). Electrical energy may be generated from the kinetic energy of water or wind—as shown in this chapter's opening photo. A small electric generator, driven by the car's gasoline engine, is used to recharge a car's battery.

Lenz's law, the conservation of energy in electromagnetic induction, is very much applicable to electric generators. Were it not for Lenz's law, which requires that induced currents *oppose* the changes giving rise to them, generators would turn on their own and happily supply electricity without the need for coal, oil, or uranium! The voluminous quantities of fuel (Fig. 31-18) consumed by power plants are dramatic testimony to the minus sign appearing on the right-hand side of Equation 31-2!

An instructive introduction to Lenz's law comes about if you have access to a hand-cranked electric generator. Without any electrical load across the generator, it is easy to turn. But as you switch on increasingly heavy loads the generator gets

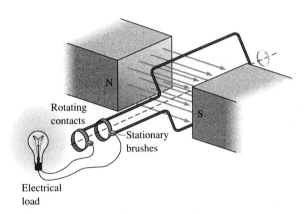

FIGURE 31-15 Simplified diagram of an electric generator. As the loop rotates in the magnetic field, the changing flux induces an emf that drives a current through the rotating contacts and stationary brushes and on through the electrical load.

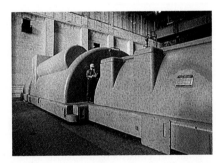

FIGURE 31-17 This large power-plant generator produces over 1000 MW of electric power. It's basically a large version of the generator shown in Fig. 31-15.

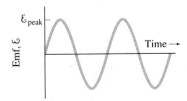

FIGURE 31-16 A generator such as that shown in Fig. 31-15 produces an alternating emf whose period is the rotation period of the conducting loop.

FIGURE 31-18 A 110-car trainload of coal arriving at a power plant in Texas. Some fourteen such trains arrive at the plant each week—a testimony to the minus sign in Equation 31-2!

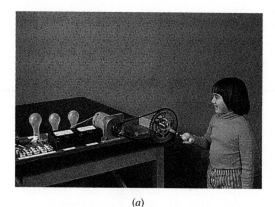
(a)

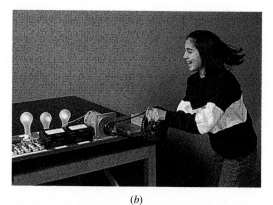
(b)

FIGURE 31-19 (a) With no electrical load, a hand-cranked generator is easy to turn. (b) With 200 watts of light bulbs connected, turning the generator becomes much more difficult. The generator emf is the same in both cases, because the generator is being turned at the same rate. But only in (b) is current flowing, giving nonzero power $P = IV$ that must be supplied by turning the generator.

harder to turn (Fig. 31-19). Most people find they can just sustain a 100-W light bulb with a hand generator. Think about this next time you leave a light on! You also experience Lenz's law when you turn on the headlights of a car that's idling slowly. You can hear the engine speed drop, and the car may even stall, as the car's generator gets harder for the engine to turn.

Got It!

If you lower the resistance across an electric generator, while turning the generator at a constant speed, will the generator get easier or harder to turn?

EXAMPLE 31-6	*Designing a Generator*

An electric generator consists of a 10-turn square wire loop 50 cm on a side. The loop is turned at 60 revolutions per second, to produce standard 60-Hz alternating current like that used throughout the United States and Canada. How strong must the magnetic field be for the peak output voltage of the generator to be 170 V? (This is actually the peak voltage of standard 120-V household wiring; 120 V is an appropriate average value.)

Solution

We need to evaluate the induced emf as a function of magnetic field strength. With a uniform magnetic field, the flux through one turn of the loop is $\int \mathbf{B} \cdot d\mathbf{A} = BA\cos\theta$, where θ is the angle between the field and the normal to the loop. But the loop rotates with angular frequency $\omega = 2\pi f$, so $\theta = 2\pi ft$. The loop area A is s^2, with s the length of the loop side, so the flux through N turns of the loop is

$$\phi_B = NBs^2 \cos(2\pi ft).$$

To find the induced emf, we take the time rate of change of this flux:

$$\mathcal{E} = -\frac{d\phi_B}{dt} = -NBs^2 \left[-2\pi f \sin(2\pi ft)\right]$$

$$= 2\pi N f B s^2 \sin(2\pi ft).$$

The peak emf is the quantity multiplying the sine; we want this to be 170 V. Solving for the unknown magnetic field B then gives

$$B = \frac{\mathcal{E}_{\text{peak}}}{2\pi N f s^2} = \frac{170 \text{ V}}{(2\pi)(10)(60 \text{ Hz})(0.50 \text{ m})^2} = 0.18 \text{ T}.$$

This is a typical field strength near the poles of a strong permanent magnet.

EXERCISE A generator includes a circular coil 30 cm in diameter, spinning at 3600 rpm in a uniform 0.50-T magnetic field. How many turns should it have if the peak output voltage is to be 2400 V?

Answer: 180

Some problems similar to Example 31-6: 24, 26, 49, 50

| **APPLICATION** | *Magnetic Recording* |

Magnetic materials are widely used as information storage media. Examples include audio- and videocassette tapes, computer disks, and the magnetic strips on credit cards. Retrieving the stored information involves electromagnetic induction.

In a typical magnetic recording system the magnetic medium—usually a plastic tape or a circular disk coated with ferromagnetic oxides—moves past a small coil called the **head**. While recording, current passing through the coil creates a magnetic field that impresses a magnetization pattern on the tape or disk (Fig. 31-20). With analog systems, like most audio- and videotapes, the current varies continuously and produces a smoothly varying magnetization pattern. With digital systems, including computer data storage and the newer digital audio and video formats, coil currents of the same magnitude but opposite polarity produce regions of oppositely directed magnetization; these represent the 1's and 0's in which digital information is coded.

To retrieve the stored information, the magnetic medium is again moved past a coil, which may be the same one used for recording. The changing magnetization on the medium results in a varying magnetic flux through the coil, which induces an emf that's amplified and processed to produce images, sound, or digital data.

The rate at which information can be stored and extracted depends on how densely the regions of varying magnetization can be packed without interfering and on how fast the medium moves in relation to the heads. Audiocassette tapes move past the heads at a mere 4.8 cm/s, a speed that limits these tapes' ability to record high-frequency sound faithfully. The much higher information content of video images requires higher tape-to-head speeds; in standard videocassette recorders a speed of 39.52 m/s is achieved by moving the tape past rapidly spinning heads. High-speed computer disks boast even greater speeds, allowing rapid data storage and retrieval (Fig. 31-21).

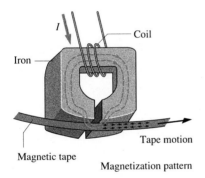

FIGURE 31-20 Recording on magnetic tape. The iron body of the head confines the magnetic field of the coil except at the gap, where a fringing field emerges to impose a magnetization pattern on the moving tape. When the tape is played back, its changing magnetization pattern imposes a changing magnetic flux at the head, inducing an emf in the head coil.

FIGURE 31-21 Mechanism of a computer disk drive includes a head (arrow) that literally flies as close as 0.25 μm above a spinning aluminum disk coated with ferromagnetic material.

| **APPLICATION** | *Eddy Currents* |

Our discussion of induced currents has centered on conducting loops. But induced currents also appear in solid conductors through which magnetic flux is changing. The resistance of a solid piece of conductor is low, so the induced currents are large, resulting in substantial energy dissipation. The presence of these **eddy currents** can make it difficult to move a conduc-

tor rapidly through a magnetic field. For example, if you try to push a piece of metal—it need not be a ferrous metal like iron—between the poles of a magnet, you'll find yourself working against a magnetic force.

A common demonstration of eddy currents consists of a pendulum with a metal bob that swings between the poles of a

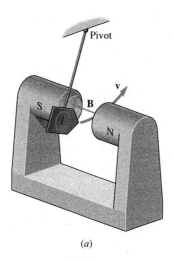

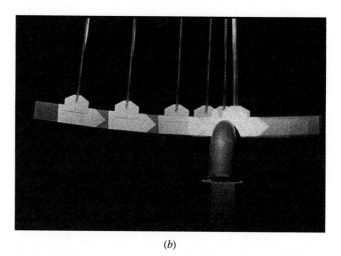

(a)

(b)

FIGURE 31-22 (a) An eddy-current pendulum consists of a conductor swinging between magnet poles. As it enters the field region, the conductor experiences a changing magnetic flux that induces a current. You should convince yourself that the current is in the direction shown as the bob begins to enter the field region. (b) The current dissipates energy in the resistance of the conductor, at the expense of its kinetic energy. Strobe photo shows rapid deceleration as the bob passes between the magnet poles.

magnet (Fig. 31-22). As it swings toward the magnet, the pendulum experiences an increasing magnetic flux that induces eddy currents. The energy dissipated by these currents comes ultimately from the kinetic energy of the pendulum, which therefore slows abruptly between the magnet poles.

Eddy currents provide an alternative to friction brakes for stopping moving machinery. Rapidly rotating saw blades, for example, can be stopped abruptly by an electromagnet activated next to the blade. Similarly, eddy-current brakes are

sometimes used on trains and in other applications involving rotating conductors.

In some instances eddy currents are a nuisance, acting just like friction in reducing the efficiency of machinery. To solve this problem, slots are often cut into moving conductors to make the current paths longer, thus increasing the electrical resistance and reducing the eddy currents. For example, if the solid pendulum bob in Fig. 31-22 is replaced by a slotted piece, it then swings more freely through the magnet.

Lenz's Law and Changing Magnetic Fields

Lenz's law—conservation of energy applied to electromagnetic induction—determines the direction of the induced current even when no motion is involved. Figure 31-23 shows a conducting loop in a magnetic field that points into the page. Suppose the field strength—and, therefore, the magnetic flux through the loop—is *decreasing.* Then the direction of the induced current must be such that the magnetic field it creates *opposes* this decrease. Therefore, the loop's field must reinforce the existing field, which means that the loop's field points into the page. Applying the right-hand rule then shows that the loop current is clockwise in Fig. 31-23.

What if the magnetic field in Fig. 31-23 had been increasing in strength? Then the loop current would have been in the opposite direction, to create a magnetic field opposite the existing field in order to oppose its increase.

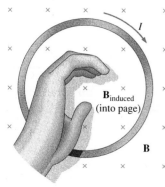

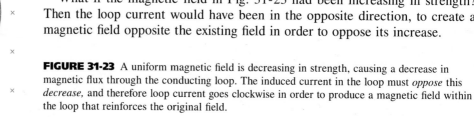

FIGURE 31-23 A uniform magnetic field is decreasing in strength, causing a decrease in magnetic flux through the conducting loop. The induced current in the loop must *oppose* this *decrease,* and therefore loop current goes clockwise in order to produce a magnetic field within the loop that reinforces the original field.

Tip

Induction Opposes Change Faraday's law relates the induced emf to the *rate of change* of magnetic flux. Lenz's law says that the induced emf and current are in such a direction as to oppose that *change* in flux—not the flux or the field itself. Figure 31-23 is a case in point; here the induced current is in a direction that actually reinforces the original field and flux—precisely because they are both *decreasing*. The same thing happened in Fig. 31-13, where movement of the loop decreased the flux, giving an induced current that reinforced the existing field.

EXAMPLE 31-7	*Lenz's Law*

Two coils are arranged as shown in Fig. 31-24. If the resistance of the variable resistor is being increased, what is the direction of the induced current in the fixed resistor *R*?

Solution

Applying the right-hand rule, we find that the magnetic field of coil *A* emerges from the right side of the coil, pointing toward coil *B*. As the resistance increases, the current in coil *A* decreases, and with it the strength of coil *A*'s magnetic field. This results in a decrease in the magnetic flux through coil *B*. The induced current in coil *B* acts to oppose this decrease in flux, so the magnetic field resulting from the induced current reinforces the field from coil *A*. Thus the field of coil *B* emerges from the right end of the coil and enters on the left end. By the right-hand rule, this requires a current from right to left in the fixed resistor.

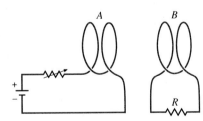

FIGURE 31-24 As the variable resistance is increased, the current in coil *A* decreases. This decreases the magnetic flux through coil *B*, resulting in an induced current whose direction is such that the magnetic field it creates in the interior of coil *B* reinforces the field from coil *A*, thereby opposing the decrease in flux through *B*.

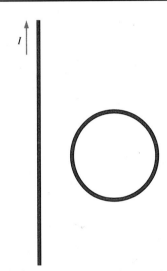

FIGURE 31-25 Which way is the current in the circular loop?

EXERCISE A circular conducting loop lies next to a long, straight wire carrying current in the direction indicated in Fig. 31-25. In which direction is the induced current in the loop when the current in the wire is (a) increasing and (b) decreasing?

Answers: (a) counterclockwise; (b) clockwise

Some problems similar to Example 31-7: 4, 10, 19, 27, 32

Got It!

A wire loop lies in the plane of this page, and a uniform magnetic field points directly out of the page. What is the direction of the current in the loop if the magnetic field strength is (a) increasing or (b) decreasing?

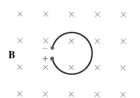

FIGURE 31-26 An open loop. In a changing magnetic field, there is an induced emf that results in charge buildup at the gap. The polarity shown results when the magnetic field strength is decreasing.

Induction in Open Circuits

An induced emf also arises in an open circuit subject to a changing magnetic field, but here the emf cannot drive a steady current. Figure 31-26 shows the loop and magnetic field of Fig. 31-23, but now with a small gap in the loop. Although the loop is not quite closed, there is still an induced emf. In response to this emf, charge piles up on either side of the gap, creating a voltage across it. Once the gap voltage equals the induced emf, the electric field associated with the separated charge opposes the emf's tendency to move charge, and a steady state is reached. In the open-circuit case, the entire emf implied by Equation 31-2 is available at the gap. The polarity can be determined by considering what would happen if current did flow. Since current flowed clockwise in the closed loop of Fig. 31-23, positive charge will accumulate at the bottom of the gap, as shown in Fig. 31-26.

Another example of an induced emf in an open circuit is the motional emf arising as a single conductor moves through a magnetic field. Example 31-8 treats this case quantitatively.

EXAMPLE 31-8	*The Tethered Satellite*

In 1996 astronauts on the space shuttle Columbia performed a novel experiment to explore a new method of generating electric power in space. Once in orbit, Columbia deployed a 520-kg satellite attached to the shuttle through a 20-km long conducting tether (Fig. 31-27). With the tethered satellite flying vertically above Columbia, the two moved at approximately right angles to Earth's magnetic field, whose strength was about 30 μT at the orbital position. Find the motional emf that developed between the tethered satellite and the shuttle with the tether extended its full 20-km length. (Unfortunately the tether broke just short of its full length, but five hours of data collected during deployment clearly demonstrated the power-generating potential of the tethered satellite.)

Solution

Figure 31-28 shows the pair flying at right angles to the magnetic field. We can imagine forming a closed circuit by letting the satellite and shuttle slide along a system of conducting rails, just like that of Example 31-4. The system is then identical to that example, and we have

$$\mathcal{E} = B\ell v = (30 \times 10^{-6} \text{ T})(20 \times 10^3 \text{ m})(7.8 \times 10^3 \text{ m/s})$$

$$= 4.7 \text{ kV},$$

where we used the orbital speed calculated in Example 9-3.

FIGURE 31-27 Tethered satellite being deployed from the space shuttle.

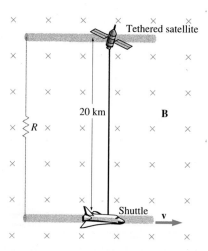

FIGURE 31-28 The tethered satellite generates electric power from the motional emf developed between the spacecraft and a satellite connected by a conducting tether. The system is analogous to the bar and rails shown in Fig. 31-8.

Since the magnetic flux through the rail arrangement would be increasing, the current would flow counterclockwise so that the magnetic field of the induced current would oppose this increase. That means positive charge will accumulate on the satellite and negative charge on the shuttle—a result that can also be obtained by considering the magnetic force on free charges in the tether.

At the shuttle's orbital altitude there are enough free electrons from ionization of the upper atmosphere for the tenuous gas surrounding the shuttle to carry a current, completing a circuit and allowing exploitation of the induced emf for electric power generation.

EXERCISE An airplane with a wingspan of 44 m is in level flight at 300 m/s over the north pole, where Earth's magnetic field has magnitude 0.62 G and points vertically downward. Find the induced emf between the wing tips.

Answer: 0.82 V

Some problems similar to Example 31-8: 10, 13, 56

31-4 INDUCED ELECTRIC FIELDS

What do we really mean by an induced emf? In a circuit containing a battery, the notion of emf is clear—the emf arises in a specific device where chemical energy is converted to electrical energy associated with charge separation. This charge separation sets up an electric field that drives current in an external circuit, as we discussed in Chapter 28. In the case of motional induced emf we also have a clear picture: the emf arises from the separation of charge associated with magnetic forces on the free charges in a moving conductor; again, the electric field associated with this charge separation may drive a current.

Now consider the current induced in a conducting loop by a magnetic field that changes with time. No motion is involved, yet there must be a force on the free charges in the conductor. The one force we know that acts on stationary charges is the electric force. Electric forces arise from electric fields, so there must be an electric field in a conducting loop in a changing magnetic field. This field is called an **induced electric field**. It has the same effect on charges—exerting a force $q\mathbf{E}$—as do the electric fields we considered earlier. The field itself, however, originates not in electric charges but in changing magnetic fields.

An induced electric field results whenever a magnetic field changes with time—whether or not an electric circuit is present. When a circuit is present, then the induced field may drive a current. But the induced field, not the current, is fundamental. A single, stationary electron placed in a changing magnetic field will experience an *electric* force—clear evidence for the existence of an electric field.

Until now we've been thinking of Faraday's law as a relation between the emf induced in a circuit and the rate of change of magnetic flux through that circuit. But we've just seen that induced electric fields are the fundamental manifestation of changing magnetic flux, and that these fields arise whether or not circuits are present. So we need to reformulate Faraday's law to describe induced electric fields without reference to circuits. The induced emf $\mathscr{E}$ that we've been writing on the left-hand side of Faraday's law means simply the work per unit charge gained by a test charge moved around a circuit. Since work is the line integral of force over distance, and electric field is the force per unit charge, we can write the emf as the line integral of the electric field. Then Faraday's law becomes

$$\oint \mathbf{E} \cdot d\boldsymbol{\ell} = -\frac{d\phi_B}{dt} \qquad \text{(Faraday's law)} \qquad (31\text{-}3)$$

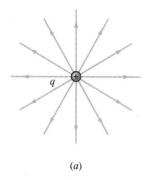

(a)

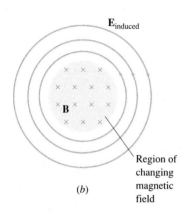

$E_{induced}$

B

Region of changing magnetic field

(b)

FIGURE 31-29 *(a)* Electric field lines arising from electric charges begin and end on the charges, or extend to infinity. *(b)* In contrast, the lines of induced electric fields have no beginning or ending points, but generally form closed loops encircling regions of changing magnetic field.

Here the line integral on the left-hand side is taken over *any* closed loop, which need not coincide with a circuit. The flux on the right-hand side is the surface integral of the magnetic field over *any* open surface bounded by the loop on the left-hand side.

Faraday's law in the form 31-3 makes no reference to wires or other circuits. It simply describes induced electric fields, which occur whenever there are changing magnetic fields. If electric circuits are present, then induced currents occur as well—but it is the induced electric fields that are fundamental. We can state Faraday's law loosely but powerfully by saying the following:

▌ **A changing magnetic field creates an electric field.**

This direct interaction between the fields is the basis for numerous practical devices and, as we'll see in Chapter 34, is essential to the existence of light.

Note the similarity between Faraday's law and Ampère's law (Equation 30-7). Faraday's law gives the line integral of the electric field around a closed loop in terms of the rate of change of magnetic flux through the loop. Ampère's law gives the line integral of the magnetic field around a closed loop in terms of the current through the loop. Both give fields that *encircle* their sources—current for the source of magnetic field and changing magnetic field for the induced electric field. That means the configuration of an induced electric field is very different from that of an electric field originating in electric charge. Induced fields have no beginning or end; their field lines generally form closed loops encircling regions of changing magnetic field (see Fig. 31-29).

When a changing magnetic field has sufficient symmetry, we can evaluate the induced electric field in the same way we did the magnetic field of a symmetric current distribution. Example 31-9 illustrates this procedure.

EXAMPLE 31-9	*An Induced Electric Field*

A long solenoid has circular cross section of radius R. The current in the solenoid is increasing and, as a result, the uniform magnetic field within the solenoid increases with time; the field magnitude is given by $B = bt$, with b a constant and t the time. Find the induced electric field outside the solenoid, a distance r from the solenoid axis.

Solution

The induced electric field has no beginning or end, so the field lines must encircle the solenoid. The only field consistent with the symmetry consists of circular field lines centered on the solenoid axis, as suggested in Fig. 31-30. Since the solenoid field points into the page and is increasing in strength, the direction of the induced electric field must be such that any current it might drive would produce a magnetic field *opposing* the increase in the solenoid field. Applying the right-hand rule then shows that the induced electric field runs counterclockwise.

Faraday's law relates the line integral of the electric field to the rate of change of the encircled magnetic flux. Here a suit-

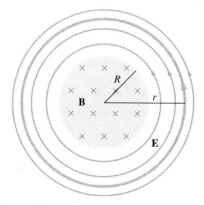

FIGURE 31-30 Cross section of a solenoid of radius R whose magnetic field is increasing with time. Field lines of the induced electric field are circles concentric with the solenoid axis. Also shown is a circular loop (gray) of radius r for evaluating the line integral in Faraday's law.

able integration loop is itself a circle centered on the solenoid axis. Symmetry shows that the field magnitude is constant over this loop, and if we circle the loop in the direction of the field then $\cos\theta$ in the dot product $\mathbf{E} \cdot d\boldsymbol{\ell}$ is 1. Thus

$$\oint \mathbf{E} \cdot d\boldsymbol{\ell} = \oint E \, d\ell = E \oint d\ell = 2\pi r E ,$$

since $\oint d\ell$ is just the loop circumference. Faraday's law relates this quantity to the rate of change of the encircled magnetic flux. Here the flux is due to the uniform magnetic field inside the solenoid, perpendicular to our loop and confined to a circular area of radius R. (We use the long-solenoid approximation, neglecting the small magnetic field that must exist outside a solenoid of finite length.) So the encircled flux is just $\phi_B = \pi R^2 B = \pi R^2 bt$, and its rate of change is

$$\frac{d\phi_B}{dt} = \frac{d}{dt}(\pi R^2 bt) = \pi R^2 b .$$

Then Faraday's law gives

$$2\pi r E = -\pi R^2 b ,$$

or

$$E = -\frac{R^2 b}{2r} .$$

We've already accounted for the minus sign in arguing that the field circles counterclockwise. The $1/r$ dependence of the field strength on distance should come as no surprise; points with $r > R$ are outside a cylindrically symmetric distribution, in this case a distribution of changing magnetic flux. We found the same $1/r$ dependence for the electric and magnetic fields outside, respectively, a cylindrically symmetric charge distribution and a cylindrically symmetric current distribution.

EXERCISE Show that the electric field at points *inside* the solenoid has magnitude $br/2$.

Some problems similar to Example 31-9: 36–38, 41, 42

In Chapter 30 we derived the magnetic field of a solenoid using Ampère's law—which, as we've formulated it so far, applies only to steady currents. But a solenoid whose field is changing—as in Example 31-9—must have a changing current, so how can we talk about it? In fact, Ampère's law gives a good approximation to the field produced by changing current, provided that change is sufficiently slow. In the examples and problems of this chapter we assume that to be the case. In Chapter 34 we'll see just what "sufficiently slow" means, and will explore what happens if we relax the assumption of slowly changing currents.

Conservative and Nonconservative Electric Fields

We've seen that static electric fields—those beginning and ending on stationary charge distributions—are conservative, meaning that the work required to move a charge between two points is independent of the path taken. A consequence is that it takes no work to move around a closed path in an electrostatic field; mathematically, we express this by writing

$$\oint \mathbf{E} \cdot d\boldsymbol{\ell} = 0 . \qquad \text{(electrostatic field)}$$

In contrast, induced electric fields generally form closed loops, and Faraday's law shows that the line integral of the electric field around a closed path in such a field is decidedly not zero. That means the induced electric field does work on a charge moved around a *closed* path and that the work done in moving between two points cannot be independent of the path taken (Fig. 31-31). The induced electric field is therefore not conservative.

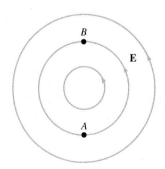

FIGURE 31-31 Two points in an induced electric field. If a positively charged particle moves counterclockwise along the field line from A to B the field does work on it. But if it moves from A to B in the clockwise direction the field does negative work; that is, an external force must do work on the charge. The work done is not path independent, and the induced electric field is not conservative.

FIGURE 31-32 This induction cooktop has no burners. Instead, coils beneath the cooktop produce time-varying magnetic fields that induce currents in the conducting cookware. Resistance in the cookware then results in heating. The cooktop itself remains cool because it's not a conductor.

The work done on charges moving around closed paths in nonconservative electric fields can be useful. A simple example is the induction cooktop (Fig. 31-32), where food cooks in a special conducting pan heated by currents in the pan itself. Those currents are driven by an induced electric field originating from a changing magnetic field in coils just below the cooktop's surface. Much more generally, any electrical device that derives its power from a generator—and that includes almost every electrical thing you use—is part of a circuit in which a nonconservative electric field drives the current.

APPLICATION	*The Tokamak*

In Chapter 29 we described fusion reactors, devices that may someday yield copious amounts of energy through nuclear fusion of hydrogen nuclei, using fuel derived from seawater. We saw how magnetic fields confine very hot plasma in fusion reactors and showed why most reactors have a toroidal shape. The most promising of the toroidal reactor designs is the **tokamak**, in which the confining magnetic field arises in part from current within the plasma itself. Discharging a large capacitor bank through a coil produces a rapidly changing magnetic field in the "hole" of the toroidal "doughnut," resulting in an induced electric field within the torus. This field drives the plasma current that produces a magnetic field component around the minor radius of the device. Other coils around the torus provide a magnetic field component around the long dimension of the torus, giving a net magnetic field that spirals around the plasma (Fig. 31-33).

As in any conductor, particle collisions dissipate energy gained from the electric field, in this case heating the plasma. Unfortunately the resistance of a plasma drops at high temperature, making it difficult to achieve the temperature needed for fusion with resistive heating alone. Nevertheless, the induced electric field helps bring the plasma close to the fusion temperature, as well as driving currents that produce the confining magnetic field.

Since the tokamak uses an induced electric field, its operation requires a changing magnetic field. Therefore, the tokamak

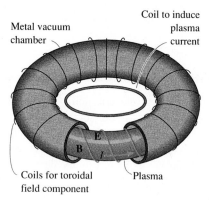

FIGURE 31-33 A tokamak fusion reactor. Current in the plasma is driven by an electric field induced by the magnetic field change associated with a rapid change in current through the central coil. Additional coils wound around the toroid give a steady magnetic field in the same direction as the plasma current. Combining with the field from the plasma current gives a net field that spirals around the plasma.

cannot run continuously but operates instead in a pulsed mode as current builds up rapidly and then decays in preparation for another pulse. Today's experimental tokamaks can achieve pulse durations of 10 s or more, during which they produce significant fusion energy.

| *Nonconservative Electric Fields*

The nonconservative nature of the induced electric field is strikingly demonstrated if you attempt to measure potential differences in nonconservative fields. In Chapter 25, we defined potential difference as the work required to move a unit charge between two points, and stressed that this work is independent of path for a conservative field. But when the field is nonconservative, the work is not independent of path, and the concept of potential becomes ambiguous.

Figure 31-34 shows an end view of a long solenoid surrounded by three identical resistors bent into circular arcs. If the solenoid current is increasing, an induced electric field appears in the resistors, and drives a current *I* in the counterclockwise direction.

Because they have the same resistance and carry the same current, the potential difference across each resistor should be the same. We could try to measure the potential difference across one resistor, for example, by connecting a voltmeter as with the right-hand meter in Fig. 31-34. With current *I* flowing through the resis-tance *R*, this meter reads *IR*. Since the current flows counterclockwise, we must connect the positive voltmeter terminal to point *B*.

But now try to measure the potential difference across the other two resistors together, as with the left-hand meter in Fig. 31-34. With the current *I* flowing through the total resis-tance *2R*, the meter now reads *2IR*. We have two voltmeters with their terminals connected to the same points, and yet they indicate different voltages. Not only are the magnitudes of the voltages different, but even their polarities differ. How can this be? It's because of the nonconservative nature of the induced

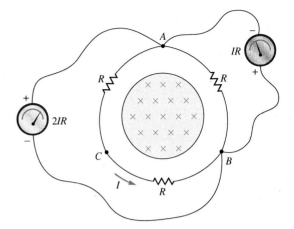

FIGURE 31-34 End view of a long solenoid surrounded by three resistors in series. A changing magnetic field in the solenoid induces an emf in the resistors, and the same current *I* flows through each. A voltmeter connected between points *A* and *B* indicates the voltage *IR* across one resistor. A second voltmeter connected to the *same points* indicates voltage *2IR* with the opposite sign.

electric field. The two voltmeters are positioned differently with respect to the changing magnetic flux, so they sample different regions of the induced electric field. Even though the meters are connected to the same points, they measure the line integral of the induced electric field over *different* paths, and so they don't read the same voltage.

31-5 DIAMAGNETISM

In Section 30-6 we discussed paramagnetic and ferromagnetic materials, in which atomic magnetic dipoles align with an applied magnetic field, causing an attractive interaction between the material and a magnet. We also mentioned diamagnetic materials, in which induced magnetic dipoles align antiparallel to the applied field, causing a repulsive force. We are now ready to understand diamagnetism as a manifestation of Faraday's law at the microscopic level.

In a purely diamagnetic material, current loops associated with pairs of atomic electrons exactly cancel, leaving atoms with no intrinsic magnetic moments. Figure 31-35*a* shows a simplified model to describe such an atom.

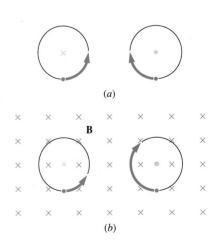

FIGURE 31-35 Simplified, classical model for a diamagnetic atom. (*a*) In the absence of an applied field, magnetic moments (cross and dot) associated with a pair of electrons exactly cancel. (*b*) The changing flux associated with an increasing magnetic field induces an electric field that speeds up one electron and slows down the other, giving rise to a net magnetic moment. (In applying the right-hand rule, remember that the electrons are negative.)

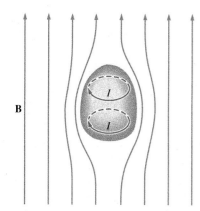

FIGURE 31-36 Induced currents in a superconductor completely cancel an applied magnetic field. Net result is that a magnetic field cannot penetrate the superconductor.

FIGURE 31-37 A small magnet is levitated above a wafer of high-temperature superconductor in a bath of liquid nitrogen at 77 K.

The picture should not be taken too literally, for it uses classical physics to describe a phenomenon properly within the domain of quantum mechanics. Nevertheless, it shows qualitatively how diamagnetism is an electromagnetic induction effect.

The electron orbiting clockwise in Fig. 31-35*a* has a magnetic moment pointing out of the page (apply the right-hand rule and remember that the electron carries a negative charge). In the absence of an applied magnetic field, this moment is exactly cancelled by the equal but oppositely directed moment of the other electron. But now suppose a magnetic field is applied, for example by moving the north pole of a magnet down toward the plane of Fig. 31-35. This produces a changing magnetic field in the plane of the figure, resulting in an induced electric field that alters the speeds of the orbiting electrons. The direction of this effect must be such as to oppose the increase in field. Thus the electron whose magnetic moment points out of the page has its moment increase, while the moment pointing into the page decreases. Figure 31-35*b* shows how these changes result from the alteration of electron speeds by the induced electric field.

Once the field is applied and the orbital speeds of the two electrons are no longer identical, the atom now has a net magnetic moment that points out of the page in Fig. 31-35, opposing the incoming magnet and resulting in a repulsive force. This repulsion is the distinguishing characteristic of diamagnetism. We listed a number of diamagnetic materials in Table 30-2.

A material that is entirely superconducting is perfectly diamagnetic, with magnetic susceptibility -1. This means that the magnetic field resulting from induced currents within the material completely cancels any applied field. Since these induced currents persist in the zero-resistance superconductor, the material completely excludes magnetic fields from its interior, a phenomenon known as the Meissner effect (Fig. 31-36). The repulsive force associated with the magnetic moments of a permanent magnet and a nearby superconductor results in the widely publicized phenomenon of magnetic levitation (Fig. 31-37). Readers of the extended version of this text will explore superconductivity further in Chapter 42.

CHAPTER SYNOPSIS

Summary

1. **Electromagnetic induction** is a fundamental phenomenon linking magnetism and electricity. Induction is described by **Faraday's law**, which states that a **changing magnetic field** produces an **induced electric field**. Unlike the conservative electrostatic field of an electric charge, this induced field is **nonconservative**, meaning it can do work on charges as they move around a closed loop. Faraday's law relates the line integral of this nonconservative electric field around an arbitrary loop to the rate of change of magnetic flux through a surface bounded by that same loop:

$$\oint \mathbf{E} \cdot d\boldsymbol{\ell} = -\frac{d\phi_B}{dt}.$$

2. In order for energy to be conserved, the induced electric field is in such a direction as to oppose the change in flux that gives rise to it. This energy-conserving aspect of Faraday's law is called **Lenz's law** and is reflected mathematically in the minus sign on the right-hand side of Faraday's law.

3. When a conductor is present, the nonconservative electric field manifests itself as an **induced emf**:

$$\mathcal{E} = -\frac{d\phi_B}{dt}.$$

This emf drives an **induced current** in any circuit with finite resistance. It does not matter whether the magnetic flux is changed by moving a conductor in a magnetic field, or by moving a magnetic field near a conductor, or by altering the shape or orientation of the conductor. The generation of electric power by moving conducting loops in magnetic fields is an important technological example of induced currents.

4. **Diamagnetism** is a manifestation of electromagnetic induction on the atomic scale. Application of a magnetic field to a diamagnetic material results in induced atomic magnetic moments that cause the material to be repelled from a magnet.

Terms You Should Understand

(Pairs are closely related terms whose distinction is important; number in parentheses is chapter section where term first appears.)

electromagnetic induction (31-1)
induced current, induced emf (31-1, 31-2)
magnetic flux (31-2)
Faraday's law, Lenz's law (31-2, 31-3)
motional emf (31-3)

generator (31-3)
eddy currents (31-3)
induced electric field (31-4)

Symbols You Should Recognize

ϕ_B (31-2)
$\oint \mathbf{E} \cdot d\boldsymbol{\ell}$ (31-4)

Problems You Should Be Able to Solve

calculating magnetic flux (31-2)
calculating induced emf's (31-2)
finding directions of induced emf's and currents (31-3)
calculating induced electric fields (31-4)

Limitations to Keep in Mind

Electromagnetic induction requires a *change* in magnetic flux. Values of magnetic field or flux alone don't matter; only the rate of change of those quantities is important.

QUESTIONS

1. A copper penny falls on a vertical path that takes it between the poles of a magnet. Does it hit the ground faster or slower than if no magnet were present?

2. A bar magnet is moved toward a conducting ring, as shown in Fig. 31-38. What is the direction of the induced current in the ring?

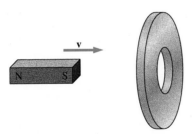

FIGURE 31-38 Question 2.

3. Figure 31-39 shows two concentric conducting loops, the outer connected to a battery and a switch. The switch is initially open. It is then closed, left closed for a while, then

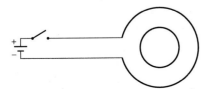

FIGURE 31-39 Question 3.

opened again. Describe the currents in the inner loop during the entire procedure.

4. An electric generator is being turned at constant speed. A load resistor R is connected across the generator terminals. If the electrical resistance of the load is lowered, does the generator get easier or harder to turn?

5. Service manuals for cars often tell you to set the idle speed of the engine with the headlights on. Why? What does this have to do with electromagnetic induction?

6. Figure 31-40 shows two square wire loops, the first containing a battery and variable resistor. The resistor is initially at the midpoint of its resistance range. Should its resistance be lowered or raised in order to induce a clockwise current in the right-hand loop?

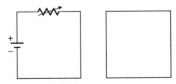

FIGURE 31-40 Question 6.

7. Consider the simple motor shown in Fig. 29-36. What happens if you connect a resistor across the motor terminals, and turn the motor by hand? What is the difference between a motor and a generator?

8. Figure 31-41 shows an open wire loop in a magnetic field. The field is changing, and charge has piled up at the loop gap with the polarity indicated. Is the magnetic field strength increasing or decreasing?

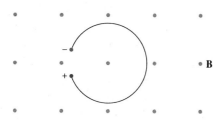

FIGURE 31-41 Question 8.

9. A constant, uniform magnetic field points into the page. A flexible, circular conducting ring lies in the plane of the page. If the ring is stretched, maintaining its circular shape, what is the direction of the induced current?

10. When a magnet is moved near a superconductor, the magnetic field lines never enter the superconductor. Why not?

11. Is it possible to produce an induced current that never changes? How or why not? Could you produce an induced current that was steady for some finite time? How or why not?

12. When you push a bar magnet into a conducting loop, you do work. What happens when you pull it out the other side?

13. You are turning a generator in such a way that the current it delivers remains constant. As you lower the load resistance across the generator, does the generator get easier or harder to turn?

14. Devise a way of measuring a magnetic field using Faraday's law.

15. In Fig. 31-42, a copper ring was originally resting on the wooden structure, surrounding the coil. When a rapidly

FIGURE 31-42 Question 15.

changing current was applied to the coil, the ring was ejected into the air. Explain this phenomenon.

16. Fluctuations in Earth's magnetic field due to changing solar activity can wreak havoc with communications, even those using underground cables. How is this possible?

17. Why is it not possible to run a tokamak on a continuous basis?

18. Conventional brakes on a car need large surface areas to dissipate the heat of friction when the brakes are applied. Would eddy-current brakes have the same problem?

19. Which way would the eddy currents flow in Fig. 31-22a as the bob continues its swing and begins to emerge from the field?

20. In Chapter 29, we pointed out that a static magnetic field cannot change the energy of a charged particle. Is this true of a changing magnetic field? Discuss.

21. A long solenoid of circular cross section is oriented so that its magnetic field points out of the page, as shown in Fig. 31-43. The solenoid current is increasing. (a) What is the direction of the induced electric field at points A and B in the figure? (b) What is the magnitude of the induced electric field in the center of the solenoid? (Don't calculate! Argue from symmetry.)

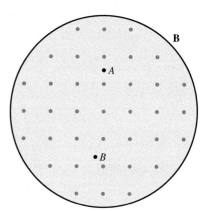

FIGURE 31-43 Question 21.

22. Is the concept of electric potential (Chapter 25) useful in a nonconservative electric field? Give an example to substantiate your answer.

23. Can an induced electric field exist in the absence of a conductor?

24. Could you tell whether a given electric field arises from electric charge or from a changing magnetic field? How or why not?

25. Does a diamagnetic material experience a force in a uniform magnetic field?

PROBLEMS

ActivPhysics can help with these problems:
Activities 13.9, 13.10

Sections 31-2 and 31-3 Faraday's Law and Induction and the Conservation of Energy

1. Show that the volt is the correct SI unit for the rate of change of magnetic flux, making Faraday's law dimensionally correct.

2. A bar magnet is moved steadily through a conducting ring, as shown in Fig. 31-44. Sketch qualitatively the current and power dissipation in the ring as functions of time. Take as positive a current flowing out of the plane of the page at the top of the ring, and indicate the position of the magnet on your time axis.

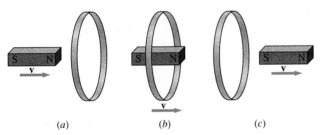

(a)   (b)   (c)

FIGURE 31-44 Problem 2.

3. Find the magnetic flux through a circular loop 5.0 cm in diameter oriented with the loop normal at 30° to a uniform 80-mT magnetic field.

4. A circular wire loop 40 cm in diameter has 100-Ω resistance and lies in a horizontal plane. A uniform magnetic field points vertically downward, and in 25 ms it increases linearly from 5.0 mT to 55 mT. Find the magnetic flux through the loop at (a) the beginning and (b) the end of the 25 ms period. (c) What is the loop current during this time? (d) Which way does this current flow?

5. A conducting loop of area 240 cm² and resistance 12 Ω lies at right angles to a spatially uniform magnetic field. The loop carries an induced current of 320 mA. At what rate is the magnetic field changing?

6. A conducting loop of area A and resistance R lies at right angles to a spatially uniform magnetic field. At time $t = 0$ the magnetic field and loop current are both zero. Subsequently, the current increases according to $I = bt^2$, where b is a constant with the units A/s². Find an expression for the magnetic field strength as a function of time.

7. A conducting loop with area 0.15 m² and resistance 6.0 Ω lies in the x-y plane. A spatially uniform magnetic field points in the z direction. The field varies with time according to $B_z = at^2 - b$, where $a = 2.0$ T/s² and $b = 8.0$ T.

Find the loop current (a) when $t = 3.0$ s and (b) when $B_z = 0$.

8. The magnetic field inside a 20-cm-diameter solenoid is increasing at the rate of 2.4 T/s. How many turns should a coil wrapped around the outside of the solenoid have in order that the emf induced in the coil be 15 V?

9. A square wire loop of side ℓ and resistance R is pulled with constant speed v from a region of no magnetic field until it is fully inside a region of constant, uniform magnetic field **B** perpendicular to the loop plane. The boundary of the field region is parallel to one side of the loop. Find an expression for the total work done by the agent pulling the loop.

10. A 1.8-m high runner sprints eastward at 9.5 m/s along the equator, where Earth's magnetic field points horizontally with a strength of 31 μT. (a) What is the magnitude of the emf induced between the runner's head and feet? (b) Which end is positive?

11. In Fig. 31-26 the loop radius is 15 cm, and the magnetic field is decreasing at the rate of 550 T/s. If the gap width is small compared with the loop circumference, what is the voltage across the gap?

12. A 5-turn coil 1.0 cm in diameter is rotated at 10 rev/s about an axis perpendicular to a uniform magnetic field. A voltmeter connected to the coil through rotating contacts reads a peak value of 360 μV. What is the magnetic field strength?

13. The wingspan of a 747 jetliner is 60 m. If the plane is flying at 960 km/h in a region where the vertical component of Earth's magnetic field is 0.20 G, what emf develops between the plane's wingtips?

14. A square wire loop 3.0 m on a side is perpendicular to a uniform magnetic field of 2.0 T. A 6-V light bulb is in series with the loop, as shown in Fig. 31-45. The magnetic field is reduced steadily to zero over a time Δt. (a) Find Δt such that the light will shine at full brightness during this time. (b) Which way will the loop current flow?

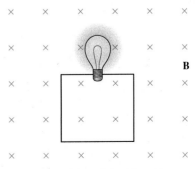

FIGURE 31-45 Problem 14.

15. In Example 31-2 take $a = 1.0$ cm, $w = 3.5$ cm, and $\ell = 6.0$ cm. Suppose the rectangular loop is a conductor with resistance 50 mΩ and that the current I in the long wire is increasing at the rate of 25 A/s. Find the induced current in the loop. In what direction does it flow?

16. A windmill with conducting blades of length ℓ is rotating with angular speed ω about a horizontal axis; the horizontal component of Earth's magnetic field at its location is B_x. Find an expression for the emf developed between the blade tips and the central axis.

17. A square conducting loop of side $s = 0.50$ m and resistance $R = 5.0$ Ω moves to the right with speed $v = 0.25$ m/s. At time $t = 0$ its rightmost edge enters a uniform magnetic field $B = 1.0$ T pointing into the page, as shown in Fig. 31-46. The magnetic field covers a region of width $w = 0.75$ m. Plot (a) the current and (b) the power dissipation in the loop as functions of time, taking a clockwise current as positive and covering the time until the entire loop has exited the field region.

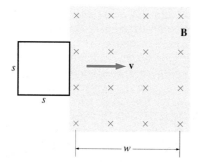

FIGURE 31-46 Problem 17.

18. A 2.0-m-long solenoid is 15 cm in diameter and consists of 2000 turns of wire. The current in the solenoid is increasing at the rate of 1.0 kA/s. (a) Find the current in a wire loop with diameter 10 cm and resistance 5.0 Ω, lying inside the solenoid in a plane perpendicular to the loop axis. (b) Repeat for a similarly oriented loop with diameter 25 cm, lying entirely outside the solenoid.

19. A solenoid 2.0 m long and 30 cm in diameter consists of 5000 turns of wire. A 5-turn coil with negligible resistance is wrapped around the solenoid and connected to a 180-Ω resistor, as shown in Fig. 31-47. The direction of the current in the solenoid is such that the solenoid's magnetic field points to the right. At time $t = 0$ the solenoid current begins to decay exponentially, being given by $I = I_0 e^{-t/\tau}$, where $I_0 = 85$ A, $\tau = 2.5$ s, and t is the time in seconds. (a) What is the direction of the current in the resistor as the solenoid current decays? What is the value of the resistor current at (b) $t = 1.0$ s and (c) $t = 5.0$ s?

20. Make a qualitative plot of the resistor current in the preceding problem as a function of time if the solenoid current

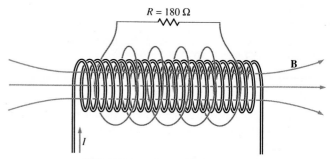

FIGURE 31-47 Problems 19–21.

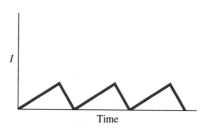

FIGURE 31-48 Problem 20.

has the form shown in Fig. 31-48. Take a left-to-right resistor current as positive.

21. (a) Find an expression for the resistor current in Problem 19 if the solenoid current is given by $I = I_0 \sin \omega t$, where $I_0 = 85$ A and $\omega = 210$ s^{-1}. (b) What is the peak current in the resistor? (c) What is the resistor current when the solenoid current is a maximum?

22. A magnetic field is described by $\mathbf{B} = B_0 \sin \omega t\, \hat{\mathbf{k}}$, where $B_0 = 2.0$ T and $\omega = 10$ s^{-1}. A conducting loop with area 150 cm^2 and resistance 5.0 Ω lies in the x-y plane. Find the induced current in the loop (a) at $t = 0$ and (b) at $t = 0.10$ s.

23. In the preceding problem, what is the first time after $t = 0$ when the loop current will be zero?

24. A car alternator consists of a 250-turn coil 10 cm in diameter in a magnetic field of 0.10 T. If the alternator is turning at 1000 revolutions per minute, what is its peak output voltage?

25. A credit-card reader extracts information from the card's magnetic stripe as it is pulled past the reader's head. At some instant the card motion results in a magnetic field at the head that is changing at the rate of 450 μT/ms. If this field passes perpendicularly through a 5000-turn head coil 2.0 mm in diameter, what will be the induced emf?

26. A generator consists of a rectangular coil 75 cm by 1.3 m, spinning in a 0.14-T magnetic field. If it is to produce a 60-Hz alternating emf (i.e., $\mathcal{E} = \mathcal{E}_0 \sin 2\pi ft$, where $f = 60$ Hz) with peak value 6.7 kV, how many turns must it have?

27. Figure 31-49 shows a pair of parallel conducting rails a distance ℓ apart in a uniform magnetic field **B**. A resistance R is connected across the rails, and a conducting bar of negligible resistance is being pulled along the rails with velocity **v** to the right. (a) What is the direction of the current in the resistor? (b) At what rate must work be done by the agent pulling the bar?

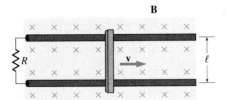

FIGURE 31-49 Problems 27–29, 33, 60.

28. The resistor in the preceding problem is replaced by an ideal voltmeter. (a) To which rail should the positive meter terminal be connected if the meter is to indicate a positive voltage? (b) At what rate must work be done by the agent pulling the bar?

29. A battery of emf $\mathscr{E}$ is inserted in series with the resistor in Fig. 31-49, with its positive terminal toward the top rail. The bar is initially at rest, and now no agent pulls it. (a) Describe the bar's subsequent motion. (b) The bar eventually reaches a constant speed. Why? (c) What is that constant speed? Express in terms of the magnetic field, the battery emf, and the rail spacing ℓ. Does the resistance R affect the final speed? If not, what role does it play?

30. A toroidal coil of square cross section has inner radius a and outer radius b. It consists of N turns of wire and carries a time-varying current $I = I_0 \sin \omega t$. A single-turn wire loop encircles the toroid, passing through its center hole as shown in Fig. 31-50. Find an expression for the peak emf induced in the loop.

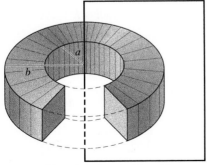

FIGURE 31-50 Problem 30.

31. A pair of parallel conducting rails 10 cm apart lie at right angles to a uniform magnetic field **B** of magnitude 2.0 T, as shown in Fig. 31-51. A 5.0-Ω and a 10-Ω resistor lie across the rails and are free to slide along them. (a) The 5-Ω resistor is held fixed, and the 10-Ω resistor is pulled to the right at 50 cm/s. What are the direction and magnitude of the induced current? (b) Now the 10-Ω resistor is held fixed, and the 5-Ω resistor is pulled to the left at 50 cm/s. What are the direction and magnitude of the induced current? (c) What is the power dissipation in the 10-Ω resistor in both cases?

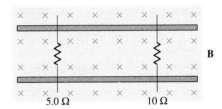

FIGURE 31-51 Problems 31, 32, and 64.

32. In Fig. 31-51 the 10-Ω resistor is being moved to the right at a constant 50 cm/s. The 5-Ω resistor, initially at rest, is placed across the conducting rails. Describe qualitatively its subsequent motion, and determine its final speed.

33. In Fig. 31-49, take $\ell = 10$ cm, $B = 0.50$ T, $R = 4.0\ \Omega$, and $v = 2.0$ m/s. Find (a) the current in the resistor, (b) the magnetic force on the bar, (c) the power dissipation in the resistor, and (d) the mechanical work done by the agent pulling the bar. Compare your answers to (c) and (d).

34. A rectangular conducting loop of resistance R, mass m, and width w falls into a uniform magnetic field **B**, as shown in Fig. 31-52. If the loop is long enough and the field region has a great enough vertical extent, the loop will reach a terminal speed. (a) Why? (b) Find an expression for the terminal speed. (c) What will be the direction of the loop current as the loop enters the field?

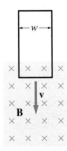

FIGURE 31-52 Problem 34.

35. A circular loop 40 cm in diameter is made from a flexible conductor and lies at right angles to a uniform 12-T magnetic field. At time $t = 0$ the loop starts to expand, its radius increasing at the rate of 5.0 mm/s. Find the induced emf in the loop (a) at $t = 1.0$ s and (b) at $t = 10$ s.

Section 31-4 Induced Electric Fields

36. The induced electric field 12 cm from the axis of a solenoid with 10 cm radius is 45 V/m. Find the rate of change of the solenoid's magnetic field.

37. Find the electric force on a 50-μC charge inside the solenoid of Problem 18, if the charge is 5.0 cm from the solenoid axis.

38. Figure 31-53 shows a top view of a tokamak. The magnetic field in the center is confined to a circular area of radius 50 cm, and during a pulse it increases at the rate of 5.1 T/ms. (a) What is the magnitude of the induced electric field in the tokamak, 1.2 m from the center of the field region in Fig. 31-53? (b) What is the field direction? (c) If a proton circles the tokamak once at this radius, going with the electric field, how much energy does it gain?

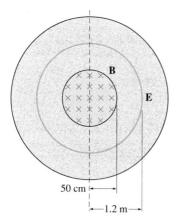

FIGURE 31-53 Top view of a tokamak. (Problem 38)

39. A uniform magnetic field points into the page in Fig. 31-54. In the same region an electric field points straight up, but increases with position at the rate of 10 V/m² as you move to the right. Apply Faraday's law to a rectangular loop to show that the magnetic field must be changing with time, and calculate the rate of change.

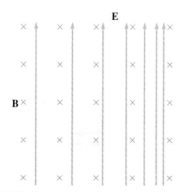

FIGURE 31-54 The magnetic field must be changing. Why? (Problem 39)

40. Use Faraday's law to show that the electric field produced by charges on the plates of a parallel-plate capacitor cannot end abruptly at the edges of the plates. *Hint:* Apply Faraday's law to the loop shown in Fig. 31-55.

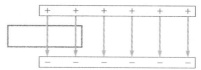

FIGURE 31-55 Problem 40.

41. Figure 31-56 shows a magnetic field pointing into the page; the field is confined to a layer of thickness h in the vertical direction but extends infinitely to the left and right. The field strength is increasing with time: $B = bt$, where b is a constant. Find an expression for the electric field at all points outside the field region. *Hint:* Consult Example 30-5.

FIGURE 31-56 Problem 41.

42. The magnetic field inside a solenoid of circular cross section is given by $\mathbf{B} = bt\,\hat{\mathbf{k}}$, where $b = 2.1$ T/ms. At time $t = 0.40$ μs a proton is inside the solenoid at the point $x = 5.0$ cm, $y = 0$, $z = 0$ and is moving with velocity $\mathbf{v} = 4.8\times10^6\,\hat{\mathbf{j}}$ m /s. Find the net electromagnetic force on the proton.

Paired Problems

(Both problems in a pair involve the same principles and techniques. If you can get the first problem, you should be able to solve the second one.)

43. A magnetic field is given by $\mathbf{B} = B_0(x/x_0)^2\,\hat{\mathbf{k}}$, where B_0 and x_0 are constants. Find an expression for the magnetic flux through a square of side $2x_0$ that lies in the x-y plane with one corner at the origin and two sides coinciding with the positive x and y axes.

44. A circular region of radius R lies in the x-y plane and contains a magnetic field given by $\mathbf{B} = B_0\dfrac{r}{R}\hat{\mathbf{k}}$, where r is the radial distance from the central axis of the field region. Find an expression for the magnetic flux through this region.

45. A uniform magnetic field is given by $\mathbf{B} = bt\,\hat{\mathbf{k}}$, where $b = 0.35$ T/s. Find the current in a conducting loop with area 240 cm² and resistance 0.20 Ω that lies in the x-y plane. In what direction is the current, as viewed from the positive z axis?

46. A uniform magnetic field is given by $\mathbf{B} = bt^3\,\hat{\mathbf{k}}$. A square conducting loop 15 cm on a side has 0.32-Ω resistance and lies in the x-y plane. At time $t = 2.5$ s, the current in the loop is 4.1 A. Find b.

47. A pair of vertical conducting rods are a distance ℓ apart and are connected at the bottom by a resistance R. A conducting bar of mass m runs horizontally between the rods and can slide freely down them while maintaining electrical contact. The whole apparatus is in a uniform magnetic field **B** pointing horizontally and perpendicular to the bar. When the bar is released from rest it soon reaches a constant speed. Find this speed.

48. A conducting bar of mass m slides down the conducting wedges shown in Fig. 31-57. The wedges are separated by a distance ℓ, connected at the top by a resistance R, and make an angle θ with the vertical. A uniform magnetic field **B** points horizontally, as shown. When released from rest the bar soon reaches a constant speed. Find an expression for this speed.

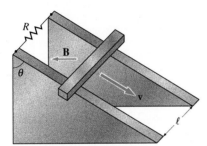

FIGURE 31-57 Problem 48.

49. Figure 31-58 shows an unusual design for a generator, consisting of a conducting bar that rotates about a central axis while making contact with a conducting ring of radius R. A uniform magnetic field is perpendicular to the ring. Wires from the axis and ring carry power to a load. Find an expression for the emf induced in this generator when the bar rotates with angular speed ω.

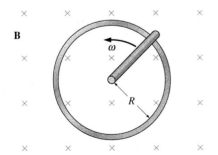

FIGURE 31-58 Problem 49.

50. A copper disk 90 cm in diameter is spinning at 3600 rpm about a conducting axle through its center, as shown in Fig. 31-59. A uniform 1.5-T magnetic field is perpendicular to the disk, as shown. A stationary conducting brush maintains contact with the disk's rim, and a voltmeter is

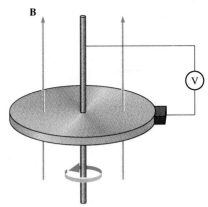

FIGURE 31-59 Problem 50.

connected between the brush and the axle. (a) What does the voltmeter read? (b) Which voltmeter lead is positive?

51. An electron is inside a solenoid, 28 cm from the solenoid axis. It experiences an electric force of magnitude 1.3 fN. At what rate is the solenoid's magnetic field changing?

52. It takes 0.43 J to push a 84-μC charge around a closed path surrounding a 1.5-m-diameter solenoid. At what rate is the solenoid's magnetic field changing?

Supplementary Problems

53. At times prior to $t = 0$, there is no current in either the solenoid or the small coil of Problem 19. Subsequently, the current in the small coil is observed to increase at 10 μA/s. What is the solenoid current as a function of time?

54. A conducting loop of area A and resistance R lies perpendicular to a uniform magnetic field B. The loop is then rotated at a uniform rate until it is upside down; this takes time Δt. Find an expression for the work done in flipping the loop.

55. So-called magnetohydrodynamic generators have been proposed as a means of extracting electrical energy from charged particles released in fusion reactions; they've also been suggested as a way to generate electricity from flowing water. An MHD generator consists of two metal plates on either side of a channel carrying conducting fluid in a magnetic field, as shown in Fig. 31-60. The magnetic force on free charges in the fluid drives positive charge to one plate, negative to the other. If there's no electrical load connected across the plates, the electric field that develops eventually halts any further charge motion. (a) Show in this case that the voltage between the plates is $V = vBd$, where v is the fluid velocity and d the plate spacing. (b) Now suppose a resistance R is connected between the plates. Show that the current through R is $I = \dfrac{vABd}{\rho d + AR}$, where A is the plate area and ρ is the resistivity of the fluid.

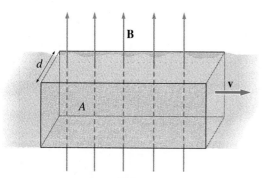

FIGURE 31-60 Problem 55.

56. The tethered satellite system of Example 31-8 is flown in a low circular orbit about a planet of mass M and radius R. If the tether has length ℓ and generates an emf $\mathcal{E}$, find an expression for the planet's magnetic field strength.

57. Clever farmers whose lands are crossed by large power lines have been known to steal power by stringing wire near the power line and making use of the induced current—a practice that has been ruled legally to be theft. The scene of a particular crime is shown in Fig. 31-61. The power line carries 60-Hz alternating current with a peak current of 10 kA (that is, the current is given by $I = I_0 \sin \omega t$, where $I_0 = 10$ kA and $\omega = 2\pi f$, with $f = 60$ Hz). (a) If the farmer wants a peak voltage of 170 V, what should be the length ℓ of the loop shown in Fig. 31-61? (170 V is the peak of standard 120-V AC power.) (b) If all the equipment the farmer connects to the loop has an equivalent resistance of 5.0 Ω, what is the farmer's average power consumption? *Note:* The *average* power consumption is half the product of the peak voltage and peak current. (c) If the power company charges 10¢ per kWh, what is the monetary value of the energy stolen each day? (d) Without examining the farmer's lands, how, in principle, could the power company know that a crime is being committed?

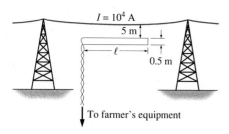

FIGURE 31-61 Problem 57.

58. A circular wire loop of resistance R and radius a lies with its plane perpendicular to a uniform magnetic field. The field strength changes from an initial value B_1 to a final value B_2. Show, by integrating the loop current over time, that the total charge that moves around the ring is

$$q = \frac{\pi a^2}{R}(B_2 - B_1).$$

Note that this result is independent of how the field changes with time.

59. A conducting disk with radius a, thickness h, and resistivity ρ is inside a solenoid of circular cross section. The disk axis coincides with the solenoid axis. The magnetic field in the solenoid is given by $B = bt$, with b a constant. Find expressions for (a) the current density in the disk as a function of the distance r from the disk center and (b) the rate of power dissipation in the entire disk. *Hint:* Consider the disk to be made up of infinitesimal conducting loops.

60. The bar in Problem 27 has mass m and is initially at rest. A constant force F is applied to the bar, pulling it to the right. (a) Formulate Newton's second law for the bar as an equation involving both v and $a = dv/dt$. (b) Use your equation to show that the bar's acceleration becomes zero when its speed reaches the value $FR/B^2\ell^2$. (c) Show by direct substitution that your equation is satisfied if v as a function of time is given by $v(t) = \dfrac{FR}{B^2\ell^2}(1 - e^{-B^2\ell^2 t/mR})$.

61. Find an expression for the speed of the left-hand resistor in Problem 32 as a function of time, in terms of its mass m, the field strength B, the speed v of the right-hand bar, the time t, and the resistances R_{left} and R_{right}.

62. A pendulum consists of a mass m suspended from two identical copper wires of negligible mass. At equilibrium the mass is a vertical distance ℓ below its supports, and the wires make 45° angles with the vertical, as shown in Fig. 31-62. A uniform magnetic field **B** points into the page. The pendulum is displaced from the plane of the page by a small angle θ_0, and at time $t = 0$ it is released. Find an expression for the voltmeter reading as a function of time.

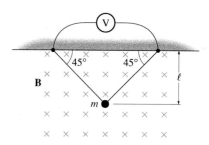

FIGURE 31-62 Problem 62.

63. A *flip coil* consists of a small coil used to measure magnetic fields. The flip coil is placed in a magnetic field with its plane perpendicular to the field, and then rotated abruptly through 180° about an axis in the plane of the coil. The coil is connected to instrumentation to measure the total charge Q that flows during this process. If the coil has N turns of area A and if its rotation axis is perpendicular to the magnetic field, show that the field strength is given by $B = QR/2NA$, where R is the coil resistance.

Inductance and Magnetic Energy

This transformer at an electrical substation uses mutual inductance to change the voltage at which power is transmitted.

Faraday's law implies that a changing magnetic flux through a circuit produces an induced emf in the circuit. In this chapter we consider the special case when that changing flux is itself caused by a changing current in an electric circuit. We then speak of the **inductance** of the circuit.

32-1 MUTUAL INDUCTANCE

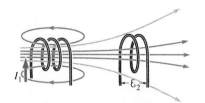

FIGURE 32-1 The mutual inductance between two coils is the ratio of magnetic flux through one coil to the current in the other coil. A changing current in one coil induces an emf in the other.

Consider two coils arranged so that some of the magnetic flux associated with current in one coil also passes through the second coil, as in Fig. 32-1. If we change the current I_1 in the first coil, an induced emf $\mathscr{E}_2$ appears in the second. As we discussed in the preceding chapter, $\mathscr{E}_2$ depends on the rate of change of magnetic flux through the second coil. The magnetic flux depends, in turn, on the current in the first coil and on the geometrical arrangement of the two coils which determines how much flux from the first coil actually links the second. We characterize this geometrical arrangement by the ratio of the total magnetic flux through the second coil to the current in the first coil. This ratio defines the **mutual inductance**, M, of the two coils:

$$M = \frac{\phi_2}{I_1}. \qquad (32\text{-}1)$$

Solving Equation 32-1 for ϕ_2 and differentiating, we obtain

$$\frac{d\phi_2}{dt} = M\frac{dI_1}{dt}.$$

Faraday's law says that $d\phi_2/dt$ is $-\mathscr{E}_2$, the induced emf in coil 2. So we have

$$\mathscr{E}_2 = -M\frac{dI_1}{dt}, \qquad (32\text{-}2)$$

where the minus sign describes the polarity of the induced emf.

In the context of Fig. 32-1, our discussion of mutual inductance assumed that a changing current in the left-hand coil caused an induced emf in the right-hand coil. But we could have equally well considered the effect a changing current in the right-hand coil would have on the left-hand coil. Although it's not at all obvious, the mutual inductance M is the same either way; it's a constant that characterizes the physical arrangement of two coils regardless of which is the source of the changing magnetic flux.

From Equation 32-2, we see that the unit of mutual inductance is the volt-second/ampere. This unit is given the name henry (H) in honor of the American scientist Joseph Henry (1797–1878), who was also the first secretary of the Smithsonian Institution. Mutual inductances found in common electronic circuits usually range from microhenrys (μH) on up to several henrys.

EXAMPLE 32-1	*Mutual Inductance*

A 2-turn coil is wrapped around a long solenoid with cross-sectional area $A = 26$ cm^2, wound with $n = 3500$ turns per meter of length (Fig. 32-2). Find the mutual inductance of this arrangement.

Solution

Since the solenoid field is uniform and confined to the solenoid interior, the flux through each turn of the small coil is just BA. Accounting for the two turns and using Equation 30-11 for the solenoid's magnetic field, the total magnetic flux through the small coil becomes

$$\phi_2 = 2BA = 2\mu_0 nIA,$$

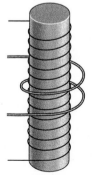

FIGURE 32-2 What is the mutual inductance of the two coils? (Example 32-1)

where I is the solenoid current. Equation 32-1 shows that mutual inductance is the ratio of the flux in one coil to the current in the other, or

$$M = \frac{\phi_2}{I} = \frac{2\mu_0 nIA}{I} = 2\mu_0 nA$$

$$= (2)(4\pi \times 10^{-7} \text{ N/A}^2)(3500)(26 \times 10^{-4} \text{ m}^2)$$

$$= 23 \ \mu\text{H} .$$

EXERCISE Suppose the solenoid of Example 32-1 has circular cross section, and that the smaller coil is *inside* the solenoid, with its diameter half that of the solenoid. Find the mutual inductance.

Answer: 5.7 μH

Some problems similar to Example 32-1: 6, 7, 10

Mutual inductance is the basis of **transformers** and similar devices that use the mutual inductance of two adjacent coils to transfer electric power from one circuit to another without direct electrical contact. Transformers also shift voltage levels, allowing great flexibility in the handling and use of electric power. But because they're based fundamentally on Faraday's law, these devices work only with alternating current or in situations where current is interrupted to make it change with time. We'll discuss transformers more in Chapter 33; for now, Example 32-2 and its exercise illustrate two transformer-like devices using mutual induction.

EXAMPLE 32-2	Spark Plugs and Toothbrushes

Solution

Electric sparks ignite the gasoline that powers your car's engine. High voltage to fire the spark plugs is provided by the ignition coil, an arrangement of two different coils with mutual inductance. Current from the car's 12-V battery flows through the coil with fewer turns, and is interrupted periodically by a switch in the car's distributor. The sudden change in current induces a large emf in the coil with more turns, and this emf drives the spark.

A typical ignition coil draws 3.0 A and supplies 20 kV to the spark plugs. If the current decays in 0.10 ms when the switch opens, what is the mutual inductance of the ignition coil?

Solution

The rate of change of current is

$$\frac{dI}{dt} = \frac{3.0 \text{ A}}{0.10 \times 10^{-3} \text{ s}} = 3.0 \times 10^4 \text{ A/s} .$$

Solving Equation 32-2 for M then gives

$$M = \frac{|\mathcal{E}|}{|dI/dt|} = \frac{20 \times 10^3 \text{ V}}{3.0 \times 10^4 \text{ A}} = 0.67 \text{ H} .$$

EXERCISE An electric toothbrush has no electrical connection to the power line (Fig. 32-3). But when the toothbrush is in its stand, a coil inside the toothbrush itself rests inside another coil in the stand, and alternating current from the power line flows in the stand coil. The mutual inductance of the two coils results in an induced current in the toothbrush

FIGURE 32-3 The batteries in this electric toothbrush are charged with energy transferred via mutual induction of coils located in the base unit, which is connected to the AC power line, and in the bottom of the brush unit. There is no direct electrical connection to the brush unit.

coil, and this current charges the batteries that power the toothbrush. Suppose the mutual inductance of this arrangement is 100 mH. At an instant when the current in the stand coil is changing at the rate of 40 A/s, what is the emf in the toothbrush coil?

Answer: 4.0 V

Some problems similar to Example 32-2: 1–4

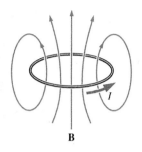

FIGURE 32-4 Magnetic flux from a circular current loop passes through the loop itself.

32-2 SELF-INDUCTANCE

So far we've considered emf and current induced in a circuit by changes—like moving a magnet or varying the current in another circuit—that were external to the circuit in question. But the changing magnetic field associated with the changing current in a circuit also affects that same circuit.

Consider a circular loop carrying current I, as shown in Fig. 32-4. Magnetic field lines arising from this current loop pass through the loop, making a magnetic flux through the loop. If the current is steady, this flux is constant, and there is no induced electric field. But if we change the loop current, then the flux changes, and an induced electric field arises. In order to conserve energy this field opposes the change that causes it—in this case the change in loop current. If the current is counterclockwise and we increase its strength, an induced electric field will appear in the clockwise direction to oppose the current increase. If we decrease the current, the induced electric field will have the opposite sense, now trying to maintain the current. The induced electric field therefore makes it difficult to change the current in the circuit.

This property of a circuit whereby its own magnetic field opposes changes in current is termed **self-inductance**. All circuits possess self-inductance, but this inductance is important only when the circuit encircles a great many of its own magnetic field lines or when current changes very rapidly. A simple piece of wire exhibits very little opposition to current changes in the 60-Hz alternating current used in electric power systems. But in a TV or computer, where currents change on time scales of billionths of a second, self-inductance of the wires themselves must be taken into account.

An **inductor** is a device designed specifically to exhibit self-inductance. Inductors have many uses in electric circuits, including establishing the frequencies of radio transmitters or the channel settings of TV sets, and helping "steer" high and low frequency signals to the tweeters and woofers of loudspeaker systems. We'll explore some of these uses in the next chapter. A typical inductor consists of a coil of wire, constructed so that a great deal of its own magnetic flux is encircled. Some inductors are wound on iron cores to promote flux concentration (Fig. 32-5). Ideally, the only electrical property of an inductor is its inductance. But real inductors are made from wire, so they have resistance as well.

As long as the current in an inductor is steady, the magnetic flux is constant, so there's no induced emf and the inductor acts just like a piece of wire. But when the current changes, the changing magnetic flux induces an emf that opposes the change in current. The more rapidly the current changes, the greater the rate of change of flux and so the greater the emf. The induced emf depends also on how much of its own magnetic flux the inductor encircles; consequently, we define self-inductance, L, as the ratio of magnetic flux through the inductor to current in the inductor:

$$L = \frac{\phi_B}{I}. \tag{32-3}$$

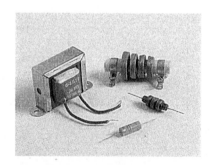

FIGURE 32-5 Typical inductors. At left is a 20-H unit, wound on an iron core for increased inductance. The others have inductances in the mH range.

The unit of self-inductance, like that of mutual inductance, is the henry. Inductance is a constant determined by the physical design of an inductor. In principle, we can calculate the inductance of any inductor, but in practice this is difficult unless the geometry is particularly simple. Inductors for use in electronic circuits are available commercially in a wide range of inductance values.

EXAMPLE 32-3	*Inductance of a Solenoid*

A long solenoid of cross-sectional area A and length ℓ has n turns per unit length. What is its self-inductance?

Solution

Equation 32-3 shows that self-inductance is the ratio of magnetic flux to current. In Chapter 30 we used Ampère's law to find the magnetic field of a long solenoid: $B = \mu_0 n I$. Since the field is uniform and perpendicular to the solenoid coils, the flux through each turn is just BA. With n turns per unit length, our solenoid has $N = n\ell$ turns. The total flux through the solenoid is then

$$\phi_B = NBA = (n\ell)(\mu_0 n I)(A) = \mu_0 n^2 A \ell I.$$

Then Equation 32-3 gives

$$L = \frac{\phi_B}{I} = \mu_0 n^2 A \ell. \qquad (32\text{-}4)$$

Does this result make sense? As the area increases, so does the flux and therefore the inductance. As the length increases so does the number of turns, and therefore the flux and the inductance increase. Equation 32-4 reflects these trends. Can you see why the inductance should be proportional to the *square* of the number of turns per unit length?

EXERCISE What is the self-inductance of the MRI solenoid in Example 30-6 (page 787)?

Answer: 0.53 H

Some problems similar to Example 32-3: 11, 15, 20

The induced emf in an inductor is determined by Faraday's law, which relates the emf to the rate of change of magnetic flux:

$$\mathcal{E} = -\frac{d\phi_B}{dt}.$$

Differentiating Equation 32-3, the definition of inductance, gives

$$\frac{d\phi_B}{dt} = L\frac{dI}{dt}.$$

Then Faraday's law becomes

$$\mathcal{E} = -L\frac{dI}{dt}. \qquad (32\text{-}5)$$

This equation gives the emf $\mathcal{E}$ induced in an inductor L when the current in the inductor is changing at the rate dI/dt. The minus sign again tells us that the emf *opposes* the change in current. For this reason the inductor emf is often called a **back emf**; it works *against* changes brought about by an externally applied emf. Figure 32-6 shows how to interpret the signs in Equation 32-5.

When the current in an inductor is steady, then $dI/dt = 0$ and there is no emf in the inductor. In this case, the inductor acts just like a piece of wire. But when the current changes the inductor responds by producing a back emf that opposes the change in current. Now the inductor acts very much like a battery, with the magnitude of its emf dependent on how fast the current changes. If we try to start or stop current suddenly, dI/dt is very large and a very large back emf appears. This is not just mathematics! Rapid switching of inductive devices such as solenoids, solenoid valves, or motors can result in destruction of delicate electronic devices by induced currents. And people have been killed opening switches in circuits containing large inductors. In the next section we'll take a closer look at the effect the rapid opening and closing of switches has in circuits containing inductors.

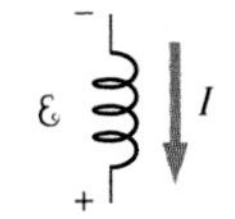

FIGURE 32-6 The inductor emf of Equation 32-5 is positive if, when going in the direction of the inductor current, you encounter the negative end of the inductor first. Because of the minus sign in Equation 32-5, this happens when the current is *decreasing* ($dI/dt < 0$).

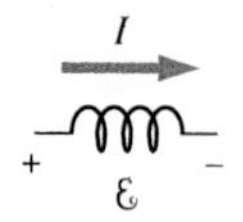

FIGURE 32-7 Is the current increasing, decreasing, or steady?

Got It!

Current flows from left to right through the inductor shown in Fig. 32-7. A voltmeter connected across the inductor gives a constant reading, and shows that the left end of the inductor is positive. Is the current in the inductor increasing, decreasing, or steady?

EXAMPLE 32-4	*A Dangerous Inductor*

A current of 5.0 A is flowing in a 2.0-H inductor. The current is reduced steadily to zero in 1.0 ms. What is the magnitude of the emf in the inductor while the current is being turned off?

Solution

Because the current changes steadily, its time rate of change has magnitude

$$\frac{dI}{dt} = \frac{5.0 \text{ A}}{1.0 \text{ ms}} = 5000 \text{ A/s},$$

so

$$|\mathcal{E}| = L\frac{dI}{dt} = (2.0 \text{ H})(5000 \text{ A/s}) = 10,000 \text{ V},$$

enough to produce a lethal shock. Note that this voltage is quite unrelated to the voltage of the battery or whatever else was supplying the inductor current. We could have a 6-volt battery and still be electrocuted trying to open the circuit rapidly when a large inductance is present.

EXERCISE A neon lamp that glows only when the voltage across it exceeds 90 V is connected across a 1.2-H inductor carrying 750 mA. When the current is interrupted the lamp flashes. Find the maximum time over which the current could have dropped to zero, assuming a steady decrease.

Answer: 10 ms

Some problems similar to Example 32-4: 12–14

32-3 INDUCTORS IN CIRCUITS

Here we examine circuits containing batteries, resistors, and inductors, analogous to the *RC* circuits of Chapter 28. In the qualitative analysis of *RC* circuits we found a useful guiding principle: The voltage across a capacitor cannot change instantaneously. We can make an analogous statement for inductors. Because the inductor emf is proportional to the rate of change of current in the inductor and because an infinite emf is physically impossible, we conclude that

▌ The current through an inductor cannot change instantaneously.

Thus, the effect an inductor has on current is analogous to the effect a capacitor has on voltage. Much of our understanding of capacitors can be applied to inductors if we interchange the words *voltage* and *current*.

Building Up the Current

Figure 32-8a shows a circuit containing a battery, switch, resistor, and inductor (symbol ⌇⌇⌇). What happens when we close the switch? Initially the inductor current is zero; since it can't change instantaneously, it must remain zero immediately after the switch is closed. But this is a series circuit, so the inductor

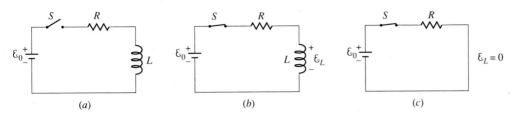

FIGURE 32-8 (*a*) An *RL* circuit. With the switch open no current flows. (*b*) Immediately after the switch is closed there is still no current. The inductor produces a back emf equal but opposite the battery emf, and therefore the rate of change of current is not zero. (*c*) After a long time, the rate of change of current and therefore the inductor emf approach zero. The inductor then acts like a piece of wire.

and resistor currents are equal. With zero current immediately after the switch is closed, there must be no voltage across the resistor. Therefore the inductor must produce a back emf equal to that of the battery, with the polarity shown in Fig. 32-8*b*. Even though there is, at this instant, no current in the inductor, the presence of an emf indicates that the *rate of change* of the current is not zero. Going around the circuit in the direction that the battery would drive a current, the inductor polarity indicated in Fig. 32-8*b* shows that the inductor emf is *negative* —and Equation 32-5 therefore shows that dI/dt is *positive* —i.e., the current is *increasing*.

As the current rises, so does the voltage across the resistor (since $V_R = IR$). Since the battery emf is constant, that means the inductor emf goes *down*—and that means the rate of change of current goes down. Thus, the current in the circuit builds up, but at an ever-decreasing rate. Concurrently, the inductor emf goes down. Eventually the current reaches a steady value, at which point dI/dt and, therefore, the inductor emf are zero. In this ultimate steady state the inductor acts like a piece of wire, and the circuit looks like Fig. 32-8*c*. The steady-state current is just $\mathcal{E}_0/R$, where $\mathcal{E}_0$ is the battery emf. Figure 32-9 summarizes this qualitative analysis of the *RL* circuit, while Fig. 32-10 shows the behavior of the current and inductor emf over time.

14.1

The *RL* Circuit

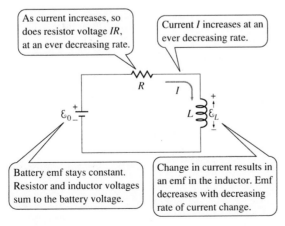

FIGURE 32-9 Interrelationships among circuit quantities as current builds up in an *RL* circuit. Compare with Fig. 28-30, which is a related diagram for a charging capacitor.

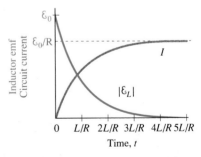

FIGURE 32-10 Inductor current and magnitude of the inductor emf as functions of time. Vertical axis represents either current or voltage.

To analyze the *RL* circuit quantitatively, we apply the loop law. Going clockwise from the negative terminal of the battery, we first encounter a voltage increase $\mathcal{E}_0$ due to the battery. Then the voltage decreases by *IR* in the resistor. Finally, there is a voltage change $\mathcal{E}_L$ in the inductor. This change is actually a decrease, because the inductor emf opposes the increase in current. However, we'll simply call the inductor emf $\mathcal{E}_L$ and let Equation 32-5 take care of the signs. Then the loop law becomes

$$\mathcal{E}_0 - IR + \mathcal{E}_L = 0. \tag{32-6a}$$

If we differentiate this equation with respect to time, the battery emf $\mathcal{E}_0$ drops out because it's constant, giving

$$\frac{d\mathcal{E}_L}{dt} = R\frac{dI}{dt}.$$

Equation 32-5 shows that $dI/dt = -\mathcal{E}_L/L$, so our differentiated loop equation becomes

$$\frac{d\mathcal{E}_L}{dt} = -R\frac{\mathcal{E}_L}{L}. \tag{32-6b}$$

This differential equation describes a quantity—$\mathcal{E}_L$—whose rate of change is proportional to itself. We discussed such equations in Chapter 28 when we considered the *RC* circuit. Equation 32-6*b* is similar to Equation 28-4, but with current *I* replaced by the inductor emf $\mathcal{E}_L$, capacitance *C* by *L*, and *R* by $1/R$. The solution to Equation 32-6*b* is that of Equation 28-4, provided we make the appropriate substitutions for *I*, *C*, and *R*:

$$\mathcal{E}_L = -\mathcal{E}_0 e^{-Rt/L}. \tag{32-7}$$

This equation shows that the inductor emf decays exponentially to zero, starting from an initial value of $-\mathcal{E}_0$ (negative because the inductor emf *opposes* the battery emf). We can now solve for the current using Equation 32-6*a*:

$$I = \frac{\mathcal{E}_0 + \mathcal{E}_L}{R} = \frac{\mathcal{E}_0 + (-\mathcal{E}_0 e^{-Rt/L})}{R} = \frac{\mathcal{E}_0}{R}(1 - e^{-Rt/L}). \tag{32-8}$$

With a capacitor, we characterized the exponentially changing quantities in terms of the capacitive time constant *RC*. With an inductor, we have an **inductive time constant** L/R. Significant changes in current cannot occur on time scales much shorter than L/R. On the other hand, an *RL* circuit will approach a steady state, with zero $\mathcal{E}_L$, only after many inductive time constants.

We include inductors in circuits when we want to limit the rate at which current can change, and we select *L* in conjunction with the circuit resistance *R* to give the desired time constant. But self-inductance occurs in *any* circuit, whether or not there's an explicit inductor present, and in high-speed circuits such as computers and TVs it's important to keep the time constant L/R small to allow rapid current changes.

Why is the inductive time constant a quotient of *L* and *R* rather than a product, as in the capacitor case? In Problem 23 you can convince yourself that L/R has the units of seconds. But you can also understand this physically. The instant the switch is closed in Fig. 32-8, the inductor emf must equal the battery emf to keep the current instantaneously at zero. The *larger* the inductance *L*, the smaller the rate of current change, *dI/dt*, needed to produce that emf—and so the longer it will take to build up the current. And the *smaller* the resistance, the larger the final current and therefore, again, the longer it will take to build up that current.

EXAMPLE 32-5	*Firing Up an Electromagnet*

A large electromagnet used for lifting scrap metal has a self-inductance of 56 H. It is connected through a switch to a constant 440-V power source; the total resistance of the circuit is 2.8 Ω. When the switch is closed, how long does it take to bring the magnet current to 75% of its final value?

Solution

Letting $t \to \infty$ in Equation 32-8 shows that the final current is $I_{final} = \mathcal{E}_0/R$, as we argued in our qualitative analysis. Setting the current I in Equation 32-8 to $0.75\mathcal{E}_0/R$ gives

$$0.75 = 1 - e^{-Rt/L},$$

or

$$e^{-Rt/L} = 0.25.$$

Taking the natural logarithm of both sides (recall that $\ln e^x = x$) gives

$$-Rt/L = \ln(0.25),$$

or

$$t = -\frac{L}{R}\ln(0.25) = -\frac{56\text{ H}}{2.8\text{ }\Omega}\ln(0.25) = 28\text{ s}.$$

(The minus sign canceled since the logarithm of a number less than 1 is negative.) Our answer is approximately one time constant ($L/R = 20$ s). This should not be surprising since we found with RC circuits that quantities following equations such as Equation 28-6 (and, therefore, its analog, Equation 32-8) reach $1 - 1/e$, or about two-thirds, of their final value in one time constant.

EXERCISE A 1.0-kΩ resistor is in series with an inductor, and a 12-V battery is connected across the pair. The current rises to 8.5 mA in 21 μs. Find the inductance.

Answer: 17 mH

Some problems similar to Example 32-5: 27–29, 32

The Current Decays

Figure 32-11a shows an *RL* circuit with a two-way switch. Throwing the switch to position *A* allows current to build up in the inductor as we've already described. Then, at time $t = 0$, we throw it to position *B*. This disconnects the battery, leaving a circuit electrically equivalent to Fig. 32-11b. Just prior to $t = 0$ there was some current I_0 flowing downward in the inductor. Since the inductor current cannot change instantaneously, that current must continue just after the switch is closed, as shown in Fig. 32-11b. To drive this current, the inductor must develop an emf in the direction shown. Now the inductor emf is positive, so Equation 32-5 shows that the current is *decreasing,* as we might well expect since the battery has been disconnected. As the current decreases, so does the voltage across the resistor. So, therefore, does the inductor emf and, therefore, the rate of change of current. We thus expect both the current and the inductor emf to decrease, but at an ever decreasing rate.

Note that the inductor emf here is like any other induced emf: it *opposes* the change giving rise to it. In this case that change is the decrease in current caused by disconnecting the battery. The inductor responds with an emf in such a direction as to keep that current flowing.

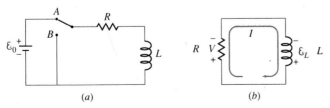

(a) (b)

FIGURE 32-11 (*a*) Throwing the switch to position *A* allows current to build up in the inductor. (*b*) Throwing it to position *B* gives a circuit containing only the inductor and resistor. The current then decays exponentially.

Applying the loop law to Fig. 32-11b gives

$$\mathcal{E}_L - IR = 0.$$

Using $\mathcal{E}_L = -L\, dI/dt$ from Equation 32-5, the loop equation becomes

$$\frac{dI}{dt} = -\frac{R}{L}I.$$

This is just like Equation 32-6b, but with I replacing $\mathcal{E}_L$. The solution follows by analogy with Equation 32-7:

$$I = I_0 e^{-Rt/L}, \tag{32-9}$$

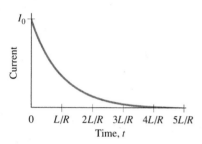

FIGURE 32-12 Exponential decay of the current in the circuit of Fig. 32-11b.

where I_0 is the inductor current when the switch is thrown from A to B. Equation 32-9 shows that the current decays with the same exponential time constant L/R that described its buildup (Fig. 32-12). The resistor voltage IR and therefore the inductor emf also decay in the same way.

It is not always necessary to use Equations 32-8 and 32-9 in describing RL circuits. For times very short compared with the time constant L/R, it suffices to use the fact that inductor currents cannot change instantaneously. And after many time constants, inductors in a circuit containing only steady sources will act like wires. Example 32-6 explores this situation.

EXAMPLE 32-6	*Short Times, Long Times*

In the circuit of Fig. 32-13a, the switch is initially open. What is the current in resistor R_2 immediately after the switch is closed? A long time after the switch is closed? Long after the switch is closed, it is again opened. What is the current in R_2 just after it is opened? A long time after?

Solution

Just before we close the switch, the current in the inductor is zero. The current cannot change instantaneously, so it remains zero just after the switch is closed. At this instant the inductor might as well be an open circuit, giving the circuit shown in Fig. 32-13b. Then all the current from R_1 flows through R_2, so

$$I = \frac{\mathcal{E}_0}{R_1 + R_2}.$$

If we wait long enough, the circuit will reach a steady state in which $dI/dt = 0$. So then there is no inductor emf, and the inductor acts like a wire. We can redraw the circuit as Fig. 32-13c, in which all the current from R_1 goes through L, and none through R_2. The resulting current in R_1 and L is just $\mathcal{E}_0/R_1$.

Now the switch is opened again. Current in R_1 stops abruptly since there is no way charge can get through the open switch. But the current through the inductor, which was $\mathcal{E}_0/R_1$ just before the switch was opened, remains $\mathcal{E}_0/R_1$ the instant after the switch is opened. There is only one place this current can

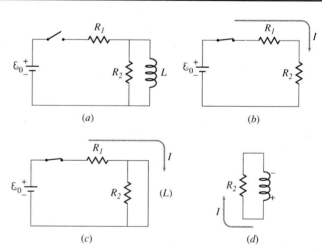

FIGURE 32-13 (a) Circuit for Example 32-6. (b) Just after the switch is closed the inductor acts like an open circuit. (c) A long time later the inductor emf is zero, so it acts like a wire. (d) When the switch opens again, current continues to flow in the inductor and on through R_2.

go—through R_2, from bottom to top (Fig. 32-13d). So just after the switch is opened, the current in R_2 is $\mathcal{E}_0/R_1$. Notice that the value of R_2 has no effect on this current, which is determined entirely by the battery emf and the resistance R_1.

What about the voltage across R_2? This is given by Ohm's law:

$$V_2 = I_2 R_2 = \frac{\mathcal{E}_0 R_2}{R_1}.$$

The larger R_2, the larger the voltage that appears when the switch is opened. If there's no resistor connected across the inductor (i.e., $R_2 = \infty$), then the voltage will be arbitrarily large as the inductor seeks at all cost to keep the current flowing. This dangerous situation can result in arcing and vaporization of circuit conductors, and even in electric shock. In circuits with large inductance, resistors are often placed in parallel with inductors to alleviate these dangers.

Finally, the current in Fig. 32-13*d* decays exponentially to zero. Plots of the currents in R_2 and L as functions of time are shown in Fig. 32-14.

EXERCISE In Fig. 32-13 take $\mathcal{E}_0 = 12$ V, $R_1 = 56\ \Omega$, $L = 48$ mH, and suppose the switch has been closed for a long time. What is the maximum value of R_2 for which the inductor emf will not exceed 100 V when the switch is opened?

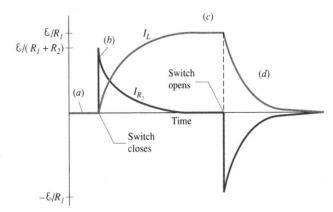

FIGURE 32-14 Currents in R_2 and L for Example 32-6. Note that the time constants before and after the switch opens are different; this reflects the fact that R_1 is out of the circuit after the switch opens. (*a*)–(*d*) indicate portions of the graph that correspond to the diagrams in Fig. 32-13.

Answer: 467 Ω

Some problems similar to Example 32-6: 36, 37, 61, 62

Got It!

In a circuit such as that of Fig. 32-13*a*, can the inductor emf ever exceed the battery emf? If so, can that happen (a) when the switch is closed or (b) when it's opened?

32-4 MAGNETIC ENERGY

In the situations we considered in Figs. 32-11*b* and 32-13*d*, current flows in circuits containing only a resistor and an inductor. Energy is dissipated, heating the resistor. Where does this energy come from?

Because there is a current in the inductor, there is also a magnetic field. The change in that magnetic field is what produces the emf that drives current around the circuit. As the current decreases, so does the inductor's magnetic field. Eventually the circuit reaches a state where there is no current, no magnetic field—and a hot resistor. So where did the resistor's thermal energy come from? It came from the magnetic field.

Like the electric field, the magnetic field contains stored energy. Our decaying *RL* circuit is analogous to a discharging *RC* circuit, in which the electric field between the capacitor plates disappears as thermal energy appears in the resistor. As in the electric case, magnetic energy is not limited to circuits. *Any* magnetic field contains energy. Release of magnetic energy drives a number of practical devices and also powers violent events throughout the universe (Fig. 32-15).

We can reinterpret the *RL* circuit of Fig. 32-11 in terms of energy. With the switch in position *A*, the battery supplies energy to the resistor and inductor. In the resistor the energy is dissipated as heat, but in the inductor it gets stored as magnetic field energy. When the switch is thrown to position *B* the battery—the

FIGURE 32-15 This eruption of a huge prominence from the Sun's surface involves the release of energy stored in magnetic fields. The intense magnetic fields responsible for such eruptive solar events are often associated with sunspots.

FIGURE 32-16 Energy transfers in the circuit of Fig. 32-11.

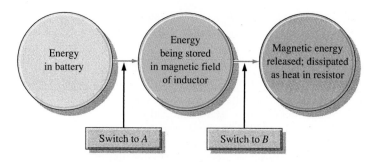

ultimate energy source for the circuit—is disconnected. Energy dissipated in the resistor now comes from the decaying magnetic field of the inductor. That energy came originally from the battery but was stored temporarily in the magnetic field. Figure 32-16 outlines these energy transfers.

Magnetic Energy in an Inductor

How much energy is stored in an inductor's magnetic field? We can answer this by considering first the *rate* of energy storage. If we multiply Equation 32-6a—the loop law for an *RL* circuit—by the current *I*, the result is

$$I\mathscr{E}_0 - I^2R + I\mathscr{E}_L = 0\,,$$

or, using Equation 32-5 for $\mathscr{E}_L$,

$$I\mathscr{E}_0 - I^2R - LI\frac{dI}{dt} = 0\,.$$

What do the terms in this equation mean? The first is the product of the battery's current and emf—a product we know gives electrical power. That this term is positive means the battery supplies energy *to* the circuit at the rate $I\mathscr{E}_0$. The second term, I^2R, is the rate of energy dissipation in the resistor (recall Equation 27-9). The negative sign means that this energy is taken *from* the circuit. The third term is also negative (since the current is increasing, dI/dt is positive) and represents the rate at which the inductor takes energy from the circuit. But the inductor does not dissipate this energy; instead, it stores the energy in its growing magnetic field. The rate at which the inductor stores energy is thus

$$P = LI\frac{dI}{dt}\,.$$

Suppose we increase the current in an inductor by some small amount dI over a small time interval dt. Since the power is the rate of energy storage, the energy dU stored during this time is thus

$$dU = P\,dt = LI\,dI$$

We find the total energy stored in bringing the inductor current from zero to some final value *I* by summing—that is, integrating—all the dU's:

$$U = \int dU = \int P\,dt = \int_0^I LI\,dI = \tfrac{1}{2}LI^2\big|_0^I$$

Evaluating at the two limits then gives the stored energy:

$$U = \tfrac{1}{2}LI^2\,. \tag{32-10}$$

This much energy is therefore released when the magnetic field decays.

| EXAMPLE 32-7 | *Quenching a Superconducting Magnet* |

Loss of coolant is a danger in superconducting electromagnets. The current is suddenly left without its zero-resistance path, and energy stored in the magnetic field is rapidly released. To prevent explosive energy release, copper or silver is incorporated into the conducting system to lengthen the time constant L/R in the event of such a "quench" (Fig. 32-17). A superconducting MRI solenoid carries a 2.4-kA current and has 0.53-H inductance. In its nonsuperconducting state, the total resistance is 31 mΩ. (a) How much energy is stored in the solenoid's magnetic field? (b) If the coils suddenly lose their superconductivity, what is the initial rate of energy release?

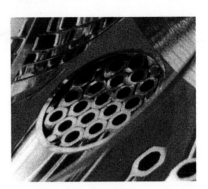

FIGURE 32-17 Superconducting cables in various stages of manufacture. The hollow tubes are made of silver, and are packed with superconducting material. In the event of a coolant loss, the silver—the best metallic conductor—will carry the current and thus prevent explosive release of magnetic energy.

Solution

(a) Equation 32-10 gives the magnetic energy:

$$U = \tfrac{1}{2}LI^2 = (\tfrac{1}{2})(0.53 \text{ H})(2.4\times10^3 \text{ A})^2 = 1.53 \text{ MJ} .$$

(b) When superconducting ceases, the current decays according to Equation 32-9. At the instant the decay starts the current still has its original value. Since the magnetic energy released is dissipated in the resistor, the rate of energy release is just I^2R, or

$$P = I^2R = (2.4\times10^3 \text{ A})^2(0.031 \ \Omega) = 180 \text{ kW} .$$

This is a substantial power; equivalent to 1,800 100-W light bulbs burning in the space of this roughly human-size device.

The following exercise explores the duration of this power surge.

EXERCISE How long is it before 90% of the magnetic energy in Example 32-7 has been dissipated?

Answer: 20 s

Some problems similar to Example 32-7: 42, 44, 47

Magnetic Energy Density

A long solenoid is a particularly simple inductor in which the magnetic field is essentially uniform. We can readily evaluate the energy density using this magnetic field, just as we found the electric field energy density using a parallel-plate capacitor.

In Example 32-3 we found that the inductance of a long solenoid of length ℓ and cross-sectional area A is $L = \mu_0 n^2 A\ell$, with n the number of turns per unit length. Equation 32-10 then gives the magnetic energy stored in the solenoid when it carries current I:

$$U = \tfrac{1}{2}LI^2 = \tfrac{1}{2}\mu_0 n^2 A\ell I^2 = \frac{1}{2\mu_0}(\mu_0 nI)^2 A\ell = \frac{B^2}{2\mu_0}A\ell ,$$

where we recognized the quantity $\mu_0 nI$ as B, the magnetic field in the solenoid (Equation 30-11). The quantity $A\ell$ is the volume containing this field, so the energy per unit volume—the **magnetic energy density**—is

$$u_B = \frac{B^2}{2\mu_0}. \qquad \text{(magnetic energy density)} \qquad (32\text{-}11)$$

Although we derived this expression for the field of a solenoid, it is, in fact, a universal expression for the local magnetic energy density. Wherever there is a magnetic field, there is stored energy.

Compare Equation 32-11 with Equation 26-3 for the energy density in an electric field:

$$u_E = \tfrac{1}{2}\varepsilon_0 E^2.$$

The expressions for electric and magnetic energy densities are similar. Each is proportional to the *square* of the field strength, and each contains the appropriate constant. That the constant appears in the numerator in one case and the denominator in the other has no deep significance; it is merely a consequence of the way SI units are defined.

| **EXAMPLE 32-8** | *Energy in Earth's Magnetic Field* |

The magnetic field strength near Earth's surface is about 50 μT. (a) How much energy is contained in 1 cubic kilometer of this field? (b) How does this compare with the electrical energy in the same volume, given a fair-weather electric field of 100 V/m?

Solution

(a) The magnetic field is essentially constant over this volume, so the total energy is the product of the energy density with the volume V:

$$U = u_B V = \frac{B^2}{2\mu_0}V = \frac{(50\times10^{-6}\ \text{T})^2}{(2)(4\pi\times10^{-7}\ \text{N/A}^2)}(1\times10^3\ \text{m})^3$$

$$= 1\ \text{MJ}.$$

This is not a particularly large energy; a mere gallon of gasoline, for example, stores about 100 times as much.

(b) Since we're considering equal volumes, it suffices to compare energy densities. Then

$$\frac{u_B}{u_E} = \frac{B^2/2\mu_0}{\tfrac{1}{2}\varepsilon_0 E^2} = \frac{B^2}{\mu_0\varepsilon_0 E^2}$$

$$= \frac{(50\times10^{-6}\ \text{T})^2}{(4\pi\times10^{-7}\ \text{N/A}^2)(8.85\times10^{-12}\ \text{F/m})(100\ \text{V/m})^2}$$

$$= 2\times10^4$$

Thus the electrical energy is even smaller, by a factor of 20,000. The energy stored in both of Earth's electromagnetic fields is very small compared, for example, with the gravitational energy or thermal energy of an equivalent volume of air. In other systems, though, including the atmospheres of stars or lab experiments in plasma physics, magnetic energy may dominate.

EXERCISE A typical sunspot is about 50,000 km in diameter, and extends into the Sun as a cylinder about 30,000 km long. Its magnetic field is about 0.2 T. What is the magnetic energy in such a spot?

Answer: 9×10^{26} J

Some problems similar to Example 32-8: 51, 52

CHAPTER SYNOPSIS

Summary

1. The **mutual inductance** of a pair of coils is defined as the ratio of the total flux in the second coil to the current in the first:

$$M = \frac{\phi_2}{I_1}.$$

By Faraday's law, the emf in the second coil is proportional to the rate of change of current in the first:

$$\mathcal{E}_2 = -M\frac{dI_1}{dt}.$$

The same mutual inductance M describes the emf developed in the first coil as a result of changing current in the second coil.

2. A changing current in a coil or circuit results in a changing magnetic flux that gives rise to an induced electric field opposing the original change in current. A device constructed to exploit this property of **self-inductance** is called an **inductor**. The self-inductance L of an inductor is the ratio of magnetic flux to current:

$$L = \frac{\phi}{I}.$$

Faraday's law relates the emf in an inductor to the rate of change of current:

$$\mathcal{E} = -L\frac{dI}{dt}.$$

The direction of the emf is such as to oppose changes in the inductor current. Self-inductance prevents the inductor current from changing instantaneously.

3. In a circuit containing a resistor R and inductor L, changes occur exponentially with an **inductive time constant** L/R. The rising current in a series RL circuit is given by

$$I = \frac{\mathscr{E}_0}{R}(1 - e^{-Rt/L}),$$

where $\mathscr{E}_0$ is the battery emf and t the time. If the current is subsequently allowed to decay, it goes exponentially to zero:

$$I = I_0 e^{-Rt/L},$$

where t is measured from the start of the decay.

4. Electrical energy supplied to an inductor ends up stored in the inductor's magnetic field. When an inductance L carries current I, the stored magnetic energy is

$$U = \tfrac{1}{2}LI^2.$$

5. All magnetic fields, not only those of inductors, contain stored energy, with the **magnetic energy density** given by

$$u_B = \frac{B^2}{2\mu_0}.$$

Terms You Should Understand

(Pairs are closely related terms whose distinction is important; number in parentheses is chapter section where term first appears.)

mutual inductance, self-inductance (32-1, 32-2)
inductor (32-2)
back emf (32-2)
inductive time constant (32-3)
magnetic energy, magnetic energy density (32-4)

Symbols You Should Recognize

M, L (32-1, 32-2)
u_B (32-4)

Problems You Should Be Able to Solve

calculating mutual inductance for simple coil configurations (32-1)
finding induced emf in a second coil given mutual inductance and rate of change of current in the first coil (32-1)
calculating self-inductance for simple configurations (32-2)
calculating back emf given self-inductance and rate of change of current (32-2)
analyzing time-dependent behavior of RL circuits (32-3)
calculating magnetic energy (32-4)

Limitations to Keep in Mind

Real inductors, other than those made from superconductors, have resistance as well as inductance.

QUESTIONS

1. Figure 32-18 shows two pairs of identical coils in different geometrical arrangements. For which arrangement is the mutual inductance greatest? Why?

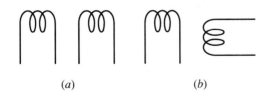

(a)   (b)

FIGURE 32-18 Question 1.

2. A car battery has an emf of 12 V, yet energy from the battery provides the 20,000-V spark that ignites the gasoline. How is this possible?

3. When two coils are connected in series but are physically far apart, they behave as a single inductor whose inductance is the sum of the individual inductances. Why might this not be true if they are close together?

4. You have a fixed length of wire to wind into an inductor. Will you get more inductance if you wind a short coil with large diameter, or a long coil with small diameter?

5. You have a fixed length of wire of resistance R. You want to wind the wire into a small space and use it as a resistor. How would you wind it so as to minimize its self-inductance?

6. In wiring circuits that operate at high frequencies, like TV sets or computers, it is important to avoid extraneous loops in wires. Why?

7. In a popular demonstration of induced emf, a light bulb is connected across a large inductor in an LR circuit, as shown in Fig. 32-19. When the switch is opened, the bulb flashes brightly and burns out. Why?

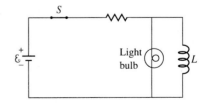

FIGURE 32-19 Question 7.

8. In the RL circuit of Fig. 32-8a, can the inductor emf exceed the battery emf (a) when the switch is first closed?

(b) When the switch is opened after being closed for a long time?

9. Does it take more or less than one time constant for current in an *RL* circuit to build up to half its steady-state value?

10. If you increase the resistance in an *RL* circuit, what effect does this have on the inductive time constant?

11. Speculate on what would happen if you connected an ideal battery directly across an ideal inductor, with no resistance anywhere in the circuit.

12. How could you modify the simple *RL* circuit of Fig. 32- 8*a* to prevent dangerous voltages from developing when the switch is opened?

13. List some similarities and differences between inductors and capacitors.

14. A 1-H inductor carries 10 A, and a 10-H inductor carries 1 A. Which inductor contains more stored energy?

15. Does the energy density in a magnetic field depend on the direction of the field?

16. The field of a magnetic dipole extends to infinity. Is there an infinite amount of energy stored in the dipole field? Why or why not?

17. It takes work to push two bar magnets together with like poles facing each other. Where does this energy go?

PROBLEMS

ActivPhysics can help with these problems:
Activity 14.1

Section 32-1 Mutual Inductance

1. Two coils have a mutual inductance of 2.0 H. If current in the first coil is changing at the rate of 60 A/s, what is the emf in the second coil?

2. A 500-V emf appears in a coil when the current in an adjacent coil changes at the rate of 3.5 A/ms. What is the mutual inductance of the coils?

3. The current in one coil is given by $I = I_p \sin 2\pi ft$, where $I_p = 75$ mA, $f = 60$ Hz, and $t = $ time. Find the peak emf in a second coil if the mutual inductance between the coils is 440 mH.

4. Two coils have a mutual inductance of 580 mH. One coil is supplied with a current given by $I = 3t^2 - 2t + 4$, where I is in amperes and t in seconds. What is the induced emf in the other coil at time $t = 2.5$ s?

5. An alternating current given by $I_p \sin 2\pi ft$ is supplied to one of two coils whose mutual inductance is M. (a) Find an expression for the emf in the second coil. (b) When $I_p = 1.0$ A and $f = 60$ Hz, the peak emf in the second coil is measured at 50 V. What is the mutual inductance?

6. Find the mutual inductance of the two-coil system described in Problem 19 of Chapter 31.

7. Two long solenoids of length ℓ both have n turns per unit length. They have circular cross sections with radii R and $2R$, respectively. The smaller solenoid is mounted inside the larger one, with their axes coinciding. Find the mutual inductance of this arrangement, neglecting any nonuniformity in the magnetic field near the ends.

8. Coils A and B have mutual inductance 25 mH. At time $t = 0$ the current in coil A is zero. Subsequently a time-varying current is supplied to A, and the induced emf in coil B is given by $\mathcal{E} = 50 + 0.2t$, with $\mathcal{E}$ in V and t in ms. Find an expression for the time-varying current in coil A.

9. A rectangular loop of length ℓ and width w is located a distance a from a long, straight wire, as shown in Fig. 32-20. What is the mutual inductance of this arrangement?

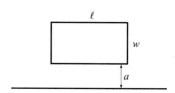

FIGURE 32-20 Problem 9.

10. Two wire loops of radii a and b lie in the same plane and have a common center. Find the mutual inductance of this arrangement, assuming $b \gg a$. *Hint:* With $b \gg a$ the magnetic field will be essentially uniform over the smaller loop. See Example 30-1.

Section 32-2 Self-Inductance

11. What is the self-inductance of a solenoid 50 cm long and 4.0 cm in diameter that contains 1,000 turns of wire?

12. The current in an inductor is changing at the rate of 100 A/s, and the inductor emf is 40 V. What is its self-inductance?

13. A 2.0-A current is flowing in a 20-H inductor. A switch is opened, interrupting the current in 1.0 ms. What emf is induced in the inductor?

14. A 60-mA current is flowing in a 100-mH inductor. Over a period of 1.0 ms the current is reversed, going steadily to 60 mA in the opposite direction. What is the inductor emf during this time?

15. A cardboard tube measures 15 cm long by 2.2 cm in diameter. How many turns of wire must be wound on the full length of the tube to make a 5.8-mH inductor?

16. The current in a 2.0-H inductor is given by $I = 3t^2 + 15t + 8$, where t is in seconds and I in amperes. Find an expression for the magnitude of the inductor emf.

17. The emf in a 50-mH inductor has magnitude $|\mathcal{E}| = 0.020t$, with t in seconds and $\mathcal{E}$ in volts. At $t = 0$ the inductor current is 300 mA. (a) If the current is increasing, what will be its value at $t = 3.0$ s? (b) Repeat for the case when the current is decreasing.

18. The current in a 40-mH inductor is given by $I = I_0 e^{-bt}$, where $I_0 = 10$ A and $b = 20$ s^{-1}. What is the magnitude of the inductor emf at (a) $t = 0$, (b) $t = 25$ ms, and (c) $t = 50$ ms?

19. A 2,000-turn solenoid is 65 cm long and has cross-sectional area 30 cm^2. What rate of change of current will produce a 600-V emf in this solenoid?

20. You have a plastic rod 20 cm long and 1.5 cm in diameter. What inductance will you get if you wind the entire rod with a single layer of (a) 22-gauge (0.64-mm-diameter) and (b) 34-gauge (0.16-mm-diameter) wire? Assume adjacent turns are touching, separated only by a negligible thickness of enamel insulation.

21. The emf in a 50-mH inductor is given by $\mathcal{E} = \mathcal{E}_p \sin \omega t$, where $\mathcal{E}_p = 75$ V and $\omega = 140$ s^{-1}. What is the peak current in the inductor? (Assume the current swings symmetrically about zero.)

22. A coaxial cable consists of an inner conductor of radius a and outer conductor of radius b, as shown in Fig. 32-21. Current flows along one conductor and back along the other. Show that the inductance per unit length of the cable is

$$\frac{\mu_0}{2\pi} \ln(b/a).$$

FIGURE 32-21 Problems 22, 68.

Section 32-3 Inductors in Circuits

23. Show that the inductive time constant has the units of seconds.

24. What inductance should you put in series with a 100-Ω resistor to give a time constant of 2.2 ms?

25. The current in a series RL circuit rises to 20% of its final value in 3.1 μs. If $L = 1.8$ mH, what is the resistance R?

26. The current in a series RL circuit rises to half its final value in 7.6 s. What is the time constant?

27. A 10-H inductor is wound of wire with resistance 2.0 Ω. If the inductor is connected across an ideal 12-V battery, how long will it take the current to reach 95% of its final value?

28. In a series RL circuit like Fig. 32-8a, $\mathcal{E}_0 = 45$ V, $R = 3.3$ Ω, and $L = 2.1$ H. If the current is 9.5 A, how long has the switch been closed?

29. In Fig. 32-8a, take $R = 2.5$ kΩ and $\mathcal{E}_0 = 50$ V. When the switch is closed, the current through the inductor rises to 10 mA in 30 μs. (a) What is the inductance? (b) What will be the current in the circuit after many time constants?

30. A series RL circuit like Fig. 32-8a has $\mathcal{E}_0 = 60$ V, $R = 22$ Ω, and $L = 1.5$ H. Find the rate of change of the current (a) immediately after the switch is closed and (b) 0.10 s later.

31. In Fig. 32-8a, take $R = 100$ Ω, $L = 2.0$ H, and $\mathcal{E}_0 = 12$ V. At 20 ms after the switch is closed, what are (a) the circuit current, (b) the inductor emf, (c) the resistor voltage, (d) the rate of change of the circuit current, and (e) the power dissipation in the resistor?

32. Show that a series RL circuit reaches 99% of its final current in approximately 5 time constants.

33. Resistor R_2 in Fig. 32-22 is to limit the emf that develops when the switch is opened. What should be its value in order that the inductor emf not exceed 100 V?

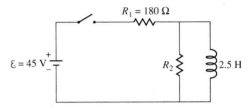

FIGURE 32-22 Problem 33.

34. In Fig. 32-11a take $\mathcal{E}_0 = 12$ V, $R = 2.7$ Ω, and $L = 20$ H. Initially the switch is in position B and there is no current anywhere. At $t = 0$ the switch is thrown to position A, and at $t = 10$ s it is thrown back to position B. Find the inductor current at (a) $t = 5.0$ s and (b) $t = 15$ s.

35. A 5.0-A current is flowing through a nonideal inductor with $L = 500$ mH. If the inductor is suddenly short circuited, the inductor current drops to 2.5 A in 6.9 ms. What is the resistance of the inductor?

36. In Fig. 32-23, take $\mathcal{E}_0 = 12$ V, $R_1 = 4.0$ Ω, $R_2 = 8.0$ Ω, $R_3 = 2.0$ Ω, and $L = 2.0$ H. What is the current I_2 (a) immediately after the switch is first closed and (b) a long time after the switch is closed? (c) After a long time the switch is again opened. Now what is I_2?

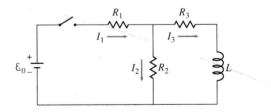

FIGURE 32-23 Problem 36.

37. In Fig. 32-24, take $\mathcal{E}_0 = 20$ V, $R_1 = 10$ Ω, $R_2 = 5.0$ Ω, and assume the switch has been open for a long time. (a) What is the inductor current immediately after the switch is closed? (b) What is the inductor current a long time after the switch is closed? (c) If after a long time the switch is again opened, what will be the voltage across R_1 immediately afterward?

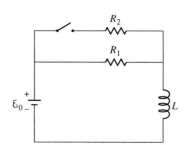

FIGURE 32-24 Problem 37.

Section 32-4 Magnetic Energy

38. How much energy is stored in a 5.0-H inductor carrying 35 A?

39. What is the current in a 10-mH inductor when the stored energy is 50 μJ?

40. A 220-mH inductor carries 350 mA. How much energy must be supplied to the inductor in raising the current to 800 mA?

41. A 12-V battery, 5.0-Ω resistor, and 18-H inductor are connected in series and allowed to reach a steady state. (a) What is the energy stored in the inductor? (b) Once in the steady state, over what time interval is the energy dissipated in the resistor equal to that stored in the inductor?

42. A battery, switch, resistor, and inductor are connected in series. When the switch is closed the current rises to half its steady-state value in 1.0 ms. How long does it take for the magnetic energy in the inductor to rise to half its steady-state value?

43. The current in a 2.0-H inductor is decreased linearly from 5.0 A to zero over 10 ms. (a) What is the average rate at which energy is being extracted from the inductor during this time? (b) Is the instantaneous rate constant?

44. When a nonideal 1.0-H inductor is short-circuited, its magnetic energy drops to one-fourth of its original value in 3.6 s. What is its resistance?

45. The current in a 2.0-H inductor is increasing. At some instant, the current is 3.0 A and the inductor emf is 5.0 V. At what rate is the inductor's magnetic energy increasing at this instant?

46. A 500-turn solenoid is 23 cm long, 1.5 cm in diameter, and carries 65 mA. How much magnetic energy does it contain?

47. A superconducting solenoid with inductance $L = 3.5$ H carries 1.8 kA. Copper is embedded in the coils to carry the current in the event of a quench (see Example 32-7). (a) What is the magnetic energy in the solenoid? (b) What is the maximum resistance of the copper that will limit the power dissipation to 100 kW immediately after a loss of superconductivity? (c) With this resistance, how long will it take the power to drop to 50 kW?

48. Show that the quantity $B^2/2\mu_0$ has the units of energy density (J/m³).

49. The Alcator fusion experiment at MIT has a 50-T magnetic field. What is the magnetic energy density in Alcator?

50. What is the magnetic field strength in a region where the magnetic energy density is 7.8 J/cm³?

51. The magnetic field of a neutron star is about 10^8 T. How does the energy density in this field compare with the energy density stored in (a) gasoline and (b) pure uranium-235 (mass density 19×10^3 kg/m³)? Consult Appendix C.

52. A loop of magnetic field arches above the Sun's surface, forming a tube approximately 10^5 km long and 10^4 km in diameter. If the magnetic field strength in the tube is 50 G, what is its magnetic energy content?

53. A single-turn loop of radius R carries current I. How does the magnetic energy density at the loop center compare with that of a long solenoid of the same radius, carrying the same current, and consisting of n turns per unit length?

54. A magnetic field is given by $\mathbf{B} = B_0(x/a)^2\hat{\mathbf{j}}$, where B_0 and a are constants. Find an expression for the magnetic energy in a cube of side a with one corner at the origin and sides extending along the coordinate axes.

55. A toroidal coil has inner radius R and a square cross section of side ℓ (Fig. 32-25). It is wound with N turns of wire, and carries a current I. Show that the magnetic energy in the toroid is given by

$$U = \frac{\mu_0 N^2 I^2 \ell}{4\pi} \ln\left(\frac{R + \ell}{R}\right).$$

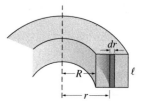

FIGURE 32-25 Cross section of a toroidal coil. Also shown is a part of a volume element, in the shape of a ring of thickness dr.

56. A toroid of inner radius 1.5 m and square cross section is wound with 2,500 turns. What must be the length ℓ of its cross-sectional square if the toroid contains 80 J of magnetic energy at a current of 63 A?

Paired Problems

(Both problems in a pair involve the same principles and techniques. If you can get the first problem, you should be able to solve the second one.)

57. Two coils have mutual inductance M. The current supplied to coil A is given by $I = bt^2$. Find an expression for the magnitude of the induced emf in coil B.

58. Two coils have mutual inductance M, and a time-varying current is supplied to coil A; at time $t = 0$ that current is zero. The magnitude of the induced emf in coil B is given by $\mathcal{E} = b\sqrt{t}$. Find an expression for the current in coil A.

59. In the circuit of Fig. 32-8a, take $\mathcal{E}_0 = 5.0$ V and $R = 1.8\ \Omega$. At 2.5 s after the switch is closed, the circuit current is 250 mA. Find the inductance.

60. In the circuit of Fig. 32-8a, take $\mathcal{E}_0 = 5.0$ V and $R = 1.8\ \Omega$. At 2.5 s after the switch is closed, the inductor emf is 2.1 V. Find the inductance.

61. In Fig. 32-13a, take $\mathcal{E}_0 = 25$ V, $R_1 = 1.5\ \Omega$, and $R_2 = 4.2\ \Omega$. What is the voltage across R_2 (a) immediately after the switch is first closed and (b) a long time after the switch is closed? (c) Long after the switch is closed it is again opened. Now what is the voltage across R_2?

62. In Fig. 32-13, take $R_2 = 5R_1$. If the maximum possible value for the inductor emf in this circuit is 300 V, what is the battery emf $\mathcal{E}_0$?

63. A wire of radius R carries a current I distributed uniformly over its cross section. Find an expression for the magnetic energy per unit length in the region from R to $100R$.

64. A wire of radius R carries a current I distributed uniformly over its cross section. Find an expression for the total magnetic energy per unit length *within* the wire.

Supplementary Problems

65. (a) Use the result of Problem 55 to determine the inductance of a toroid. (b) Show that your result reduces to the inductance of a long solenoid when $R \gg \ell$.

66. Two long, flat parallel bars of width w and spacing d carry equal but opposite currents I, as shown in Fig. 32-26. (a) Use Ampère's law to find the magnetic field between the bars. Take $d \ll w$ so you can neglect fringing fields. (b) Use your result to find the magnetic energy per unit length stored between the bars. (c) Compare your result in (b) with the expression $U = \frac{1}{2}LI^2$ to find an expression for the inductance per unit length of the bars.

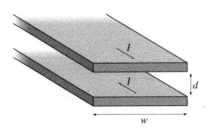

FIGURE 32-26 Problem 66.

67. (a) Use Equation 32-9 to write an expression for the power dissipation in the resistor as a function of time, and (b) integrate from $t = 0$ to $t = \infty$ to show that the total energy dissipated is equal to the energy initially stored in the inductor, namely, $\frac{1}{2}LI_0^2$.

68. (a) Find the magnetic energy density as a function of radial distance for the coaxial cable of Problem 22. (b) Integrate over the volume between the cable conductors to show that the total energy per unit length of the cable is

$$U = \frac{\mu_0}{4\pi}I^2 \ln(b/a) .$$

Hint: Your volume element should be a cylindrical shell of radius r, thickness dr, and length ℓ. What is its volume dV? (c) Use the expression $U = \frac{1}{2}LI^2$ to find the inductance per unit length, and show that your result agrees with that of Problem 22.

69. An electric field and a magnetic field have the same energy density. Obtain an expression for the ratio E/B, and evaluate this ratio numerically. What are its units? Is your answer close to any of the fundamental constants listed inside the front cover?

70. Two long, straight, parallel wires are a distance d apart. The wires have radius a, where $a \ll d$. Current flows down one wire and back along the other. Find the inductance per unit length of the parallel wires. Assume the wire radius is so small that you can neglect the magnetic flux within the wires themselves.

71. The switch in the circuit of Fig. 32-27 is closed at time $t = 0$, at which instant the inductor current is zero. Write the loop and node laws for this circuit, and show that they are satisfied if the inductor current is given by $I = (\mathcal{E}_0/R_1)(1 - e^{-R_\parallel t/L})$, where $R_\parallel$ is the resistance of R_1 and R_2 were they connected in parallel.

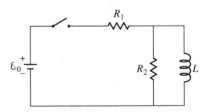

FIGURE 32-27 Problem 71.

72. Earth's magnetic field ends abruptly on the sunward side at approximately the point where the magnetic energy density has dropped to the same value as the kinetic energy density in the solar wind. Near Earth, the solar wind contains about 5 protons and 5 electrons per cubic centimeter, and flows at 400 km/s. Treating Earth's field as that of a dipole with dipole moment 8×10^{22} J/T, estimate the distance to the point above the equator where the field ends.

33 Alternating-Current Circuits

Nearly all electric power systems use alternating current (AC) at a frequency of 50–60 Hz. Higher frequency AC is essential to radio, television, and computers.

Chapter 28 considered direct-current (DC) circuits, in which the source of electrical energy is a battery or other device whose emf does not change with time. When we turn on a circuit containing only resistors and a DC emf, current starts to flow immediately and remains steady until the circuit is turned off. Even when we add capacitance, as in Section 28-6, or inductance, as in Section 32-3, all currents and voltages eventually reach steady values.

We now turn our attention to alternating-current (AC) circuits, in which sources of electrical energy vary with time. Alternating current is used almost universally for electric power, for reasons we'll discuss in Section 33-6, so you make use of AC circuits every time you switch on a light, a toaster, a stereo, or another device plugged into your household wiring. More rapidly varying alternating currents include the audio and video signals inside stereos and TVs, and the "clock" signal that sets the basic speed of your computer.

In this chapter we'll show first how to characterize AC current and voltage, and then will look at the behavior of resistors, capacitors, and inductors in AC circuits.

33-1 ALTERNATING CURRENT

We saw in Chapter 31 how the rotation of conducting loops in electric power generators naturally leads to voltage and current that vary sinusoidally with time. In audio and video equipment, computers, and other electronic devices, AC signals may exhibit more complicated time variation. But, as we described in Section 16-6, these more complicated variations can be analyzed as superpositions of sinusoidal functions. For that reason we can limit our description of AC circuits to those where current and voltage vary sinusoidally with time.

A sinusoidal AC voltage or current is characterized by its amplitude, frequency, and phase constant—the same quantities we developed in Chapter 15 to describe simple harmonic motion. Amplitude is specified by giving the peak value (V_p, I_p) or the **root-mean-square** value (V_{rms}, I_{rms}). The rms value is an average obtained by squaring the signal, taking the time average, and then taking the square root. This procedure is used because the direct average of an AC signal is zero since it spends as much time below zero as above. Use of rms values also facilitates the calculation of power in AC circuits. For a sine wave, rms and peak values are related by

$$V_{rms} = \frac{V_p}{\sqrt{2}} \quad \text{and} \quad I_{rms} = \frac{I_p}{\sqrt{2}}, \tag{33-1}$$

as you can show in Problem 7. When we speak of 120-V household wiring, for example, we are giving the rms voltage. Figure 33-1 shows graphically the relation between rms and peak values.

In practical and engineering situations we usually describe frequency f in cycles per second, or hertz (Hz). In mathematical analysis of alternating current, it's usually more convenient to use the angular frequency ω, measured in radians per second or, equivalently, inverse seconds (s^{-1}). The relation between the two,

$$\omega = 2\pi f, \tag{33-2}$$

is the same as for rotational and simple harmonic motion, and for the same reason: a full cycle contains 2π radians.

Sometimes we are interested in the phase constant ϕ of an AC signal, which describes when the sine curve crosses zero (see Fig. 33-1). A full mathematical description of an AC voltage or current then includes its amplitude (V_p, I_p), frequency (ω), and phase constant (ϕ):

$$V = V_p \sin(\omega t + \phi_V) \quad \text{and} \quad I = I_p \sin(\omega t + \phi_I). \tag{33-3}$$

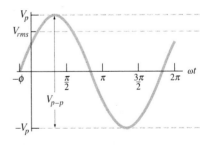

FIGURE 33-1 A sinusoidally varying AC voltage, showing peak, rms, and peak-to-peak amplitudes; the latter is just the difference between the extreme values, here equal to $2V_p$. The waveform completes a full cycle as ωt increases by 2π. The phase constant ϕ is $\pi/6$ or $30°$; note that a positive phase constant shifts the curve to the left.

Here we've labeled the phase constants with subscripts V and I to indicate that voltage and current—even in the same circuit element—need not have the same phase constant. We will often take one phase constant to be zero; then the other describes the *phase difference* between the voltage and current. Phase difference, rather than the actual value of the phase constant, is the important quantity in AC circuits.

EXAMPLE 33-1	*Household Voltage*

Standard household wiring in North America supplies 120 V rms at 60 Hz. Express this voltage mathematically in the form of Equation 33-3, assuming that the voltage is rising through zero at time $t = 0$.

Solution

The rms and peak voltages are related by Equation 33-1, so

$$V_p = \sqrt{2}V_{rms} = (\sqrt{2})(120 \text{ V}) = 170 \text{ V}.$$

The angular frequency is 2π times the frequency in Hz, so

$$\omega = 2\pi f = (2\pi)(60 \text{ Hz}) = 377 \text{ s}^{-1}.$$

When $t = 0$ we want Equation 33-3 to give $V = 0$; that requires $\phi = 0$ or $\phi = \pi$. But only with $\phi = 0$ will the curve be *rising* at $t = 0$, so Equation 33-3 becomes

$$V = 170\sin(377t),$$

with V in volts and t in seconds. We will frequently take the phase constant to be zero as in this example; only when we're

comparing signals with different phase does the value of ϕ become significant.

Although household outlets in North America provide 120 V rms (or 170 V peak, as we just calculated), wires entering the house actually carry a 240-V potential difference. The full 240 V is available for major appliances such as electric dryers, stoves, and water heaters; it's split into separate 120-V circuits that supply groups of outlets and lights. In Europe, in contrast, the standard outlet voltage is about 230 V, and the frequency is 50 Hz.

EXERCISE A 1.0-kHz sinusoidal current with rms amplitude 1.5 A drives a loudspeaker in a test of a stereo system. Express this current in the form of Equation 33-3, assuming zero phase constant.

Answer: $I = 2.12\sin(6.28\times10^3 t)$, with I in A and t in s.

Some problems similar to Example 33-1: 1, 4, 5

33-2 CIRCUIT ELEMENTS IN AC CIRCUITS

Here we examine separately the AC behavior of resistors, capacitors, and inductors so we can subsequently understand what happens when we combine these elements in AC circuits.

Resistors

An ideal resistor is a device whose current and voltage are always proportional:

$$I = \frac{V}{R}.$$

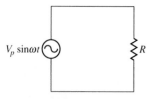

$V_p \sin\omega t$ R

FIGURE 33-2 A resistor connected across an AC generator (symbol ⊝).

Figure 33-2 shows a resistor R connected across an AC generator, making the voltage across the resistor equal to the generator voltage. The generator voltage is described by Equation 33-3, where we take the phase constant $\phi_V = 0$. Then the current is

$$I = \frac{V}{R} = \frac{V_p \sin\omega t}{R} = \frac{V_p}{R}\sin\omega t.$$

The current has the same frequency as the voltage, and, since its phase constant is also zero, the voltage and current are *in phase*—that is, they peak at the same time. The peak current is simply the peak voltage divided by the resistance: $I_p = V_p/R$. Because both voltage and current are sinusoidal, their rms values are in the same ratio as their peak values; thus $I_{rms} = V_{rms}/R$.

Capacitors

Figure 33-3 shows a capacitor connected across an AC generator. In Chapter 26, we defined a capacitor as a device in which voltage and charge are directly proportional:

$$q = CV.$$

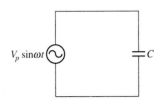

FIGURE 33-3 A capacitor across an AC generator.

Differentiating this relation gives

$$\frac{dq}{dt} = C\frac{dV}{dt}.$$

But dq/dt is the current flowing to the capacitor plates (which we'll call the "capacitor current" even though charge doesn't actually flow through the space between the capacitor plates). So we have

$$I = C\frac{dV}{dt}.$$

The generator voltage $V_p \sin \omega t$ appears directly across the capacitor, so the capacitor voltage V is the generator voltage, and therefore

$$I = C\frac{d}{dt}(V_p \sin \omega t)$$

$$= \omega C V_p \cos \omega t = \omega C V_p \sin(\omega t + \pi/2). \qquad (33\text{-}4)$$

This equation shows clearly the phase and amplitude relations between current and voltage in a capacitor. Because the cosine curve is just a sine curve shifted left by $\pi/2$ or 90°, Equation 33-4 tells us that:

> The current in a capacitor leads the voltage by 90°.

Figure 33-4 shows graphically this relation between current and voltage in a capacitor.

The term $\omega C V_p$ multiplying the cosine in Equation 33-4 is the amplitude of the current, so we can write

$$I_p = \omega C V_p,$$

or, in a form resembling Ohm's law,

$$I_p = \frac{V_p}{1/(\omega C)} = \frac{V_p}{X_C}, \qquad (33\text{-}5)$$

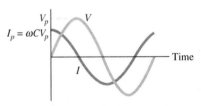

FIGURE 33-4 Current in a capacitor leads the voltage by $\pi/2$ or 90°, meaning that the current peaks *before* the voltage by one-fourth of a full cycle.

where we have defined $X_C = 1/\omega C$.

Equation 33-5 shows that the capacitor acts somewhat like a resistor of resistance $X_C = 1/\omega C$. But not quite! This "resistance" does give the relation between the peak voltage and peak current, but it doesn't tell the whole story. The capacitor also introduces a phase difference between voltage and current. This phase difference reflects a fundamental physical difference between resistors and capacitors. A resistor dissipates electrical energy as heat. A capacitor stores and releases electrical energy. Over a complete cycle, the agent turning the generator in Fig. 33-3 does no net work, while the agent turning the generator with the resistive load of Fig. 33-2 continually does work that gets dissipated as heat in the resistor. Because the quantity X_C in Equation 33-5 does not act quite like a resistance, we give it the special name **capacitive reactance**. Like resistance, reactance is measured in ohms (Ω).

Does it make sense that X_C depends on frequency? Yes—as frequency goes to zero, X_C goes to infinity. At zero frequency nothing is changing; there is no need to move charge on or off the plates, so no current flows, and the capacitor might as well be an open circuit. As frequency increases, larger currents flow to move charge on and off the capacitor plates in ever shorter times, so the capacitor looks increasingly like a short circuit. We often summarize this behavior qualitatively by saying that a capacitor at low frequencies acts like an open circuit, while at high frequencies it acts like a short circuit.

Why does the capacitor current *lead* the voltage? Because the capacitor voltage is proportional to its charge, and it takes current to move charge onto the capacitor plates. Therefore current must flow *before* the voltage can change significantly. We found the same thing with the *RC* circuit of Chapter 28; there current flowed as soon as the switch was closed, but it took time to build up the capacitor voltage.

Inductors

Figure 33-5 shows an inductor connected across an AC generator. The loop law for this circuit is

$$V_p \sin \omega t + \mathscr{E}_L = 0 .$$

From the preceding chapter, we know that the inductor emf is given by $\mathscr{E}_L = -L\dfrac{dI}{dt}$, so the loop law becomes

$$V_p \sin \omega t = L \frac{dI}{dt} .$$

To obtain a relation involving the current I rather than its derivative, we integrate this equation:

$$\int V_p \sin \omega t \, dt = \int L \frac{dI}{dt} dt = \int L \, dI ,$$

or

$$-\frac{V_p}{\omega} \cos \omega t = LI .$$

Here we have set the integration constants to zero because nonzero values would represent a DC emf and current that are absent in this circuit. Solving for I then gives

$$I = -\frac{V_p}{\omega L} \cos \omega t = \frac{V_p}{\omega L} \sin(\omega t - \pi/2) , \tag{33-6}$$

where the last step follows because $\sin(\alpha - \pi/2) = -\cos \alpha$ for any α.

Equation 33-6 shows that the current in the inductor lags the applied voltage by $\pi/2$ or 90° (i.e., Equation 33-6 is Equation 33-3 with $\phi = -\pi/2$). Equivalently:

> **The voltage across an inductor leads the inductor current by 90°.**

Figure 33-6 plots this phase relation.

Equation 33-6 also shows that the peak current is

$$I_p = \frac{V_p}{\omega L} = \frac{V_p}{X_L} . \tag{33-7}$$

FIGURE 33-5 An inductor across an AC generator.

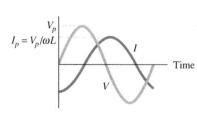

FIGURE 33-6 Voltage across an inductor leads the current by $\pi/2$ or 90°.

TABLE 33-1 *Phase and Amplitude Relations in Circuit Elements*

CIRCUIT ELEMENT	PEAK CURRENT/VOLTAGE	PHASE RELATION
Resistor	$I_p = \dfrac{V_p}{R}$	V, I in phase
Capacitor	$I_p = \dfrac{V_p}{X_C} = \dfrac{V_p}{1/\omega C}$	I leads V by 90°
Inductor	$I_p = \dfrac{V_p}{X_L} = \dfrac{V_p}{\omega L}$	V leads I by 90°

Again, this equation resembles Ohm's law, with a "resistance" $X_L = \omega L$. But as with the capacitor, no power is dissipated in the inductor. Instead, energy is alternately stored and released as the inductor's magnetic field builds up, then decays. To distinguish it from dissipative resistance, we call X_L the **inductive reactance**. Inductive reactance, too, is measured in ohms.

Does it make sense that the inductive reactance increases with increasing ω and increasing L? An inductor is a device that, through its induced back emf, opposes changes in current. The greater the inductance, the greater the opposition to changing current. And the more rapidly the current is changing, the more vigorously the inductor opposes the change, so the inductive reactance increases at high frequencies. In the extreme case of very high frequencies, an inductor looks like an open circuit. But at very low frequencies it looks more and more like a short circuit, until with direct current (zero frequency), an inductor exhibits zero reactance because there is no change in current.

Why does the inductor voltage *lead* the current? Because a changing current in an inductor induces an emf. *Before* the current can build up significantly there must first, therefore, be voltage across the inductor.

Table 33-1 summarizes the phase and amplitude relations in resistors, capacitors, and inductors.

Got It!

A capacitor and an inductor are connected across separate but identical electric generators, and the same current flows in each. If the frequency of the generators is doubled, which component will now carry the most current?

EXAMPLE 33-2	*Inductors and Capacitors*

A capacitor is connected across the 60-Hz, 120-V rms power line, and an rms current of 200 mA flows. What is the capacitance? What inductance would have to be connected across the power line for the same current to flow? Would there be anything different about the circuit containing the inductor?

Solution

The peak current and voltage are related through Equation 33-5: so

$$I_p = \frac{V_p}{1/\omega C},$$

$$C = \frac{I_p}{\omega V_p}.$$

We are given the rms voltage and current, but since only the ratio of these quantities appears in our equation, it doesn't matter whether we use rms or peak values. With $f = 60$ Hz, $\omega = 2\pi f$ or 377 s^{-1}, so

$$C = \frac{I}{\omega V} = \frac{0.20 \text{ A}}{(377 \text{ s}^{-1})(120 \text{ V})} = 4.4 \ \mu\text{F}.$$

An inductor that passes the same current must have the same reactance, so

$$\omega L = \frac{1}{\omega C},$$

or $\quad L = \dfrac{1}{\omega^2 C} = \dfrac{1}{(377 \text{ s}^{-1})^2(4.4 \times 10^{-6} \text{ F})} = 1.6 \text{ H}.$

Although the currents are the same, the two situations differ in that current leads voltage by 90° in the capacitor and lags by 90° in the inductor.

EXERCISE Inductors (called "ballast") are often used to limit the current in fluorescent lamps. In a particular lamp operating at 60 Hz, 80 V (rms) appears across a 0.53-H ballast inductor.

(a) What is the rms inductor current? (b) What capacitance could be used in place of the inductor to provide the same current?

Answers: (a) 400 mA; (b) 13 μF

Some problems similar to Example 33-2: 13, 14, 17, 20

Phasor Diagrams

Phase and amplitude relations in AC circuits may be summarized graphically in **phasor diagrams**. A phasor is an arrow whose fixed length represents the amplitude of an AC voltage or current. The phasor rotates counterclockwise about the origin with the angular frequency ω of the AC quantity. The component of the phasor on the vertical axis then represents the sinusoidally varying AC signal. Figure 33-7a shows phasors for the current and voltage in a resistor.

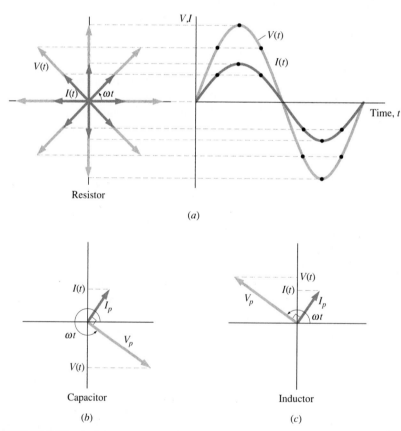

FIGURE 33-7 Phasor diagrams showing voltage and current in (*a*) a resistor, (*b*) a capacitor, and (*c*) an inductor. Lengths of phasors correspond to amplitudes V_p and I_p, while projection on the vertical axis gives the instantaneous value. Angle between voltage and current phasors gives their relative phase. In (*a*), the phasors are shown at several times; projection of the vertical components onto a plot of current and voltage versus time then shows that these quantities vary sinusoidally with time.

The lengths of the phasors are related by Ohm's law, $V_p = I_p R$. The current and voltage phasors always point in the same direction, showing that current and voltage in the resistor are in phase. For this case we show the phasors at several times in the cycle, to illustrate how, through their rotation, the phasors contain information about the time variation of the quantities they represent. Normally, however, it suffices to show phasors at one arbitrary time. We've done this in Figs. 33-7b and c for a capacitor and an inductor. The phasors are at right angles in each case, indicating the phase relations between current and voltage. Their lengths are related by the appropriate reactance, so $V_p = I_p X$. As phasors rotate, a diagram such as Fig. 33-7a would show them tracing out current and voltage graphs like those of Figs. 33-4 and 33-6. You should convince yourself that all the relationships of Table 33-1 are correctly described by the phasor diagrams of Fig. 33-7. Although phasor diagrams do not add much to our understanding of AC circuits containing only one circuit element, they will greatly simplify the analysis of more complicated circuits.

Capacitors and Inductors: A Comparison

Here and in previous chapters, we have considered separately the behavior of capacitors and inductors. Many of the properties of these devices are analogous. A capacitor opposes instantaneous changes in voltage, while an inductor opposes instantaneous changes in current. In an RC circuit with a DC emf, voltage builds up exponentially across the capacitor, with time constant RC. In the analogous RL circuit, current builds up exponentially in the inductor, with time constant L/R. A capacitor stores electrical energy given by $\frac{1}{2}CV^2$. An inductor stores magnetic energy given by $\frac{1}{2}LI^2$. A capacitor acts like an open circuit at low frequencies, an inductor like a short circuit at low frequencies. Each exhibits the opposite behavior at high frequencies.

Capacitors and inductors are complementary devices, reflecting a deeper complementarity between electric and magnetic fields. Any verbal description of a capacitor applies to an inductor if we replace the words "capacitor" with "inductor," "electric" with "magnetic," and "voltage" with "current." Table 33-2 summarizes the complementary aspects of capacitors and inductors.

TABLE 33-2 *Capacitors and Inductors*

	CAPACITOR	**INDUCTOR**
Defining relation	$C = \dfrac{q}{V}$	$L = \dfrac{\phi_B}{I}$
Defining relation, differential form	$I = C\dfrac{dV}{dt}$	$\mathscr{E} = -L\dfrac{dI}{dt}$
Opposes changes in	Voltage	Current
Energy storage	In electric field $U = \frac{1}{2}CV^2$	In magnetic field $U = \frac{1}{2}LI^2$
Behavior in low-frequency limit	Open circuit	Short circuit
Behavior in high-frequency limit	Short circuit	Open circuit
Reactance	$X_C = 1/\omega C$	$X_L = \omega L$
Phase	Current leads by 90°	Voltage leads by 90°

APPLICATION	*Loudspeaker Systems*

Loudspeakers in high-quality audio systems invariably contain two or more individual *drivers*—devices for converting electrical energy to sound—within the same enclosure (Fig. 33-8a). The most common form of driver includes a wire coil attached to a diaphragm and suspended in the field of a permanent magnet (Fig. 33-8b). Varying current in the coil then leads to a varying force that drives the diaphragm back and forth to produce sound.

Faithful reproduction of low-frequency sound requires a large driver, called a *woofer*. The woofer is large both because much of the sound power in music lies in the low-frequency range (think of a drum versus a flute!) and because the human ear is much less sensitive to low frequencies (recall Fig. 17-3). But the woofer's large size gives it a large mechanical inertia, so it can't undergo the rapid movements needed to reproduce high-frequency sound. Consequently, a much smaller driver, the *tweeter,* is used for high frequencies.

Power from an amplifier doesn't "know" about the mechanical properties of the drivers, so connecting both drivers directly to the same amplifier would result in low-frequency power being dissipated ineffectually in the tweeter and high-

frequency power in the woofer. To prevent this inefficiency, a speaker system contains a *crossover network* to "steer" power to the appropriate drivers. Figure 33-8c shows a simple crossover network that exploits the frequency-dependent behavior of capacitors and inductors. At low frequencies the inductor reactance ωL is low, and current flows readily through the inductor to the woofer coil. But at high frequencies the inductor reactance is high, and little high-frequency power reaches the woofer. The capacitor's behavior is the opposite: It blocks low-frequency power from reaching the tweeter, while passing high-frequency power. Many speaker systems also employ a *midrange* driver, with a capacitor and inductor in series to block power at both high- and low-frequency extremes. Example 33-4, later in this chapter, explores quantitatively the behavior of the midrange circuitry.

The circuits of Fig. 33-8c are examples of *filters,* widely used in electronic systems to pass preferentially a range of frequencies. For instance, bass and treble controls on audio systems adjust filter properties to boost low or high frequencies as desired. Problem 74 explores a simple filter.

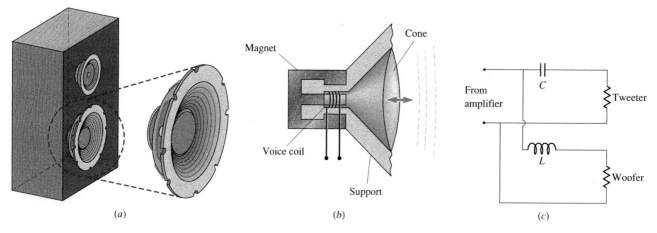

(a)   (b)   (c)

FIGURE 33-8 (a) A loudspeaker system, showing the woofer and tweeter drivers for low- and high-frequency sound production. (b) Cutaway view of a moving-coil driver. (c) The crossover network "steers" power at the appropriate frequencies to the woofer and tweeter. Resistances represent the coils in the two drivers.

33-3 *LC* CIRCUITS

In this section we consider circuits containing both inductors and capacitors. The properties of these circuits reflect directly the complementary nature of the two devices.

LC Oscillations

Figure 33-9 shows a circuit with a capacitor C and inductor L. Suppose the capacitor is initially charged to some voltage V_p and corresponding charge q_p, and is then connected to the inductor. What happens?

Initially, the capacitor is fully charged, while the inductor current is zero. There is electrical energy stored in the capacitor, but none in the inductor. This initial state is shown in Fig. 33-10*a*. Then the capacitor begins to discharge through the inductor. It cannot do so all at once, because the inductor opposes changes in current. So current in the inductor rises gradually, and with it the magnetic energy stored in the inductor. At the same time the capacitor voltage, charge, and stored electrical energy decrease. Some time later, the initial energy is divided equally between the capacitor and inductor, as in Fig. 33-10*b*. But the capacitor keeps discharging, eventually reaching zero charge, as in Fig. 33-10*c*. Now there is no voltage across the capacitor and no stored electrical energy. All the energy that was initially in the electric field of the capacitor is in the magnetic field of the inductor.

Does everything stop at this point? No, because current is flowing in the inductor. Current in an inductor cannot change abruptly, so the current keeps flowing and piles positive charge on the bottom plate of the capacitor (Fig. 33-10*d*). Stored electrical energy increases as the capacitor charges,

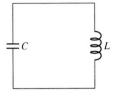

FIGURE 33-9 An *LC* circuit.

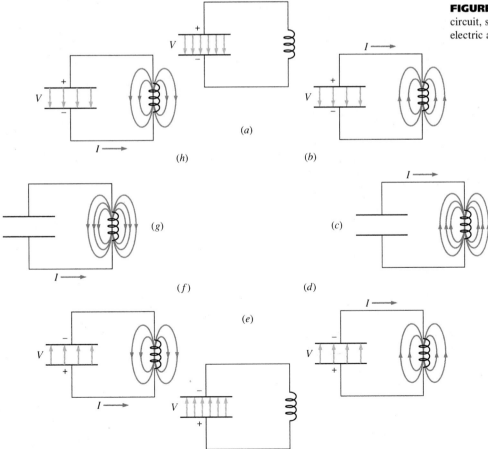

FIGURE 33-10 Oscillation in an *LC* circuit, showing energy transfer between electric and magnetic fields.

(*a*)

(*h*)

(*b*)

(*g*)

(*c*)

(*f*)

(*d*)

(*e*)

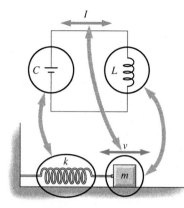

FIGURE 33-11 An LC circuit is the electrical analog of a mass-spring system. The capacitor corresponds to the spring, the inductor to the mass, and current to velocity.

TABLE 33-3 *LC Circuits and Mass-Spring Systems*

LC CIRCUIT	**MASS-SPRING**
Charge q	Displacement x
Current $I = dq/dt$	Velocity $v = dx/dt$
Inductance L	Mass m
Capacitance C	$1/k$ (k = spring constant)
Magnetic energy $U_B = \frac{1}{2}LI^2$	Kinetic energy $U_K = \frac{1}{2}mv^2$
Electric energy $U_E = \frac{1}{2}(1/C)q^2$	Potential energy $U = \frac{1}{2}kx^2$
Frequency $\omega = 1/\sqrt{LC}$	Frequency $\omega = \sqrt{k/m}$
Resistance	Friction

and the inductor current and stored magnetic energy decrease. Eventually (Fig. 33-10e), the capacitor is fully charged in the opposite direction from its initial state. Again all the energy is in the capacitor. Again the capacitor begins to discharge, and the process repeats, now with a counterclockwise current (Fig. 33-10f). All the energy is transferred to the inductor (Fig. 33-10g), and then back to the capacitor, which again attains its initial state (Fig. 33-10a). Provided there is no energy loss, the oscillation repeats indefinitely.

This LC oscillation should remind you of the mass-spring system we studied in Chapter 15. There, energy was transferred back and forth between kinetic energy of the mass and potential energy of the spring. Here, energy is transferred back and forth between magnetic energy of the inductor and electrical energy of the capacitor. The mass-spring system oscillates with frequency determined by the mass m and spring constant k. Similarly, the LC circuit oscillates with frequency determined by the inductance L and capacitance C. Figure 33-11 shows the corresponding elements of each system and Table 33-3 shows some analogies between mass-spring systems and LC circuits. We will develop these analogies more rigorously in the next section.

Analogies with LC circuits are so useful that engineers sometimes simulate complicated systems, such as bridges, automobile suspensions, or world energy usage, with networks of LC circuits. Such a network is called an analog computer because its behavior is analogous to that of the system under study.

Analyzing the *LC* Circuit

We described the LC circuit qualitatively in terms of transfer between electric and magnetic energy. This description suggests a way to analyze the circuit quantitatively. The total energy in the circuit is the sum of the magnetic and electric energy:

$$U = U_B + U_E = \tfrac{1}{2}LI^2 + \tfrac{1}{2}\frac{q^2}{C}.$$

The time derivative of this equation is

$$\frac{dU}{dt} = \frac{d}{dt}\left(\tfrac{1}{2}LI^2 + \tfrac{1}{2}\frac{q^2}{C}\right).$$

But since the total energy in our ideal circuit does not change, $dU/dt = 0$. Carrying out the differentiations in our expression for dU/dt, we then have

$$LI\frac{dI}{dt} + \frac{q}{C}\frac{dq}{dt} = 0. \qquad (33\text{-}8)$$

Substituting $I = dq/dt$ and $dI/dt = d^2q/dt^2$ gives

$$L\frac{d^2q}{dt^2} + \frac{1}{C}q = 0. \qquad (33\text{-}9)$$

Equation 33-9 is a differential equation describing the capacitor charge as a function of time. We encountered a similar equation in Chapter 15 when we studied the mass-spring system:

$$m\frac{d^2x}{dt^2} + kx = 0. \qquad (15\text{-}4)$$

We found that Equation 15-4 could be satisfied by a sinusoidal function of time, with frequency given by

$$\omega = \sqrt{k/m}. \qquad (15\text{-}11)$$

Equation 33-9 is identical to Equation 15-4 except that q replaces x, L replaces m, and $1/C$ replaces k. Therefore the solution of Equation 33-9 is a sinusoidal oscillation,

$$q(t) = q_p \cos \omega t, \qquad (33\text{-}10)$$

whose frequency is given by Equation 15-8a with L replacing m and $1/C$ replacing k:

where
$$\omega = \frac{1}{\sqrt{LC}}. \qquad (33\text{-}11)$$

Here we chose cosine rather than sine since our qualitative description (Fig. 33-10) started with the capacitor charge at its peak value. Differentiating the charge (Equation 33-10) gives the current:

$$I(t) = \frac{dq}{dt} = \frac{d}{dt}(q_p \cos \omega t) = -\omega q_p \sin \omega t. \qquad (33\text{-}12)$$

All other circuit quantities follow from Equations 33-10 and 33-12. The capacitor voltage, obtained from the relation $q = CV$, is

$$V_C(t) = \frac{q}{C} = \frac{q_p}{C}\cos \omega t.$$

The electrical energy in the capacitor is, therefore,

$$U_E = \tfrac{1}{2}CV^2 = (\tfrac{1}{2}C)\left(\frac{q_p}{C}\cos \omega t\right)^2 = \frac{q_p^2}{2C}\cos^2 \omega t,$$

while the magnetic energy in the inductor is

$$U_B = \tfrac{1}{2}LI^2 = \tfrac{1}{2}L(-\omega q_p \sin \omega t)^2 = \tfrac{1}{2}L\omega^2 q_p^2 \sin^2 \omega t.$$

We can verify that our solution conserves energy by adding the electric and magnetic energies:

$$U_{\text{total}} = U_E + U_B = \frac{q_p^2}{2C}\cos^2 \omega t + \tfrac{1}{2}L\omega^2 q_p^2 \sin^2 \omega t.$$

FIGURE 33-12 Electric and magnetic energies in an LC circuit. Their sum is constant.

14.2
The RLC Oscillator

But Equation 33-11 shows that $\omega^2 = 1/LC$, so we have

$$U_{total} = \frac{q_p^2}{2C}\cos^2 \omega t + \frac{1}{2}\frac{L}{LC}q_p^2 \sin^2 \omega t$$

$$= \frac{q_p^2}{2C}(\cos^2 \omega t + \sin^2 \omega t) = \frac{q_p^2}{2C},$$

since $\cos^2 \omega t + \sin^2 \omega t = 1$. Thus the total energy is independent of time and is equal to the initial energy stored in the capacitor. Figure 33-12 is a plot of the electric and magnetic energies as functions of time, showing that the two always sum to a constant.

You can simulate the LC circuit we've just analyzed with ActivPhysics Activity 14.2 if you set $R = 0$ in that simulation.

Got It!

You have an LC circuit that oscillates at a typical AM radio frequency, namely 1 MHz. If you want to change the capacitor so that the circuit will now oscillate at a typical FM radio frequency of 100 MHz, should you make the capacitance larger or smaller? By what factor?

EXAMPLE 33-3	*A Piano Tuner*

You wish to make an LC circuit oscillate at 440 Hz (the note A above middle C); connected to an amplifier and loudspeaker it will produce a pure tone to be used in tuning pianos. You have available a 2.0-H inductor. What value of capacitance should you use? If you initially charge the capacitor to 5.0 V, what will be the peak charge on the capacitor and the peak current in the circuit?

Solution
The oscillation frequency is given by Equation 33-11. Solving for C gives

$$C = \frac{1}{\omega^2 L} = \frac{1}{(2\pi f)^2 L} = \frac{1}{[(2\pi)(440 \text{ Hz})]^2(2.0 \text{ H})} = 65.4 \text{ nF}.$$

The capacitor charge and voltage are related through $C = q/V$, so

$$q_p = CV_p = (65.4 \text{ nF})(5.0 \text{ V}) = 327 \text{ nC}.$$

Equation 33-12 then shows that the peak current is

$$I_p = \omega q_p = 2\pi f q_p = (2\pi)(440 \text{ Hz})(327 \text{ nC}) = 0.90 \text{ mA}.$$

Problem 38 shows how the current also follows from energy considerations.

EXERCISE An FM radio transmitter requires an LC circuit that oscillates at the 89.5-MHz transmitter frequency. What should be the inductance if the circuit capacitance is 47 pF?

Answer: 67 nH

Some problems similar to Example 33-3: 27, 28, 31, 32

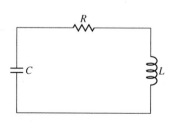

FIGURE 33-13 An RLC circuit.

Resistance in LC Circuits—Damping

Real inductors, capacitors, and wires have resistance. Both this intrinsic resistance and any external resistance are represented by the resistor R in Fig. 33-13. What happens in such a resistive LC circuit?

Provided the resistance is small—small enough that only a small fraction of the energy is lost in one cycle—then our analysis of the preceding section applies. The circuit oscillates at a frequency given very nearly by Equation 33-11. But as current flows back and forth through the resistor, energy is dissipated as heat. On each successive cycle, the total energy decreases. Consequently, the amplitude of the oscillations decreases with time.

We can analyze this *RLC* circuit by starting with Equation 33-8, except that now energy is being lost at the rate I^2R (the power dissipation in a resistor; recall Equation 27-9a). So instead of zero, the right side of Equation 33-8 becomes $-I^2R$, with the minus sign indicating energy loss from the circuit:

$$LI\frac{dI}{dt} + \frac{q}{C}\frac{dq}{dt} = -I^2R\,.$$

Writing $I = dq/dt$ as we did in the preceding section leads to

$$L\frac{d^2q}{dt^2} + R\frac{dq}{dt} + \frac{q}{C} = 0\,.$$

This equation is mathematically identical to Equation 15-19 for damped simple harmonic motion, showing that our analogies of Table 33-3 continue to hold when resistance is present. Using Equation 15-20, which is the solution to Equation 15-19, and the appropriate analogies from Table 33-3, we can construct the solution for our decaying *RLC* circuit:

$$q(t) = q_p e^{-Rt/2L}\cos\omega t\,. \tag{33-13}$$

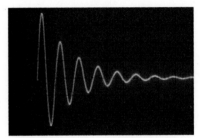

Other quantities show similar behavior, with oscillation amplitude decaying exponentially with time constant $2L/R$. Figure 33-14 shows an oscilloscope trace of the capacitor voltage in a circuit undergoing damped oscillations.

As the electrical resistance increases, the oscillations decay more rapidly and the frequency of oscillation decreases. Finally, when the exponential time constant $2L/R$ equals the inverse of the natural frequency given by Equation 33-11, much of the energy is lost in the time of one undamped oscillation period. This situation is termed **critical damping**, and at this value of R circuit quantities decay exponentially to zero, in analogy with a critically damped mechanical system (Section 15-6). For greater values of R, the circuit is **overdamped** and also exhibits no oscillation. In circuits that are designed to oscillate, such as radio transmitters or TV tuners, engineers obviously want to minimize damping. But in other situations, circuit oscillations would be a nuisance, and then it's important to introduce enough resistance to suppress oscillation. You can simulate the *RLC* circuit with ActivPhysics Activity 14.2.

FIGURE 33-14 An oscilloscope displays the capacitor voltage in an *RLC* circuit. Note the exponential decline in amplitude of the oscillations.

33-4 DRIVEN *RLC* CIRCUITS AND RESONANCE

Figure 33-15 shows an *RLC* circuit connected across an AC generator. The *RLC* circuit itself is analogous to a mass-spring system, so adding the generator is like adding the external driving force on the mechanical oscillator that we considered in Section 15-7. We'll call the generator frequency ω_d, the driving frequency, just as we did in Chapter 15. Pursuing the mechanical analogy, we expect the driven *RLC* circuit to exhibit resonant behavior as we discussed in Section 15-7. Such electrical resonance is crucial to the operation of radio, television, and other frequency-specific devices.

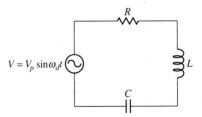

FIGURE 33-15 A series *RLC* circuit driven by an AC generator.

Resonance in the *RLC* Circuit

Suppose we vary the generator frequency ω_d in Fig. 33-15 while keeping the generator's peak voltage constant. How much current flows in the *RLC* circuit? At low frequencies the capacitor acts almost like an open circuit (its reactance $X_C = 1/\omega C$ is large), so little current flows. At high frequencies the inductor acts almost like an open circuit (its reactance $X_L = \omega L$ is large), so little current

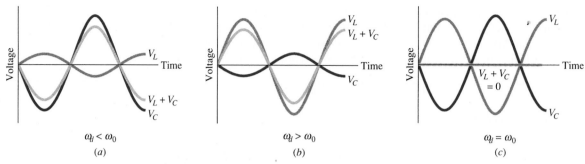

FIGURE 33-16 In a series RLC circuit, capacitor and inductor voltages are 180° out of phase at all frequencies. (*a*) At low frequencies, the voltage is greatest across the capacitor. (*b*) At high frequencies, the voltage is greatest across the inductor. (*c*) At resonance, capacitor and inductor voltages have equal amplitude, and therefore they cancel completely.

flows. At some intermediate frequency the current must be a maximum. We now show that this **resonant frequency** is in fact the undamped natural frequency $\omega_0 = 1/\sqrt{LC}$.

Figure 33-15 is a series circuit, so the *same* current flows through all the components. We know that the voltage in a capacitor lags the current by 90°, while the voltage in an inductor leads by 90°. Since the same current flows through the inductor and capacitor, the inductor and capacitor voltages are therefore 180° out of phase. This phase relation holds at *any* frequency. At low frequencies, however, the capacitor's reactance is greatest and the capacitor voltage is therefore greater than the inductor voltage (Fig. 33-16*a*). At high frequencies the opposite is true, with the inductor voltage being greatest (Fig. 33-16*b*). Since the two voltages are 180° out of phase, they tend to cancel, but at high or low frequencies Figs. 33-16*a* and *b* show that their different amplitudes mean this cancellation is not complete.

Is there some frequency, ω_0, at which the capacitor and inductor voltages exactly cancel? The peak current and voltage in these two components are related by Equations 33-5 and 33-7, respectively. Since the current is the same, comparison of these equations shows that the voltages will be the same when the capacitive reactance $1/\omega C$ is equal to the inductive reactance ωL, which gives

$$\omega_0^2 = \frac{1}{LC}. \quad \text{(resonant frequency)}$$

This is precisely Equation 33-11's condition for the undamped natural frequency.

At resonance, then, the capacitor and inductor voltages completely cancel. The voltage across the pair together is zero, and—at the resonant frequency only—the pair behave just like a wire. The circuit current at resonance is determined entirely by the resistance. At any other frequency the effects of capacitance and inductance do not cancel completely, and the current is lower.

14.3

The Driven Oscillator

Got It!

You measure the capacitor and inductor voltages in a driven RLC circuit, and find 10 V for the rms capacitor voltage and 15 V for the rms inductor voltage. Is the driving frequency above or below resonance?

Frequency Response of the *RLC* Circuit

Here we derive a general expression for the current as a function of frequency in the series *RLC* circuit, using the phasor diagrams introduced in Section 33-2. Since the same current flows through all components of the series circuit, we represent this current by a single phasor of length I_p in Fig. 33-17. Also shown are phasors for the resistor, capacitor, and inductor voltages. The resistor voltage phasor is in the same direction as the current because these two are in phase, but the capacitor and inductor voltages are at 90° relative to the current.

In analyzing circuits, we've often used the fact that the sum of the voltage differences around a circuit is zero. This statement is true *at each instant*, meaning that it applies to *instantaneous* values of the voltages. Because they have different phases, the voltages in the circuit of Fig. 33-15 peak at different times—so we can't simply sum the peak voltages around the circuit and set the result to zero. Instead, we have to sum the instantaneous voltages. We can do that by adding the voltage phasors *vectorially*—a process that accounts for both magnitude and phase. Figure 33-17*b* shows that this vector addition gives the following relation between the peak generator voltage, V_p, and the voltages across the individual components:

$$V_p^2 = V_{Rp}^2 + (V_{Lp} - V_{Cp})^2 .$$

Expressing this in terms of the current and the resistances and reactances gives

$$V_p^2 = I_p^2 R^2 + (I_p X_L - I_p X_C)^2 ,$$

or

$$I_p = \frac{V_p}{\sqrt{R^2 + (X_L - X_C)^2}} = \frac{V_p}{Z} , \qquad (33\text{-}14)$$

where we have defined

$$Z = \sqrt{R^2 + (X_L - X_C)^2} .$$

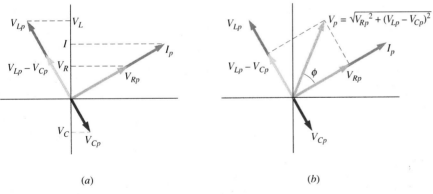

(a)   (b)

FIGURE 33-17 Phasor diagrams for the driven *RLC* circuit. As usual, the length of each phasor indicates the peak value of voltage or current, while the projection on the vertical axis is the instantaneous value. As the phasors rotate with angular frequency ω_d, the instantaneous values vary sinusoidally with time. (*a*) The current in the three circuit elements is the same, and is in phase with the resistor voltage. The voltages differ, and are out of phase with each other. (*b*) Voltage phasors for the inductor, capacitor, and resistor sum vectorially to give the generator voltage *V*. In this case the inductor voltage exceeds the capacitor voltage, so the driving voltage *V* leads the current. The phase difference ϕ between *V* and *I* is given by Equation 33-16.

Equation 33-14 has the form of Ohm's law, with Z playing the role of resistance. We call Z the **impedance** of the circuit. Impedance is a generalization of resistance to include the frequency-dependent effects of capacitance and inductance. Putting in our expressions for the reactances gives

$$Z = \sqrt{R^2 + \left(\omega L - \frac{1}{\omega C}\right)^2}. \tag{33-15}$$

In agreement with our earlier analysis, this equation shows that the circuit impedance becomes very large at high and low frequencies, and has its lowest value, R, at resonance.

Figure 33-18 is a plot of Equation 33-14, showing peak current versus frequency for several values of resistance. As we lower the resistance, the peak current at resonance rises. Although the current at other frequencies rises, too, it does so to a much lower extent than at resonance. This is because the impedance at resonance depends only on the resistance, but includes reactive effects at other frequencies. As a result, the resonance curve becomes more sharply peaked as the resistance drops. For a circuit with very low resistance, the current at resonance is dramatically different from that at even a slightly different frequency. Such a circuit, called a **high-Q** (for high-quality) circuit, does a good job of distinguishing its resonant frequency from nearby frequencies. A rigorous definition of Q can be given in terms of the width of the resonance curve (see Problem 81). High-Q circuits are important in radio and TV transmitters, where they help establish the precise broadcast frequency. At the receiving end, when you tune a simple radio, you're adjusting the variable capacitor in a high-Q LC circuit that selects the desired station from among the hodgepodge of radio signals reaching the antenna (Fig. 33-19).

Equation 33-14 relates the peak current in the RLC circuit and the voltage across it, but that equation doesn't tell the whole story. In general, current and voltage are not in phase. Figure 33-17b shows that the phase difference ϕ between the driving voltage and the circuit current is

$$\tan \phi = \frac{V_{Lp} - V_{Cp}}{V_{Rp}}.$$

Because the voltages are proportional to the reactances and resistance, this expression may be written

$$\tan \phi = \frac{X_L - X_C}{R} = \frac{\omega L - 1/\omega C}{R}. \tag{33-16}$$

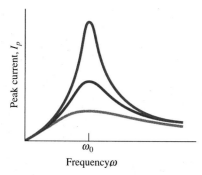

FIGURE 33-18 Resonance curves for an RLC circuit with three different resistance values. Upper curve is for half the resistance, and lower curve for twice the resistance, of the middle curve.

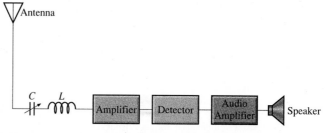

FIGURE 33-19 Diagram of a simple radio, using an LC circuit with a variable capacitor to select the desired station frequency. The signal is subsequently amplified, the audio information is extracted in the detector, and the amplified audio signal drives the loudspeaker. More sophisticated receivers often use digital circuitry in place of the LC frequency selector.

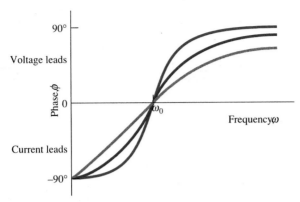

FIGURE 33-20 Phase relations for the *RLC* circuits whose resonance curves are shown in Fig. 33-18.

Does this equation make sense? At resonance, $X_L = X_C$ and the phase difference is zero. Here the effects of capacitance and inductance cancel, and the circuit behaves like a pure resistance. At frequencies below resonance, capacitive reactance is greatest and the phase difference is negative, indicating that current leads voltage—as we expect in a circuit dominated by capacitance. Above resonance $X_L > X_C$ and the phase difference is positive, indicating that voltage leads current—as we expect in a circuit dominated by inductance. At high- and low-frequency extremes, $\tan \phi$ becomes arbitrarily large and the phase differences approach 90°, as shown in Fig. 33-20.

We've defined the phase difference ϕ in Equation 33-16 as negative when the current leads. This means that if we describe voltage and current with Equation 33-3, then the arbitrary choice $\phi_V = 0$ requires $\phi_I = -\phi$. Conversely, if we choose $\phi_I = 0$, then $\phi_V = +\phi$.

Tip

Phase Matters You can't analyze an AC circuit by treating resistors, capacitors, and inductors all as "resistors" with resistances R, X_C, and X_L. Why not? Because associated with each component is a different phase relation between current and voltage. Only a phasor diagram—or mathematical analysis that includes phase relations—correctly characterizes the circuit. The phase relations in a series *RLC* circuit show up in the minus sign joining the capacitive and inductive reactance, and in the Pythagorean-like addition of the resistance and reactances in Equations 33-14 and 33-15.

EXAMPLE 33-4	*Designing a Loudspeaker System*

Current flows to the midrange speaker in a loudspeaker system through a 2.2-mH inductor and a capacitor, in series. (See *Application: Loudspeaker Systems,* earlier in this chapter.) (a) What should be the capacitance in order that a given applied voltage produces the maximum current at a frequency of 1.0 kHz? (b) What should be the speaker's resistance in order that the same voltage produces a current with half the maximum value at 600 Hz? (c) If the peak output voltage of the amplifier is 20 V, what should be the capacitor's peak voltage rating?

Solution

(a) Inductor, capacitor, and resistor comprise a series *RLC* circuit, with resonant frequency $f_0 = \omega_0/2\pi = 1/2\pi\sqrt{LC}$. Solving for C gives

$$C = \frac{1}{4\pi^2 f_0^2 L} = \frac{1}{(4\pi^2)(1.0\times10^3 \text{ Hz})^2(2.2\times10^{-3} \text{ H})} = 11.5 \ \mu\text{F}.$$

(b) Equation 33-14 gives the current in an *RLC* circuit. The denominator in this equation—the impedance $Z = \sqrt{R^2 + (X_L - X_C)^2}$—has the value R at resonance, when

$X_L = X_C$. Thus the current will have half its maximum value where the $Z = 2R$. Using $X_L = \omega L$ and $X_C = 1/\omega C$, we want R such that

$$ Z = \sqrt{R^2 + \left(\omega L - \frac{1}{\omega C} \right)^2} = 2R $$

when $f = \omega/2\pi = 600$ Hz, or $\omega = 3.77 \times 10^3$ s^{-1}. Squaring and solving for R gives

$$ R = \frac{1}{\sqrt{3}} \left| \omega L - \frac{1}{\omega C} \right| = 8.53 \; \Omega , $$

where we used the 11.5-μF answer to part (a) for the capacitance C. This resistance value is typical for a loudspeaker. The exercise below shows that the current also has half its maximum value at 1.7 kHz, so the midrange speaker gets at least half its maximum current in the range from about 600 to 1700 Hz.

(c) The maximum current flows at the resonant frequency, so the Ohm's-law-like Equation 33-5 shows that the maximum capacitor voltage also occurs at this frequency and is given by

$$ V_{Cp} = I_p X_C = \left(\frac{V_p}{R} \right) \left(\frac{1}{\omega C} \right) $$

$$ = \left(\frac{20 \; V}{8.53 \; \Omega} \right) \left(\frac{1}{(2\pi)(1000 \; Hz)(11.5 \times 10^{-6} \; F)} \right) $$

$$ = 32 \; V . $$

How can this value be *greater* than the peak applied voltage? Remember that there's another source of emf in the circuit—the inductor, whose emf depends on the rate of change of current and may therefore exceed the applied voltage. In this relatively low-Q circuit the peak capacitor voltage is not too much greater than the peak applied voltage, but in high-Q circuits like those used in radio transmitters, capacitors may have to withstand voltages hundreds of times those applied to the circuit.

EXERCISE Find a second frequency where the speaker current in Example 33-4 has half its maximum value. *Hint:* Square Equation 33-15, isolate the frequency-dependent terms, take a square root, and solve a quadratic equation. Or use graphical techniques.

Answer: 1.7 kHz

Some problems similar to Example 33-4: 43, 44, 46, 69, 70, 76

33-5 POWER IN AC CIRCUITS

In Section 33-2, we noted that average power dissipation is zero in a circuit containing only a capacitor or an inductor. We can understand this physically because the reactive element alternately stores and releases energy rather than dissipating it as heat. Mathematically, we can see this from Fig. 33-21a, which

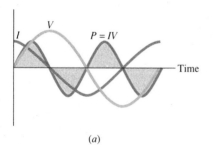

(a)

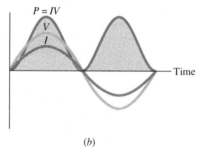

(b)

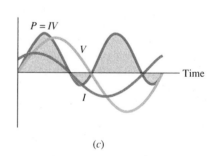

(c)

FIGURE 33-21 Current I, voltage V, and power consumption IV. (a) Current and voltage in a capacitor are out of phase by 90°. The power is alternately positive (absorbing energy from the source) and negative (returning energy to the source), and the net energy consumption (shaded area) over one cycle is zero. (b) Current and voltage are in phase in a resistor and therefore the power is always positive, meaning that the resistor is a net energy consumer. (c) Average power consumption decreases as current and voltage go out of phase.

shows the current, voltage, and instantaneous power in a capacitor. The power is the product of the current and voltage. Because these two are out of phase, the power is positive half the time, and negative half the time. When the power is positive, the capacitor absorbs energy from the source that drives the current. When the power is negative, the capacitor returns energy to the driving source. The net energy transferred to the capacitor over one cycle is $\int P\,dt$, or the area under the power-versus-time curve, and is zero in this case. Figure 33-21*b*, in contrast, shows current, voltage, and instantaneous power in a resistor. Since current and voltage are always in phase, the power is always positive, and the resistor always takes energy from the source. Comparison of Figs. 33-21*a* and *b* suggests that the phase difference between current and voltage is important in determining the average power consumption of an AC circuit. We can see this more clearly if we imagine slipping the current and voltage just slightly out of phase, as in Fig. 33-21*c*. Then there are narrow regions where the power is negative, so the average power over one cycle is slightly less than in the resistor case. As the phase difference increases, so does the time that the power is negative, until at 90° phase difference, the time-average power is zero.

We can develop a general expression for power in AC circuits by considering the time-average product of voltage and current with arbitrary phase difference ϕ:

$$\langle P \rangle = \langle [I_p \sin(\omega t + \phi)][V_p \sin \omega t]\rangle ,$$

where $\langle\,\rangle$ indicates a time average over one cycle. Expanding the current term using a trig identity (see Appendix A) gives

$$\langle P \rangle = I_p V_p \langle (\sin^2 \omega t)(\cos \phi) + (\sin \omega t)(\cos \omega t)(\sin \phi)\rangle .$$

The average of $(\sin \omega t)(\cos \omega t)$ is zero, as we've just shown for two signals 90° out of phase. The quantity $\sin^2 \omega t$ swings from 0 to 1, and is symmetric about $\frac{1}{2}$, so its average value is $\frac{1}{2}$ recall (recall Fig. 16-16). Then we have

$$\langle P \rangle = \tfrac{1}{2} I_p V_p \cos \phi .$$

Writing the peak values as $\sqrt{2}$ times the rms values gives

$$\langle P \rangle = \tfrac{1}{2}\sqrt{2}I_{\text{rms}} \sqrt{2}V_{\text{rms}} \cos \phi = I_{\text{rms}} V_{\text{rms}} \cos \phi . \qquad (33\text{-}17)$$

This equation confirms our earlier graphical arguments. When the voltage and current are in phase, the average power is just the product $I_{\text{rms}} V_{\text{rms}}$. (This, in fact, is a principal reason for using rms values: with them, the expression for average power is the same as in the DC case.) But with current and voltage out of phase, the average power is smaller; at 90° phase difference it is zero.

The factor $\cos \phi$ is called the **power factor**. A purely resistive circuit has a power factor of 1, while a circuit with only inductance and capacitance has a power factor of zero. In circuits containing resistance along with capacitance and/or inductance, the power factor generally depends on frequency; in the series *RLC* circuit, for example, it is 1 at resonance but lower at other frequencies.

Equation 33-17 shows that delivering a given average power at a fixed voltage requires greater current when the power factor is less than 1. Because energy is dissipated at the rate I^2R in the resistance of transmission lines, motor coils, and the like, electrical loads with low power factors result in wasted energy. For that reason, electric power engineers often add capacitance to inductive devices such as motors, bringing the power factor closer to 1 and thus lowering the current and therefore the resistive energy losses.

33-6 TRANSFORMERS AND POWER SUPPLIES

A **transformer** is a pair of wire coils in close proximity. We analyzed such a coil pair in Section 32-1, and showed how a change in current in one coil—which we'll call the **primary**—results in a changing magnetic flux and therefore, by Faraday's law, an emf in the other coil, or **secondary**. This emf can drive a current in circuitry connected to the secondary coil. Thus, the transformer transfers electrical energy from the primary circuit to the secondary circuit, even though there is no direct electrical connection between the two.

Practical transformers are often wound on iron cores that concentrate flux, ensuring that essentially all the magnetic flux produced by the primary coil goes through the secondary. Figure 33-22 shows a simplified diagram of a transformer, along with its circuit symbol.

The transformer in Fig. 33-22a has two turns in its primary and four in its secondary. Since the same changing flux passes through each turn of each coil, the total emf induced in the secondary must be twice that of the primary. This transformer is therefore a **step-up transformer**; it steps up the voltage by a factor of 2. Interchanging primary and secondary would give a **step-down** transformer, with the secondary voltage half that of the primary. In general, the ratio of the peak (or rms) primary voltage V_1 to the peak (or rms) secondary voltage V_2 is the same as the ratio of the numbers of turns in the two coils:

$$V_2 = \frac{N_2}{N_1} V_1 . \tag{33-18}$$

Aren't we getting something for nothing with a step-up transformer? No—a step-up transformer increases voltage but not power. In an ideal transformer, all the power supplied to the primary is transferred to the secondary; therefore,

$$I_1 V_1 = I_2 V_2 . \tag{33-19}$$

If the voltage goes up, the current goes down, and vice versa. Real transformers have losses associated with resistance in their windings and heating of their iron cores, but good engineering holds these losses to a few per cent of the total power.

Transformers are widely used to provide voltages different from those of available sources. Most electronic circuits, for example, require a few tens of volts or less; step-down transformers bring the 120-V AC power line down to this level. Television tubes and computer monitors require tens of kV, calling for step-up transformers.

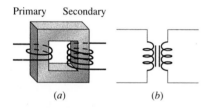

Primary   Secondary

(a)   (b)

FIGURE 33-22 (a) A transformer, consisting of two coils wound on an iron core. (b) Transformer circuit symbol.

Transformers work only with alternating current, since they make use of electromagnetic induction and therefore require *changing* current for their operation. With the sinusoidally varying currents in AC power systems, the rate of change of current is also a sinusoidal function (the derivative of sine is cosine), so both the primary and secondary currents are sinusoidally varying AC. One of the main reasons for the near-universal use of AC power is the ease with which it can be transformed from one voltage level to another. To use transformers with DC—from a battery, for example—requires that the current be interrupted periodically. The car ignition coil of Example 32-2 is, in fact, a step-up transformer that works only because the car's distributor regularly interrupts the current to the coil's primary.

APPLICATION	*Electric Power Distribution*

The power loss in a resistance R carrying current I is given by $I^2 R$. That means it's most efficient to transmit electric power at high voltage and low current. Lower voltages, on the other hand, are safer and easier to handle. How can we satisfy both these considerations in practical power systems? With transformers!

Power-plant generators operate at about 20 kV. Transformers at the power plant then step this up to several hundred kilovolts for long-distance transmission. At a city or town the voltage is dropped to several kilovolts for distribution within the municipality. Transformers reduce the voltage further for use in individual homes and businesses. The typical household voltage levels of 120 V and 240 V represent a compromise between the desire to minimize shock hazards—best met with low voltages—and the need to keep currents low. Low current allows the use of thinner wiring and also minimizes the danger of fire—but requires higher voltage to deliver a given power. Individual electrical devices within a building use transformers to meet their particular voltage requirements. Increasingly, small electrical devices such as modems, answering machines, portable stereos, and the like use external transformers that plug right into the wall; the power cord to the device then carries only low-voltage power. Figure 33-23 outlines the voltage transformations in power transmission.

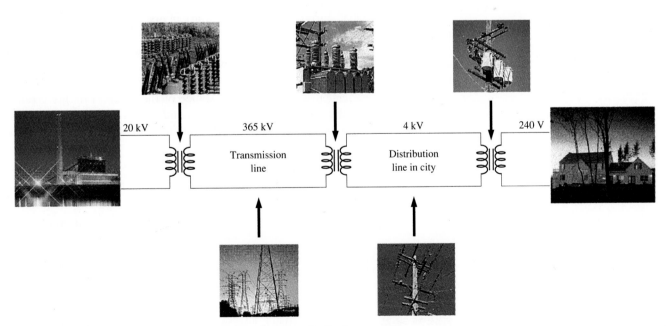

FIGURE 33-23 Transformers are used throughout the power distribution network.

FIGURE 33-24 Circuit symbol for a diode, with preferred direction of current indicated.

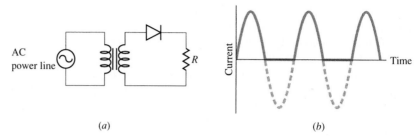

(a)   (b)

FIGURE 33-25 (a) A simple DC power supply consists of a transformer and diode, which supply current to the load resistance. (b) The diode passes current in only one direction, cutting off the negative half of each cycle (dashed gray) and giving the load current shown in blue.

DC Power Supplies

Devices such as light bulbs and electric heaters work equally well on AC or DC. But others, especially electronic circuits, require DC power. How do we get DC from the AC power line?

In Chapter 27's discussion of semiconductors, we showed how a junction between *P*-type and *N*-type semiconductors passes current in one direction but not the other. A **diode** is a *PN* junction designed specifically to be such a "one-way valve" for electric current. An ideal diode acts like a short circuit to current flowing in the preferred direction and like an open circuit in the opposite direction (Fig. 33-24).

Figure 33-25a shows a diode and resistor connected to the secondary of a transformer. The resistor represents the load—that is, whatever circuit we wish to supply with DC power. The transformer brings the 120-V AC power line to a level appropriate to the load. The diode passes current in only one direction, resulting in the load current shown in Fig. 33-25b.

Although the load current in Fig. 33-25 flows in one direction, it still varies drastically with time. If the load were a stereo amplifier, for example, its speakers would emit a loud hum. So we smooth, or **filter**, the output of the diode. The simplest filter is a capacitor, as shown in Fig. 33-26a. As the voltage on the left side of the diode rises, the capacitor voltage rises rapidly because of the short time constant associated with the low resistance of the diode in its preferred direction. But then the AC voltage begins to fall, and the diode "turns off." The capacitor cannot discharge from right to left through the diode but only through

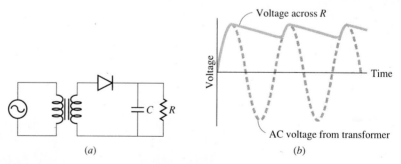

(a)   (b)

FIGURE 33-26 (a) Adding a capacitor reduces variations in the load voltage and therefore in the load current. This circuit is a complete DC power supply. (b) Load voltage as a function of time.

the load resistance. If the time constant RC is long enough, the capacitor voltage will drop only slightly before the AC voltage again rises and sends a new surge of current through the diode to bring the capacitor to its maximum charge (Fig. 33-26b). By making the capacitance large enough—so large that the time constant is much longer than the period of the AC power—we can make load current and voltage arbitrarily smooth. Large capacitors are expensive, so in practice additional filters—often using transistors or integrated circuits—are added to the simple capacitive filter in critical applications. High-quality power supplies for audio equipment or electronic instrumentation achieve so-called ripple factors—the ratio of the fluctuation amplitude to the DC level—of 10^{-5} or better. More complicated diode circuits can also be used to produce signals requiring less filtering (see Problem 80).

CHAPTER SYNOPSIS

Summary

1. **Alternating current** varies with time. A sinusoidal AC signal is characterized by its peak amplitude, frequency, and phase constant; for example:

$$I = I_p \sin(\omega t + \phi).$$

The root-mean-square (rms) amplitude of a sinusoidal AC signal is the peak value divided by $\sqrt{2}$; here $I_{rms} = I_p/\sqrt{2}$.

2. In a resistor, the ratio of voltage to current is always constant, so

$$I_p = \frac{V_p}{R},$$

and the current and voltage are in phase.

3. In a capacitor the ratio of peak voltage and current is determined by the **capacitive reactance**:

$$I_p = \frac{V_p}{X_C}, \quad \text{where} \quad X_C = \frac{1}{\omega C}.$$

The current in the capacitor **leads** the voltage by 90°.

4. In an inductor the ratio of peak voltage and current is determined by the **inductive reactance**:

$$I_p = \frac{V_p}{X_L}, \quad \text{where} \quad X_L = \omega L.$$

The current in the inductor **lags** the voltage by 90°.

5. **Phasors** are vector-like arrows showing the amplitude and phase of AC signals, and are useful in analyzing AC circuits.

6. In an undriven LC circuit, energy oscillates between electric and magnetic forms at the **resonant frequency** $\omega_0 = 1/\sqrt{LC}$. The amplitude of the oscillation decays exponentially as energy is dissipated in the circuit resistance.

7. In a series RLC circuit, the effects of inductance and capacitance exactly cancel at the resonant frequency. At this frequency the circuit exhibits the minimum **impedance**,

and therefore passes the maximum current. At resonance the current and voltage are in phase. At lower frequencies the capacitor dominates and current leads voltage, while at higher frequencies the inductor dominates and voltage leads current. The impedance of a series RLC circuit is

$$Z = \sqrt{R^2 + (X_L - X_C)^2},$$

while the phase difference between current and voltage is given by

$$\tan \phi = \frac{X_L - X_C}{R}.$$

8. The power dissipated in an AC circuit depends on the relative effects of resistance and reactance. In a purely reactive circuit, current and voltage are 90° out of phase, and no power is dissipated. In a purely resistive circuit, the average power dissipation is $I_{rms}V_{rms}$. When both resistance and reactance are present, the power dissipation depends on the **power factor**, $\cos\phi$, where ϕ is the phase difference between current and voltage. In general, the time-average power consumed in an AC circuit is

$$\langle P \rangle = I_{rms} V_{rms} \cos\phi.$$

9. A **transformer** uses electromagnetic induction to transfer electric power between two circuits. The ratio of the peak or rms voltages in the transformer's two windings is the same as the ratio of the numbers of turns in the windings:

$$V_2 = \frac{N_2}{N_1} V_1,$$

while the power VI is the same in each winding of an ideal transformer.

10. DC **power supplies** use **diodes** to change alternating to direct power. Capacitors then smooth out the remaining time variation to produce the steady voltages and currents needed to power electronic equipment.

Terms You Should Understand

(Pairs are closely related terms whose distinction is important; number in parentheses is chapter section where term first appears.)

AC, DC (introduction)
peak, rms amplitudes (33-1)
frequency, angular frequency (33-1)
capacitive reactance, inductive reactance (33-2)
phasor (33-2)
resonant frequency (33-4)
impedance (33-4)
power factor (33-5)
transformer (33-6)
diode (33-6)

Symbols You Should Recognize

I_p, V_p; I_{rms}, V_{rms} (33-1) f, ω (33-1)
ϕ (33-1) X_C, X_L (33-2)
Z (33-4)

Problems You Should Be Able to Solve

calculating current and voltage in AC circuits involving individual resistors, capacitors, and inductors (33-2)
analyzing oscillating *LC* circuits (33-3)
analyzing driven *RLC* circuits (33-4)
calculating power in AC circuits (33-5)
designing simple power supplies using transformers, diodes, and capacitive filters (33-6)

Limitations to Keep in Mind

This chapter considers only sinusoidally varying AC signals. More complex time variations must first be analyzed as sums of sinusoidal terms, using techniques mentioned in Chapter 16.
Care must be taken in adding AC signals with different phases. Phasor diagrams provide a convenient way of doing this.

QUESTIONS

1. Two AC signals have the same amplitude but different frequencies. Are their rms amplitudes the same?
2. Does it make sense to talk about the phase difference between two AC signals of different frequencies? Sketch a diagram to confirm your answer.
3. What is meant by the statement "a capacitor is a DC open circuit"?
4. How can current keep flowing in an AC circuit containing a capacitor? After all, a capacitor contains a gap between two conductors, and no charge can cross this gap.
5. Why does it make sense that inductive reactance increases with frequency?
6. The same AC voltage appears across a capacitor and a resistor, and the same rms current flows in each. Is the power dissipation the same in each?
7. When a particular inductor and capacitor are connected across the same AC voltage, the current in the inductor is larger than in the capacitor. Will this be true at all frequencies?
8. An inductor and capacitor are connected in series across an AC generator, and the rms voltage across the inductor is found to be larger than that across the capacitor. Is the generator frequency above or below resonance?
9. When the capacitor voltage in an undriven *LC* circuit reaches zero, why don't the oscillations stop?
10. Why is the quantity ωL not called the resistance of an inductor?
11. Why is Equation 33-5 not a full description of the relation between voltage and current in a capacitor?
12. If you double both the capacitance and inductance in an *LC* circuit, what effect does this have on the resonant frequency?

13. In a series *RLC* circuit, the applied voltage lags the current. Is the frequency above or below resonance?
14. In a series *RLC* circuit, the applied voltage leads the current. Is the peak voltage greater across the capacitor or the inductor?
15. What does it mean to say that the capacitor in an *RLC* circuit dominates at low frequencies?
16. The voltage across two circuit elements in series is zero. Is it possible that the voltages across the individual elements are nevertheless not zero? Give an example.
17. If you measure the rms voltages across the resistor, capacitor, and inductor in a series *RLC* circuit, will they add to the rms value of the generator voltage? Reconcile your answer with the loop law. (See also Problem 47.)
18. In a fluorescent light fixture an inductor, called the ballast, is used to limit current to the lamp. Why is an inductor preferable to a resistor?
19. What is the power factor in a circuit containing only a resistor? Does this power factor change with frequency?
20. To save electrical energy, should you strive for a large or small power factor?
21. When an AC motor runs with no significant mechanical load, its power factor is very nearly zero. What must happen when the motor begins doing mechanical work?
22. A step-up transformer increases voltage, or energy per unit charge. How is this possible without violating conservation of energy?
23. A battery charger runs off the 120-V AC power line. It supplies up to 30 A to recharge a 12-V car battery, yet it can be plugged into a 15-A circuit without blowing the circuit breaker. How is this possible?

PROBLEMS

ActivPhysics can help with these problems:
Activities 14.2, 14.3

Section 33-1 Alternating Current

1. Much of Europe uses AC power at 230 V rms and 50 Hz. Express this AC voltage in the form of Equation 33-3, taking $\phi = 0$.

2. An rms voltmeter connected across the filament of a TV picture tube reads 6.3 V. What is the peak voltage across the filament?

3. An oscilloscope displays a sinusoidal signal whose peak-to-peak voltage (see Fig. 33-1) is 28 V. What is the rms voltage?

4. An industrial electric motor runs at 208 V rms and 400 Hz. What are (a) the peak voltage and (b) the angular frequency?

5. An AC current is given by $I = 495 \sin(9.43t)$, with I in milliamperes and t in milliseconds. Find (a) the rms current and (b) the frequency in Hz.

6. What are the phase constants for each of the signals shown in Fig. 33-27?

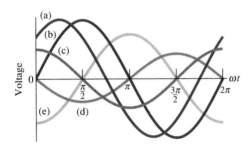

FIGURE 33-27 Problem 6.

7. The rms amplitude is defined as the square root of the average of the square of the signal. For a periodic function the time average is the integral over one period, divided by the period. For a sinusoidal voltage given by $V = V_p \sin \omega t$, show explicitly that $V_{rms} = V_p/\sqrt{2}$.

8. How are the rms and peak voltages related for the square wave shown in Fig. 33-28? See Problem 7.

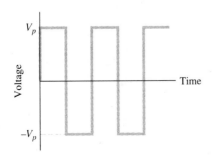

FIGURE 33-28 A square wave (Problem 8).

9. How are the rms and peak voltages related for the triangle wave in Fig. 33-29? See Problem 7.

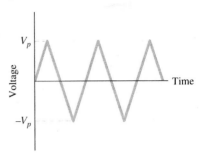

FIGURE 33-29 A triangle wave (Problem 9).

10. A 10-V rms AC signal with frequency 1.0 kHz is 90° ahead of another signal of the same frequency but with peak voltage 7.1 V. On the same graph, plot voltage versus time for both these signals. Choose scales appropriate to display one full cycle.

11. The most general expression for a sinusoidal AC current may be written either $I = I_1 \sin \omega t + I_2 \cos \omega t$ or $I = I_p \sin(\omega t + \phi)$. Find relations between I_1, I_2, I_p, and ϕ that make these expressions equivalent. (See Appendix A for trig identities.)

Section 33-2 Circuit Elements in AC Circuits

12. Show that the unit of both capacitive and inductive reactance is the ohm.

13. What is the rms current in a 1.0-μF capacitor connected across the 120-V rms, 60-Hz AC line?

14. A 470-Ω resistor, 10-μF capacitor, and 750-mH inductor are each connected across 6.3-V rms, 60-Hz AC power sources. Find the rms current in each.

15. Find the reactance of a 3.3-μF capacitor at (a) 60 Hz, (b) 1.0 kHz, and (c) 20 kHz.

16. A 15-μF capacitor carries an rms current of 1.4 A. What is the minimum safe voltage rating for the capacitor if the frequency is (a) 60 Hz or (b) 1.0 kHz?

17. A capacitor and a 1.8-kΩ resistor pass the same current when each is separately connected across a 60-Hz power line. What is the capacitance?

18. (a) A 2.2-H inductor is connected across the 120-V rms, 60-Hz power line. What is the rms inductor current? (b) Repeat if the same inductor is connected across the 230-V rms, 50-Hz power line commonly used in Europe.

19. A 50-mH inductor is connected across a 10-V rms AC generator, and an rms current of 2.0 mA flows. What is the generator frequency?

20. A 2.0-μF capacitor has a capacitive reactance of 1.0 kΩ. (a) What is the frequency of the applied voltage? (b) What inductance would give the same value for inductive reactance at this frequency? (c) How would the two reactances compare if the frequency were doubled?

21. A 1.2-μF capacitor is connected across a generator whose output is given by $V = V_p \sin 2\pi ft$, where $V_p = 22$ V, $f = 60$ Hz, and t is in seconds. (a) What is the peak current? (b) What are the magnitudes of the voltage and (c) the current at $t = 6.5$ ms?

22. A voltage $V = V_p \sin \omega t$ is applied across a capacitor. What is the minimum frequency for which the current will be zero at time $t = 20$ μs?

23. What is the maximum charge on the plates of a 16-μF capacitor connected across the 120-V rms, 60-Hz AC power line?

24. At 10 kHz an inductor has 10 times the reactance of a capacitor. At what frequency will their reactances be equal?

25. A 0.75-H inductor is in series with a fluorescent lamp, and the series combination is across the 120-V rms, 60-Hz power line. If the rms inductor voltage is 90 V, what is the rms lamp current?

26. A 2.2-nF capacitor and a capacitor of unknown capacitance are connected in parallel across a 10-V rms sine-wave generator. At 1.0 kHz, the generator supplies a total current of 3.4 mA rms. The generator frequency is then decreased until the rms current has dropped to 1.2 mA. Find (a) the unknown capacitance and (b) the lower frequency.

Section 33-3 *LC* Circuits

27. Find the resonant frequency of an *LC* circuit consisting of a 0.22-μF capacitor and a 1.7-mH inductor.

28. An *LC* circuit with $C = 18$ mF undergoes *LC* oscillations with period 2.4 s. What is the inductance?

29. You have a 2.0-mH inductor and wish to make an *LC* circuit whose resonant frequency spans the AM radio band (550 kHz to 1600 kHz). What range of capacitance should your variable capacitor cover?

30. The FM radio band covers the frequency range from 88 MHz to 108 MHz. If the variable capacitor in an FM receiver ranges from 10.9 pF to 16.4 pF, what inductor should be used to make an *LC* circuit whose resonant frequency spans the FM band?

31. You want to use an *LC* circuit in a timing application. The circuit is to start with the capacitor fully charged, and the voltage should drop to zero in 15 s. You have available a 25-H inductor. What capacitance should you use?

32. An *LC* circuit includes a 20-μF capacitor and has a period of 5.0 ms. The peak current is 25 mA. Find (a) the inductance and (b) the peak voltage.

33. An *LC* circuit includes a 0.025-μF capacitor and a 340-μH inductor. (a) If the peak voltage on the capacitor is 190 V, what is the peak current in the inductor? (b) How long after the voltage peak does the current peak occur?

34. If the capacitor in the preceding problem is rated at 600 V, what is the maximum inductor current that will keep the capacitor within its rating?

35. At the instant when the electric and magnetic energies are equal in the *LC* circuit of Problem 33, the current is 540 mA. (a) What is the instantaneous voltage? Find (b) the peak voltage, (c) the peak current, and (d) the total energy.

36. In an *LC* circuit, what fraction of a cycle passes before the energy in the capacitor falls to one-fourth of its peak value?

37. One-eighth of a cycle after the capacitor in an *LC* circuit is fully charged, what are each of the following as fractions of their peak values: (a) capacitor charge, (b) energy in the capacitor, (c) inductor current, (d) energy in the inductor?

38. Show from conservation of energy that the peak voltage and current in an *LC* circuit are related by $I_p = V_p \sqrt{\dfrac{C}{L}}$.

39. The 2000-μF capacitor in Fig. 33-30 is initially charged to 200 V. (a) Describe how you would manipulate switches A and B to transfer all the energy from the 2000-μF capacitor to the 500-μF capacitor. Include the times you would throw the switches. (b) What will be the voltage across the 500-μF capacitor once you've finished?

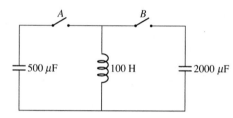

FIGURE 33-30 Problem 39.

40. A damped *LC* circuit consists of a 0.15-μF capacitor and a 20-mH inductor with resistance 1.6 Ω. How many cycles will the circuit oscillate before the peak voltage on the capacitor drops to half its initial value?

41. A damped *RLC* circuit includes a 5.0-Ω resistor and a 100-mH inductor. If half the initial energy is lost after 15 cycles, what is the capacitance?

Section 33-4 Driven *RLC* Circuits and Resonance

42. A series *RLC* circuit has $R = 75$ Ω, $L = 20$ mH, and a resonant frequency of 4.0 kHz. (a) What is the capacitance? (b) What is the impedance of the circuit at resonance? (c) What is the impedance at 3.0 kHz?

43. If the speaker system of Example 33-4 is driven by a 10-V peak, 1.0-kHz sine wave, what will be the peak voltage across the capacitor?

44. An *RLC* circuit includes a 1.5-H inductor and a 250-μF capacitor rated at 400 V. The circuit is connected across a sine-wave generator whose peak voltage is 32 V. What minimum resistance must the circuit have to ensure that the capacitor voltage does not exceed its rated value when the generator is at the resonant frequency?

45. TV channel 2 occupies the frequency range from 54 MHz to 60 MHz. A series *RLC* tuning circuit in a TV receiver includes an 18-pF capacitor and resonates in the middle of the channel 2 band. (a) What is the inductance? (b) To let the whole signal in, the resonance curve must be broad enough that the current throughout the band be no less than 70% of the current at the resonant frequency. What constraint does this place on the circuit resistance?

46. An *RLC* circuit includes a 10-Ω resistor, 1.5-μF capacitor, and 50-mH inductor. The capacitor is rated at 1200 V. The circuit is driven by an AC source whose peak voltage is 100 V. (a) What would be the peak capacitor voltage at resonance? (b) Make a graph of the peak capacitor voltage as a function of frequency, and from it determine the frequency range that should be avoided for the capacitor to stay within its voltage rating.

47. A 2.0-H inductor and a 3.5-μF capacitor are connected in series with a 50-Ω resistor, and the combination is connected to an AC generator supplying 24 V peak at 60 Hz. (a) At the instant the generator voltage is at its peak, what is the instantaneous voltage across each circuit element? Show explicitly that these sum to the generator voltage. (b) If rms voltmeters are connected across each of the three components, what will they read? Do their readings sum to the rms generator voltage? Does this contradict the loop law?

48. Show that the impedance of an *RLC* circuit driven at frequency ω_d can be written

$$Z = \sqrt{R^2 + \omega_d^2 L^2 (1 - \omega_0^2/\omega_d^2)^2},$$

where ω_0 is the resonant frequency.

49. Figure 33-31 shows the phasor diagram for an *RLC* circuit. (a) Is the driving frequency above or below resonance? (b) Complete the diagram by adding the applied voltage phasor, and from your diagram determine the phase difference between applied voltage and current.

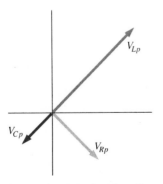

FIGURE 33-31 Problem 49.

50. An AC voltage of fixed amplitude is applied across a series *RLC* circuit. The component values are such that the cur-

rent at half the resonant frequency is half the current at resonance. (a) Show that the current at twice the resonant frequency is also half that at resonance. (b) Sketch phasor diagrams for both off-resonance cases.

51. For the circuit of Problem 46, find the phase relation between applied voltage and current at frequencies of (a) 550 Hz and (b) 700 Hz.

52. For the circuit of Problem 46, find two frequencies at which the voltage and current will be 60° out of phase. Which leads in each case?

Section 33-5 Power in AC Circuits

53. An electric drill draws 4.6 A rms at 120 V rms. If the current lags the voltage by 25°, what is the drill's power consumption?

54. A series *RLC* circuit has resistance 100 Ω and impedance 300 Ω. (a) What is the power factor? (b) If the rms current is 200 mA, what is the power dissipation?

55. A series *RLC* circuit has power factor 0.80 and impedance 100 Ω at 60 Hz. (a) What is the circuit resistance? (b) If the inductance is 0.10 H, what is the resonant frequency?

56. An *RLC* circuit with $R = 10\ \Omega$, $C = 2.0\ \mu$F, and $L = 500$ mH is connected to an AC generator supplying 80 V rms. (a) Find the power factor when the generator frequency is half the resonant frequency. Find the power dissipation (b) at half the resonant frequency and (c) at the resonant frequency.

57. A power plant produces 60-Hz power at 365 kV rms and 200 A rms. The plant is connected to a small city by a transmission line with total resistance 100 Ω. What fraction of the power is lost in transmission if the city's power factor is (a) 1.0 or (b) 0.60? (c) Is it more economical for the power company if the load has a large power factor or a small one? Explain.

Section 33-6 Transformers and Power Supplies

58. A rural power line carries 2.3 A rms at 4000 V. A step-down transformer reduces this to 235 V rms to supply a house. Find (a) the turns ratio of the transformer and (b) the current in the 235-V line to the house.

59. A transformer steps up the 120-V rms AC power line voltage to 23 kV rms for a TV picture tube. If the rms current in the primary is 1.0 A, and the transformer is 95% efficient, what is the secondary current?

60. A car battery charger runs off the 120-V rms AC power line, and supplies 10 A DC at 14 V. (a) If the charger is 80% efficient in converting the line power to the DC power it supplies to the battery, how much current does it draw from the AC line? (b) If electricity costs 9.5¢/kWh, how much does it cost to run the charger for 10 hours? Assume the power factor is 1.

61. The transformer in the power supply of Fig. 33-26a has an output voltage of 6.3 V rms at 60 Hz, and the capacitance is 1200 μF. (a) With an infinite load resistance, what would be the output voltage of the power supply? (b) What is the minimum load resistance for which the output would not drop more than 1% from this value? Assume that the discharge time in Fig. 33-26b is essentially a full cycle.

62. A power supply like that in Fig. 33-26a is supposed to deliver 22 V DC at a maximum current of 150 mA. The transformer's peak output voltage is appropriate to charge the capacitor to a full 22 V, and the primary is supplied with 60 Hz AC. What value of capacitance will ensure that the output voltage stays within 3% of the rated 22 V?

Paired Problems

(Both problems in a pair involve the same principles and techniques. If you can get the first problem, you should be able to solve the second one.)

63. A sine-wave generator delivers a signal whose peak voltage is independent of frequency. Two identical capacitors are connected in parallel across the generator, and the generator supplies a peak current I_p at frequency f_1. The capacitors are then connected in series across the generator. To what frequency should the generator be tuned to bring the current back to I_p?

64. A 1.0-μF capacitor and a 2.0-μF capacitor are connected in parallel across a sine-wave generator, and the generator supplies a total rms current of 25 mA at 1.0 kHz. Assuming the generator voltage is independent of frequency, at what frequency will it supply the same current when the capacitors are in series?

65. The peak current in an oscillating LC circuit is 850 mA. If $L = 1.2$ mH and $C = 5.0$ μF, what is the peak voltage?

66. An LC circuit with $C = 470$ pF is oscillating at 7.3 MHz. If the peak voltage is 95 V, what is the peak current?

67. An RLC circuit includes a 3.3-μF capacitor and a 27-mH inductor. The capacitor is charged to 35 V, and the circuit begins oscillating. Ten full cycles later the capacitor voltage peaks at 28 V. What is the resistance?

68. An RLC circuit with $R = 1.2$ Ω and $C = 10$ μF loses 2% of its initial energy in one oscillation cycle. What is its inductance?

69. A series RLC circuit with $R = 5.5$ Ω, $L = 180$ mH, and $C = 0.12$ μF is connected across a sine-wave generator. If the inductor can handle a maximum current of 1.5 A, what is the maximum safe value for the generator's peak output voltage when it is tuned to resonance?

70. A series RLC circuit with $R = 1.3$ Ω, $L = 27$ mH, and $C = 0.33$ μF is connected across a sine-wave generator. If the capacitor's peak voltage rating is 600 V, what is the maximum safe value for the generator's peak output voltage when it is tuned to resonance?

Supplementary Problems

71. Two capacitors are connected in parallel across a 10-V rms, 10-kHz sine-wave generator, and the generator supplies a total rms current of 30 mA. When the capacitors are rewired in series, the rms generator current drops to 5.5 mA. Find the values of the two capacitances.

72. An LC circuit starts at $t = 0$ with its 2000-μF capacitor at its peak voltage of 14 V. At $t = 35$ ms the voltage has dropped to 8.5 V. (a) What will be the peak current? (b) When will the peak current occur?

73. An undriven RLC circuit with inductance L and resistance R starts oscillating with total energy U_0. After N cycles the energy is U_1. Find an expression for the capacitance, assuming the circuit is not heavily damped.

74. Figure 33-32 shows a **low-pass filter**. When an alternating voltage is applied at the V_{in} terminals, the output voltage V_{out} depends on frequency. (a) Show that $V_{out} = V_{in}/\sqrt{1 + (RC\omega)^2}$, where the voltages are either peak or rms values (there is also a phase difference). (b) At what frequency is the output voltage down from the input voltage by a factor of $1/\sqrt{2}$? (This is called the *half-power point* since the power—proportional to V^2—is down by a factor of $\frac{1}{2}$.) *Hint:* You can repeat the phasor analysis of Section 33-4, but without the inductor. Or you can start from Equation 33-14, with X_L set to zero.

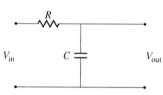

FIGURE 33-32 Problem 74.

75. You wish to make a "black box" with two input connections and two output connections, as shown in Fig. 33-33. When you put a 12-V rms, 60-Hz sine wave across the input, a 6.0-V, 60-Hz signal should appear at the output, with the output voltage leading the input voltage by 45°. Design a circuit that could be used in the "black box."

FIGURE 33-33 Problem 75.

76. A series RLC circuit with $R = 47$ Ω, $L = 250$ mH, and $C = 4.0$ μF is connected across a sine-wave generator whose peak output voltage is independent of frequency.

Find the frequency range over which the peak current will exceed half its value at resonance. *Hint:* You can solve this problem graphically or, with appropriate algebraic manipulations, using quadratic equations.

77. A sine-wave generator with peak output voltage of 20 V is applied across a series *RLC* circuit. At the resonant frequency of 2.0 kHz the peak current is 50 mA, while at 1.0 kHz it is 15 mA. Find R, L, and C.

78. Use phasor analysis to show that the parallel *RLC* circuit of Fig. 33-34 has impedance $Z = \left[\dfrac{1}{R^2} + \left(\dfrac{1}{X_L} - \dfrac{1}{X_C} \right)^2 \right]^{-1/2}$.

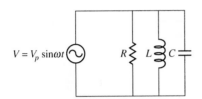

FIGURE 33-34 Problem 78.

79. A 2.5-H inductor is connected across a 1500-μF capacitor. A 5.0-kg mass is connected to a spring. What should be the spring constant if the mechanical and electrical systems have the same resonant frequency?

80. Figure 33-35 shows a diode circuit called a *full-wave bridge,* whose output requires less filtering than the single-diode circuit of Fig. 33-25. (a) Sketch a graph of the resis-

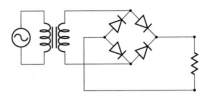

FIGURE 33-35 A full-wave diode bridge (Problem 80).

tor current as a function of time, covering two full cycles of the AC generator, and (b) explain why less filtering is needed.

81. For *RLC* circuits in which the resistance is not too large, the Q factor may be defined as the ratio of the resonant frequency to the difference between the two frequencies where the power dissipated in the circuit is half that dissipated at resonance. Show, using suitable approximations, that this definition leads to the expression $Q = \omega_0 L / R$, with ω_0 the resonant frequency.

82. Consider a series circuit containing an AC generator, a resistor, and a capacitor. Construct a phasor diagram, and derive expressions for the circuit impedance and the phase angle between the applied voltage and the current. Show that the current always leads the voltage.

83. Consider a series circuit containing an AC generator, a resistor, and an inductor. Construct a phasor diagram, and derive expressions for the circuit impedance and the phase angle between the applied voltage and the current. Show that the voltage always leads the current.

34 Maxwell's Equations and Electromagnetic Waves

Electromagnetic waves include light and the radio waves essential to modern communications. This antenna communicates with orbiting satellites.

At this point we have introduced the four fundamental laws of electromagnetism—Gauss's law for electricity, Gauss's law for magnetism, Ampère's law, and Faraday's law—that govern the behavior of electric and magnetic fields throughout the universe. We have seen how these laws describe the electric and magnetic interactions that make matter act as it does and have explored many practical devices that exploit the laws of electromagnetism. Here we extend the fundamental laws to their most general form and show how they predict the existence of electromagnetic waves. Those waves include the light, radio, TV, microwaves, X-rays, ultraviolet, and infrared with which we see, communicate, cook our food, diagnose our diseases, learn about the universe beyond Earth, and perform a myriad of other tasks from the mundane to the profound.

Electromagnetic waves are certainly among the most important manifestations of electromagnetism. After showing how electromagnetic waves arise from fundamental principles, we'll take a brief look at some of their properties. The next three chapters, on optics, then examine in detail the behavior of the electromagnetic waves we call visible light.

34-1 THE FOUR LAWS OF ELECTROMAGNETISM

Table 34-1 summarizes the four laws as we introduced them in earlier chapters. As you look at these four laws together, you can't help noticing some strong similarities. On the left-hand sides of the equations, the two laws of Gauss are identical but for the interchanging of **E** and **B**. Similarly, the laws of Ampère and Faraday have left-hand sides that differ only in the interchange of **E** and **B**.

On the right-hand sides, things are more different. Gauss's law for electricity involves the charge enclosed by the surface of integration, while Gauss's law for magnetism has zero on the right-hand side. Actually, though, these laws are similar. Since we have no experimental evidence for the existence of isolated magnetic charge, the enclosed magnetic charge on the right-hand side of Gauss's law for magnetism is zero. If and when magnetic monopoles are discovered, then the right-hand side of Gauss's law for magnetism would be nonzero for any surface enclosing net magnetic charge.

The right-hand sides of Ampère's and Faraday's laws are distinctly different. In Ampère's law we find the current—the flow of electric charge—as a source of magnetic field. We can understand the absence of a similar term in Faraday's law because we have never observed a flow of magnetic monopoles. If we had such a flow, then we would expect this magnetic current to produce an electric field.

Two of the differences among the laws of electromagnetism would be resolved if we knew for sure that magnetic monopoles exist. That current theories of elementary particles suggest the existence of monopoles is a tantalizing hint that there may be a fuller symmetry between electric and magnetic phenomena. The search for symmetry, based not on logic or experimental evidence but on an intuitive sense that nature should be simple, has motivated some of the most important discoveries in physics. We'll see next how symmetry considerations help lead us, finally, to the complete set of fundamental laws of electromagnetism.

TABLE 34-1 *Four Laws of Electromagnetism (still incomplete)*

LAW	MATHEMATICAL STATEMENT	WHAT IT SAYS
Gauss for **E**	$\oint \mathbf{E} \cdot d\mathbf{A} = \dfrac{q}{\varepsilon_0}$	How charges produce electric field; field lines begin and end on charges
Gauss for **B**	$\oint \mathbf{B} \cdot d\mathbf{A} = 0$	No magnetic charge; magnetic field lines do not begin or end
Faraday	$\oint \mathbf{E} \cdot d\boldsymbol{\ell} = -\dfrac{d\phi_B}{dt}$	Changing magnetic flux produces electric field
Ampère (steady currents only)	$\oint \mathbf{B} \cdot d\boldsymbol{\ell} = \mu_0 I$	Electric current produces magnetic field

34-2 AMBIGUITY IN AMPÈRE'S LAW

There remains one difference between the equations of electricity and magnetism that would not be resolved by the discovery of magnetic monopoles. On the right-hand side of Faraday's law we find the term $d\phi_B/dt$ that describes changing magnetic flux as a source of electric field. We find no comparable term in Ampère's law. Are we missing something? Is it possible that a changing electric flux produces a magnetic field? So far, we've given no experimental evidence for such a conjecture. It's suggested only by our sense that the near symmetry between electricity and magnetism is not a coincidence. If a changing electric flux did produce a magnetic field, just as a changing magnetic flux produces an electric field, then we would expect a term $d\phi_E/dt$ on the right-hand side of Ampère's law.

When we first stated Ampère's law in Chapter 30, we emphasized that it applied only to *steady* currents. Why that restriction? Figure 34-1 shows a situation in which current is *not* steady, namely the *RC* circuit we discussed in Chapter 28. Initially current flows in this circuit to carry charge onto the plates of the capacitor. But the current gradually decreases to zero as the capacitor becomes fully charged. While it's flowing, the current should produce a magnetic field. Let's try to use Ampère's law to calculate that field.

Ampère's law says that the line integral of the magnetic field around any closed loop is proportional to the encircled current:

$$\oint \mathbf{B} \cdot d\boldsymbol{\ell} = \mu_0 I .$$

By the encircled current, we mean the current through *any open surface* bounded by the loop. Figure 34-2 shows four such surfaces. The same current flows through surfaces 1, 2, and 4, because each of them is pierced by a current-carrying wire. But no current pierces surface 3, because the right end of that surface lies in the insulating gap between the capacitor plates. Charge flows onto the plates of the capacitor, but it doesn't flow through that gap. So for surfaces 1, 2, and 4, the right-hand side of Ampère's law is $\mu_0 I$, but for surface 3 it's zero. Thus Ampère's law is ambiguous in this case of a changing current.

This ambiguity does not arise with steady currents. In an *RC* circuit the steady-state current is everywhere zero, and thus the right-hand side of Ampère's law is zero for *any* surface. It's only when currents are changing with time that there may be situations like that of Fig. 34-2 where Ampère's law becomes ambiguous. That's why the form of Ampère's law we have used until now is strictly valid only for steady currents.

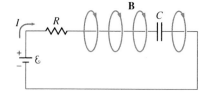

FIGURE 34-1 A charging *RC* circuit, showing some magnetic field lines surrounding the current-carrying wire.

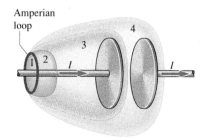

FIGURE 34-2 Ampère's law relates the line integral around an amperian loop to the current through *any open surface* bounded by that loop. Figure 34-2 shows four such surfaces, all bounded by the same circular loop. Surface 1 is the flat, circular disk bounded by the loop. The others are all like soap bubbles in the process of being blown after dipping the loop into a soap solution; they're open at the left end, so if current does pass through a surface, it does so at the right end only. Current in the wires passes through surfaces 1, 2, and 4, but not 3, so Ampère's law is ambiguous.

Can we salvage Ampère's law, extending it to cover unsteady currents without affecting its validity in the steady case? Symmetry between Ampère's and Faraday's laws has already suggested that a changing electric flux might produce a magnetic field. Between the plates of a charging capacitor there is an electric field whose magnitude is increasing (Fig. 34-3). That means there is a changing electric flux through surface 3 of Fig. 34-2.

It was the Scottish physicist James Clerk Maxwell who, about 1860, suggested that a changing electric flux should give rise to a magnetic field. Since that time many experiments, including direct measurement of the magnetic field inside a charging capacitor, have confirmed Maxwell's remarkable insight. Maxwell quantified his idea by introducing a new term into Ampère's law:

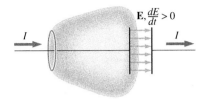

FIGURE 34-3 There is a changing electric field in the charging capacitor and, therefore, a changing electric flux through surface 3 of Fig. 34-2.

$$\oint \mathbf{B} \cdot d\boldsymbol{\ell} = \mu_0 I + \mu_0 \varepsilon_0 \frac{d\phi_E}{dt}. \qquad (34\text{-}1)$$

Now there's no ambiguity. The integral is taken around any loop, I is the current through *any* surface bounded by the loop, and ϕ_E is the electric flux through that surface. With our charging capacitor, Equation 34-1 gives the same magnetic field no matter which surface we choose. For surfaces 1, 2, and 4 of Fig. 34-2, the current I makes all the contribution to the right-hand side of the equation. For surface 3, through which no current flows, the right-hand side of Equation 34-1 comes entirely from the changing electric flux. You can readily verify that the term $\varepsilon_0 d\phi_E/dt$ has the units of current, and that, for the charging capacitor, this term is numerically equal to the current I (see Problem 3).

Although changing electric flux is not the same thing as electric current, it has the same effect as a current in producing a magnetic field. For this reason Maxwell called the term $\varepsilon_0 d\phi_E/dt$ the **displacement current**. The word "displacement" has historical roots that don't provide much physical insight. But the word "current" is meaningful in that the effect of displacement current is indistinguishable from that of real current in producing magnetic fields. Although we developed the idea of displacement current using the specific example of a charging capacitor, we emphasize that Ampère's law in its now complete form (Equation 34-1) is truly universal: *any* changing electric flux results in a magnetic field. That fact will prove crucial in establishing the existence of electromagnetic waves.

EXAMPLE 34-1	*Displacement Current Produces Magnetic Field*

A parallel-plate capacitor with circular plates a distance d apart is charged through long, straight wires as shown in Fig. 34-4. The potential difference between the plates is increasing at the rate dV/dt. Find an expression for the magnetic field as a function of position between the plates.

Solution

With long, straight feed wires, the situation has cylindrical symmetry. The only magnetic field with this symmetry has

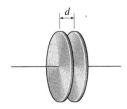

FIGURE 34-4 A circular capacitor (Example 34-1).

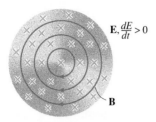

FIGURE 34-5 Electric and magnetic fields between the circular capacitor plates. The electric field strength is increasing, so the displacement current is in the same direction as the electric field. Pointing the right thumb in this direction then shows that the magnetic field circles clockwise.

circular field lines and a magnitude that depends only on the radial distance r from the symmetry axis, as shown in Fig. 34-5. A magnetic field line within the capacitor encircles no conduction current—no flow of charge—but it does encircle a changing electric field and therefore a displacement current. If the field line has radius r, the encircled electric flux is

$$\phi_E = \int \mathbf{E} \cdot d\mathbf{A} = \pi r^2 E = \pi r^2 \frac{V}{d},$$

where the uniformity of the field allows us to calculate the field as the ratio of potential difference to plate spacing and the flux as a simple product of field and area. Then the displacement current is

$$I_D = \varepsilon_0 \frac{d\phi_E}{dt} = \frac{\varepsilon_0 \pi r^2}{d} \frac{dV}{dt}.$$

With cylindrical symmetry, the line integral on the left-hand side of Ampère's law becomes

$$\oint \mathbf{B} \cdot d\boldsymbol{\ell} = 2\pi r B.$$

Equating this quantity to μ_0 times the encircled displacement current gives

$$2\pi r B = \frac{\mu_0 \varepsilon_0 \pi r^2}{d} \frac{dV}{dt},$$

so

$$B = \frac{\mu_0 \varepsilon_0 r}{2d} \frac{dV}{dt}.$$

This field, with its magnitude increasing linearly with r, should remind you of the magnetic field inside a cylindrical wire (see Example 30-4). Problem 4 extends this calculation to the field outside the capacitor.

We can find the direction of the induced magnetic field just as we did for the fields of ordinary conduction currents: Point your right thumb in the direction of the current and your right fingers curl in the direction of the magnetic field. But which way does the displacement current go? In this example the electric field strength is increasing, so $d\phi_E/dt$ is positive, and the displacement current is in the direction of the electric field (see Fig. 34-5). If the electric field strength were decreasing, the displacement current would be opposite the field.

The induced magnetic field in a practical capacitor is minuscule, as the following exercise illustrates. We'll soon see, however, that the significance of displacement-current-induced magnetic fields is vastly greater than in this simple example.

EXERCISE In 1984 D. F. Bartlett and T. R. Corle of the University of Colorado first measured the magnetic field inside a charging capacitor using a sensitive magnetometer called a superconducting quantum interference detector (SQUID). They used a capacitor with circular plates spaced 1.22 cm, connected across a 340-V peak sine-wave generator operating at 1.25 kHz. What was the peak magnetic field strength 3.0 cm from the capacitor axis?

Answer: 3.65×10^{-11} T, less than one millionth of Earth's magnetic field

Some problems similar to Example 34-1: 4–6

34-3 MAXWELL'S EQUATIONS

It was Maxwell's genius to recognize that Ampère's law should be modified to reflect the symmetry suggested by Faraday's law. The consequences of Maxwell's discovery go far beyond anything he could have imagined. To honor Maxwell, the four complete laws of electromagnetism are given the collective name **Maxwell's equations**. This full and complete set of equations, first published in 1864, governs the behavior of electric and magnetic fields everywhere. Table 34-2 summarizes Maxwell's equations.

These four simple, compact statements are all it takes to describe classical electromagnetic phenomena. Everything electric or magnetic that we have considered and will consider—from polar molecules to electric current; resistors, capacitors, inductors, and transistors; solar flares and cell membranes; electric generators and thunderstorms; computers and TV sets; the northern lights and fusion reactors—all these can be described using Maxwell's

TABLE 34-2 *Maxwell's Equations*

LAW	MATHEMATICAL STATEMENT	WHAT IT SAYS	EQUATION NUMBER
Gauss for $\mathbf{E}$	$\oint \mathbf{E} \cdot d\mathbf{A} = \dfrac{q}{\varepsilon_0}$	How charges produce electric field; field lines begin and end on charges	(34-2)
Gauss for $\mathbf{B}$	$\oint \mathbf{B} \cdot d\mathbf{A} = 0$	No magnetic charge; magnetic field lines do not begin or end	(34-3)
Faraday	$\oint \mathbf{E} \cdot d\boldsymbol{\ell} = -\dfrac{d\phi_B}{dt}$	Changing magnetic flux produces electric field	(34-4)
Ampère	$\oint \mathbf{B} \cdot d\boldsymbol{\ell} = \mu_0 I + \mu_0\varepsilon_0 \dfrac{d\phi_E}{dt}$	Electric current and changing electric flux produce magnetic field	(34-5)

equations. And despite this wealth of phenomena, we have yet to discuss a most important manifestation of electromagnetism, namely electromagnetic waves. We've put off waves until now because they, unlike electromagnetic phenomena we've already introduced, depend crucially on Maxwell's extension of Ampère's law. It's easiest to understand electromagnetic waves when they propagate through empty space, so before beginning our study of waves we'll first simplify Maxwell's equations for the case of a vacuum.

Maxwell's Equations in Vacuum

Consider Maxwell's equations in a region free of any matter—in vacuum. We've learned enough about electromagnetism to anticipate that the fields themselves will still be able to interact, change, and carry energy even in the absence of matter. To express Maxwell's equations in vacuum, we simply remove all reference to matter—that is, to electric charge:

$$\oint \mathbf{E} \cdot d\mathbf{A} = 0 \qquad (\text{Gauss, } \mathbf{E}) \qquad\qquad (34\text{-}6)$$

$$\oint \mathbf{B} \cdot d\mathbf{A} = 0 \qquad (\text{Gauss, } \mathbf{B}) \qquad\qquad (34\text{-}7)$$

$$\oint \mathbf{E} \cdot d\boldsymbol{\ell} = -\frac{d\phi_B}{dt} \qquad (\text{Faraday}) \qquad\qquad (34\text{-}8)$$

$$\oint \mathbf{B} \cdot d\boldsymbol{\ell} = \mu_0\varepsilon_0 \frac{d\phi_E}{dt}. \qquad (\text{Ampère}) \qquad\qquad (34\text{-}9)$$

In vacuum the symmetry is complete, with electric and magnetic fields appearing in the equations on an equal footing. With charge and current absent in a vacuum, the only source of either field is a change in the other field—as shown by the time derivatives on the right-hand sides of Faraday's and Ampère's laws.

34-4 ELECTROMAGNETIC WAVES

Faraday's law shows that a changing magnetic field induces an electric field. Ampère's law shows that a changing electric field induces a magnetic field. Together, the two laws suggest the possibility of **electromagnetic waves**, in which each type of field continually induces the other, resulting in an electromagnetic disturbance that propagates through space as a wave. We'll now confirm this qualitative suggestion with a rigorous demonstration, directly from Maxwell's equations, that electromagnetic waves are indeed possible. In the process we'll discover the properties of electromagnetic waves and will come to a deep understanding of the nature of light.

A Plane Electromagnetic Wave

Here we describe the simplest type of electromagnetic wave—a plane wave in vacuum. Recall from Chapter 16 that a plane wave is one whose properties don't vary in directions perpendicular to the wave propagation, so its wavefronts are planes (see Fig. 16-18). A plane wave is an approximation to the more realistic case of a spherical wave expanding from a localized source, but it's a good approximation at distances from the wave source that are large compared with the wavelength. Light waves reaching Earth from the Sun, for example, or radio waves miles from the transmitter, are essentially plane waves.

In vacuum, it turns out that the electric and magnetic fields of an electromagnetic wave are perpendicular to each other. They're both also perpendicular to the direction of wave propagation—making the electromagnetic wave a transverse wave, as defined in Chapter 16. To be concrete, we'll take the x direction to be the direction of propagation, the y direction that of the electric field, and the z direction that of the magnetic field (Fig. 34-6). We won't prove that this configuration of three mutually perpendicular directions is the only

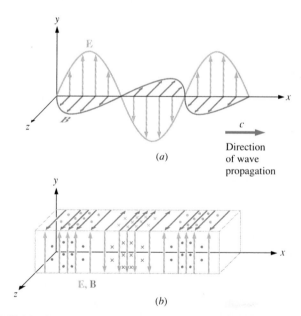

FIGURE 34-6 Fields of a plane electromagnetic wave, shown at a fixed instant of time. (a) Field vectors for points on the x axis show the sinusoidal variation in the fields. The electric and magnetic fields are perpendicular but in phase; they're also perpendicular to the propagation direction. (b) A partial representation of the field lines, which actually extend forever in both directions. Here the lines are pictured only in a finite rectangular slab. Lines on the facing surfaces of the slab are shown as arrows; lines going through the slab appear as dots or crosses depending on whether they're emerging from or going into the slab. Spacing of the field lines reflects the sinusoidal variation shown in (a).

one possible for an electromagnetic wave (although in vacuum it is; see Problem 11). What we will do, though, is prove that this configuration satisfies Maxwell's equations—thus showing that such electromagnetic waves are indeed possible. Before we can do that, we need a mathematical description of our plane electromagnetic wave.

In Chapter 16 we found that a sinusoidal wave propagating in the x direction is represented by a function of the form $A \sin(kx - \omega t)$, where A is the wave amplitude, k the wave number, and ω the angular frequency. For the mechanical waves of Chapters 16 and 17, the function $A \sin(kx - \omega t)$ described some physical quantity such as the height of a water wave or pressure variation in a sound wave. In an electromagnetic wave, the corresponding physical quantities are the electric and magnetic fields—which are vector quantities. It turns out that these two wave fields, although perpendicular, are in phase—meaning that their peaks and troughs coincide, as shown in Fig. 34-6. Having chosen the y direction for the electric field and the z direction for the magnetic field, we can then write the fields of our plane electromagnetic wave as

$$\mathbf{E}(x, t) = E_p \sin(kx - \omega t)\hat{\mathbf{j}} \qquad (34\text{-}10)$$

and

$$\mathbf{B}(x, t) = B_p \sin(kx - \omega t)\hat{\mathbf{k}}, \qquad (34\text{-}11)$$

where the peak amplitudes E_p and B_p are constants and where $\hat{\mathbf{j}}$ and $\hat{\mathbf{k}}$ are unit vectors in the y and z directions. Figure 34-6a is a "snapshot" of some field vectors of this wave at points on the x axis, shown at a fixed instant of time. That $\mathbf{E}$ and $\mathbf{B}$ are perpendicular is obvious from the figure, as is the fact that they're perpendicular to the propagation direction, in this case the x direction. You can also see the sinusoidal variation, as the field vectors get alternately longer, then shorter, then reverse direction, and so on. And you can see that $\mathbf{E}$ and $\mathbf{B}$ are in phase: they peak at the same points, and are zero at the same points. We emphasize that Fig. 34-6a shows field *vectors* for points on the x axis only; the fields extend forever throughout space, and because this is a plane wave, a picture of field vectors along any line parallel to the x axis would look just the same.

We can also draw field *lines* for our wave, in contrast to the field vectors of Fig. 34-6a. We can't draw complete field lines, because they extend forever in both directions. So in Fig. 34-6b we've shown the field lines only in a rectangular slab; that's enough to give a picture of what the fields look like everywhere. You should convince yourself that Figs. 34-6a and 34-6b show exactly the same thing, namely a plane electromagnetic wave described by Equations 34-10 and 34-11. In one case we use field *vectors,* whose lengths are proportional to the field magnitudes, and in the other we use field *lines,* which extend forever and whose spacing indicates the field magnitudes.

We'll now use Maxwell's equations to show that the electric and magnetic fields pictured in Fig. 34-6 and described by Equations 34-10 and 34-11 really do satisfy Maxwell's equations. We've chosen a sinusoidal waveform for our wave fields because of its mathematical simplicity. But the superposition principle holds for electric and magnetic fields, and we know from Section 16-6 that by superposition we can represent *any* waveform in terms of sinusoidal waveforms. So our proof that electromagnetic waves can exist actually holds for any wave shape (see Problem 74 here and Problem 54 in Chapter 16). That means we can use electromagnetic waves to communicate the complex waveforms of music, TV images, or computer data encoded as pulses of light.

We have four Maxwell equations to satisfy: the two Gauss's laws, and the laws of Faraday and Ampère.

Gauss's Laws

In vacuum, Gauss's laws for the electric and magnetic fields both have zero on the right-hand side (Equations 34-6 and 34-7), reflecting the absence of charge. That means, as we've seen many times before, that the field lines can't begin or end; they either form closed loops or extend to infinity. Our electromagnetic wave is a plane wave, meaning that no wave property varies in directions perpendicular to the wave propagation. Therefore the field lines shown partially in Fig. 34-6b must extend, straight, forever in both directions. So they don't begin or end, and thus the two Gauss laws are satisfied.

Faraday's Law

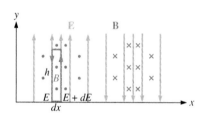

FIGURE 34-7 Cross section of Fig. 34-6 in the *x-y* plane. Also shown is a rectangular loop for evaluating the line integral in Faraday's law.

To see that Faraday's law is satisfied, consider an observer looking directly toward the *x-y* plane in Fig. 34-6. Such an observer would see electric field lines going up and down and magnetic field lines coming straight in and out, as shown in Fig. 34-7. Consider the small rectangular loop of height *h* and infinitesimal width *dx* shown in the figure. Evaluating the line integral of the electric field **E** around this loop, we get no contribution from the short ends because they are at right angles to the field. Going around counterclockwise, we get a contribution $-Eh$ as we go down the left side against the field direction. Then we get a positive contribution going up the right side. Because of the variation in field strength with position, the field strength on the right side of the loop is different from that on the left. Let the change in field be dE, so the field on the right side of the loop is $E + dE$, giving a contribution of $(E + dE)h$ to the line integral. Then the line integral of **E** around the loop is

$$\oint \mathbf{E} \cdot d\boldsymbol{\ell} = -Eh + (E + dE)h = h\, dE.$$

Physically, this nonzero line integral implies an induced electric field. Induced by what? By a changing magnetic flux through the loop. The electric field of the wave arises because of the changing magnetic field of the wave. The area of the loop is $h\, dx$, and the magnetic field **B** is at right angles to this area, so the magnetic flux through the loop is just

$$\phi_B = Bh\, dx.$$

The rate of change of flux through the loop is then

$$\frac{d\phi_B}{dt} = h\, dx\, \frac{dB}{dt}.$$

Faraday's law relates the line integral of the electric field to the rate of change of flux:

$$\oint \mathbf{E} \cdot d\boldsymbol{\ell} = -\frac{d\phi_B}{dt},$$

or, using our expressions for the line integral and the rate of change of flux,

$$h\, dE = -h\, dx\, \frac{dB}{dt}.$$

Dividing through by $h\,dx$, we have

$$\frac{dE}{dx} = -\frac{dB}{dt}. \qquad (34\text{-}12a)$$

In deriving this equation, we considered changes in E with position at a fixed instant of time, as pictured in Fig. 34-7, so our derivative dE/dx means the rate of change of E with position while time is held fixed. Similarly, in evaluating the derivative of magnetic flux, we were concerned only with the time rate of change at the fixed position of our loop. Both our derivatives represent rates of change with respect to one variable while the other variable is held fixed, and are therefore partial derivatives (see Math Toolbox on p. 400 if you're not familiar with partial derivatives). Equation 34-12a should then be written more properly:

$$\frac{\partial E}{\partial x} = -\frac{\partial B}{\partial t}. \qquad (34\text{-}12b)$$

Equation 34-12b—which is just Faraday's law applied to our electromagnetic wave—tells us that the rate at which the electric field changes with *position* is related to the rate at which the magnetic field changes with *time*.

Ampère's Law

Now imagine an observer looking down on Fig. 34-6 from above. This observer sees the magnetic field lines lying in the x-z plane, and electric field lines emerging perpendicular to the x-z plane as shown in Fig. 34-8. We can apply Ampère's law (Equation 34-9) to the infinitesimal rectangle shown, just as we applied Faraday's law to a similar rectangle in the x-y plane. Going counterclockwise around the rectangle, we get no contribution to the line integral of the magnetic field on the short sides, since they lie perpendicular to the field. Going down the left side, we get a contribution Bh to the line integral. Going up the right side, against the field, we get a negative contribution $-(B + dB)h$, where dB is the change in B from one side of the rectangle to the other. So the line integral in Ampère's law is

$$\oint \mathbf{B} \cdot d\boldsymbol{\ell} = Bh - (B + dB)h = -h\,dB.$$

The electric flux through the rectangle is simply $Eh\,dx$, so the rate of change of electric flux is

$$\frac{d\phi_E}{dt} = h\,dx\,\frac{dE}{dt}.$$

Ampère's law relates the line integral of the magnetic field to this time derivative of the electric flux, giving

$$-h\,dB = \varepsilon_0\mu_0 h\,dx\,\frac{dE}{dt}.$$

Dividing through by $h\,dx$ and noting again that we are really dealing with partial derivatives, we have

$$\frac{\partial B}{\partial x} = -\varepsilon_0\mu_0\frac{\partial E}{\partial t}. \qquad (34\text{-}13)$$

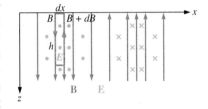

FIGURE 34-8 Cross section of Fig. 34-6 in the x-z plane, showing a rectangular loop for evaluating the line integral in Ampère's law.

Equations 34-12 and 34-13—derived from Faraday's and Ampère's laws—express fully the requirements that Maxwell's universal laws of electromagnetism pose on the field structure of Fig. 34-6. The two equations are remarkable in that each describes an induced field that arises from the changing of the other field. That other field, in turn, arises from the changing of the first field. Thus we have a self-perpetuating electromagnetic structure, whose fields exist and change without the need for charged matter. If Equations 34-10 and 34-11, which describe the fields in Fig. 34-6, can be made consistent with Equations 34-12 and 34-13, then we will have demonstrated that our electromagnetic wave does indeed satisfy Maxwell's equations and is thus a possible configuration of electric and magnetic fields.

Faraday, Ampère, and the Wave Fields

To see that Equation 34-12 is satisfied, we differentiate the electric field of Equation 34-10 with respect to x, and the magnetic field of Equation 34-11 with respect to t:

$$\frac{\partial E}{\partial x} = \frac{\partial}{\partial x}[E_p \sin(kx - \omega t)] = kE_p \cos(kx - \omega t)$$

and
$$\frac{\partial B}{\partial t} = \frac{\partial}{\partial t}[B_p \sin(kx - \omega t)] = -\omega B_p \cos(kx - \omega t).$$

Putting these expressions in for the derivatives in Equation 34-12 gives

$$kE_p \cos(kx - \omega t) = -[-\omega B_p \cos(kx - \omega t)].$$

The cosine term cancels from this equation, showing that the equation holds if

$$kE_p = \omega B_p. \tag{34-14}$$

To see that Equation 34-13 is also satisfied, we differentiate the magnetic field of Equation 34-11 with respect to x and the electric field of Equation 34-10 with respect to t:

$$\frac{\partial B}{\partial x} = kB_p \cos(kx - \omega t)$$

and
$$\frac{\partial E}{\partial t} = -\omega E_p \cos(kx - \omega t).$$

Using these expressions in Equation 34-13 then gives

$$kB_p \cos(kx - \omega t) = -\varepsilon_0 \mu_0 [-\omega E_p \cos(kx - \omega t)].$$

Again, the cosine term cancels, showing that this equation is satisfied if

$$kB_p = \varepsilon_0 \mu_0 \omega E_p. \tag{34-15}$$

Our analysis has shown that electromagnetic waves whose form is given by Fig. 34-6 and Equations 34-10 and 34-11 can exist, provided that the amplitudes E_p and B_p, and the frequency ω and wave number k, are related by Equations 34-14 and 34-15. Physically, the existence of these waves is possible because a change in either kind of field—electric or magnetic—induces the other kind of field, giving rise to a self-perpetuating electromagnetic field structure. Maxwell's theory thus leads to the prediction of an entirely new phenomenon—the electromagnetic wave. We will now explore some properties of these waves.

34-5 THE SPEED OF ELECTROMAGNETIC WAVES

In Chapter 16 we found that the speed of a sinusoidal wave is given by the ratio of the angular frequency and wave number:

$$\text{wave speed} = \frac{\omega}{k}.$$

To determine the speed of our electromagnetic wave, we solve Equation 34-14 for E_p:

$$E_p = \frac{\omega B_p}{k},$$

and use this expression in Equation 34-15:

$$kB_p = \varepsilon_0 \mu_0 \omega E_p = \frac{\varepsilon_0 \mu_0 \omega^2 B_p}{k}.$$

Solving for the wave speed ω/k then gives

$$\text{wave speed} = \frac{\omega}{k} = \frac{1}{\sqrt{\varepsilon_0 \mu_0}}. \tag{34-16}$$

This remarkably simple result shows that the speed of an electromagnetic wave in vacuum depends only on the electric and magnetic constants ε_0 and μ_0. All electromagnetic waves in vacuum, regardless of frequency or amplitude, share this speed. Although we derived this result for sinusoidal waves, the superposition principle ensures that it holds for any wave shape.

We can easily calculate the speed given in Equation 34-16:

$$\frac{1}{\sqrt{\varepsilon_0 \mu_0}} = \frac{1}{[(8.85 \times 10^{-12} \text{ F/m})(4\pi \times 10^{-7} \text{ H/m})]^{1/2}} = 3.00 \times 10^8 \text{ m/s}.$$

But this is precisely the speed of light!

As early as 1600, Galileo had tried to measure the speed of light by uncovering lanterns on different mountaintops. He was able to conclude only that "If not instantaneous, it is extraordinarily rapid." The first evidence for a finite speed of light came in the 1670s from observations by the Danish astronomer Ole Römer. He noted that eclipses of Jupiter's moons occurred at different times than predicted as Jupiter's distance from Earth changed. Römer interpreted the changes as being due to the different times for light traveling at a finite speed from Jupiter to Earth. Römer's data implied a speed of 2.3×10^8 m/s, about three quarters of the actual value. In 1728, James Bradley used changes in the apparent positions of stars resulting from Earth's orbital motion to calculate a value of 2.95×10^8 m/s for the speed of light—in error by less than 2%. As we saw in Chapter 1, the exact value $c = 2.99792458 \times 10^8$ m/s was adopted in

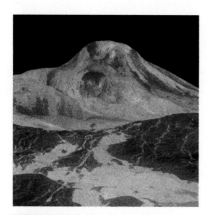

FIGURE 34-9 This image of Venus was made using data that include surface altitude determined by very accurate measurements of the travel time for radar signals reflected from Venus' surface. Radar, like all electromagnetic waves, travels at the speed of light.

1983 to define the meter. So we no longer measure the speed of light; instead, that speed provides an accurate way to measure distances (Fig. 34-9).

Do other properties of light besides its speed fit our picture of electromagnetic waves? In 1678—some 200 years before Maxwell—the Dutch physicist Christian Huygens had suggested that light is a wave. In 1801, Thomas Young experimented with a 2-slit system to show that light undergoes interference, giving conclusive evidence for the wave nature of light (see Fig. 16-25). But neither experiment nor theory could say what kind of wave light might be. Then, in the 1860s, came Maxwell. Using a theory developed from laboratory experiments involving electricity and magnetism, with no reference whatever to optics or light, Maxwell showed how the interplay of electric and magnetic fields could result in electromagnetic waves. The speed of those waves—calculated from the quantities ε_0 and μ_0 that were determined in laboratory experiments having nothing to do with light—was precisely the known speed of light. Maxwell was led inescapably to the conclusion that light is an electromagnetic wave.

Maxwell's identification of light as an electromagnetic phenomenon is a classic example of the unification of knowledge toward which science is ever striving. With one simple calculation, Maxwell brought the entire science of optics under the umbrella of electromagnetism. Maxwell's work stands as a crowning intellectual triumph, an achievement whose implications are still expanding our view of the universe.

34-6 PROPERTIES OF ELECTROMAGNETIC WAVES

Our demonstration that electromagnetic waves satisfy Maxwell's equations places definite constraints on the properties of those waves. The wave frequency ω and wave number k are not both arbitrary, but must be related through

$$\frac{\omega}{k} = c, \tag{34-17a}$$

where $c = 1/\sqrt{\varepsilon_0 \mu_0}$ is the speed of light. In Chapter 16 we related the angular frequency ω and wave number k to the more familiar frequency f and wavelength λ through the equations $\omega = 2\pi f$ and $k = 2\pi/\lambda$. Therefore we can also write Equation 34-17a in the form

$$f\lambda = c. \tag{34-17b}$$

Furthermore, Equation 34-14 shows that

$$E = \frac{\omega}{k}B = cB. \tag{34-18}$$

Thus, the field magnitudes in the wave are not independent but are in the ratio of the speed of light. Also, Fig. 34-6 and Equations 34-10 and 34-11 have the electric and magnetic fields perpendicular to each other and to the direction of wave propagation, with the electric and magnetic fields in phase. It is in fact the case that only waves with this form—**E** and **B** in phase and with **E**, **B**, and the propagation direction all perpendicular—can satisfy Maxwell's equations in vacuum (see Problem 11).

EXAMPLE 34-2	*Laser Light*

A laser beam with wavelength 633 nm is propagating in the $+z$ direction. Its electric field is parallel to the x axis and has amplitude 6.0 kV/m. Find the wave frequency, and the direction and amplitude of the magnetic field.

Solution

Equation 34-17b relates the wavelength and frequency to the speed of light. Solving for f gives

$$f = \frac{c}{\lambda} = \frac{3.00\times10^8 \text{ m/s}}{633\times10^{-9} \text{ m}} = 4.74\times10^{14} \text{ Hz}.$$

If we imagine reorienting the wave of Fig. 34-6 so it propagates along the z direction, then rotate it about the z direction so the electric field is parallel to the x axis, we find that the magnetic field is parallel to the y axis. The magnetic field amplitude follows from Equation 34-18:

$$B_p = \frac{E_p}{c} = \frac{6.0\times10^3 \text{ V/m}}{3.00\times10^8 \text{ m/s}} = 2.0\times10^{-5} \text{ T}.$$

EXERCISE An electromagnetic wave is propagating in the $-y$ direction, with its magnetic field parallel to the x axis. The magnetic field amplitude is 8.0 μT. Write an expression for the wave's electric field vector at the point where the magnetic field points in the $+x$ direction and is at its peak value.

Answer: $\mathbf{E} = -2.4\hat{\mathbf{k}}$ kV/m

Some problems similar to Example 34-2: 24–27

Got It!

Light and radio waves are both electromagnetic waves; of the two, light has a much higher frequency. Does that mean light waves travel faster than radio waves? Regardless of your answer, are any other properties of these waves different?

34-7 THE ELECTROMAGNETIC SPECTRUM

Although an electromagnetic wave's frequency and wavelength must be related by Equation 34-17b, one or the other of these quantities is completely arbitrary. That means we can have electromagnetic waves of any frequency, or, equivalently, any wavelength. Direct measurement shows that visible light occupies a wavelength range from about 400 nm to 700 nm, corresponding to frequencies from 7.5×10^{14} Hz to 4.3×10^{14} Hz. The different wavelengths or frequencies correspond to different colors, with red at the long-wavelength, low-frequency end of the visible region and blue at the short-wavelength, high-frequency end (see the enlargement in Fig. 34-10).

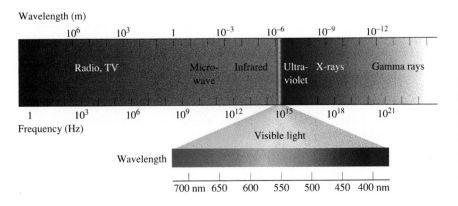

FIGURE 34-10 The electromagnetic spectrum ranges from radio waves to gamma rays, with visible light occupying only a narrow range of wavelengths and frequencies. Note the logarithmic scale, in which intervals between numbered tick marks correspond to factors-of-1000 changes in frequency and wavelength.

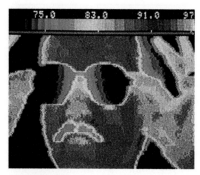

FIGURE 34-11 Subtle variations in body temperature are color coded in this infrared image of a human face. Regions at different temperatures emit different frequencies of infrared; these are coded into the image's visible colors according to the temperature scale at the top.

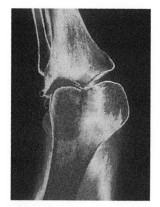

FIGURE 34-12 X rays are high-frequency, short wavelength electromagnetic waves that readily penetrate soft tissues but not bone. Here, an X-ray image reveals rheumatoid arthritis in a human knee joint.

Figure 34-10 shows the entire **electromagnetic spectrum**, including frequencies and wavelengths that differ by many orders of magnitude either way from those of visible light. The invisible electromagnetic waves beyond the narrow visible range were unknown in Maxwell's time. A brilliant confirmation of Maxwell's theory came in 1888, when the German physicist Heinrich Hertz succeeded in generating and detecting electromagnetic waves of much lower frequency than visible light. Hertz intended his work only to verify Maxwell's modification of Ampère's law, but the practical consequences have proven enormous. In 1896, the Italian scientist Guglielmo Marconi demonstrated that he could generate and detect the so-called Hertzian waves. In 1901, he transmitted electromagnetic waves across the Atlantic Ocean, creating a public sensation. From the pioneering work of Hertz and Marconi, spurred by the theoretical efforts of Maxwell, came the entire technology of radio, television, and microwaves that so dominates modern society. We now consider all electromagnetic waves in the frequency range from a few Hz to about 3×10^{11} Hz as radio waves, with ordinary AM radio at about 10^6 Hz, FM radio at 10^8 Hz, and microwaves used for radar, cooking, and satellite communications at 10^9 Hz and above.

Between radio waves and visible light lies the infrared frequency range. Electromagnetic waves in this region are emitted by warm objects, even when they are not hot enough to glow visibly. For this reason, infrared cameras are used to determine subtle body temperature differences in medical diagnosis, to examine buildings for heat loss, and to study the birth of stars in clouds of interstellar gas and dust (Fig. 34-11).

Beyond the visible region are the ultraviolet rays responsible for sunburn, then the highly penetrating X rays (Fig. 34-12), and finally the gamma rays whose primary terrestrial source is radioactive decay. All these phenomena, from radio to gamma rays, are fundamentally the same: They are all electromagnetic waves, differing only in frequency and wavelength. All travel with speed c, and all consist of electric and magnetic fields produced from each other through the induction processes described by Faraday's and Ampère's laws. Naming the different types of electromagnetic waves is just a matter of convenience; there are no gaps in the continuous range of allowed frequencies and wavelengths. Practical differences arise because waves of different wavelengths interact differently with matter; in particular, shorter wavelengths tend to be generated and absorbed most efficiently by smaller systems.

APPLICATION	*The New Astronomy*

Figure 34-10 shows that visible light occupies only a small part of the electromagnetic spectrum. For centuries our only information about the universe beyond Earth—except for an occasional meteorite—came from visible light. Processes like those occurring on the visible surface of our Sun and many other stars produce predominantly visible light. Optical astronomy, utilizing visible light, gave a good picture of the universe to the extent that it consists of objects not too different from the visible part of the Sun. The restriction to optical astronomy was in part imposed by Earth's atmosphere. Transparent to visible light, the atmosphere is largely opaque to other forms of electromagnetic radiation, although "windows" of relative transparency exist in parts of the radio and infrared bands. The

discovery by Bell Telephone Laboratories electrical engineer Karl Jansky in 1931 that radio waves from outer space can be detected on Earth led to the development of radio astronomy. For decades, radio astronomy has given a picture of the universe that complements the optical view, showing phenomena that are simply not detectable by optical means (Fig. 34-13).

The onset of the space age in the late 1950s finally opened the rest of the electromagnetic spectrum to astronomers. Before this time there were surprisingly few suggestions that anything interesting might be found beyond the visible range. But satellites carrying infrared, ultraviolet, X-ray, and gamma-ray detectors have literally revolutionized our view of the universe

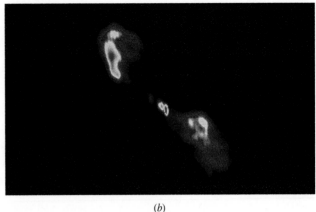

(a)

(b)

FIGURE 34-13 (a) Some of the 27 dish antennas that comprise the Very Large Array (VLA) radio telescope in New Mexico. Each dish is 25 m in diameter, and the array can be configured to occupy an area larger than metropolitan Washington, DC. (b) The galaxy Centaurus A, a powerful radio emitter, imaged with the VLA. The two lobes are jets of material ejected from the galaxy's central core. The VLA was tuned to a wavelength of 20 cm for this observation.

FIGURE 34-14 This false-color infrared image of the Andromeda galaxy was taken with the Infrared Astronomical Satellite. Yellow indicates regions of brightest infrared emission, corresponding to places where new stars are probably forming.

(Fig. 34-14). Exotic objects such as neutron stars and black holes are now objects of astronomical study. The opening of the entire electromagnetic spectrum has brought a new richness to astronomy, showing that our universe contains some of the most unusual objects that the laws of physics permit. Phenom-

ena that were once bizarre conjectures of theoreticians are now observed regularly. For example, astronomers are convinced that massive black holes—with the mass of a million Suns—lurk at the centers of galaxies, including our own. Closer to home, observations of the Sun with ultraviolet and X-ray instruments have brought new understandings of the star that sustains us. And by turning space-borne infrared detectors toward Earth, we have learned much about the structure and resources of our own planet (Fig. 34-15).

FIGURE 34-15 This satellite image documents destruction of the Brazilian rainforest by human activities. False colors enhance the distinction between healthy forest (dark green) and cleared areas (light green, pink).

34-8 POLARIZATION

The fields of an electromagnetic wave in vacuum (and in common materials such as air and glass) are perpendicular to the propagation direction, but within the plane perpendicular to the wave propagation the orientation of one field is still arbitrary. **Polarization** is a wave property that specifies the electric field

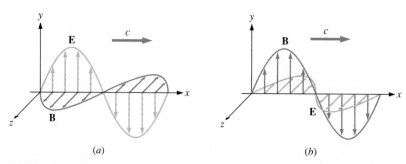

FIGURE 34-16 Field vectors for two electromagnetic waves. Both are propagating in the $+x$ direction, but have different polarizations. The polarization direction is that of the electric field, so the wave in (*a*) is vertically polarized (i.e., its electric field is in the *y* direction), while the wave in (*b*) is horizontally polarized (i.e., in the *z* direction). Unpolarized light would be a mix of such waves with their electric fields oriented at random in many different directions.

16.4
Polarizer

direction; since the two fields are perpendicular, polarization also determines the magnetic field direction (Fig. 34-16).

Electromagnetic waves used in radio, TV, and radar originate from antennas whose configuration gives the waves a definite polarization. The light waves produced by most lasers are also polarized. In contrast, visible light from hot sources such as the Sun or a light bulb is **unpolarized**, consisting of a mixture of electromagnetic waves with random field orientations.

Unpolarized light may be polarized either by reflection off surfaces or when it passes through substances whose molecular or crystal structure has a preferred direction called the **transmission axis**. Many crystals and synthetic materials such as the plastic Polaroid have this property. For example, sunlight reflecting off the hood of a car becomes partially polarized in the horizontal direction. Polaroid sunglasses, with their transmission axis vertical, block this reflected glare with only a modest reduction in overall light intensity.

A polarizing material passes unattenuated only that component of the wave's electric field that lies along its preferred direction. If θ is the angle between the field and the polarizer's preferred direction, then the field component in the preferred direction is $E\cos\theta$. As we will show shortly, the intensity S of an electromagnetic wave is proportional to the square of the field strength; as a result a wave of intensity S_0 incident on a polarizer emerges with intensity given by the so-called **Law of Malus**:

$$S = S_0\cos^2\theta. \qquad (34\text{-}19)$$

This equation shows that electromagnetic waves will be blocked completely if $\theta = 90°$, a situation that occurs when unpolarized light passes through one polarizer to give it a definite polarization, then through another oriented at 90° to the first (Fig. 34-17).

When unpolarized light passes through a polarizer its intensity is cut in half. You can see this from Equation 34-19 because the unpolarized light includes a mix of waves with random polarization angles θ. Averaging over all possible angles in Equation 34-19 amounts to taking the average of $\cos^2\theta$ over a full cycle. We've seen on several occasions that the average of the square of a sinusoidal function is $\frac{1}{2}$ (recall Fig. 16-16), so a polarizer does indeed cut the intensity of unpolarized light in half.

FIGURE 34-17 Two pairs of Polaroid sunglasses with their transmission axes at right angles. Where they overlap, no light can get through.

| EXAMPLE 34-3 | *Multiple Polarizers* |

Unpolarized light with intensity S_0 is incident on a "stack" of three polarizers. The first has its polarization axis vertical, the second is at 25° to the vertical, and the third is at 70° to the vertical (Fig. 34-18). What is the intensity of light emerging from this stack?

Solution

We've just seen that the first polarizer cuts the unpolarized intensity in half, giving $\frac{1}{2}S_0$ for the intensity incident on the second polarizer. Equation 34-19 shows that the second and third polarizers each reduce the intensity by a factor $\cos^2 \theta$, where θ is the angle between the incident polarization direction—established by one polarizer—and the next polarizer's axis. For the second polarizer this angle is 25°; for the third it is 70° − 25° = 45°. Thus light emerges from the stack with intensity

$$S = (\tfrac{1}{2})(\cos^2 25°)(\cos^2 45°)S_0 = 0.205 S_0 .$$

Interestingly, this is greater than the intensity we would get passing light through a vertical polarizer followed by a single polarizer at 70°. And, as the exercise below shows, it is much

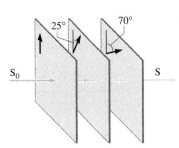

FIGURE 34-18 A stack of polarizers. Arrows on the sheets indicate directions of the polarization axes.

greater than what we would get by interchanging the second and third polarizers. Can you see why?

EXERCISE Rework Example 34-3 with the second and third polarizers interchanged.

Answer: $S = 0.029 S_0$

Some problems similar to Example 34-3: 35, 36, 72

Polarization can tell us much about sources of electromagnetic waves or about materials through which the waves travel. Many astrophysical processes produce polarized waves; measuring the polarization then gives clues to the mechanisms operating in distant objects. Polarization of light as it passes through materials helps geologists to understand the composition and formation of rocks (Fig. 34-19) and helps engineers to locate stresses in structures (Fig. 34-20).

FIGURE 34-19 Photomicrograph of a thin section of rock placed between crossed polarizers. Individual mineral crystals, here a few mm in size, rotate the light's electric field, altering the transmitted light intensity.

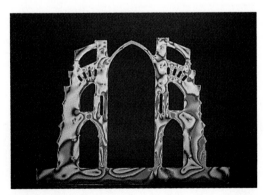

FIGURE 34-20 Plastic model of a Gothic cathedral, photographed between polarizing sheets. The resulting patterns reveal stresses, helping architects and engineers understand the response of the building to wind and weight loading—topics related to our study of static equilibrium in Chapter 14.

APPLICATION	*Liquid Crystal Displays and Electro-Optic Modulation*

They're everywhere, from watches, calculators, and gas pumps to laptop computers—the **liquid-crystal displays** (LCDs) that convert electrical signals into letters, numbers, pictures, and graphs that we can read. Fundamental to their operation is the polarization of light.

In Fig. 34-17 we saw that two polarizers oriented at right angles block all light from getting through the pair. But if we could rotate the light's polarization direction through 90° while it's between the polarizers, then light from the first polarizer would reach the second aligned with the latter's preferred direction, and so would pass through. That's just what happens in an LCD—but it happens selectively, under control of an electrical signal, allowing the transmission of light to be turned on or off.

In Chapter 23 we introduced liquid crystals as systems of long dipole-like molecules that align with an applied electric field. Figure 34-21 shows how this property is used to make a display. The liquid crystal is contained between two transparent striated plates that cause the molecules to align with their striations. The two plates' striations are mutually perpendicular, so the molecules' alignment gradually changes through the device. The electric field of a light wave interacts with the molecules, with the result that the polarization direction of the light rotates through 90° as it passes through the liquid crystal. The whole system is between crossed polarizers and so, because of the 90° rotation of the polarization, light incident on the system gets through (Fig. 34-21a).

Now suppose a voltage is applied between the plates confining the liquid crystal. This results in an electric field that aligns the molecules as shown in Fig. 34-21b. In this new orientation the liquid crystal no longer rotates the polarization of the light, so the situation is just like that of Fig. 34-17, and the light is blocked. There's one such system for each of the segments that make up the numbers and letters of a liquid crystal display, and each segment can be turned on or off to make the desired symbol

FIGURE 34-21 Polarization plays a central role in the operation of a liquid-crystal display.

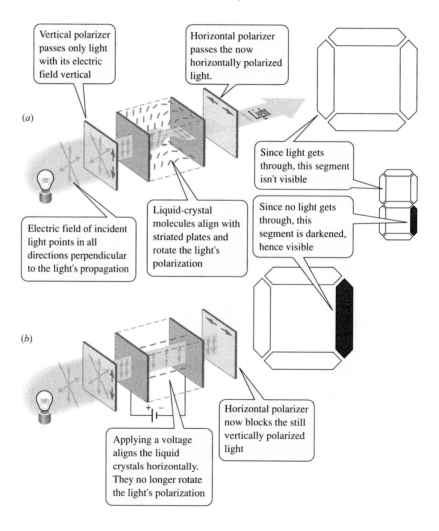

In Fig. 34-21 we show light incident from the back of the display and emerging from the front for viewing. In many LCDs the light at the back is replaced by a mirror that reflects ambient light. Then there's no power needed to provide light, and the LCD operates at minimal electrical power. Low power consumption is one of the key advantages of liquid-crystal displays.

Liquid crystals are rather slow in their response, so they aren't good for rapid switching of light. But some solid crystals have much the same property as the liquid-crystal system of Fig. 34-21, in that they selectively rotate the polarization of light depending on the presence or absence of an electric field (in this case, it takes a field to produce the rotation). This is known as the **electro-optic effect**.

Placing an electro-optic crystal between crossed polarizers makes an **electro-optic modulator** (EOM) that can switch light on timescales as short as 10^{-10} s. Such devices, used as electronic shutters to interrupt laser beams and thus produce very short pulses of light, have been used to make some of the most accurate measurements of the speed of light. Applying a varying voltage to the EOM causes the light transmission to vary continuously. Voice or music, for example, can be transmitted on a laser beam by applying the amplified signal from a microphone to an EOM. EOMs are used in a wide variety of scientific and commercial applications. An especially important use is the conversion of electrical signals to light pulses on the highest-speed fiber optic communications systems.

34-9 PRODUCING ELECTROMAGNETIC WAVES

We have shown that electromagnetic waves can exist, and have explored some of their properties. But how do these waves originate?

All that's necessary is to produce a changing electric or magnetic field. Once a changing field of either type exists, Faraday's and Ampère's laws ensure the production of the other type—and so on, to give a propagating electromagnetic wave. Ultimately, changing fields of either type occur when we alter the motion of electric charge. Therefore:

> ❙ *Accelerated* electric charge is the source of electromagnetic waves.

In a radio transmitter, the accelerated charges are electrons moving back and forth in an antenna, driven by an alternating voltage from an *LC* circuit (Fig. 34-22). In an X-ray tube, high-energy electrons decelerate rapidly as they

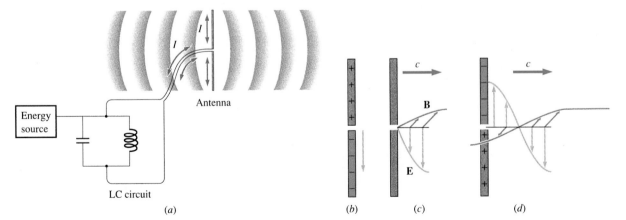

FIGURE 34-22 (*a*) Simplified diagram of a radio transmitter. Oscillations of an *LC* circuit drive alternating current (green arrows) in the antenna, while a power source replenishes energy carried away in electromagnetic waves. (*b*)–(*d*) A changing electric field arises from the changing charge distribution in the antenna. The changing electric field induces a changing magnetic field, and the field structure propagates away from the antenna at the speed of light. Frames (*b*) and (*d*) are half a wave period apart in time, at times when charge separation in the antenna is a maximum.

slam into a target; their deceleration is the source of the electromagnetic waves, now in the X-ray region of the spectrum. In the magnetron tube of a microwave oven, electrons circle in a magnetic field; their centripetal acceleration is the source of the microwaves that cook your food. And the altered movement of electrons in atoms—although described accurately only by quantum mechanics—is the source of most visible light. If the motion of the accelerated charges is periodic, then the wave frequency is that of the motion; more generally, systems are most efficient at producing (and receiving) electromagnetic waves whose wavelength is comparable to the size of the system. That's why TV antennas are on the order of 1 m in size, while nuclei—some 10^{-15} m in diameter—produce gamma rays.

Calculation of electromagnetic waves emitted by accelerated charges presents challenging but important problems for physicists and communications engineers. Figure 34-23a shows a "snapshot" of the electric field produced by a single point charge undergoing simple harmonic motion, while Fig. 34-23b shows the field of an oscillating dipole—a configuration approximated by many systems from antennas to atoms and molecules. Both figures show that the waves are strongest in the direction at right angles to the acceleration of the charge distribution and that there is no radiation in the direction of the acceleration. This accounts for, among other phenomena, the directionality of radio and TV antennas, which transmit and receive most effectively perpendicular to the long direction of the antenna.

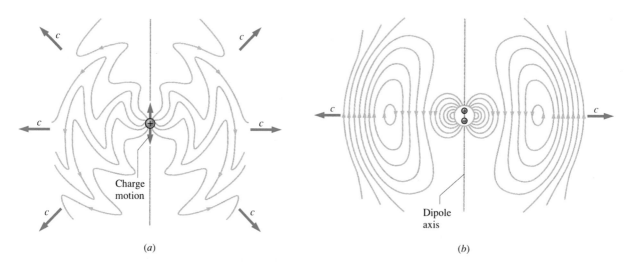

(a)

(b)

FIGURE 34-23 "Snapshots" showing the electric fields of oscillating charge distributions. (a) A single point charge executing simple harmonic motion in the horizontal plane. Note that the field close to the charge approximates the radial field of a stationary point charge, but that farther out the "kinks" in the field—resulting from the accelerated motion—are more prominent and become essentially perpendicular to the radial direction. These transverse kinks move outward at the speed of light, and constitute the wave fields. (b) The electric field of an oscillating dipole. Note that the field forms closed loops, detached from the dipole. These are the outward propagating wave fields. The larger field loops shown were formed when the oscillating dipole had the opposite orientation. Not shown in either figure are the equally important magnetic fields.

The fields shown in Fig. 34-23 seem to bear little resemblance to the plane-wave fields of Fig. 34-7 that we used to demonstrate the possibility of electromagnetic waves. We could produce true plane waves only with an infinite sheet of accelerated charge—an obvious impossibility. But far from the source, the curved field lines evident in Fig. 34-23b, for example, would appear straight, and the wave would begin to approximate a plane wave. So our plane-wave analysis is a valid approximation at great distances—typically many wavelengths—from a localized wave source. Closer to the source more complicated expressions for the wave fields apply, but these, too, satisfy Maxwell's equations.

34-10 ENERGY IN ELECTROMAGNETIC WAVES

We showed in previous chapters that electric and magnetic fields contain energy. Here we have considered electromagnetic waves, in which a combination of electric and magnetic fields propagates through space. As the wave moves, it must transport the energy contained in those fields.

We define **intensity**, S, as the rate at which an electromagnetic wave transports energy across a unit area. This is the same definition we used for wave intensity in Chapter 16, and the units are also the same: power per unit area, or W/m^2. We can calculate the intensity of a plane electromagnetic wave by considering a rectangular box of thickness dx and cross-sectional area A with its face perpendicular to the wave propagation (Fig. 34-24). Within this box are wave fields **E** and **B** whose energy densities are given by Equations 26-3 and 32-11:

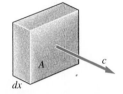

FIGURE 34-24 A box of length dx and cross-sectional area A at right angles to the propagation of an electromagnetic wave.

$$u_E = \tfrac{1}{2}\varepsilon_0 E^2$$

$$u_B = \frac{B^2}{2\mu_0}.$$

If dx is sufficiently small, the fields don't change much over the box, so the total energy in the box is just the sum of the electric and magnetic energy densities multiplied by the box volume $A\,dx$:

$$dU = (u_E + u_B)\,A\,dx = \frac{1}{2}\left(\varepsilon_0 E^2 + \frac{B^2}{\mu_0}\right)A\,dx.$$

This energy moves with speed c, so all the energy contained in the box length dx moves out of the box in a time $dt = dx/c$. The rate at which energy moves through the cross-sectional area A is then

$$\frac{dU}{dt} = \frac{1}{2}\left(\varepsilon_0 E^2 + \frac{B^2}{\mu_0}\right)\frac{A\,dx}{dx/c} = \frac{c}{2}\left(\varepsilon_0 E^2 + \frac{B^2}{\mu_0}\right)A.$$

So the intensity S, or rate of energy flow per unit area, is

$$S = \frac{c}{2}\left(\varepsilon_0 E^2 + \frac{B^2}{\mu_0}\right).$$

We can recast this equation in simpler form by noting that, for an electromagnetic wave, $E = cB$ and $B = E/c$. Using these expressions to replace one of

(a)

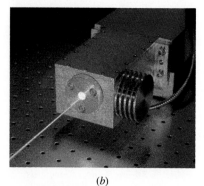

(b)

FIGURE 34-25 (a) The intensity of candle light is only a few W/m². (b) This laser produces a modest 3W of power, but because its beam diameter is less than 0.5 mm, its intensity is some 20 MW/m²—2000 times that of bright sunlight.

the E's in the term E^2 with B and similarly one of the B's in the term B^2 with E, we have

$$S = \frac{c}{2}\left(\varepsilon_0 c E B + \frac{EB}{\mu_0 c}\right) = \frac{1}{2\mu_0}(\varepsilon_0 \mu_0 c^2 + 1)\, EB.$$

But $c = 1/\sqrt{\varepsilon_0 \mu_0}$, so $\varepsilon_0 \mu_0 c^2 = 1$, giving

$$S = \frac{EB}{\mu_0}. \tag{34-20a}$$

Although we derived Equation 34-20a for an electromagnetic wave, it is in fact a special case of the more general result that nonparallel electric and magnetic fields are accompanied by a flow of electromagnetic energy. In general, the rate of energy flow per unit area is given by

$$\mathbf{S} = \frac{\mathbf{E} \times \mathbf{B}}{\mu_0}. \tag{34-20b}$$

Here a vector $\mathbf{S}$ is used to signify not only the magnitude of the energy flow, but also its direction. For an electromagnetic wave in vacuum, in which $\mathbf{E}$ and $\mathbf{B}$ must be at right angles, Equation 34-20b reduces to Equation 34-20a, with the direction of energy flow the same as the direction of wave travel. The vector intensity $\mathbf{S}$ is called the **Poynting vector** after the English physicist J. H. Poynting, who suggested it in 1884. Poynting's name is especially fortuitous, for the Poynting vector points in the direction of energy flow. Problem 76 explores an important application of the Poynting vector to fields that do not constitute an electromagnetic wave.

Equations 34-20 give the intensity at the instant when the fields have magnitudes E and B. In an electromagnetic wave the fields oscillate, and so does the intensity. We're usually not interested in this rapid oscillation. For example, an engineer designing a solar collector doesn't care that sunlight intensity oscillates at about 10^{14} Hz. What she really wants is the *average* intensity, $\bar{S}$. Because the instantaneous intensity of Equation 34-20a contains a product of sinusoidally varying terms, which are in phase, the average intensity is just half the peak intensity:

$$\bar{S} = \frac{\overline{EB}}{\mu_0} = \frac{E_p B_p}{2\mu_0} \quad \text{(average intensity)} \tag{34-21a}$$

(This follows because, as we've seen on several occasions, the average of $\sin^2 \omega t$ over one cycle is $\frac{1}{2}$.) Typical values for $\bar{S}$ in visible light range from a few W/m² in the faint light of a candle to many MW/m² in the most intense laser beams (Fig. 34-25).

We wrote Equation 34-21a in terms of both the electric and magnetic fields, but we can use the wave condition $E = cB$ to eliminate either field in terms of the other:

$$\bar{S} = \frac{E_p^{\,2}}{2\mu_0 c} \tag{34-21b}$$

and

$$\bar{S} = \frac{cB_p^{\,2}}{2\mu_0}. \tag{34-21c}$$

Got It!

Lasers 1 and 2 emit light of the same color, and the electric field in the beam from laser 1 is twice as strong as that in laser 2's beam. How do their (a) magnetic fields, (b) intensities, and (c) wavelengths compare?

EXAMPLE 34-4	*Solar Energy*

The average intensity of sunlight on a clear day at noon is about 1 kW/m² (Fig. 34-26). What are the electric and magnetic fields in sunlight? How many solar collectors would you need to replace a 4.8-kW electric water heater in noonday sun, if each collector has an area of 2.0 m² and converts 40% of the incident sunlight to heat?

Solution

Solving Equation 34-21b for the electric field gives

$$E_p = \sqrt{2\mu_0 c\overline{S}}$$

$$= [(2)(4\pi \times 10^{-7} \text{ H/m})(3.0 \times 10^8 \text{ m/s})(1 \times 10^3 \text{ W/m}^2)]^{1/2}$$

$$= 0.87 \text{ kV/m}.$$

The peak magnetic field is then given by $B_p = E_p/c$, so

$$B_p = \frac{E_p}{c} = \frac{870 \text{ V/m}}{3.0 \times 10^8 \text{ m/s}} = 3 \times 10^{-6} \text{ T}.$$

At 1 kW/m², we would then need 4.8 m² of collector area if the collectors were 100% efficient. At 40% efficiency, we therefore need 4.8 m²/0.40 = 12 m², for a total of 6 collectors.

FIGURE 34-26 In bright sunlight, energy is incident on each square meter of these solar collectors at the rate of about 1000 watts.

EXERCISE A laser produces an average power of 7.0 W in a light beam 1.0 mm in diameter. Find (a) the average intensity and (b) the peak electric field of the laser light.

Answers: (a) 8.9 MW/m²; (b) 82 kV/m

Some problems similar to Example 34-4: 38–41, 43

Waves from Localized Sources

As an electromagnetic wave propagates through empty space, its total energy does not change. With plane waves the intensity—power per unit area—does not change either. But when a wave originates in a localized source such as an atom, a radio transmitting antenna, a light bulb, or a star, its wavefronts are not planes but expanding spheres (recall Fig. 16-18). The wave's total energy remains the same, but as it expands that energy is spread over the area of an ever larger sphere—whose area increases as the square of the distance from the source. Therefore, as we found in Chapter 16, the power per unit area—the intensity—decreases as the inverse square of the distance:

$$S = \frac{P}{4\pi r^2}. \tag{34-22}$$

Here S and P can be either the peak or average intensity and power, respectively, and r is the distance from a localized source. This intensity decrease occurs not because electromagnetic waves "weaken" and lose energy but because that energy gets spread ever more thinly.

Because the intensity of an electromagnetic wave is proportional to the *square* of the field strengths (Equations 34-21), Equation 34-22 shows that the *fields* of a spherical wave decrease as $1/r$. Contrast that with the $1/r^2$ decrease in the electric field of a stationary point charge, and you can see why the electromagnetic wave fields associated with an accelerated charge dominate in all but the immediate vicinity of the charge (see Fig. 34-23a).

EXAMPLE 34-5	A Garage-Door Opener

A radio-activated garage-door opener responds to signals with average intensity as weak as 20 μW/m². If the transmitter unit produces a 240-mW signal, broadcast in all directions, what is the maximum distance at which the transmitter will activate the door opener? What is the minimum value for the peak electric field to which the unit responds?

Solution

Since the waves spread out in all the directions, Equation 34-22 applies. Solving for r gives

$$r = \sqrt{\frac{P}{4\pi S}} = \sqrt{\frac{240\times10^{-3}\ \text{W}}{(4\pi)(20\times10^{-6}\ \text{W/m}^2)}} = 31\ \text{m}.$$

Solving Equation 34-21b gives the electric field corresponding to the unit's 20-μW/m² sensitivity:

$$E_p = \sqrt{2\mu_0 c \bar{S}}$$

$$= \sqrt{(2)(4\pi\times10^{-7}\ \text{H/m})(3.00\times10^8\ \text{m/s})(20\times10^{-6}\ \text{W/m}^2)}$$

$$= 0.12\ \text{V/m}.$$

The sensitivity of radio receiving equipment is often expressed in terms of the minimum electric field strength.

EXERCISE A stereo receiver's AM tuner section has a rated sensitivity of 2.1 mV/m. What is the maximum distance at which this unit can receive broadcasts from a radio station's 5.0-kW transmitter, assuming the signal is broadcast in all directions?

Answer: 261 km

Some problems similar to Example 34-5: 49, 51, 52, 61, 62

34-11 WAVE MOMENTUM AND RADIATION PRESSURE

We know from mechanics that moving objects carry both energy and momentum. The same is true for electromagnetic waves. Maxwell showed that the wave energy U and momentum p are related by

$$p = \frac{U}{c}. \tag{34-23}$$

If an electromagnetic wave is incident on an object and the object absorbs the wave energy (as, for example, a black object exposed to sunlight), then the object also absorbs the momentum given by Equation 34-23. If the wave's average intensity is $\bar{S}$, then it carries energy per unit area at the average rate $\bar{S}$ J/s/m². According to Equation 34-23 it therefore carries momentum per unit area at the rate $\bar{S}/c$. Newton's law in its general form $\mathbf{F} = d\mathbf{p}/dt$ tells us that the rate of change of an object's momentum is equal to the net force on the object. Therefore, if an object absorbs electromagnetic wave momentum $\bar{S}/c$ per unit area per unit time, it experiences a force per unit area of this magnitude. Since force per unit area is pressure, we call this quantity the **radiation pressure**:

$$P_{\text{rad}} = \frac{\bar{S}}{c}. \tag{34-24}$$

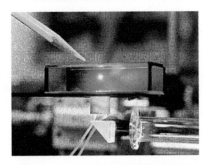

FIGURE 34-27 The bright dot at the center of this picture is a 20-micron particle levitated by a laser beam reflected upward by the prism shown at the bottom.

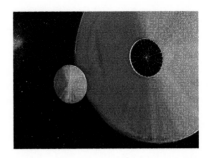

FIGURE 34-28 Two-stage sailing spacecraft proposed for interstellar travel. At the target star, laser light beamed all the way from the solar system would reflect from the large sail to the smaller one, bringing the latter to a stop. The diameter of the large sail is 1000 km.

The radiation pressure is doubled if an object reflects electromagnetic waves, in the same way that bouncing a basketball off a backboard changes the ball's momentum by $2mv$ and, therefore, delivers momentum $2mv$ to the backboard.

The pressure exerted by ordinary light is very small, but Dartmouth College physicists E. F. Nichols and G. F. Hull demonstrated its existence in a sensitive experiment performed in 1903. With high-energy laser light or with objects of low mass and large area, radiation pressure can be appreciable. Lasers exert enough light pressure to levitate small particles (Fig. 34-27), and the pressure of light has been suggested as a means of driving interstellar "sailing ships" (Fig. 34-28). Finally, the idea that electromagnetic waves carry momentum played a crucial role in Einstein's development of his famous equation $E = mc^2$.

EXAMPLE 34-6	*Star Wars*

A proposed ballistic missile defense system calls for a laser that can focus 25 MW of light on an attacking warhead. The weapon works by heating the warhead to the point of destruction, but it also delivers momentum that alters the warhead's trajectory. If the beam dwells on a 200-kg warhead for 15 s, what velocity change does it impart to the warhead? Estimate the distance by which the warhead will be knocked off course over its remaining 30 minutes of flight.

Solution

The energy delivered in a 25-MW beam acting for 15 s is $(25\ \text{MW})(15\ \text{s}) = 375\ \text{MJ}$. According to Equation 34-23, the associated momentum is

$$p = \frac{U}{c} = \frac{375 \times 10^6\ \text{J}}{3.00 \times 10^8\ \text{m/s}} = 1.25\ \text{kg·m/s}\,.$$

The change in the warhead's velocity is given by $m\Delta v = \Delta p$, where Δp is the change in its momentum. Assuming the warhead absorbs all the beam's momentum, we then have

$$\Delta v = \frac{\Delta p}{m} = \frac{1.25\ \text{kg·m/s}}{200\ \text{kg}} = 0.00625\ \text{m/s}\,.$$

This is insignificant compared with a typical warhead speed of 7 km/s. Even though we don't know the direction of the velocity change, we can estimate crudely the error Δx in the impact point by multiplying this change by the flight time:

$$\Delta x = \Delta v\,t = (0.00625\ \text{m/s})(30\ \text{min})(60\ \text{s/min}) = 11\ \text{m}\,.$$

This is totally negligible, especially for a nuclear warhead. Even with this enormously powerful laser, radiation pressure has an insignificant effect. It's the energy delivered, not the momentum, that matters here.

EXERCISE A laser delivers 5.0 MW/m². If the beam is directed upward, what is the maximum mass for a 100-μm-diameter particle to be suspended in the beam?

Answer: 1.3×10^{-11} kg

Some problems similar to Example 34-6: 56–59

CHAPTER SYNOPSIS

Summary

1. Maxwell's modification of Ampère's law adds a **displacement current** term $\varepsilon_0 d\phi_E/dt$, showing that changing electric flux is a source of magnetic field. This modified law completes the set of **Maxwell's equations**—the four equations that govern the behavior of electromagnetic fields.

2. The interplay of electric and magnetic fields described by Faraday's and Ampère's laws gives rise to **electromagnetic waves**. When they propagate through vacuum, these waves
   a. Travel at the speed of light, $c = 1/\sqrt{\varepsilon_0\mu_0} = 3.00\times10^8$ m/s.
   b. Have their electric and magnetic fields at right angles to each other and to the direction of wave propagation.
   c. Have their fields in phase, with magnitudes related by $E = cB$.
   d. Can have any frequency or wavelength, provided the two are related by the equivalent expressions $f\lambda = c$ or $\omega/k = c$.

3. Radio waves, television, microwaves, infrared, visible light, ultraviolet, X rays, and gamma rays are all forms of electromagnetic radiation. They differ only in frequency and wavelength, and together comprise the **electromagnetic spectrum**.

4. **Polarization** describes the orientation of a wave's electric field in the plane perpendicular to the propagation direction. When a polarized wave passes through a polarizing material, its intensity is reduced by a factor $\cos^2\theta$, where θ is the angle between the wave polarization and the preferred axis of the material.

5. Electromagnetic waves are produced by accelerated electric charges, as in the alternating current of a radio antenna.

6. Electromagnetic waves carry energy. The rate at which energy is transported per unit area is the wave **intensity**. The **Poynting vector**,

$$\mathbf{S} = \frac{\mathbf{E} \times \mathbf{B}}{\mu_0},$$

describes this energy transport for any configuration of electromagnetic fields. The average intensity has half the peak value, or

$$\bar{S} = \frac{E_p B_p}{2\mu_0}.$$

The intensity of a plane wave remains constant, while the intensity from a localized source decreases as the inverse square of the distance from the source.

7. An electromagnetic wave with energy U also carries momentum $p = U/c$. As a result, it exerts a **radiation pressure** $P_{rad} = \bar{S}/c$ on an object that absorbs the wave and twice this pressure on a reflecting object.

Terms You Should Understand

(Pairs are closely related terms whose distinction is important; number in parentheses is chapter section where term first appears.)

displacement current (34-2)
Maxwell's equations (34-3)
electromagnetic wave (34-4)
electromagnetic spectrum (34-7)
polarization (34-8)
intensity, Poynting vector (34-10)
radiation pressure (34-11)

Symbols You Should Recognize

$\varepsilon_0 d\phi_E/dt$ (34-2)
$S, \mathbf{S}, \bar{S}$ (34-10)
c (34-5)
P_{rad} (34-11)

Problems You Should Be Able to Solve

evaluating induced magnetic fields in symmetric situations (34-2)
relating frequency and wavelength of electromagnetic waves (34-6)
relating electric and magnetic field strengths in electromagnetic waves (34-6)
calculating light intensity emerging from one or more polarizers (34-8)
relating wave intensity and fields (34-10)
evaluating wave intensity and fields as a function of distance from localized sources (34-10)
calculating radiation pressure and its effects (34-11)

Limitations to Keep in Mind

The description of electromagnetic waves developed in this chapter applies strictly only in vacuum.

QUESTIONS

1. Why is Maxwell's modification of Ampère's law essential to the existence of electromagnetic waves?
2. The presence of magnetic monopoles would require modification of Gauss's law for magnetism. Which of the other Maxwell equations would also need modification?
3. There is displacement current between the plates of a charging capacitor, yet no charge is moving between the plates. In what sense is the word "current" appropriate here?
4. Is there displacement current in an electromagnetic wave? Is there ordinary conduction current?
5. List some similarities and differences between electromagnetic waves and sound waves.
6. What aspect of the electromagnetic wave considered in Section 34-4 ensures that Gauss's laws for electricity and magnetism are satisfied?
7. Explain why parallel electric and magnetic fields in vacuum could not constitute an electromagnetic wave.
8. The speed of an electromagnetic wave is given by $c = \lambda f$. How does the speed depend on frequency? On wavelength?
9. When astronomers observe a supernova explosion in a distant galaxy, they see a sudden, simultaneous rise in visible light and other forms of electromagnetic radiation. How is this evidence that the speed of light is independent of frequency?
10. Turning a TV antenna so its rods point vertically may change the quality of your TV reception. Why? Think about polarization.
11. Unpolarized light is incident on two sheets of Polaroid with their polarization directions at right angles, and no light gets through. A third sheet is inserted between the other two, and now some light gets through. How can this be?
12. Why is it not possible to define exactly where the visible region of the spectrum ends?
13. Why did the field of X-ray astronomy flourish only after the advent of space flight?
14. The Sun emits most of its electromagnetic wave energy in the visible region of the spectrum, with the peak in the yellow-green. Our eyes are sensitive to the same range, with peak sensitivity in the yellow-green. Is this a coincidence?
15. Suppose your eyes were sensitive to radio waves rather than light. What things would look bright?
16. An *LC* circuit is made entirely from superconducting materials, yet its oscillations eventually damp out. Why?
17. If you double the field strength in an electromagnetic wave, what happens to the intensity?
18. The intensity of light falls off as the inverse square of the distance from the source. Does this mean that electromagnetic wave energy is lost? Explain.
19. When your picture is taken with a flash camera, why doesn't the momentum of the light flash knock you over?
20. Some long-distance power transmission lines use DC rather than AC, despite the need to convert between DC and AC at either end. Why might this be? What energy loss mechanism occurs with AC but not DC?
21. Electromagnetic waves do not readily penetrate metals. Why might this be?

PROBLEMS

Section 34-2 Ambiguity in Ampère's Law

1. A uniform electric field is increasing at the rate of 1.5 V/m·μs. What is the displacement current through an area of 1.0 cm² at right angles to the field?
2. A parallel-plate capacitor has square plates 10 cm on a side and 0.50 cm apart. If the voltage across the plates is increasing at the rate of 220 V/ms, what is the displacement current in the capacitor?
3. A parallel-plate capacitor of plate area A and spacing d is charging at the rate dV/dt. Show that the displacement current in the capacitor is equal to the conduction current flowing in the wires feeding the capacitor.
4. A capacitor with circular plates is fed with long, straight wires along the axis of the plates. Show that the magnetic field *outside* the capacitor, in a plane that passes through the interior of the capacitor and is perpendicular to the

axis, is given by $B = \dfrac{\mu_0 \varepsilon_0 R^2}{2rd} \dfrac{dV}{dt}$. Here R is the plate radius, d the spacing, dV/dt the rate of change of the capacitor voltage, and r the distance from the axis.
5. A parallel-plate capacitor has circular plates with radius 50 cm and spacing 1.0 mm. A uniform electric field between the plates is changing at the rate 1.0 MV/m·s. What is the magnetic field between the plates (a) on the symmetry axis, (b) 15 cm from the axis, and (c) 150 cm from the axis?
6. An electric field points into the page and occupies a circular region of radius 1.0 m, as shown in Fig. 34-29. There are no electric charges in the region, but there is a magnetic field forming closed loops pointing clockwise, as shown. The magnetic field strength 50 cm from the center of the

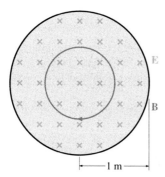

FIGURE 34-29 Problem 6.

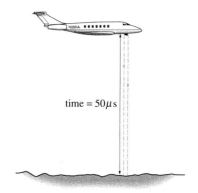

time = $50\mu s$

FIGURE 34-30 Problem 14.

region is 2.0 μT. (a) What is the rate of change of the electric field? (b) Is the electric field increasing or decreasing?

Section 34-4 Electromagnetic Waves

7. At a particular point the instantaneous electric field of an electromagnetic wave points in the $+y$ direction, while the magnetic field points in the $-z$ direction. In what direction is the wave propagating?

8. The fields of an electromagnetic wave are $\mathbf{E} = E_p\sin(kz + \omega t)\hat{\jmath}$ and $\mathbf{B} = B_p\sin(kz + \omega t)\hat{\imath}$. Give a unit vector in the direction of propagation.

9. The electric field of a radio wave is given by $\mathbf{E} = E\sin(kz - \omega t)(\hat{\imath} + \hat{\jmath})$. (a) What is the peak amplitude of the electric field? (b) Give a unit vector in the direction of the magnetic field at a place and time where $\sin(kz - \omega t)$ is positive.

10. Show by differentiation and substitution that Equations 34-12b and 34-13 can be satisfied by fields of the form $E(x, t) = E_pf(kx \pm \omega t)$ and $B(x, t) = B_pf(kx \pm \omega t)$, where f is any function of the argument $kx \pm \omega t$.

11. Show that it is impossible for an electromagnetic wave in vacuum to have a time-varying component of its electric field in the direction of its magnetic field. *Hint:* Assume **E** does have such a component, and show that you cannot satisfy both Gauss and Faraday.

Section 34-5 The Speed of Electromagnetic Waves

12. A light-minute is the distance light travels in one minute. Show that the Sun is about 8 light-minutes from Earth.

13. Your intercontinental telephone call is carried by electromagnetic waves routed via a satellite in geosynchronous orbit at an altitude of 36,000 km. Approximately how long does it take before your voice is heard at the other end?

14. An airplane's radar altimeter works by bouncing radio waves off the ground and measuring the round-trip travel time (Fig. 34-30). If that time is 50 μs, what is the altitude?

15. Roughly how long does it take light to go 1 foot?

16. If you speak via radio from Earth to an astronaut on the moon, how long is it before you can get a reply?

17. "Ghosts" on a TV screen occur when part of the signal goes directly from transmitter to receiver, while part takes a longer route, reflecting off mountains or buildings (Fig. 34-31). The electron beam in a 50-cm-wide TV tube "paints" the picture by scanning the beam from left to right across the screen in about 10^{-4} s. If a "ghost" image appears displaced about 1 cm from the main image, what is the difference in path lengths of the direct and indirect signals?

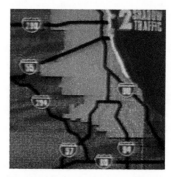

FIGURE 34-31 Ghost images of highways appear on this TV traffic report (Problem 17).

18. A computer can fetch information from its memory in 3.0 ns, a process that involves sending a signal from the central processing unit (CPU) to memory and awaiting the return of the information. If signals in the computer's wiring travel at $0.60c$, what is the maximum distance between the CPU and the memory? Your answer shows why high-speed computers are necessarily compact.

19. Problem 69 shows that the speed of electromagnetic waves in a transparent dielectric is given by $1/\sqrt{\kappa\varepsilon_0\mu_0}$, where κ is the dielectric constant described in Chapter 26. An experimental measurement gives 1.97×10^8 m/s for the speed of light in a piece of glass. What is the dielectric constant of this glass at optical frequencies?

Section 34-6 Properties of Electromagnetic Waves

20. What are the wavelengths of (a) a 100-MHz FM radio wave, (b) a 3.0-GHz radar wave, (c) a 6.0×10^{14}-Hz light wave, and (d) a 1.0×10^{18}-Hz X ray?

21. A 60-Hz power line emits electromagnetic radiation. What is the wavelength?

22. Antennas for transmitting and receiving electromagnetic radiation usually have typical dimensions on the order of half a wavelength. Look at a TV antenna, and estimate the wavelength and frequency of a TV signal.

23. A CB radio antenna is a vertical rod 2.75 m high. If this length is one-fourth of the CB wavelength, what is the CB frequency?

24. A microwave oven operates at 2.4 GHz. What is the distance between wave crests in the oven?

25. What would be the electric field strength in an electromagnetic wave whose magnetic field equalled that of Earth, about 50 μT?

26. Dielectric breakdown in air occurs at an electric field strength of about 3×10^6 V/m. What would be the peak magnetic field in an electromagnetic wave with this value for its peak electric field?

27. A radio receiver can detect signals with electric fields as low as 320 μV/m. What is the corresponding magnetic field?

Section 34-8 Polarization

28. An electromagnetic wave is propagating in the z direction. What is its polarization direction, if its magnetic field is in the y direction?

29. Polarized light is incident on a sheet of polarizing material, and only 20% of the light gets through. What is the angle between the electric field and the polarization axis of the material?

30. Vertically polarized light passes through a polarizer whose polarization axis is oriented at 70° to the vertical. What fraction of the incident intensity emerges from the polarizer?

31. A polarizer blocks 75% of a polarized light beam. What is the angle between the beam's polarization and the polarizer's axis?

32. An electro-optic modulator is supposed to switch a laser beam between fully off and fully on, as its crystal rotates the beam polarization by 90° when a voltage is applied. But a power-supply failure results in only enough voltage for a 72° beam rotation. What fraction of the laser light is transmitted when it is supposed to be fully on?

33. Unpolarized light of intensity S_0 passes first through a polarizer with its polarization axis vertical, then through one with its axis at 35° to the vertical. What is the light intensity after the second polarizer?

34. Vertically polarized light passes through two polarizers, the first at 60° to the vertical and the second at 90° to the vertical. What fraction of the light gets through?

35. Unpolarized light with intensity S_0 passes through a stack of five polarizing sheets, each with its axis rotated 20° with respect to the previous one. What is the intensity of the light emerging from the stack?

36. Unpolarized light of intensity S_0 is incident on a "sandwich" of three polarizers. The outer two have their transmission axes perpendicular, while the middle one has its axis at 45° to the others. What is the light intensity emerging from this "sandwich?"

37. Polarized light with average intensity S_0 passes through a sheet of polarizing material which is rotating at 10 rev/s. At time $t = 0$ the polarization axis is aligned with the incident polarization. Write an expression for the transmitted intensity as a function of time.

Section 34-10 Energy in Electromagnetic Waves

38. A typical laboratory electric field is 1000 V/m. What is the average intensity of an electromagnetic wave with this value for its peak field?

39. What would be the average intensity of a laser beam so strong that its electric field produced dielectric breakdown of air (which requires $E_p = 3 \times 10^6$ V/m)?

40. Estimate the peak electric field inside a 625-W microwave oven under the simplifying approximation that the microwaves propagate as a plane wave through the oven's 750-cm^2 cross-sectional area.

41. A radio receiver can pick up signals with peak electric fields as low as 450 μV/m. What is the average intensity of such a signal?

42. Show that the electric and magnetic energy densities in an electromagnetic wave are equal.

43. A laser blackboard pointer delivers 0.10 mW average power in a beam 0.90 mm in diameter. Find (a) the average intensity, (b) the peak electric field, and (c) the peak magnetic field.

44. The laser of Example 34-6 produces a spot 80 cm in diameter at its target. What are the rms electric and magnetic fields at the target?

45. The United States' safety standard for continuous exposure to microwave radiation is 10 mW/cm^2. The glass door of a microwave oven measures 40 cm by 17 cm and is covered with a metal screen that blocks microwaves. What fraction of the oven's 625-W microwave power can leak through the door window without exceeding the safe exposure to someone right outside the door? Assume the power leaks uniformly through the window area.

46. A 1.0-kW radio transmitter broadcasts uniformly in all directions. What is the intensity of its signal at a distance of 5.0 km from the transmitter?

47. Use the fact that sunlight intensity at Earth's orbit is 1368 W/m^2 to calculate the Sun's total power output.

48. About two-thirds of the solar energy at Earth's orbit reaches the planet's surface. At what rate is solar energy incident on the entire Earth? See the previous problem,

and compare your result with the roughly 10^{13} W rate at which humanity consumes energy.

49. During its 1989 encounter with Neptune, the Voyager 2 spacecraft was 4.5×10^9 km from Earth (Fig. 34-32). Its images of Neptune were broadcast by a radio transmitter with a mere 21-W average power output. What would be (a) the average intensity and (b) the peak electric field received at Earth if the transmitter broadcast equally in all directions? (The received signal was actually somewhat stronger because Voyager used a directional antenna.)

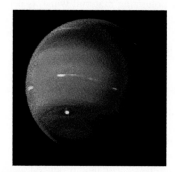

FIGURE 34-32 Neptune, photographed by the Voyager II spacecraft when it was 4.5×10^9 km from Earth. How long did it take the radio signal carrying this image to reach Earth? (Problem 49)

50. A quasar 10 billion light-years from Earth appears the same brightness as a star 50,000 light-years away. How does the power output of the quasar compare with that of the star?

51. At 1.5 km from the transmitter, the peak electric field of a radio wave is 350 mV/m. (a) What is the transmitter's power output, assuming it broadcasts uniformly in all directions? (b) What is the peak electric field 10 km from the transmitter?

52. The peak electric field at a point 25 m from a point source of electromagnetic waves is 4.2 kV/m. What is the peak magnetic field 1.0 m from the source?

53. A typical fluorescent lamp is a little over 1 m long and a few cm in diameter. How do you expect the light intensity to vary with distance (a) near the lamp but not near either end and (b) far from the lamp?

Section 34-11 Wave Momentum and Radiation Pressure

54. A camera flash delivers 2.5 kW of light power for 1.0 ms (Fig. 34-33). Find (a) the total energy and (b) the total momentum carried by the flash.

55. What is the radiation pressure exerted on a light-absorbing surface by a laser beam whose intensity is 180 W/cm²?

56. A laser beam shines vertically upward. What laser power is necessary for this beam to support a flat piece of aluminum foil with mass 30 μg and diameter equal to that of the beam? Assume the foil reflects all the light.

FIGURE 34-33 How much energy and momentum are in light from the camera flash? (Problem 54)

57. The average intensity of noonday sunlight is about 1 kW/m². What is the radiation force on a solar collector measuring 60 cm by 2.5 m if it is oriented at right angles to the incident light and absorbs all the light?

58. Serious proposals have been made to "sail" spacecraft to the outer solar system using the pressure of sunlight. How much sail area must a 1000-kg spacecraft have if its acceleration at Earth's orbit is to be 1 m/s²? Assume the sails are made from reflecting material. You can neglect the Sun's gravity. (Why?)

59. A 65-kg astronaut is floating in empty space. If the astronaut shines a 1.0-W flashlight in a fixed direction, how long will it take the astronaut to accelerate to a speed of 10 m/s?

60. A "photon rocket" emits a beam of light instead of the hot gas of an ordinary rocket. How powerful a light source would be needed for a photon rocket with thrust equal to that of a space shuttle (35 MN)? Compare your answer with humanity's total electric power-generating capability, about 10^{12} W.

Paired Problems

(Both problems in a pair involve the same principles and techniques. If you can get the first problem, you should be able to solve the second one.)

61. Find the peak electric and magnetic fields 1.5 m from a 60-W light bulb that radiates equally in all directions.

62. At 4.6 km from a radio transmitter, the peak electric field in the radio wave measures 380 mV/m. What is the transmitter's power, assuming it broadcasts equally in all directions?

63. Unpolarized light is incident on two polarizers with their axes at 45°. What fraction of the incident light gets through?

64. Find the angle between two polarizers if unpolarized light incident on the pair emerges with 10% of its incident intensity.

65. What is the radiation force on the door of a microwave oven if 625 W of microwave power hits the door at right angles and is reflected?

66. What is the power output of a laser whose beam exerts a 55-mN force on an absorbing object oriented at right angles to the beam? The object is larger than the beam's cross section.

67. A 60-W light bulb is 6.0 cm in diameter. What is the radiation pressure on an opaque object at the bulb's surface?

68. A white dwarf star is approximately the size of Earth but radiates about as much energy as the Sun. Estimate the radiation pressure on an absorbing object at the white dwarf's surface.

Supplementary Problems

69. Maxwell's equations in a dielectric resemble those in vacuum (Equations 34-6 through 34-9), but with ϕ_E in Ampère's law replaced by $\kappa\phi_E$, where κ is the dielectric constant introduced in Chapter 26. Show that the speed of electromagnetic waves in such a dielectric is $c/\sqrt{\kappa}$.

70. Use appropriate data from Appendix E to calculate the radiation pressure on a light-absorbing object at the Sun's surface.

71. A radar system produces pulses consisting of 100 full cycles of a sinusoidal 70-GHz electromagnetic wave. The average power while the transmitter is on is 45 MW, and the waves are confined to a beam 20 cm in diameter. Find (a) the peak electric field, (b) the wavelength, (c) the total energy in a pulse, and (d) the total momentum in a pulse. (e) If the transmitter produces 1000 pulses per second, what is its average power output?

72. In a stack of polarizing sheets, each sheet has its polarization axis rotated 14° with respect to the preceding sheet. If the stack passes 37% of the incident, unpolarized light, how many sheets does it contain?

73. The peak electric field measured at 8.0 cm from a light source is 150 W/m², while at 12 cm it measures 122 W/m². Describe the shape of the source.

74. Show that Equations 34-12b and 34-13 may be combined to yield a wave equation like Equation 16-13. *Hint:* Take the partial derivative of one equation with respect to x and of the other with respect to t, and use the fact that

$$\frac{\partial}{\partial x}\left(\frac{\partial f}{\partial t}\right) = \frac{\partial}{\partial t}\left(\frac{\partial f}{\partial x}\right)$$

for any well-behaved function $f(x, t)$.

75. Studies of the origin of the solar system suggest that sufficiently small particles might be blown out of the solar system by the force of sunlight. To see how small such particles must be, compare the force of sunlight with the force of gravity, and solve for the particle radius at which the two are equal. Assume the particles are spherical and have density 2 g/cm³. Why do you not need to worry about the distance from the Sun?

76. A cylindrical resistor of length ℓ, radius a, and resistance R carries a current I. Calculate the electric and magnetic fields at the surface of the resistor, assuming the electric field is uniform throughout, including at the surface. Calculate the Poynting vector, and show that it points into the resistor. Calculate the flux of the Poynting vector (that is, $\int \mathbf{S} \cdot d\mathbf{A}$) over the surface of the resistor to get the rate of electromagnetic energy flow into the resistor, and show that the result is just I^2R. Your result shows that the energy heating the resistor comes from the fields surrounding it. These fields are sustained by the source of electrical energy that drives the current.

PART 4 *Cumulative Problems*

These problems combine material from chapters throughout the entire part or, in addition, from chapters in earlier parts, or they present special challenges.

1. An air-insulated parallel-plate capacitor has plate area 100 cm² and spacing 0.50 cm. The capacitor is charged and then disconnected from the charging battery. A thin-walled, nonconducting box of the same dimensions as the capacitor is filled with water at 20.00°C. The box is released at the edge of the capacitor and moves without friction into the capacitor (Fig. 1). When it reaches equilibrium the water temperature is 21.50°. What was the original voltage on the capacitor?

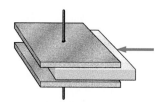

FIGURE 1 Cumulative Problem 1.

2. A wire of length ℓ and resistance R is formed into a closed rectangular loop twice as long as it is wide. It is mounted on a nonconducting horizontal axle parallel to its longer dimension, as shown in Fig. 2. A uniform magnetic field **B** points into the page, as shown. A long string of negligible mass is wrapped many times around a drum of radius a attached to the axle, and a mass m is attached to the string. When the mass is released it falls and eventually reaches a speed that, averaged over one cycle of the loop's rotation, is constant from one rotation to the next. Find an expression for that average terminal speed.

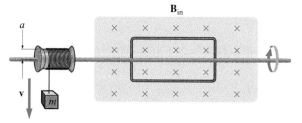

FIGURE 2 Cumulative Problem 2.

3. Five wires of equal length 25 cm and resistance 10 Ω are connected as shown in Fig. 3. Two solenoids, each 10 cm in diameter, extend a long way perpendicular to the page. The magnetic fields of both solenoids point out of the page; the field strength in the left-hand solenoid is increasing at 50 T/s while that in the right-hand solenoid is decreasing at 30 T/s. Find the current in the resistance wire shared by both triangles. Which way does the current flow?

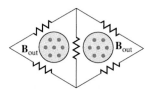

FIGURE 3 Cumulative Problem 3.

4. A long solenoid of length ℓ and radius R has a total of N turns. The solenoid current is increasing linearly with time: $I(t) = bt$, where b is a constant. (a) Find an expression for the rate at which the magnetic energy in the solenoid is increasing. (b) Find an expression for the induced electric field at the inner edge of the solenoid coils. (c) Evaluate the Poynting vector at the inner edge of the coils, and show by integration that electromagnetic energy is flowing into the solenoid at a rate equal to the buildup of magnetic energy.

5. A coaxial cable consists of an inner conductor of radius a and an outer conductor of radius b; the space between the conductors is filled with insulation of dielectric constant κ (Fig. 4). The cable's axis is the z axis. The cable is used to carry electromagnetic energy from a radio transmitter to a broadcasting antenna. The electric field between the conductors points radially from the axis, and is given by $E = E_0(a/r) \cos(kz - \omega t)$. The magnetic field encircles the axis, and is given by $B = B_0(a/r) \cos(kz - \omega t)$. Here E_0, B_0, k, and ω are constants. Show, using appropriate closed surfaces and loops, that these fields satisfy Maxwell's equations. Your result shows that the cable acts as a "waveguide," confining an electromagnetic wave to the space between the conductors.

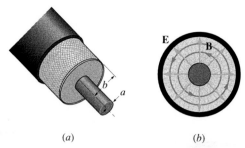

(a)   *(b)*

FIGURE 4 Cumulative Problem 5. *(a)* A coaxial cable. *(b)* Cross section, showing the electric and magnetic fields. The fields also vary with position z along the cable axis, according to the equations given.

APPENDIX A
Mathematics

A-1 ALGEBRA AND TRIGONOMETRY

Quadratic Formula

If $ax^2 + bx + c = 0$ then $x = \dfrac{-b \pm \sqrt{b^2 - 4ac}}{2a}$

Circumference, Area, Volume

Where $\pi \simeq 3.14159\ldots$

circumference of circle	$2\pi r$
area of circle	πr^2
surface area of sphere	$4\pi r^2$
volume of sphere	$\frac{4}{3}\pi r^3$
area of triangle	$\frac{1}{2}bh$
volume of cylinder	$\pi r^2 \ell$

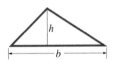

Trigonometry

definition of angle (in radians): $\theta = \dfrac{s}{r}$

2π radians in complete circle
1 radian $\simeq 57.3°$

Trigonometric Functions

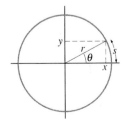

$$\sin\theta = \frac{y}{r}$$

$$\cos\theta = \frac{x}{r}$$

$$\tan\theta = \frac{\sin\theta}{\cos\theta} = \frac{y}{x}$$

Values at Selected Angles

$\theta \rightarrow$	0	$\dfrac{\pi}{6}$ (30°)	$\dfrac{\pi}{4}$ (45°)	$\dfrac{\pi}{3}$ (60°)	$\dfrac{\pi}{2}$ (90°)
$\sin\theta$	0	$\dfrac{1}{2}$	$\dfrac{\sqrt{2}}{2}$	$\dfrac{\sqrt{3}}{2}$	1
$\cos\theta$	1	$\dfrac{\sqrt{3}}{2}$	$\dfrac{\sqrt{2}}{2}$	$\dfrac{1}{2}$	0
$\tan\theta$	0	$\dfrac{\sqrt{3}}{3}$	1	$\sqrt{3}$	∞

Graphs of Trigonometric Functions

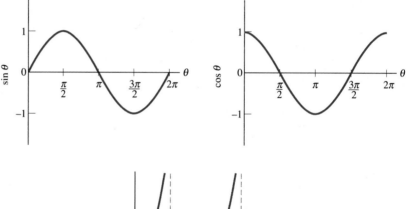

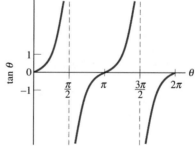

Trigonometric Identities

$\sin(-\theta) = -\sin\theta$

$\cos(-\theta) = \cos\theta$

$\sin\left(\theta \pm \dfrac{\pi}{2}\right) = \pm\cos\theta$

$\cos\left(\theta \pm \dfrac{\pi}{2}\right) = \mp\sin\theta$

$\sin^2\theta + \cos^2\theta = 1$

$\sin 2\theta = 2\sin\theta\cos\theta$

$$\cos 2\theta = \cos^2 \theta - \sin^2 \theta =: 1 - 2\sin^2 \theta = 2\cos^2 \theta - 1$$

$$\sin(\alpha \pm \beta) = \sin\alpha\cos\beta \pm \cos\alpha\sin\beta$$

$$\cos(\alpha \pm \beta) = \cos\alpha\cos\beta \mp \sin\alpha\sin\beta$$

$$\sin\alpha \pm \sin\beta = 2\sin[\tfrac{1}{2}(\alpha \pm \beta)]\cos[\tfrac{1}{2}(\alpha \mp \beta)]$$

$$\cos\alpha + \cos\beta = 2\cos[\tfrac{1}{2}(\alpha + \beta)]\cos[\tfrac{1}{2}(\alpha - \beta)]$$

$$\cos\alpha - \cos\beta = -2\sin[\tfrac{1}{2}(\alpha + \beta)]\sin[\tfrac{1}{2}(\alpha - \beta)]$$

Laws of Cosines and Sines

Where A, B, C are the sides of an arbitrary triangle and α, β, γ the angles opposite those sides:

Law of cosines

$$C^2 = A^2 + B^2 - 2AB\cos\gamma$$

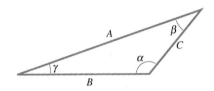

Law of sines

$$\frac{\sin\alpha}{A} = \frac{\sin\beta}{B} = \frac{\sin\gamma}{C}$$

Exponentials and Logarithms

Graphs

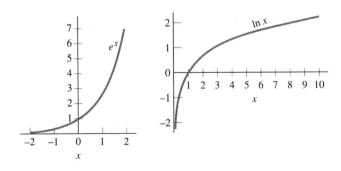

Exponential and Natural Logarithms Are Inverse Functions

$$e^{\ln x} = x, \quad \ln e^x = x \quad e = 2.71828 \ldots .$$

Exponential and Logarithmic Identities

$$a^x = e^{x \ln a} \qquad \ln(xy) = \ln x + \ln y$$

$$a^x a^y = a^{x+y} \qquad \ln\left(\frac{x}{y}\right) = \ln x - \ln y$$

$$(a^x)^y = a^{xy} \qquad \ln\left(\frac{1}{x}\right) = -\ln x$$

$$\log x \equiv \log_{10} x = \ln(10)\ln x \simeq 2.3\ln x$$

Expansions and Approximations

Series Expansions of Functions

Note: $n! = n(n - 1)(n - 2)(n - 3) \cdots (3)(2)(1)$

$$e^x = 1 + x + \frac{x^2}{2!} + \frac{x^3}{3!} + \cdots \quad \text{(exponential)}$$

$$\left.\begin{array}{l} \sin x = x - \dfrac{x^3}{3!} + \dfrac{x^5}{5!} - \cdots \quad \text{(sine)} \\[2em] \cos x = 1 - \dfrac{x^2}{2!} + \dfrac{x^4}{4!} - \cdots \quad \text{(cosine)} \end{array}\right\} (x \text{ in radians})$$

$$\ln(1 + x) = x - \frac{x^2}{2} + \frac{x^3}{3} - \cdots \quad \text{(natural logarithm)}$$

$$(1 + x)^p = 1 + px + \frac{p(p - 1)}{2!}x^2 + \frac{p(p - 1)(p - 2)}{3!}x^3 + \cdots$$

(binomial, valid for $|x| < 1$)

Approximations

For $|x| \ll 1$, the first few terms in the series provide a good approximation; that is,

$$\left.\begin{array}{l} e^x \simeq 1 + x \\[0.5em] \sin x \simeq x \\[0.5em] \cos x \simeq 1 - \frac{1}{2}x^2 \\[0.5em] \ln(1 + x) \simeq x \\[0.5em] (1 + x)^p \simeq 1 + px \end{array}\right\} \text{for } |x| \ll 1$$

Expressions that do not have the forms shown may often be put in the appropriate form. For example:

$$\frac{1}{\sqrt{a^2 + y^2}} = \frac{1}{a\sqrt{1 + \dfrac{y^2}{a^2}}} = \frac{1}{a}\left(1 + \frac{y^2}{a^2}\right)^{-1/2}.$$

For $y^2 \ll a^2$, this may be approximated using the binomial expansion $(1 + x)^p \simeq 1 + px$, with $p = -\frac{1}{2}$ and $x = y^2/a^2$:

$$\frac{1}{a}\left(1 + \frac{y^2}{a^2}\right)^{-1/2} \simeq \frac{1}{a}\left(1 - \frac{1}{2}\frac{y^2}{a^2}\right).$$

Vector Algebra

Vector Products

$\mathbf{A} \cdot \mathbf{B} = AB\cos\theta$

$|\mathbf{A} \times \mathbf{B}| = AB\sin\theta$, with direction of $\mathbf{A} \times \mathbf{B}$ given by right-hand rule:

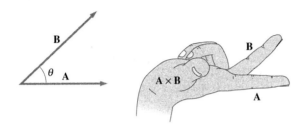

Unit Vector Notation

An arbitrary vector $\mathbf{A}$ may be written in terms of its components A_x, A_y, A_z and the unit vectors $\hat{\mathbf{i}}$, $\hat{\mathbf{j}}$, $\hat{\mathbf{k}}$ that have length 1 and lie along the x, y, z axes:

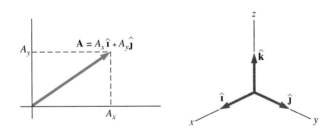

In unit vector notation, vector products become

$\mathbf{A} \cdot \mathbf{B} = A_x B_x + A_y B_y + A_z B_z$

$\mathbf{A} \times \mathbf{B} = (A_y B_z - A_z B_y)\hat{\mathbf{i}} + (A_z B_x - A_x B_z)\hat{\mathbf{j}} + (A_x B_y - A_y B_x)\hat{\mathbf{k}}$

Vector Identities

$\mathbf{A} \cdot \mathbf{B} = \mathbf{B} \cdot \mathbf{A}$

$\mathbf{A} \times \mathbf{B} = -\mathbf{B} \times \mathbf{A}$

$\mathbf{A} \cdot (\mathbf{B} \times \mathbf{C}) = \mathbf{B} \cdot (\mathbf{C} \times \mathbf{A}) = \mathbf{C} \cdot (\mathbf{A} \times \mathbf{B})$

$\mathbf{A} \times (\mathbf{B} \times \mathbf{C}) = (\mathbf{A} \cdot \mathbf{C})\mathbf{B} - (\mathbf{A} \cdot \mathbf{B})\mathbf{C}$

A-2 CALCULUS

Derivatives

Definition of the Derivative

If y is a function of x $[y = f(x)]$, then the **derivative of y with respect to x** is the ratio of the change Δy in y to the corresponding change Δx in x, in the limit of arbitrarily small Δx:

$$\frac{dy}{dx} = \lim_{\Delta x \to 0} \frac{\Delta y}{\Delta x}.$$

Algebraically, the derivative is the rate of change of y with respect to x; geometrically, it is the slope of the y versus x graph—that is, of the tangent line to the graph at a given point:

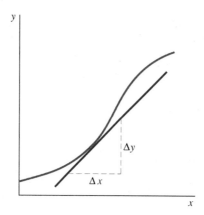

Derivatives of Common Functions

Although the derivative of a function can be evaluated directly using the limiting process that defines the derivative, standard formulas are available for common functions:

$$\frac{da}{dx} = 0 \quad (a \text{ is a constant})$$

$$\frac{dx^n}{dx} = nx^{n-1} \quad (n \text{ need not be an integer})$$

$$\frac{d}{dx}\sin x = \cos x$$

$$\frac{d}{dx}\cos x = -\sin x$$

$$\frac{d}{dx}\tan x = \frac{1}{\cos^2 x}$$

$$\frac{de^x}{dx} = e^x$$

$$\frac{d}{dx}\ln x = \frac{1}{x}$$

Derivatives of Sums, Products, and Functions of Functions

1. Derivative of a constant times a function

$$\frac{d}{dx}[af(x)] = a\frac{df}{dx} \quad (a \text{ is a constant})$$

2. Derivative of a sum

$$\frac{d}{dx}[f(x) + g(x)] = \frac{df}{dx} + \frac{dg}{dx}$$

3. Derivative of a product

$$\frac{d}{dx}[f(x)g(x)] = g\frac{df}{dx} + f\frac{dg}{dx}$$

Examples

$$\frac{d}{dx}(x^2\cos x) = \cos x\frac{dx^2}{dx} + x^2\frac{d}{dx}\cos x = 2x\cos x - x^2\sin x$$

$$\frac{d}{dx}(x\ln x) = \ln x\frac{dx}{dx} + x\frac{d}{dx}\ln x = (\ln x)(1) + x\left(\frac{1}{x}\right) = \ln x + 1$$

4. Derivative of a quotient

$$\frac{d}{dx}\left[\frac{f(x)}{g(x)}\right] = \frac{1}{g^2}\left(g\frac{df}{dx} - f\frac{dg}{dx}\right)$$

Example

$$\frac{d}{dx}\left(\frac{\sin x}{x^2}\right) = \frac{1}{x^4}\left(x^2\frac{d}{dx}\sin x - \sin x\frac{dx^2}{dx}\right) = \frac{\cos x}{x^2} - \frac{2\sin x}{x^3}$$

5. Chain rule for derivatives

If f is a function of u and u is a function of x, then

$$\frac{df}{dx} = \frac{df}{du}\frac{du}{dx}.$$

Examples

a. Evaluate $\dfrac{d}{dx}\sin(x^2)$. Here $u = x^2$ and $f(u) = \sin u$, so

$$\frac{d}{dx}\sin(x^2) = \frac{d}{du}\sin u\frac{du}{dx} = (\cos u)\frac{dx^2}{dx} = 2x\cos(x^2).$$

b. $\dfrac{d}{dt}\sin \omega t = \dfrac{d}{d\omega t}\sin \omega t\dfrac{d}{dt}\omega t = \omega\cos \omega t.$ (ω a constant)

c. Evaluate $\dfrac{d}{dx}\sin^2 5x$. Here $u = \sin 5x$ and $f(u) = u^2$, so

$$\frac{d}{dx}\sin^2 5x = \frac{d}{du}u^2\frac{du}{dx} = 2u\frac{du}{dx} = 2\sin 5x\frac{d}{dx}\sin 5x$$

$$= (2)(\sin 5x)(5)(\cos 5x) = 10\sin 5x\cos 5x = 5\sin 2x.$$

Second Derivative

The second derivative of y with respect to x is defined as the derivative of the derivative:

$$\frac{d^2y}{dx^2} = \frac{d}{dx}\left(\frac{dy}{dx}\right).$$

Example

If $y = ax^3$, then $dy/dx = 3ax^2$, so

$$\frac{d^2y}{dx^2} = \frac{d}{dx}3ax^2 = 6ax.$$

Partial Derivatives

When a function depends on more than one variable, then the partial derivatives of that function are the derivatives with respect to each variable, taken with all other variables held constant. If f is a function of x and y, then the partial derivatives are written

$$\frac{\partial f}{\partial x} \quad \text{and} \quad \frac{\partial f}{\partial y}.$$

Example

If $f(x, y) = x^3\sin y$, then

$$\frac{\partial f}{\partial x} = 3x^2\sin y \quad \text{and} \quad \frac{\partial f}{\partial y} = x^3\cos y.$$

Integrals

Indefinite Integrals

Integration is the inverse of differentiation. The **indefinite integral**, $\int f(x)\,dx$, is defined as a function whose derivative is $f(x)$:

$$\frac{d}{dx}\left[\int f(x)\,dx\right] = f(x).$$

If $A(x)$ is an indefinite integral of $f(x)$, then because the derivative of a constant is zero, the function $A(x) + C$ is also an indefinite integral of $f(x)$, where C is any constant. Inverting the derivatives of common functions listed in the preceding section gives the integrals on the next page (a more extensive table appears at the end of this appendix).

$$\int a\,dx = ax + C \qquad\qquad \int \cos x\,dx = \sin x + C$$

$$\int x^n\,dx = \frac{x^{n+1}}{n+1} + C, \quad n \neq -1 \qquad \int e^x\,dx = e^x + C$$

$$\int \sin x\,dx = -\cos x + C \qquad\qquad \int x^{-1}\,dx = \ln x + C$$

Definite Integrals

In physics we are most often interested in the **definite integral**, defined as the sum of a large number of very small quantities, in the limit as the number of quantities grows arbitrarily large and the size of each arbitrarily small:

$$\int_{x_1}^{x_2} f(x)\,dx \equiv \lim_{\substack{\Delta x \to 0 \\ N \to \infty}} \sum_{i=1}^{N} f(x_i)\,\Delta x,$$

where the terms in the sum are evaluated at values x_i between the limits of integration x_1 and x_2; in the limit $\Delta x \to 0$, the sum is over all values of x in the interval.

The definite integral is used whenever we need to sum over a quantity that is changing—for example, to calculate the work done by a variable force (Chapter 7), the entropy change in a system whose temperature varies (Chapter 22), or the flux of an electric field that varies with position (Chapter 24).

The key to evaluating the definite integral is provided by the **fundamental theorem of calculus**. The theorem states that, if $A(x)$ is an *indefinite* integral of $f(x)$, then the *definite integral* is given by

$$\int_{x_1}^{x_2} f(x)\,dx = A(x_2) - A(x_1) \equiv A(x)\Big|_{x_1}^{x_2}.$$

Geometrically, the definite integral is the area under the graph of $f(x)$ between the limits x_1 and x_2:

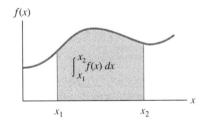

Evaluating Integrals

The first step in evaluating an integral is to express all varying quantities within the integral in terms of a single variable. For example, in evaluating $\int E\,dr$ to calculate an electric potential (Chapter 25), it is necessary first to express E as a function of r. This procedure is illustrated in many examples throughout this text; Example 23-7 provides a typical case.

Once an integral is written in terms of a single variable, it is necessary to manipulate the integrand—the function being integrated—into a form whose integral you know or can look up in tables of integrals. Two common techniques are especially useful:

1. **Change of variables**

   An unfamiliar integral can often be put into familiar form by defining a new variable. For example, it is not obvious how to integrate the expression

   $$\int \frac{x\,dx}{\sqrt{a^2 + x^2}}.$$

   where a is a constant. But let $z = a^2 + x^2$. Then

   $$\frac{dz}{dx} = \frac{da^2}{dx} + \frac{dx^2}{dx} = 0 + 2x = 2x,$$

   so $dz = 2x\,dx$. Then the quantity $x\,dx$ in our unfamiliar integral is just $\frac{1}{2}dz$, while the quantity $\sqrt{a^2 + x^2}$ is just $z^{1/2}$. So the integral becomes

   $$\int \tfrac{1}{2} z^{-1/2}\,dz = \frac{\frac{1}{2}z^{1/2}}{(1/2)} = \sqrt{z},$$

   where we have used the standard form for the integral of a power of the independent variable. Substituting back $z = a^2 + x^2$ gives

   $$\int \frac{x\,dx}{\sqrt{a^2 + x^2}} = \sqrt{a^2 + x^2}.$$

2. **Integration by parts**

   The quantity $\int u\,dv$ is the area under the curve of u as a function of v between specified limits. In the figure below, that area can also be expressed as the area of the rectangle shown minus the area under the curve of v as a function of u. Mathematically, this relation among areas may be expressed as a relation among integrals:

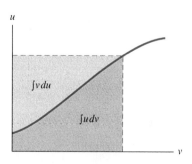

   $$\int u\,dv = uv - \int v\,du. \qquad \text{(integration by parts)}$$

This expression may often be used to transform complicated integrals into simpler ones.

Example

Evaluate $\int x \cos x\, dx$. Here let $u = x$, so $du = dx$. Then $dv = \cos x\, dx$, so $v = \int dv = \int \cos x\, dx = \sin x$. Integrating by parts then gives

$$\int x \cos x\, dx = (x)(\sin x) - \int \sin x\, dx = x \sin x + \cos x,$$

where the $+$ sign arises because $\int \sin x\, dx = -\cos x$.

Table of Integrals

[More extensive tables are available in many mathematical and scientific hand-books; see, for example, **Handbook of Chemistry and Physics** (Chemical Rubber Co.) or Dwight, **Tables of Integrals and Other Mathematical Data** (Macmillan).] Increasingly, sophisticated computer software is used instead of tables for the symbolic evaluation of integrals; among the most widely used are *Maple*, *Mathematica*, and *Derive*.

In the expressions below, a and b are constants. An arbitrary constant of integration may be added to the right-hand side.

$$\int e^{ax}\, dx = \frac{e^{ax}}{a}$$

$$\int \sin ax\, dx = -\frac{\cos ax}{a}$$

$$\int \cos ax\, dx = \frac{\sin ax}{a}$$

$$\int \tan ax\, dx = -\frac{1}{a}\ln(\cos ax)$$

$$\int \sin^2 ax\, dx = \frac{x}{2} - \frac{\sin 2ax}{4a}$$

$$\int \cos^2 ax\, dx = \frac{x}{2} + \frac{\sin 2ax}{4a}$$

$$\int x \sin ax\, dx = \frac{1}{a^2}\sin ax - \frac{1}{a}x \cos ax$$

$$\int x \cos ax\, dx = \frac{1}{a^2}\cos ax + \frac{1}{a}x \sin ax$$

$$\int \frac{dx}{\sqrt{a^2 - x^2}} = \sin^{-1}\!\left(\frac{x}{a}\right)$$

$$\int \frac{dx}{\sqrt{x^2 \pm a^2}} = \ln(x + \sqrt{x^2 \pm a^2})$$

$$\int \frac{dx}{x^2 + a^2} = \frac{1}{a}\tan^{-1}\!\left(\frac{x}{a}\right)$$

$$\int \frac{x\, dx}{\sqrt{a^2 - x^2}} = -\sqrt{a^2 - x^2}$$

$$\int \frac{x\, dx}{\sqrt{x^2 \pm a^2}} = \sqrt{x^2 \pm a^2}$$

$$\int \frac{dx}{(x^2 \pm a^2)^{3/2}} = \frac{\pm x}{a^2 \sqrt{x^2 \pm a^2}}$$

$$\int x e^{ax}\, dx = \frac{e^{ax}}{a^2}(ax - 1)$$

$$\int x^2 e^{ax}\, dx = \frac{x^2 e^{ax}}{a} - \frac{2}{a}\left[\frac{e^{ax}}{a^2}(ax - 1)\right]$$

$$\int \frac{dx}{a + bx} = \frac{1}{b}\ln(a + bx)$$

$$\int \frac{dx}{(a + bx)^2} = -\frac{1}{b(a + bx)}$$

$$\int \ln ax\, dx = x \ln ax - x$$

APPENDIX B
The International System of Units (SI)

This material is from the United States edition of the English translation of the sixth edition of "Le Système International d'Unités (SI)," the definitive publication in the French language issued in 1991 by the International Bureau of Weights and Measures (BIPM). The year the definition was adopted is given in parentheses.

unit of length (meter): The meter is the length of the path traveled by light in vacuum during a time interval of 1/299 792 458 of a second. (1983)

unit of mass (kilogram): The kilogram is the unit of mass; it is equal to the mass of the international prototype of the kilogram. (1889)

unit of time (second): The second is the duration of 9 192 631 770 periods of the radiation corresponding to the transition between the two hyperfine levels of the ground state of the cesium-133 atom. (1967)

unit of electric current (ampere): The ampere is that constant current which, if maintained in two straight parallel conductors of infinite length, of negligible circular cross section, and placed 1 meter apart in vacuum, would produce between these conductors a force equal to 2×10^{-7} newton per meter of length. (1948)

unit of thermodynamic temperature (kelvin): The kelvin, unit of thermodynamic temperature, is the fraction 1/273.16 of the thermodynamic temperature of the triple point of water. (1957) Also, the unit kelvin and its symbol K should be used to express an interval or a difference of temperature.

unit of amount of substance (mole): (1) The mole is the amount of substance of a system that contains as many elementary entities as there are atoms in 0.012 kilogram of carbon 12. (1971) (2) When the mole is used, the elementary entities must be specified and may be atoms, molecules, ions, electrons, other particles, or specified groups of such particles.

unit of luminous intensity (candela): The candela is the luminous intensity, in a given direction, of a source that emits monochromatic radiation of frequency 540×10^{12} hertz and that has a radiant intensity in that direction of (1/683) watt per steradian. (1979)

▲ *SI Base and Supplementary Units*

	SI UNIT	
QUANTITY	**NAME**	**SYMBOL**
Base Unit		
Length	meter	m
Mass	kilogram	kg
Time	second	s
Electric current	ampere	A
Thermodynamic temperature	kelvin	K
Amount of substance	mole	mol
Luminous intensity	candela	cd
Supplementary Units		
Plane angle	radian	rad
Solid angle	steradian	sr

▲ *SI Prefixes*

FACTOR	PREFIX	SYMBOL
10^{24}	yotta	Y
10^{21}	zetta	Z
10^{18}	exa	E
10^{15}	peta	P
10^{12}	tera	T
10^{9}	giga	G
10^{6}	mega	M
10^{3}	kilo	k
10^{2}	hecto	h
10^{1}	deka	da
10^{0}	—	—
10^{-1}	deci	d
10^{-2}	centi	c
10^{-3}	milli	m
10^{-6}	micro	μ
10^{-9}	nano	n
10^{-12}	pico	p
10^{-15}	femto	f
10^{-18}	atto	a
10^{-21}	zepto	z
10^{-24}	yocto	y

▲ *Some SI Derived Units with Special Names*

			SI UNIT	
QUANTITY	**NAME**	**SYMBOL**	**EXPRESSION IN TERMS OF OTHER UNITS**	**EXPRESSION IN TERMS OF SI BASE UNITS**
Frequency	hertz	Hz		s^{-1}
Force	newton	N		$m \cdot kg \cdot s^{-2}$
Pressure, stress	pascal	Pa	N/m^2	$m^{-1} \cdot kg \cdot s^{-2}$
Energy, work, heat	joule	J	$N \cdot m$	$m^2 \cdot kg \cdot s^{-2}$
Power	watt	W	J/s	$m^2 \cdot kg \cdot s^{-3}$
Electric charge	coulomb	C		$s \cdot A$
Electric potential, potential difference, electromotive force	volt	V	J/C	$m^2 \cdot kg \cdot s^{-3} \cdot A^{-1}$
Capacitance	farad	F	C/V	$m^{-2} \cdot kg^{-1} \cdot s^4 \cdot A^2$
Electric resistance	ohm	Ω	V/A	$m^2 \cdot kg \cdot s^{-3} \cdot A^{-2}$
Magnetic flux	weber	Wb	$V \cdot s$	$m^2 \cdot kg \cdot s^{-2} \cdot A^{-1}$
Magnetic field	tesla	T	Wb/m^2	$kg \cdot s^{-2} \cdot A^{-1}$
Inductance	henry	H	Wb/A	$m^2 \cdot kg \cdot s^{-2} \cdot A^{-2}$
Radioactivity	becquerel	Bq	1 decay/s	s^{-1}
Absorbed radiation dose	gray	Gy	J/kg, 100 rad	$m^2 \cdot s^{-2}$
Radiation dose equivalent	sievert	Sv	J/kg, 100 rem	$m^2 \cdot s^{-2}$

Conversion Factors

The listings below give the SI equivalents of non-SI units. To convert from the units shown to SI, multiply by the factor given; to convert the other way, divide. For conversions within the SI system see table of SI prefixes in Appendix B, Chapter 1, or inside front cover. Conversions that are not exact by definition are given to, at most, 4 significant figures.

Length

1 inch (in.) = 0.0254 m

1 foot (ft) = 0.3048 m

1 yard (yd) = 0.9144 m

1 mile (mi) = 1609 m

1 nautical mile = 1852 m

1 angstrom (Å) = 10^{-10} m

1 light-year (ly) = 9.46×10^{15} m

1 astronomical unit (AU) = 1.5×10^{11} m

1 parsec = 3.09×10^{16} m

1 fermi = 10^{-15} m = 1 fm

Mass

1 slug = 14.59 kg

1 metric ton (tonne; T) = 1000 kg

1 unified mass unit (u) = 1.660×10^{-27} kg

Force units in the English system are sometimes used (incorrectly) for mass. The units given below are actually equal to the number of kilograms multiplied by *g*, the acceleration of gravity.

1 pound (lb) = weight of 0.454 kg

1 ton = 2000 lb = weight of 908 kg

1 ounce (oz) = weight of 0.02835 kg

Time

1 minute (min) = 60 s

1 hour (h) = 60 min = 3600 s

1 day (d) = 24 h = 86 400 s

1 year (y) = 365.2422 d* = 3.156×10^7 s

* The length of the year changes very slowly with changes in Earth's orbital period.

Area

1 hectare (ha) = 10^4 m^2

1 square inch (in.^{2}) = 6.452×10^{-4} m^2

1 square foot (ft^2) = 9.290×10^{-2} m^2

1 acre = 4047 m^2

1 barn = 10^{-28} m^2

1 shed = 10^{-30} m^2

Volume

1 liter (L) = 1000 cm^3 = 10^{-3} m^3

1 cubic foot (ft^3) = 2.832×10^{-2} m^3

1 cubic inch (in.^{3}) = 1.639×10^{-5} m^3

1 fluid ounce = 1/128 gal = 2.957×10^{-5} m^3

1 barrel = 42 gal = 0.1590 m^3

1 gallon (U.S.; gal) = 3.785×10^{-3} m^3

1 gallon (British) = 4.546×10^{-3} m^3

Angle, Phase

1 degree (°) = $\pi/180$ rad = 1.745×10^{-2} rad

1 revolution (rev) = 360° = 2π rad

1 cycle = 360° = 2π rad

Speed, Velocity

1 km/h = (1/3.6) m/s = 0.2778 m/s

1 mi/h (mph) = 0.4470 m/s

1 ft/s = 0.3048 m/s

1 ly/y = 3.00×10^8 m/s

Angular Speed, Angular Velocity, Frequency, and Angular Frequency

1 rev/s = 2π rad/s = 6.283 rad/s (s^{-1})

1 Hz = 1 cycle/s = 2πs^{-1}

1 rev/min (rpm) = 0.1047 rad/s (s^{-1})

Force

1 dyne = 10^{-5} N

1 pound (lb) = 4.448 N

Pressure

1 dyne/cm^2 = 0.10 Pa

1 atmosphere (atm) = 1.013×10^5 Pa

1 torr = 1 mm Hg at 0°C = 133.3 Pa

1 bar = 10^5 Pa = 0.987 atm

1 lb/in.^{2} (psi) = 6.895×10^3 Pa

1 in. H$_2$O (60°F) = 248.8 Pa

1 in. Hg (60°F) = 3.377×10^3 Pa

Energy, Work, Heat

1 erg = 10^{-7} J

1 calorie* (cal) = 4.184 J

1 electron-volt (eV) = 1.602×10^{-19} J

1 foot-pound (ft·lb) = 1.356 J

1 Btu* = 1.054×10^3 J

1 kWh = 3.6×10^6 J

1 megaton (explosive yield; Mt)

$\quad$ = 4.18×10^{15} J

---

* Values based on the thermochemical calorie; other definitions vary slightly.

Power

1 erg/s $= 10^{-7}$ W	1 Btu/h (Btuh) $= 0.293$ W
1 horsepower (hp) $= 746$ W	1 ft·lb/s $= 1.356$ W

Magnetic Field

1 gauss (G) $= 10^{-4}$ T	1 gamma (γ) $= 10^{-9}$ T

Radiation

1 curie (ci) $= 3.7 \times 10^{10}$ Bq	1 rad $= 10^{-2}$ Gy
	1 rem $= 10^{-2}$ Sv

▲   *Energy Content of Fuels*

ENERGY SOURCE	ENERGY CONTENT
Coal	2.9×10^{7} J/kg $= 7300$ kWh/ton $= 25 \times 10^{6}$ Btu/ton
Oil	43×10^{6} J/kg $= 39$ kWh/gal $= 1.3 \times 10^{5}$ Btu/gal
Gasoline	44×10^{6} J/kg $= 36$ kWh/gal $= 1.2 \times 10^{5}$ Btu/gal
Natural gas	55×10^{6} J/kg $= 30$ kWh/100 ft^3 $= 1000$ Btu/ft^3
Uranium (fission)	
Normal abundance	5.8×10^{11} J/kg $= 1.6 \times 10^{5}$ kWh/kg
Pure U-235	8.2×10^{13} J/kg $= 2.3 \times 10^{7}$ kWh/kg
Hydrogen (fusion)	
Normal abundance	7×10^{11} J/kg $= 3.0 \times 10^{4}$ kWh/kg
Pure deuterium	3.3×10^{14} J/kg $= 9.2 \times 10^{7}$ kWh/kg
Water	1.2×10^{10} J/kg $= 1.3 \times 10^{4}$ kWh/gal $= 340$ gal gasoline/gal
H$_2$O	
100% conversion, matter to energy	9.0×10^{16} J/kg $= 931$ MeV/u $= 2.5 \times 10^{10}$ kWh/kg

APPENDIX D
The Elements

The atomic weights of stable elements reflect the abundances of different isotopes; values given here apply to elements as they exist naturally on Earth. For stable elements, parentheses express uncertainties in the last decimal place given. For elements with no stable isotopes (indicated in boldface), sets of most important isotopes are given. (Exceptions are the unstable elements thorium, protactinium, and uranium, for which atomic weights reflect natural abundances of long-lived isotopes.) See also periodic table inside back cover.

ATOMIC NUMBER	NAMES	SYMBOL	ATOMIC WEIGHT
1	Hydrogen	H	1.00794 (7)
2	Helium	He	4.002602 (2)
3	Lithium	Li	6.941 (2)
4	Beryllium	Be	9.012182 (3)
5	Boron	B	10.811 (5)
6	Carbon	C	12.011 (1)
7	Nitrogen	N	14.00674 (7)
8	Oxygen	O	15.9994 (3)
9	Fluorine	F	18.9984032 (9)
10	Neon	Ne	20.1797 (6)
11	Sodium (Natrium)	Na	22.989768 (6)
12	Magnesium	Mg	24.3050 (6)
13	Aluminum	Al	26.981539 (5)
14	Silicon	Si	28.0855 (3)
15	Phosphorus	P	30.973762 (4)
16	Sulfur	S	32.066 (6)
17	Chlorine	Cl	35.4527 (9)
18	Argon	Ar	39.948 (1)
19	Potassium (Kalium)	K	39.0983 (1)
20	Calcium	Ca	40.078 (4)
21	Scandium	Sc	44.955910 (9)
22	Titanium	Ti	47.88 (3)
23	Vanadium	V	50.9415 (1)
24	Chromium	Cr	51.9961 (6)
25	Manganese	Mn	54.93805 (1)
26	Iron	Fe	55.847 (3)
27	Cobalt	Co	58.93320 (1)

ATOMIC NUMBER	NAMES	SYMBOL	ATOMIC WEIGHT
28	Nickel	Ni	58.69 (1)
29	Copper	Cu	63.546 (3)
30	Zinc	Zn	65.39 (2)
31	Gallium	Ga	69.723 (1)
32	Germanium	Ge	72.61 (2)
33	Arsenic	As	74.92159 (2)
34	Selenium	Se	78.96 (3)
35	Bromine	Br	79.904 (1)
36	Krypton	Kr	83.80 (1)
37	Rubidium	Rb	85.4678 (3)
38	Strontium	Sr	87.62 (1)
39	Yttrium	Y	88.90585 (2)
40	Zirconium	Zr	91.224 (2)
41	Niobium	Nb	92.90638 (2)
42	Molybdenum	Mo	95.94 (1)
43	**Technetium**	**Tc**	**97, 98, 99**
44	Ruthenium	Ru	101.07 (2)
45	Rhodium	Rh	102.90550 (3)
46	Palladium	Pd	106.42 (1)
47	Silver	Ag	107.8682 (2)
48	Cadmium	Cd	112.411 (8)
49	Indium	In	114.82 (1)
50	Tin	Sn	118.710 (7)
51	Antimony (Stibium)	Sb	121.75 (3)
52	Tellurium	Te	127.60 (3)
53	Iodine	I	126.90447 (3)
54	Xenon	Xe	131.29 (2)
55	Cesium	Cs	132.90543 (5)
56	Barium	Ba	137.327 (7)
57	Lanthanum	La	138.9055 (2)
58	Cerium	Ce	140.115 (4)
59	Praseodymium	Pr	140.90765 (3)
60	Neodymium	Nd	144.24 (3)
61	**Promethium**	**Pm**	**145, 147**
62	Samarium	Sm	150.36 (3)
63	Europium	Eu	151.965 (9)
64	Gadolinium	Gd	157.25 (3)
65	Terbium	Tb	158.92534 (3)
66	Dysprosium	Dy	162.50 (3)
67	Holmium	Ho	164.93032 (3)
68	Erbium	Er	167.26 (3)
69	Thulium	Tm	168.93421 (3)
70	Ytterbium	Yb	173.04 (3)
71	Lutetium	Lu	174.967 (1)
72	Hafnium	Hf	178.49 (2)
73	Tantalum	Ta	180.9479 (1)
74	Tungsten (Wolfram)	W	183.85 (3)
75	Rhenium	Re	186.207 (1)
76	Osmium	Os	190.2 (1)
77	Iridium	Ir	192.22 (3)
78	Platinum	Pt	195.08 (3)
79	Gold	Au	196.96654 (3)
80	Mercury	Hg	200.59 (3)
81	Thallium	Tl	204.3833 (2)
82	Lead	Pb	207.2 (1)
83	Bismuth	Bi	208.98037 (3)

ATOMIC NUMBER	NAMES	SYMBOL	ATOMIC WEIGHT
84	Polonium	Po	209, 210
85	Astatine	At	210, 211
86	Radon	Rn	211, 220, 222
87	Francium	Fr	223
88	Radium	Ra	223, 224, 226, 228
89	Actinium	Ac	227
90	Thorium	Th	232.0381 (1)
91	Protactinium	Pa	231.03588 (2)
92	Uranium	U	238.0289 (1)
93	Neptunium	Np	237, 239
94	Plutonium	Pu	238, 239, 240, 241, 242, 244
95	Americium	Am	241, 243
96	Curium	Cm	243, 244, 245, 246, 247, 248
97	Berkelium	Bk	247, 249
98	Californium	Cf	249, 250, 251, 252
99	Einsteinium	Es	252
100	Fermium	Fm	257
101	Mendelevium	Md	255, 256, 258, 260
102	Nobelium	No	253, 254, 255, 259
103	Lawrencium	Lr	256, 258, 259, 261
104	Rutherfordium	Rf	257, 259, 260, 261
105	Dubnium	Db	260, 261, 262
106	Seaborgium	Sg	259, 260, 261, 263
107	Bohrium	Bh	261, 262
108	Hassium	Hs	264, 265
109	Meitnerium	Mt	266
110	—	—	269
111	—	—	272
112	—	—	277

Astrophysical Data

SUN, PLANETS, PRINCIPAL SATELLITES

BODY	MASS (10²⁴ kg)	MEAN RADIUS (10⁶ m EXCEPT AS NOTED)	SURFACE GRAVITY (m/s²)	ESCAPE SPEED (km/s)	SIDEREAL ROTATION PERIOD* (days)	MEAN DISTANCE FROM CENTRAL BODY† (10⁶ km)	ORBITAL PERIOD	ORBITAL SPEED (km/s)
Sun	1.99×10^6	696	274	618	36 at poles 27 at equator	2.6×10^{11}	200 My	250
Mercury	0.330	2.44	3.70	4.25	58.6	57.6	88.0 d	48
Venus	4.87	6.05	8.87	10.4	−243	108	225 d	35
Earth	5.97	6.37	9.81	11.2	0.997	150	365.3 d	30
Moon	0.0735	1.74	1.62	2.38	27.3	0.385	27.3 d	1.0
Mars	0.642	3.38	3.74	5.03	1.03	228	1.88 y	24.1
Phobos	9.6×10^{-9}	9-13 km	0.001	0.008	0.32	9.4×10^{-3}	0.32 d	2.1
Deimos	2×10^{-9}	5-8 km	0.001	0.005	1.3	23×10^{-3}	1.3 d	1.3
Jupiter	1.90×10^3	69.1	26.5	60.6	0.414	778	11.9 y	13.0
Io	0.0889	1.82	1.8	2.6	1.77	0.422	1.77 d	17
Europa	0.478	1.57	1.3	2.0	3.55	0.671	3.55 d	14
Ganymede	0.148	2.63	1.4	2.7	7.15	1.07	7.15 d	11
Callisto	0.107	2.40	1.2	2.4	16.7	1.88	16.7 d	8.2
and 13 smaller satellites								
Saturn	569	56.8	11.8	36.6	0.438	1.43×10^3	29.5 y	9.65
Tethys	0.0007	0.53	0.2	0.4	1.89	0.294	1.89 d	11.3
Dione	0.00015	0.56	0.3	0.6	2.74	0.377	2.74 d	10.0
Rhea	0.0025	0.77	0.3	0.5	4.52	0.527	4.52 d	8.5
Titan	0.135	2.58	1.4	2.6	15.9	1.22	15.9 d	5.6
Iapetus	0.0019	0.73	0.2	0.6	79.3	3.56	79.3 d	3.3
and 12 smaller satellites								
Uranus	86.6	25.0	9.23	21.5	−0.65	2.87×10^3	84.1 y	6.79
Ariel	0.0013	0.58	0.3	0.4	2.52	0.19	2.52 d	5.5
Umbriel	0.0013	0.59	0.3	0.4	4.14	0.27	4.14 d	4.7
Titania	0.0018	0.81	0.2	0.5	8.70	0.44	8.70 d	3.7
Oberon	0.0017	0.78	0.2	0.5	13.5	0.58	13.5 d	3.1
and 11 smaller satellites								
Neptune	103	24.0	11.9	23.9	0.768	4.50×10^3	165 y	5.43
Triton	0.134	1.9	2.5	3.1	5.88	0.354	5.88 d	4.4
and 7 smaller satellites								
Pluto	0.015	1.2	0.4	1.2	−6.39	5.91×10^3	249 y	4.7
Charon	0.001	0.6			−6.39	0.02	6.39 d	0.2

*Negative rotation period indicates retrograde motion, in opposite sense from orbital motion. Periods are sidereal, meaning the time for the body to return to the same orientation relative to the distant stars rather than the Sun.

†Central body is galactic center for Sun, Sun for planets, and planet for satellites.

Got It! Answers

Chapter 2

p. 24 Average speed and average velocity are the same for direct and Kansas City stop flights; average speed is greater for Minneapolis stop flight

p. 27 (b) has constant speed; (a) reverses direction; (d) speeds up

Chapter 3

p. 52 (c)

Chapter 4

p. 70 None are true

Chapter 5

p. 95 The straight line

p. 99 $T > F_g$ for upward a; $T < F_g$ for downward a; $T = F_g$ for constant speed in either direction

p. 102 No; for example, a car slowing down is moving in the direction opposite the force that's slowing it

p. 107 The statement is nonsense. If there were no gravity in space, spacecraft, astronauts, and the moon would all move in straight lines and we would never see them again!

p. 109 Upward acceleration does not imply upward velocity; cable tension exceeds weight in (a) and (d)

p. 111 No, the force on the larger block is 1.5 N

Chapter 6

p. 134 Both 1 N

p. 139 Because the gravitational force is just enough to keep them accelerating in a circular path

p. 144 Because the objects were on sloping surfaces, and therefore the normal force was not equal to the weight

p. 153 The larger one; it has a greater ratio of mass to surface area

Chapter 7

p. 172 No, it's only 5 J, as the spring hasn't exerted 2 N the whole way

p. 177 Both do the same work; the faster hiker produces more power

Chapter 8

p. 200 Because an *increase* in potential energy (positive dU/dx) means one is doing work moving *against* a force

Chapter 10

p. 244 Second one from the top

p. 247 $30\hat{\jmath}$ kg·m/s

p. 249 Both skaters' momenta increase; the basketball's momentum reverses sign; system momentum is unchanged

Chapter 11

p. 264 The first two

p. 271 The object initially at rest

Chapter 12

p. 290 12-6b

p. 297 Because its mass is farther from the rotation axis

p. 304 The solid ball

Chapter 13

p. 323 The boy brings no additional angular momentum to the system, while the girl does

p. 327 Upward

Chapter 14

p. 339 The diagonal pair

Chapter 15

p. 369 Frequency and period are the same; amplitude and phase constants are different

p. 375 (a) no change; (b) doubles; (c) doubles

Chapter 17

p. 422 No, it drops by 20 dB

Chapter 18

p. 450 No, the water level stays the same

p. 451 Because you'll put the center of gravity over the center of buoyancy, making the canoe unstable as in Fig. 18-17b

p. 458 Lower

Chapter 19

p. 480 The rock

p. 486 Radiation; (a) conduction; (b) convection

Chapter 20

p. 504 100°C

Chapter 21

p. 526 In an isothermal process T is constant so pressure and volume are inversely proportional. But temperature changes in an adiabatic process, so P and V are not inversely proportional. Thus there's no contradiction between the two equations

Chapter 23
p. 576 (a) $-\hat{\mathbf{i}}$; (b) $\sqrt{2}/2(-\hat{\mathbf{i}} + \hat{\mathbf{j}})$
p. 583 (a) 200 N/C; (b) 100 N/C
p. 585 Because P isn't the same distance from **all** parts of the rod

Chapter 24
p. 606 (a) $\phi = 0$ for A, B; $\phi = Es^2$ for C; (b) $\phi = 0$ for A, $\phi = s^2E\cos 45° = \sqrt{2}s^2E/2$ for B, C
p. 608 ϕ doesn't change; $\mathbf{E}$ generally does
p. 611 (a) remains zero; (b) doubles
p. 617 (a) $E = \dfrac{Q}{-(2)(1\ m)^2(\varepsilon_0)}$ (b) $E = \dfrac{kQ}{(1000\ m)^2}$
p. 619 No

Chapter 25
p. 633 (a) doubles; (b) doubles; (c) becomes zero; (d) changes sign
p. 633 $W_\alpha = 2W_p$
p. 635 Proton: toward negative ΔV; electron: toward positive ΔV
p. 636 b, a, c
p. 637 More
p. 644 (a)
p. 645 Yes to both

Chapter 26
p. 666 They're the same
p. 670 Twice the working voltage
p. 673 (a) parallel; (b) series; (c) the series combination 1/2 C

Chapter 27
p. 686 (a) current to left; (b) upward current; (c) current to left; (d) no current; (e) no current
p. 700 (a) (2); (b) (1)

Chapter 28
p. 713 (a) 3 V; (b) 0 V; (c) 6 V
p. 716 (a) 2R; (b) 1/2 R
p. 718 A will be brightest; with C disconnected both A and B will have equal brightness
p. 732 (a) 6 mA; (b) 2 mA

Chapter 29
p. 746 Greatest force in (a); least (0) in (c); direction in (a) and (b) is into page
p. 749 Counterclockwise
p. 755 Upward

Chapter 30
p. 777 (a) into the page at P, out of the page at Q; (b) stronger at P
p. 778 Tighten, independent of the current direction
p. 780 Into the page
p. 782 (b) only

Chapter 31
p. 811 Same direction as in Fig. 31-11; you still do work
p. 812 Counterclockwise
p. 814 Harder
p. 817 (a) clockwise; (b) counterclockwise

Chapter 32
p. 838 Increasing
p. 843 Only when it's opened

Chapter 33
p. 857 The capacitor
p. 864 Smaller, by a factor of 10^{-4}
p. 866 Above

Chapter 34
p. 895 Both have the same speed; light has a much smaller wavelength
p. 905 (a) $B_1 = 2B_2$; (b) $S_1 = 4S_2$; (c) $\lambda_1 = \lambda_2$

Chapter 35
p. 923 $n_3 > n_1 > n_2$

Chapter 36
p. 943 At the mirror's center of curvature
p. 950 (a) The intensity diminishes, but the full image remains (b) there would be no image (c) there would be no image, or it would be very out of focus (d) yes, but not obviously visible except when looking straight toward lens
p. 951 Virtual, convex
p. 960 +2.25 diopter

Chapter 37
p. 976 Closer together

Chapter 38
p. 1020 When the twins move at the same speed they are the same age; the twin making the longer trip is younger
p. 1029 Less, although insignificantly so at these low relative speeds
p. 1033 Very nearly c

Answers to Odd-Numbered Problems

Chapter 1
3. 100,000 times bigger
   5.0.108 782 775 7 ns
7. 10^8
9. 0.79 rad
11. 28 g
13. 10^6
15. 7%
17. Less by about 3 mi/h
19. 30 AU
21. 143 m²/kg
23. Approximately 0.0175 rad
25. L/T^2
27. (c) Actually, the speed is given by
   $v = \sqrt{\lambda g/2\pi}$
29. 2.5×10^6 m
31. 7.4×10^6 m/s²
33. (a) 2.5×10^{-11} m²; (b) 5.0 μm
35. 280 K
37. 41 m
39. 7
43. $\sim 1.3 \times 10^6$
45. About 0.1%
47. (a) $\sim 1.4 \times 10^{18}$ m³; (b) $\sim 1.3 \times 10^{12}$
49. ~ 10 times as much in stars
51. $\sim 10^4$
53. $d_{Sun}/d_{moon} = 380$;
   $R_{Sun} \sim 7 \times 10^5$ km
   (a) 4 μm; (b) 7500
55. (a) $\sim 10^{28}$; (b) $\sim 10^{14}$
59. $\sqrt{F_0/\mu}$; this is in fact the equation
   for the wave speed

Chapter 2
1. 10.16 m/s
3. 5.30 m/s
5. (a) 24 km north; (b) 9.6 km/h;
   (c) 16 km/h; (d) 0; (e) 0
7. 28.5 km/h
9. 48 mi/h

11. 1 m/s = 2.24 mi/h
13. 51 ft/s = 35 mi/h
15. (a) 84 km/h; (b) 55 h
17. 2.6 h later; 1800 km from New
   York
21. (a) 2.0 m/s; (b) 0; (c) -5.0 m/s; (d)
   1.2 m/s; (e) 0.17 m/s
23. (a) $b - 2ct$; (b) 8.4 s after launch
25. (a) $t = 0$ s, 0.13 s, 2.5 s;
   (b) $v = 3bt^2 - 2ct + d$;
   (c) $v_0 = 1.0$ m/s;
   (d) $t = 0.065$ s, 1.7 s
27. 125 m/s²
29. 15 m/s²
31. 31 s
33. (a) 126 m/s; (b) 0.46 m/s²
35. $a = 6bt - 2c$
37. 100 m by both methods
41. (a) 46 m/s²; (b) 61 s
43. (a) 2.0 m/s²; (b) 150 m
45. 5×10^{-12} m
47. 12 km/s
49. (a) 0.014 s; (b) 0.51 m
51. 886 m
53. Yes, $a = 370$ m/s²
55. No collision; 10 m apart
57. 4.6×10^{-3} m/s²
59. Collide at 12 km/h
61. 11.3 m/s
63. (a) 27 m; (b) 4.7 s
65. Mars
67. 273 m
69. 2.0 m/s
71. 2.4 s
73. (a) 25 km/h; (b) 13 km/h
75. (a) 4.6 s; (b) 8.7 m/s
77. 0.196 s
79. 5.0 s; 17 km/h
81. (a) 7.0 m/s; (b) in 2.3 s
83. 83.113 m

85. (b) 3.8 s; (c) 19 m; (d) 100 m
87. (a) $v = \omega x_0 \cos \omega t$,
   $a = -\omega^2 x_0 \sin \omega t$;
   (b) $v_{max} = \omega x_0$, $a_{max} = \omega^2 x_0$
89. (a) 20 cm
91. 1.19 m

Chapter 3
1. 266 m, 34° N of W
3. 702 km, 21.3° E of N
5. $C = 5.0$ m; 127° clockwise from **A**
7. (a) 0.68A vertically upward;
   (b) 1.88A, to the right
9. (a) L, $-x$ direction; (b) $\sqrt{3}L$,
   $+ y$ direction; (c) 0; (d) $2L$,
   $- x$ direction
11. $\mathbf{V} = 105\hat{\imath} + 58\hat{\jmath}$ km
13. $\mathbf{A} = 8.19\hat{\imath} + 5.74\hat{\jmath}$;
   $\mathbf{B} = -3.44\hat{\imath} - 4.91\hat{\jmath}$;
   $\mathbf{C} = -3.38\hat{\imath} + 7.25\hat{\jmath}$
15. $\mathbf{A} + \mathbf{B} = 4.8\hat{\imath} + 0.82\hat{\jmath}$;
   $\mathbf{A} - \mathbf{B} = 12\hat{\imath} + 11\hat{\jmath}$;
   $\mathbf{A} + \mathbf{C} = 4.8\hat{\imath} + 13\hat{\jmath}$;
   $\mathbf{A} + \mathbf{B} + \mathbf{C} = 1.4\hat{\imath} + 8.1\hat{\jmath}$
17. $\mathbf{C} = -15\hat{\imath} + 9\hat{\jmath} - 18\hat{\mathbf{k}}$
19. (a) $1.37\hat{\imath} + 8.07\hat{\jmath}$;
   (b) $8.25\hat{\imath} + 17.9\hat{\jmath}$; (c) $10.5\hat{\imath} - 17.6\hat{\jmath}$
21. $0.19\hat{\imath} + 0.88\hat{\jmath}$ km;
   (b) 1.0 km at 79° N of E
23. (a) $A_x = 5.9$, $A_y = 8.1$; $A'_x = 5.4$,
   $A'_y = 8.4$ units
25. $\hat{\imath} + \hat{\jmath} + \hat{\mathbf{k}}$; magnitude $= \sqrt{3}$
27. (a) in x-y system $\Delta \mathbf{r} = 5.0\hat{\imath} +$
   $3.5\hat{\jmath}$ km; in x'-y' system
   $\Delta \mathbf{r} = 6.1\hat{\imath} + 0.50\hat{\jmath}$ km;
   (b) $\Delta r = 6.1$ km
29. (a) 5.4 mi at 32° E of N;
   (b) 15 mi/h at 32° E of N
31. (a) 264 km/h, 29° west of north;
   (b) $-128\hat{\imath} + 231\hat{\jmath}$ km/h

33. $19\hat{\imath} + 4.5\hat{\jmath} + 0.26\hat{k}$ km/h
35. (a) $24\hat{\imath} + 10\hat{\jmath}$ m;
   (b) $12\hat{\imath} + 5.0\hat{\jmath}$ m/s;
   (c) $12\hat{\imath} - 5.0\hat{\jmath}$ m/s
37. 5.12 m/s^2, $41°$ S of W ($221°$ from x axis)
39. (a) $\bar{\mathbf{v}} = -0.8\hat{\jmath}$ cm/h;
   (b) $\bar{\mathbf{a}} = -0.42\hat{\imath}$ cm/h^2
41. (a) $10\hat{\imath} - 21\hat{\jmath}$ m/s; (b) 13.0 m/s;
   (c) $89.0°$
43. $6.7\hat{\imath}$ m/s; (b) 1.66 s; (c) 8.24 m/s
45. (a) 18 km/h, 14 km/h, 10 km/h,
   14 km/h; (b) 21 km/h, 17 km/h,
   13 km/h, 17 km/h
47. $30\hat{\imath} + 64\hat{\jmath}$ km/s
49. (a) 1.6 m, 2.8 m/s, both vertically
   downward; (b) 2.03 m, 3.57 m/s,
   both at $38.1°$ to the vertical;
   (c) 9.8 m/s^2, vertically downward in
   both frames of reference
51. 16.2 m
53. (a) 1.8 km/h/s = 0.50 m/s^2;
   (b) $142°$
55. (a) 0.32 cm/s; (b) 0.034 cm/s^2;
   (c) $90°$
57. $25°$ upstream
59. (a) 1.30×10^6 m; (b) 7.78 km/s;
   (c) 9.19 m/s^2, almost g
61. $-b\hat{\imath} + a\hat{\jmath}$, $b\hat{\imath} - a\hat{\jmath}$
63. $\frac{\sqrt{2}}{2}\hat{\imath} + \frac{\sqrt{2}}{2}\hat{\jmath}$
67. $53.8°$, 13.9 km/h

Chapter 4

1. $0°$
3. $1.3\hat{\imath} + 2.3\hat{\jmath}$ m/s
5. 6.0 m/s at $53°$ below x axis
7. (a) $23°$; (b) 5.4×10^3 km
9. 1.83 m
11. (a) $t = 18$ s; (b) 300 m; (c) 22 m/s,
   at $120°$ to x axis
13. (a) 2.6×10^{17} cm/s^2, upward;
   (b) parabolic
15. (a) 1.34 s; (b) 14.7 m
17. 5.7 m/s
19. 34 nm
21. 8.3 m/s at $61°$
23. Yes
25. -14.6 m/s
27. (a) 6.64 km/s; (b) 16.0 min;
   (c) 8.28 km/s
29. 1.1 s
31. 1090 m

35. (a) 8.8 m; (b) 0.53 m
37. 11.2 m/s
41. $31.2°$ or $65.7°$
43. 2.8×10^{-3} m/s^2
45. 54 min
47. 2.27 km
59. 5.07×10^3 s
51. $a_r = 0.947$ m/s^2;
   $a_t = 6.28\times10^{-2}$ m/s^2
53. $t = \sqrt{r/a_t}$
55. 89 m/s
57. 32 m
59. 19 m
61. 300 m, 119 m
63. $\mathbf{v}_0 = 6.36\hat{\imath} + 10.3\hat{\jmath}$ m/s,
   or 12.1 m/s at $58.3°$
65. $83°$
71. 7.2 m/s at $77°$ to horizontal
75. $38°$
77. $2v_0 \sin\theta_0/g$
79. 892 m/s^2
81. 364 m

83. (a) $\tan^{-1}\left(\tan\theta_0 - \dfrac{gt}{v_0\cos\theta_0}\right)$;

   (b) $\tan^{-1}\left(\tan\theta_0 - \dfrac{gx}{v_0^2\cos^2\theta_0}\right)$

Chapter 5

1. 3.8 MN
3. 1.5×10^3 kN
5. 10^{-4} N
7. (a) $m_B = 3.0m_A$; (b) 2.0 m/s^2
9. Quadruples
11. (a) 11 m; (b) 24 m; (c) 43 m;
   (d) 53 m
13. $F_{\text{driver}} = 5.7$ kN; $F_{\text{passenger}} = $
   125 kN, 22 times greater
15. 5.77 N at $72.2°$ to the x axis
17. Venus
19. (a) 3.3 N; (b) 12 oz
21. 9.1×10^3 kg
23. 7.7×10^{12} m/s^2
25. 4.26 m/s^2
27. 385 N
29. 2.9 m/s^2, downward
31. (a) 3.1×10^7 N; (b) 9.4×10^2 N
33. 0.53 s
35. 55 kN
37. 2.0 N
39. 1.3×10^{-21} cm

41. (a) 5.26 kN; (b) 1.08 kN;
   (c) 494 N; (d) 589 N
43. 130 N
45. 33 cm
47. 1.9 m/s^2
49. 830 g
51. (a) 132 cm; (b) 127 cm;
   (c) 120 cm; (d) 40 m/s^2
53. 30.7 kN
55. 4.1 cm
57. Apparent weight is 55% of actual
   weight
59. 240 N
61. 4.3 cm
63. 7.2 m
65. (a) $0.40mg$; (b) $2.40mg$; (c) $1.40mg$
67. (a) 16 kN; (b) 1.5 kN

69. (a) $a = \dfrac{m_f - m_s}{m_s}g$;

   (b) $y = \dfrac{m_f a_s h}{(m_f - m_s)(g + a_s)}$

71. $\ell + nm(a + g)/k$, where n is the
   spring number measured from the
   bottom
75. 900 N

Chapter 6

1. $2.7\hat{\imath} + 5.5\hat{\jmath}$ N, or 6.1 N at $64°$ to
   the x axis
3. (a) 2.0 kN; (b) 1.4 kN
7. 43 cm
9. 530 N; 3.6 times the weight
11. 98 N in horizontal string; $98\sqrt{2}$ N
   in vertical string
13. 230 N in short rope; 84 N in long
   rope
15. (a) 6.3 m/s^2; (b) 0.44 s
17. Right-hand mass 2.5 times left-hand
   mass
19. (a) 7.1 kg; (b) 3.9 kg
21. Left to right, 56.9 N, 34.4 N,
   89.2 N
23. 8.18×10^{-8} N
27. (a) 13 m/s; (b) $4.4°$
29. 132 m
31. (a) 310 N; (b) 0; (c) nothing
33. (a) $35°$; (b) $22°$
35. 24 m/s = 86 km/h
37. 17 m/s
39. 579 N
41. 5.43 kN
43. 0.21

45. 25.3 s
47. 11.4 m/s^2
49. 133 m
51. 2.7 cm
53. (a) 1.6 m/s^2; (b) 3.3 N
55. 4.2 m/s^2
57. 95 km/h
61. 0.72
63. 2.6 N
65. 4.7 m/s
67. 0.70 m/s^2, upward
69. 7.75 m/s
71. 1.40 s
73. (a) 0.12; (b) toward the inside of the turn
75. 2.0 rpm
79. (a) lower at equator, where a net downward force is needed to keep you accelerating with Earth's rotation; (b) 0.34%
85. 28 cm

Chapter 7
1. 900 J
3. 0.15 NJ
5. 9.6 MJ
7. (a) 400 J; (b) 31 kg
9. 4.4 MN
13. (a) 86.9 units^2; (b) 20.3 units^2
15. (a) 0; (b) 90°
19. 169 J
21. 622 J
23. (a) 60 kJ; (b) 20 kJ
25. (a) 360 J; (b) 350 J; (c) 357.5 J; (d) 359.375 J
27. $k_B = 8k_A$
29. 190 J
31. (a) 33 J; (b) 60 J; (c) 78 J
33. $F_0\left(x + \dfrac{x^2}{2\ell_0} + \dfrac{\ell_0^2}{\ell_0 + x} - \ell_0\right)$
35. (a) 0; (b) $2FR$; (c) πFR
37. 135 J
41. 2.56×10^{-15} J = 16.0 keV
43. 116 km/h
45. 1 : 2
47. 113 m/s
49. 2.82 kN = 635 lbs
51. (a) 83.6 MJ; (b) 256 km/h; (c) 2.14 s; (d) 33.3 m/s^2
53. (a) 60 kW; (b) 1 kW; (c) 40 W
55. 9.4 MJ
57. (a) 36 MW; (b) 1.1 MW

61. 2.7 h
63. 430 million gal/day
65. 2.1 MJ
67. 7.7°
69. 1.9 m
71. $\frac{1}{2}F_0 x_0$
73. 70.5°
75. (a) 28 kJ; (b) 18 kJ
77. (a) 450 W; (b) 8.0 kJ
79. (a) $W = \frac{1}{2}bt^2$; (b) $a = \sqrt{b/m}$
81. (a) 71 kW·y; (b) 93 kW·y
83. About 450 J
85. (a) 33 J; (b) 167 J

Chapter 8
1. (a) $-2\mu mg\ell$; (b) $-\sqrt{2}\mu mg\ell$
3. (a) 0; (b) $F_0 a$
5. (a) 1.3 MJ; (b) 59 kJ
9. (a) 1.07 J; (b) 1.12 J
11. 5.2 J
13. 55 cm
15. 2.9 J
17. $U = -\frac{1}{3}ax^3 - bx$
19. $U = F_0\left(x + \dfrac{x^2}{2\ell} + \dfrac{\ell^2}{\ell + x} - \ell\right)$
21. 50 m/s (180 km/h)
23. 92 m
27. (a) 16 m/s; (b) 29%
29. 26 MN/m
31. 3.6 m/s = 13 km/h
35. 2.6 m/s
39. ±2.0 m
43. (a) $U = -\dfrac{a}{2}x^2 + \dfrac{b}{4}x^4$; (b) $x = 0.66$ m, $x = 2.1$ m
45. (a) −6.7 N; (b) 0; (c) 4.5 N
49. (a) 30 cm; (b) 10.4 N/m
51. 35%
53. 19%
55. 0.36
57. 2.6 m/s
59. 0.036
61. 62 cm from left end of frictional zone
63. 1000 MW, twice that of the coal plant
65. $x = 2(h_1 - h_2)$
69. (a) $v = \sqrt{\sqrt{2}g\ell}$; (b) $T = \dfrac{3}{\sqrt{2}}mg$
71. ±25 cm

73. 14 m
75. (a) 2.53×10^5 m/s; (b) 2.91×10^5 m/s; (c) 2.93×10^5 m/s
77. 54.6 mJ
79. 75 cm
81. (a) 1.74 cm; (b) 0.78 cm; (c) 7.4×10^7 m/s
83. (a) $v = \left[\dfrac{x^2}{m}\left(a - \frac{1}{2}bx^2\right)\right]^{1/2}$; (c) $v_{max} = a/\sqrt{2mb}$
85. $v = [2ax^{|b+1|}/m|b + 1|]^{1/2}$
87. 14.5 m

Chapter 9
1. $R_E/\sqrt{2}$
3. 58%
5. 8.6 kg
7. 46 nN
9. $(\sqrt{2} - 1)R_{planet} \simeq 0.41R_{planet}$
11. 1.2×10^{-7}
13. 3.1 km/s
15. 1.8 days
17. 1.0 hour
19. 2.6×10^{41} kg, about 10^{11} solar masses
21. 6.3×10^{10} m
23. 2.64×10^{10} m
25. 2.47 times Earth's orbital radius
27. No
29. 3.2×10^9 J
31. 530 km
33. 58 MJ
35. $R_E/99 = 64$ km; underestimate
37. 3%
39. $\sqrt{2}$
41. 7.7 Mm
43. (a) 11.2 km/s; (b) 9.74 km/s; (c) no
47. $v = \sqrt{2GM\left(\dfrac{3}{R} + \dfrac{1}{r}\right)}$
49. 8.1×10^{11} m, just beyond Jupiter
53. 109 min
55. 15 km/s, 23 km/s
57. 7.95 km/s
59. 8.85×10^5 m
61. (a) 9.0×10^{10} m; (b) 5.3×10^{11} J; (c) 38 km/s
63. 4.60×10^{10} m
65. (b) 8.8 mm; (c) 2.9 km
67. 1400 km lower

Chapter 10

1. 0.75 m from the center
3. 14 m to the right, 4.5 m upward in Fig. 10-23
5. $\ell/2\sqrt{3}$ along the perpendicular bisector of any side
7. $X = 44$ cm, $Y = 55$ cm, with origin at lower left
9. $0.115a$ above the vertex of the missing triangle
11. 6.5 pm from the oxygen
13. $\mathbf{R} = (t^2 + \frac{10}{3}t + \frac{7}{3})\hat{\imath} + (\frac{2}{3}t + \frac{8}{3})\hat{\jmath};\ \mathbf{V} = (2t + \frac{10}{3})\hat{\imath} + \frac{2}{3}\hat{\jmath};\ \mathbf{A} = 2\hat{\imath}$
15. $\sim 10^{-10}$ m, the diameter of a hydrogen atom
17. $m_{\text{mouse}} = \frac{1}{4}m_{\text{bowl}}$
19. Moves in the opposite direction at 67 cm/s
21. 21 g, $-x$ direction
23. 498 m/s
25. 8.4 km/h
27. (a) 0.14 N/m²; (b) 0.014 mm
29. (a) 0.99 m; (b) 3.9 m/s
31. 3.9 km/h
33. $26\hat{\imath} + 16\hat{\jmath}$ m/s
35. 1100 kg
37. (a) 3.3×10^6 N (b) 3.4×10^5 kg
39. 0.22
41. $K_{\text{cm}} = 1.1 \times 10^{-14}$ J before and after; $K_{\text{int}} = 0$ before, $K_{\text{int}} = 1.3 \times 10^{-14}$ J after
43. before: $K_{\text{cm}} = 1.6$ MJ, $K_{\text{int}} = 21$ kJ; after: $K_{\text{cm}} = 1.6$ MJ, $K_{\text{int}} = 0$
45. (a) 1.7 cm above the bottom; (b) 2.7 cm above the bottom
47. 20 m
49. $-47\hat{\imath} - 68\hat{\jmath}$ m/s
51. (a) 3.5 m; (b) 1.3 m/s; (c) 0
53. (a) 0.096 m/s²; (b) 6.2 m/s
55. 9.3 m/s
57. (a) $m = \dfrac{\pi\rho h^2}{2a}$; (b) $Z = \frac{2}{3}h$
59. 3.0 mN
61. (a) 37.7°; (b) 0.657 m/s
63. 5.8 s after explosion
65. (a) thrust $= m\dfrac{dv}{dt} = [(1 + f)V_{\text{ex}} - V]\dfrac{dM_{\text{in}}}{dt}$; (b) 1504 lb

67. $v_1 = \left(\dfrac{m_2 kx^2}{m_1^2 + m_1 m_2}\right)^{1/2}$;

$v_2 = \left(\dfrac{m_1 kx^2}{m_2^2 + m_1 m_2}\right)^{1/2}$

Chapter 11

1. 52 N·s
3. 4.3×10^3 N, $7.1mg$
5. (a) $-2.6\hat{\imath} + 0.74\hat{\jmath}$ N·s; (b) $-51\hat{\imath} + 14\hat{\jmath}$ N
7. 0.46 s
9. (a) 7.3 MN·s; (b) 5.6 MN
11. (a) 6.8×10^{-3} N·s; (b) 2.3 N
13. $\Delta P/P = 2\%$
15. 12 ms
17. (a) 5.4 mi/h; (b) 13%
19. 19 kg
23. 10^{21} kg
25. $4.0\hat{\imath} + 21.5\hat{\jmath}$ Mm/s
29. 1.3 μJ
31. 120°
33. 46 m/s
35. $v_{1f} = -11$ Mm/s; $v_{2f} = 6.9$ Mm/s
37. $3 + 2\sqrt{2} \approx 5.8$; it doesn't matter which is more massive
39. $v_A = -\frac{1}{3}v$; $v_B = \frac{2}{9}v$; $v_C = \frac{8}{9}v$
45. 22°
47. $(v_{1i} = 0.833$ m/s, $v_{2i} = 1.22$ m/s, $\theta_{2i} = 28.3°)$; $(v_{1i} = 1.20$ m/s, $v_{2i} = 1.12$ m/s, $\theta_{2i} = 31.2°)$
49. 13 m/s at 27° to horizontal
51. $v_A = -\frac{1}{5}v_0\hat{\imath}$; $v_B = \frac{3}{5}v_0\hat{\imath} + \frac{1}{5}\sqrt{3}v_0\hat{\jmath}$ $v_C = \frac{3}{5}v_0\hat{\imath} - \frac{1}{5}\sqrt{3}v_0\hat{\jmath}$
53. 350 N
55. 52 km/h at 33° north of east
57. $m_{\text{truck}} = 7.6m_{\text{car}}$
59. (a) $m_1 = 3m_2$; (b) $v_{2f} = 2v$
61. $v_{1f} = 1.66$ m/s; $v_{2f} = 0.703$ m/s; $\theta_{2f} = 67°$ clockwise from initial velocity of the first ball
63. (a) 12.0 m; (b) 15.4 m/s
65. 0.88
69. $v_{1\text{kg}} = 4.0$ m/s; $v_{4\text{kg}} = 1.0$ m/s at 50° clockwise from the x axis
71. $v_{1200} = 2.2$ km/h, $v_{1800} = 18$ km/h
73. (a) $v_1 = 0.28v_0$, $v_2 = 0.48v_0$; (b) 3, $0.26v_0$, $0.31v_0$

Chapter 12

1. (a) 7.27×10^{-5} rad/s; (b) 1.75×10^{-3} rad/s; (c) 1.45×10^{-4} rad/s; (d) 31.4 rad/s

3. (a) 75.4 rad/s; (b) 0.24 mrad/s; (c) 6283 rad/s; (d) 2.0×10^{-7} rad/s
5. (a) 66 rpm; (b) 3.7 s
7. (a) 21.7 rad/s, 207 rpm; (b) 34.7 rad/s, 331 rpm
9. (a) 0.068 rpm/s; (b) 7.1×10^{-3} rad/s²
11. (a) 12 min; (b) 2.2×10^4
13. 1.3 rad/s²
15. (a) 2.0 s; (b) 1.0 rev
17. 1.2 m
19. 0.079 N·m
21. 0.15 N·m
23. (a) 0.70 N·m, counterclockwise; (b) $\mathbf{F}_1$ and $\mathbf{F}_5$
25. 614 kg·m²
27. (a) $\frac{2}{3}m\ell^2$; (b) $\frac{2}{3}m\ell^2$; (c) $\frac{4}{3}m\ell^2$
29. 45 kg·m²
33. (a) 1×10^{38} kg·m²; (b) 2.6×10^{19} N·m
35. (a) 1.29×10^{38} kg·m²; (b) 6.45×10^{33} N·m
39. (a) 430 min; (b) 1900 rev
41. 1900 N·m
43. 170 rpm
45. $m_{\text{pulley}} = 0.49$ kg; $m_1 = 0.41$ kg; $m_2 = 0.58$ kg
47. (a) 450 J; (b) 140 W
49. 0.089%
51. 12.2 rad/s
53. 7.0 m/s

55. $v = \sqrt{\dfrac{2gh}{\alpha + 1}}$

57. 17%
59. hollow
61. (a) 0.156; (b) 0.070 rad/s

63. $\dfrac{253}{512}MR^2 = 0.494MR^2$

65. (a) 310 N; (b) 165 kg
67. (a) 3.5 m/s; (b) 24%
69. $\frac{27}{10}R$
71. $\omega = \sqrt{2A/I}$
73. $I = \frac{1}{2}Mb^2$
75. $2\sqrt{2g/3R}$
77. $\frac{1}{2}Mg\ell \cos\phi$

Chapter 13

1. 63 rad/s, west
3. 0.52 rad/s², $-37°$
5. 16.6 rad/s

7. (a) $-z$; (b) z; (c) in the x-y plane, 45° clockwise from the x axis

9. (a) $-12\hat{k}$ N·m; (b) $36\hat{k}$ N·m; (c) $12\hat{i} - 36\hat{j}$ N·m

11. $-9.0\hat{k}$ N·m

13. Parallel to the x axis or 120° clockwise from x axis

17. $F_x = 1.33F_y - 3.13$ N

19. 414 kg·m²/s

21. 7.6 rad/s

23. 0.017 kg·m²/s

25. 37 kg·m²/s

27. 2.7×10^5 kg·m²/s, out of page in Fig. 13-30

29. 0.21 kg·m²

31. (a) 0.17 rev/s; (b) 386 J

33. (a) 142 rpm; (b) 21%

35. 2.5 days

37. (a) 23.7 rpm; (b) 3.49 mJ

39. (a) $\dfrac{2M\omega_0}{2M + 3m}$; (b) $\dfrac{M\omega_0}{M + 6m}$; (c) same as (b)

41. (a) 0.537 rad/s; (b) 6.44 m/s; (c) 207 N

43. 6.0 cm

45. $I = \dfrac{mgd}{2\omega\Omega}$

47. $\tan^{-1}(\tfrac{1}{2}) = 26.6°$

49. 0.37 rev/s

51. 22 g

53. $\dfrac{I}{I + mR^2}$

55. (a) 1.61; (b) 2.22

59. Sun's rotation 2.8%; Jupiter's orbital motion 60%

61. $v = \left[\dfrac{8(m + M)g\ell}{m^2}(\tfrac{1}{4}m + \tfrac{1}{3}M)\right]^{1/2}$

63. (a) $\dfrac{m\sqrt{2gh}}{(\tfrac{1}{2}M + m)R}$;

(b) $\dfrac{\sqrt{2gm[hm - (\tfrac{1}{2}M + m)R]}}{(\tfrac{1}{2}M + m)R}$;

(c) $h = \dfrac{(\tfrac{1}{2}M + m)R}{m}$

65. (a) $\tfrac{2}{7}\omega_0$; (b) $2\omega_0R/7\mu_k g$

Chapter 14

1. (a) $\tfrac{1}{3}\ell F_3 - \tfrac{2}{3}\ell F_2 + \ell F_1 = 0$;

(b) $\tfrac{1}{2}\ell F_1 - \tfrac{1}{6}\ell F_2 - \tfrac{1}{6}\ell F_3 + \tfrac{1}{2}\ell F_4 - \tfrac{1}{2}\ell F_5 = 0$

3. (b) $\tau_{\text{origin}} = -7\hat{k}$ N·m

5. (a) A vector of length $\sqrt{2}\,F$, oriented 45° clockwise from the negative y axis, applied at the point $x = 0$ m, $y = +1$ m or anywhere on the line $y = (1 + x)$ m. (b) Not possible; the first two vectors sum to zero but produce a nonzero torque, so any other vector applied to balance torques will upset force balance.

7. Both sets have $-F_1 + F_2 \sin\phi + F_3 = 0$, $-F_2 \cos\phi + F_4 = 0$; torque equations are

(a) $\ell_2 F_4 \cos\phi - \ell_2 F_3 \sin\phi - \ell_1 F_2 = 0$; (b) $(\ell_2 - \ell_1)F_2 - \ell_2 F_1 \sin\phi = 0$.

9. (a) $\tau_A = \tfrac{1}{2}\ell mg$; (b) $\tau_B = 0$; (c) $\tau_C = \tfrac{1}{2}\ell mg$

11. $\tfrac{1}{6}L$

13. (a) 61 cm from left end; (b) 1.4 m from left end

15. 120 N

17. 11.7 kN

19. (a) 40 N·m; (b) 1300 N

21. Vertical forces both 73.5 N, downward, horizontal forces both 33.6 N, away from door jamb at top, toward jamb at bottom

23. 5.0 kN; tension

25. 0.87

27. 500 N

29. 7.3°

31. 50 kN

33. 6.05 kN

35. $\tfrac{1}{8}$

37. Maximum height of CM is at sphere center; lower for clown (b)

39. Two equilibria for $|a| > 2\sqrt{3}$; one metastable, other unstable

41. 1.2 m

43. 170 N

45. 74 kg

47. $\tfrac{1}{2}(\sqrt{3} - 1)mgs$

49. $\mu = \dfrac{\sin 2\theta}{3 + \cos 2\theta}$

51. $mg/2k$

53. 28°

55. Left scale 16.3 N; right scale 22.9 N

57. Tip

59. Slide

61. (a) $0.44mg$, at 12° to Earth's polar axis; (b) $0.036mgR_E$, out of the plane of Fig. 14-57

Part 1   Cumulative Problems

1. 16.5 m from the post

3. $a = \dfrac{2g[(m_1 + m_2)\sin\theta - \mu m_1 \cos\theta]}{2m_1 + 3m_2}$

5. (a) $v = \tfrac{2}{7}\omega R$; (b) $\Delta x = \dfrac{2\omega^2 R^2}{49\mu g}$

Chapter 15

1. $T = 0.780$ s; $f = 1.28$ Hz

3. 11.5 fs

5. $A = 20$ cm, $\omega = \pi/2$ s⁻¹, $\phi = 0$; $A = 30$ cm, $\omega = 2.0$ s⁻¹, $\phi = -\pi/2$; $A = 40$ cm, $\omega = \pi/2$ s⁻¹, $\phi = \pi/4$

7. 63.3 kg

9. 1.7 kN/m

11. 0.69 s

13. (a) $\pi\sqrt{m/k}$; (b) $v_0\sqrt{m/k}$

17. (a) 1.0 cm; (b) 6.2 m; (c) 3.6 km

19. 0.11 N·m/rad

21. (a) $2\pi\sqrt{\ell/g}$; (b) $2\pi\sqrt{2\ell/3g}$; (c) $2\pi\sqrt{2\ell/g}$; (d) infinite

23. 0.34 s

25. $R = \sqrt{2\kappa/k}$

27. Within 1 μm

33. 5.0 g

35. $\omega^2 = \dfrac{k_1 k_2}{m(k_1 + k_2)}$

37. a and b are the amplitudes in the x and y directions, respectively

39. 400 J, or 1.4×10^{-3} of the total KE

41. $t = (0.14 + n)$ s, $t = (0.53 + n)$ s, n an integer; $x = \pm 37$ cm

45. $\omega = \sqrt{2k/3M}$

47. 34

49. 77% at 0.90 ω; 66% at 1.1ω

53. (a) 19 s⁻¹; (b) 0.33 s; (c) 92 m/s²

55. (a) 6.5 cm; (b) 0.51 s

57. 1.64 s

59. 300 g

61. (a) $E_2 = \tfrac{1}{4}E_1$; (b) $a_{2\max} = \tfrac{1}{4}a_{1\max}$

63. 2.1 m/s²

65. 0.44

67. $2\pi\sqrt{7/10ga}$

69. $f = 0.54$ Hz; $A = 22$ cm; $\phi = -0.11$ rad

71. $T = 2\pi\sqrt{R/g}$

73. $T = 2\pi\sqrt{mL/2F_0}$

Chapter 16

1. 3.4 s
3. 3.38 m
5. 1.81×10^8 m/s $= 0.604c$
7. (a) 400 nm; (b) 0.3 mm
9. 11 m
11. (a) 0.58 m^{-1}; (b) 1.53 s^{-1}
13. (a) 13.7 s^{-1}; (b) 0.393 cm^{-1};
    (c) $y = 2.5\cos(0.393x + 13.7t)$
15. (a) 25 cm; (b) 0.37 Hz; (c) 12 m;
    (d) 4.4 m/s
17. $y = \dfrac{2}{(x - 3t)^4 + 1}$
19. (a) 3.0 m; (b) 1.5 s; (c) 2.0 m/s;
    (d) $+x$
21. 250 m/s
23. (a) 7.6 N; (b) 1.7 m/s
25. 364 m/s
27. 94 N
29. 7.64 g/cm^3
31. 585 m/s
33. 9.9 W
35. 35 cm
37. $4\pi^2A^2F/\lambda$
39. 12 mW/m^2
41. (a) 9.1 kW/m^2; (b) 0.88 W/m^2
43. (a) 6.4 kW/m^2; (b) 4.9 W/m^2
45. 5.1 m
47. (a) 2 cm; (b) pulse 1 at $x = 0$,
    direction $+x$, pulse 2 at $x = 5$,
    direction $-x$; (c) $t = 2.5$ s
49. Every 6 s
51. 5.34 m
53. $\sqrt{gh}$
55. (a) 1.5 cm; (b) 63 cm; (c) 11 ms;
    (d) 56 m/s;
    (e) 18 W
57. $v = \sqrt{k\ell(\ell - \ell_0)/m}$
59. 10 m
61. Every 30 s
63. $u < 0.063v$
67. 5.2 km
69. 67 m

Chapter 17

3. $\lambda = 34$ cm; $T = 1.0$ ms;
   $\omega = 6.3\times10^3$ s^{-1};
   $k = 0.18$ cm^{-1}
5. 0.29 s
7. 0.14 kg/m^3
9. monatomic
11. 739 m/s
13. 190 m/s

15. 4.4 nm
17. (a) 3.8 mW/m^2; (b) 96 dB;
    (c) 1.8 N/m^2; (d) 1.6 μm
19. 1 kHz to 6.5 kHz
21. (a) 3.2 μW/m^2, 0.051 N/m^2;
    (b) 3.2×10^{-13} W/m^2;
    1.6×10^{-5} N/m^2
23. (a) 20 dB; (b) approximately
    250 Hz
27. 6.3 m
29. 1
31. 3.2 km/s
33. 0.75 mm
35. 39 μs
37. no; $F = 31$ kN
39. (a) 280 Hz; (b) 70 Hz; (c) 210 Hz
45. (a) 16.6 cm; (b) 424–457 Hz
47. 0.33 Hz
49. 91 Hz
51. 253 m/s
53. 400 Hz
55. 43 m/s $= 154$ km/h
57. (a) 2800 Hz; (b) 933 Hz
59. 25 m/s
63. $u/v = 1/\sin 45° = 1.4$
65. (a) 5.5×10^{-4} W/m^2; (b) 87 dB
67. (a) 112 m/s; (b) 4, 5
69. 960 m/s
71. 0.445 s
73. (a) $\lambda = 5.0$ m, $f = 0.56$ Hz;
    (b) $\lambda = 2.5$ m; $f = 0.79$ Hz
75. 1.36
77. $\Delta f = 2uf/(v - u)$
79. 16 kHz

Chapter 18

1. 1.2 kg
3. 10^{-14}
5. (a) 81 N; (b) 65 N
7. 1 in. $H_2O = 249$ Pa
9. 2×10^7 N, or 2000 tons
11. 21 N
13. 0.25 m^2
15. No; $F = 2.3\times10^4$ N, or 2.5 tons
17. 1700 kg/m^3
19. ~90 m
21. 890 Pa gauge
23. 8.1×10^{10} N
25. 3.6 mm
27. 93 cm higher in the eye
29. 8.11×10^3 kg
31. 44 kg
33. 0.75 %
35. 59 g

37. 27 m
39. (a) 49 kg; (b) 2500 kg
43. (a) 1.8×10^4 m^3/s; (b) 1.5 m/s
45. 1.75 m/s
47. (a) $h_2 = h_1$; (b) $h_2 = h_1 - \dfrac{3v^2}{2g}$
49. 14.3 m
51. 7.2 cm^3/s
53. (a) no; (b) yes
55. 13
57. 70%
59. $A\sqrt{2gh}$
61. (a) 14 m/s; (b) 2.2 m
65. (a) 25 L/s; (b) 55 m/s; (c) 1.8 kPa
67. $t = \dfrac{A_0}{A_1}\sqrt{\dfrac{2h}{g}}$
69. $P = P_a + \rho gh_0 + \frac{1}{2}\rho\omega^2 r^2$;
    (b) $h = h_0 + \dfrac{\omega^2 r^2}{2g}$
71. (a) $\rho(h) = \dfrac{P_0}{h_0 g}e^{-h/h_0}$; (b) 5.7 km

Part 2   Cumulative Problems

1. (a) $\ell = \dfrac{4M}{\pi d^2\rho}$; (b) $T = 4\sqrt{\dfrac{\pi M}{d^2\rho g}}$
5. 17.2 cm

Chapter 19

1. 720
3. 20°C
5. -40
7. -196°C, -321°F
9. (a) 138 kPa; (b) 33.4 kPa;
   (c) 233 kPa
11. 1.37 L
13. 586 mm
15. 240 kcal
17. 0.36 kg
19. 24 days
21. (a) 23 kJ; (b) 337 kJ; (c) 65 kJ
23. 7.5 kW
25. 2.4 kg
27. (a) 560 g; (b) 0.27 K/s
29. 1.8 kg
31. 0.70 K
33. 1.6 K/s
35. 197 g
37. 56.2°C
39. 55 kW
41. 0.293 W
43. 25 ft^2·°F·h/Btu
45. 200 W

47. (a) 12.3 ft^2·°F·h/Btu;
    (b) 715 Btu/h
49. Will save 10 gallons/month
51. 23°C
53. 80%
55. −25°C
57. Drop by 5.9 K
59. 24°C
61. 480 W
63. 1151 K
65. −2.5°C
67. (a) $87; (b) $10
69. 4.65%
71. $\Delta T_{copper} = 0.16$ K; $\Delta T_{iron} = 2.1$ K
73. 2.9 J
77. 10 hours

Chapter 20

1. 2.6 m^3
3. 1.8 MPa
5. (a) 27 L; (b) 330 K
7. 2.7×10^7
9. 11 L
11. 515 kPa
13. (a) 1.27 atm; (b) 0.0268 mol;
    (c) 0.786 atm
15. H_2
17. 268 K, compared with ideal gas
    292 K
19. 1.76 MPa
21. (a) 9.1×10^{20}; (b) 2.0×10^{20}
23. 22 kJ
25. 3.9 kg
27. 5.96 MJ
29. 1.3×10^{10} kg
31. 564 W
33. 44 minutes
35. 48 min
37. (a) 117 s
39. 3.55 MJ
41. 64°C
43. 177 g
45. 135 g solid in 865 g liquid, at 234 K
47. 5.0 kg
49. 4.9°C
51. 1.00021 cm
53. 3.9 km
55. 43.6 mm^3
57. 307 K
59. $d = \frac{1}{2}L_0\sqrt{2\alpha\,\Delta T + (\alpha\,\Delta T)^2}$
61. 120 mol/m^3
63. 19 kW
65. 79 g
67. 1.2 kg ice, 0.80 kg water, all at 0°C

69. 50 min
71. (a) 61 h; (b) 52 h
77. 34 km

Chapter 21

1. 29 kJ
3. Increases by 250 J
5. (a) 310 MW; (b) 54%
7. 0.02°C
9. $2P_1V_1$
11. 1.2 kJ
13. 4.3 kJ
15. 190 K
17. 1.99 kJ
19. (a) 399 J; (b) 264 kPa
21. (a) 571 kPa; (b) 438 J
23. 440°C
25. $V = 0.18V_0$
27. (b) Gas does 13 J of work;
    (c) 22 J heat lost from gas
29. (a) 300 K, 1.5 kJ; (b) 336 K, 0 J;
    (c) 326 K, 429 J
31. (a) 39.9 kPa; (b) 83.3 kPa;
    (c) 80.2 kJ
33. 928 J
35. (a) 211 J; (b) 12.9 L
37. 75°C
39. 128 J
41. (a) −9.0°C; (b) stable
43. 57.7%
45. 79%
47. 20 mol
49. Drops 23.1 K
51. 343 K
53. 28 kPa
55. (a) 598 J; (b) 2500 J flows in
57. 25 m
59. $\frac{4}{3}P_1V_1$
63. (a) 2.5 kJ; (b) 447 K
69. (a) $M = \dfrac{P_0 A}{g}\left[\dfrac{h_1}{h_2} - 1\right]$;

    (b) $M = \dfrac{P_0 A}{g}\left[\left(\dfrac{h_1}{h_2}\right)^{\gamma} - 1\right]$

Chapter 22

1. (a) 12!/6!, or 6.7×10^5 states;
   (b) about 1 in 1000
3. 5×10^{24} J, assuming oceans cover
   75% of Earth to an average depth
   of 3 km; this is about 20,000 times
   annual use
5. (a) 27%; (b) 7.0%; (c) 77%
7. 0.95 K
9. 52% winter, 48% summer
11. (a) 1.75 GW; (b) 43%; (c) 505 K
13. 2×10^7 kg/s, slightly more than the
    Mississippi's flow
15. (a) 39%; (b) 550 J; (c) 190°C
17. 53.3 kJ
19. (a) 4.3; (b) maximum COP = 11
23. (a) $COP_{summer} = 13$, $COP_{winter} = 3.5$;
    (b) 0.076 J; (c) 0.22 J
25. (a) 561.7 J; (b) 464.1 J;
    (c) 97.66 J; (d) 17.4%;
    (e) $T_c = 403$ K, $T_h = 487$ K
29. 718 K
31. 1.22 kJ/K
33. 8.9°C
35. 1.36×10^8 J/K
39. (a) 53 J/K; (b) 74 J/K; (c) 0
41. (a) −109 J/K; (b) 122 J/K;
    (c) 13 J/K
43. $\Delta S_{AB} = 68.5$ J/K, $\Delta S_{BC} = 45.7$ J/K,
    $\Delta S_{CA} = -114.2$ J/K
45. 470 kPa
47. (a) 69%; (b) 967 K
49. Decrease in $T_{minimum}$
51. $58
53. (a) $W = Q = 345$ J; (b) $e = 24\%$
55. 598 J/K
57. About 30 km for 200 kg of water
    and a 60 kg bather
59. 166 MW
61. (a) $1 - 5^{1-\gamma}$; (b) $3T_{min}(5^{\gamma-1})$;
    (c) $e_{Carnot} = 1 - \frac{1}{3}(5^{1-\gamma})$
63. (a) 7.94; (b) 5.26; (c) $P_n = 2.96P_s$
65. (a) $T_h = T_{h0}e^{-P_0 t/mc(T_{h0} - T_c)}$;
    (b) $P = 0$ at
    $t = \dfrac{mc(T_{h0} - T_c)}{P_0}\ln\left(\dfrac{T_{h0}}{T_c}\right)$
67.

	P	V	T	U − U$_A$	S − S$_A$
A					
B			3.4 T_0	6.0 $P_0 V_0$	3.1 $P_0 V_0/T_0$
C	1.5 P_0	2.2 V_0	3.4 T_0	6.0 $P_0 V_0$	3.8 $P_0 V_0/T_0$
D			3.0 T_0	5.0 $P_0 V_0$	3.8 $P_0 V_0/T_0$

Part 3 Cumulative Problems

1. $e = 1 - r^{1-\gamma}\left[\dfrac{r_c^\gamma - 1}{\gamma(r_c - 1)}\right]$

3. $W = an^2\left(\dfrac{1}{V_2} - \dfrac{1}{V_1}\right) +$

$nRT \ln\left(\dfrac{V_2 - bn}{V_1 - bn}\right)$

5. (a) $t_1 = \dfrac{L_f M T_h}{P_h T_0}$;

(b) $P = P_h\left[1 - \dfrac{T_0}{T_h}e^{P_h(t-t_1)/McT_h}\right]$,

(c) $t_2 = t_1 + \dfrac{McT_h}{P_h}\ln\dfrac{T_h}{T_0}$, with L_f

the heat of fusion of ice and c the specific heat of water.

Chapter 23

1. Several coulombs
3. (a) uud; (b) udd
5. About 10^9 N; about 10^6 times typical human weight
7. 8.2×10^{-8} N
9. $21.8\ \mu C$
11. $-0.18\hat{\imath} + 0.64\hat{\jmath}$ nN
13. (a) $\hat{\jmath}$; (b) $-\hat{\imath}$; (c) $(\hat{\imath} + 3\hat{\jmath})/$
$\sqrt{10} \approx 0.032\hat{\imath} + 0.95\hat{\jmath}$
15. $14\hat{\imath} - 7.4\hat{\jmath}$ N
17. $15\ \mu C$
19. $1.6\hat{\imath} - 0.33\hat{\jmath}$ N
21. $\dfrac{kq^2}{a^2}(\sqrt{2} + \tfrac{1}{2})$
23. $q_2 = 143\ \mu C$; $q_3 = 116\ \mu C$
25. 3.8×10^9 N/C
27. (a) 2.2 MN/C; (b) 77 N
29. 5.15×10^{11} N/C
31. (a) $26\hat{\jmath}$ MN/C; (b) $-5.15\hat{\jmath}$ MN/C;
(c) $-58\hat{\jmath}$ MN/C
33. $-4e$
35. (a) $\mathbf{E} = \dfrac{2kqy}{(a^2 + y^2)^{3/2}}\hat{\jmath}$;
(b) $y = \pm a/\sqrt{2}$
37. (a) $8.0\hat{\jmath}$ GN/C; (b) $190\hat{\jmath}$ MN/C;
(c) $216\hat{\jmath}$ kN/C
39. 39 pm
41. (a) $\mathbf{E} = 2\sqrt{3}\ kqa/x^3\hat{\imath}$;
(b) $p = \sqrt{3}\ qa$
43. 2.1 MN/C
45. $-\dfrac{2k\lambda_0}{\pi\ell}\hat{\imath}$

47. -137 nC
51. 1.1 kN/C
53. (a) 2.5 μC/m; (b) 3.0×10^5 N/C;
(c) 1.8 N/C
55. 3.3×10^{-12} kg
57. (a) 1.35 cm; (b) reverses direction, accelerates and exits field region at 3.8×10^5 m/s
59. $v > \ell\sqrt{qE/md}$
61. 2.8 Mm/s
63. $-14\ \mu$C/m
65. (a) 3.0 mN·m; (b) 11 mJ
67. (b) Attractive
69. $x = -8.09$ nm
71. $\dfrac{k\lambda_0}{\ell}\hat{\imath}$
73. $2\sqrt{2}kQ/\pi a^2$
75. 1.4 cm
77. 33.3 μC
79. $-4q$, a distance $3a$ to the right of $-q$
81. 50.7 kN/C, downward
83. 7.0 cm; 0.54 μC
85. (a) $(2kep/r^3)\hat{\imath}$; (b) $(-2kep/r^3)\hat{\imath}$, with the $+x$ direction to the right

Chapter 24

1. $+3\ \mu$C
5. (a) 1.7 kN·m^2/C; (b) 1.2 kN·m^2/C;
(c) 0
7. 490 N·m^2/C
9. $\pi R^2 E$
11. (a) $-q/\varepsilon_0$; (b) $-2q/\varepsilon_0$; (c) 0; (d) 0
13. 4.9×10^4 N·m^2/C
15. (a) 0.69 MN·m^2/C
(b) -0.69 MN·m^2/C (c) 0
17. 10 kN/C
19. 1.8×10^{12} N/C
21. (a) 2.2×10^5 N/C, outward;
(b) 2.5×10^4 N/C, outward;
(c) 4.0×10^3 N/C, inward
23. (a) $8kQ/R^2$, inward; (b) $kQ/4R^2$, inward; (c) (a) would not change, (b) would become 0
25. (a) 3.6 MN/C; (b) 3.8 MN/C;
(c) (a) would not change, (b) would nearly double
27. as $1/r$
29. 6.3 μC/m^3
33. 3.6 mC/m^3
35. 58 nC/m^2
37. $E_1 = \sigma/2\varepsilon_0$, left; $E_2 = \sigma/2\varepsilon_0$, right; $E_3 = 3\sigma/2\varepsilon_0$, right; $E_4 = \sigma/2\varepsilon_0$, right

39. 18 N/C
41. (a) $x < 1.83$ cm; (b) $x > 54.5$ cm
43. 1.6×10^5 N/C
45. (a) $\rho = 0$; (b) $\sigma = 4.0$ mC/m^2;
(c) other charges would destroy the symmetry, making σ nonuniform
47. (a) 0.50 μC/m^2; (b) 56 kN/C
49. (b) $-Q$
51. 1.8 MN/C
53. (a) 0; (b) 180 kN/C; (c) 0;
(d) 20 kN/C
57. (a) $4kq/R^2$; (b) $3kq/4R^2$
59. (a) 0; (b) 1.3 MN/C; (c) 0
61. (a) 1.9×10^{11} N/C;
(b) 3.6×10^{10} N/C
63. $\dfrac{\rho r}{3\varepsilon_0} - \dfrac{\rho a^3}{3\varepsilon_0 r^2}$
65. $\tfrac{1}{3}E_0 a^2$
67. 0.39 μs
69. $E_{in} = \rho_0 x^2/2\varepsilon_0 d$; $E_{out} = \rho_0 d/8\varepsilon_0$
73. (a) 0; (b) $(ac/\varepsilon_0 r^2)(e^{-1} - e^{-r/a})$;
(c) $(ac/\varepsilon_0 r^2)(e^{-1} - e^{-b/a})$
77. $+10.6\ \mu$C/m^2 on both outer faces, $\pm36.9\ \mu$C/m^2 on inner faces

Chapter 25

1. 600 μJ
3. 3.0 kV
5. 910 V
7. 5.6 kV/m
9. Proton and He$^+$ both gain
100 eV $= 1.6\times10^{-17}$ J; α gains
200 eV $= 3.2\times10^{-17}$ J
11. 4.5 V
13. 0.23 MC
17. 6.1 μC
19. 27.2 V
21. $Q = 5.4$ nC, $r = 17$ cm
23. (a) 442 kV; (b) 9.2 Mm/s
25. kQ/R.
27. $V(x) = -\tfrac{1}{2}ax^2$
29. 52 nC/m
31. $x = -a/2$, $x = a/4$
33. (a) 2.6 kV; (b) 1.8 kV; (c) 0
35. $kQ\left(\dfrac{2}{c} + \dfrac{1}{b} - \dfrac{1}{a}\right)$
37. $2kQ/R$
39. $2\pi k\sigma(\sqrt{x^2 + b^2} - \sqrt{x^2 + a^2})$
41. (a) $V(x, y) = -E_0(x + y) = -150(x + y)$ V/m; (b) 150V
45. (a) $\mathbf{E} = -ay\hat{\imath} - ax\hat{\jmath}$
47. (a) 4 V; (b) $E_x = 1$ V/m, $E_y = -12$ V/m, $E_z = 3$ V/m

49. $\mathbf{E} = \dfrac{kQx}{(x^2 + a^2)^{3/2}}\hat{\mathbf{i}}$

51. $E = V_0/R$, radially outward

53. 3 kV

55. (a) 34 kV, -9.0 kV; (b) 12.6 kV on each; (c) 24 nC

57. (a) 43 kV; (b) 1.7 MV/m; (c) 540 V; (d) 0

59. 1.55 keV $= 2.47 \times 10^{-16}$ J

61. (a) $\dfrac{2kqx}{x^2 - a^2}$; (b) $\dfrac{2kq}{x}$

63. (a) 27 kV; (b) no change

65. -7.5 V

67. (a) $x = -3$ m, 0 m, 1 m; (b) $\mathbf{E} = (3x^2 + 4x - 3)\hat{\mathbf{i}}$; (c) $x = -1.87$ m, 0.535 m

69. (a) 7.2 kV; (b) 14.4 kV

71. 14 cm, 1.7 nC

73. 23 nC/m

75. (a) $V(x) = \dfrac{k\lambda_0 x}{\ell^2}\left[x \ln\!\left(\dfrac{2x + \ell}{2x - \ell}\right) - \ell\right]$; (b) $\frac{1}{12}\lambda_0\ell$; (c) $\dfrac{k\lambda_0\ell}{12x}$

77. $y^2 + (x - \frac{5}{3}a)^2 = (\frac{4}{3}a)^2$; i.e., a circle

79. $\dfrac{kq}{2a}\ln\!\left(\dfrac{\sqrt{2} + 1}{\sqrt{2} - 1}\right) \approx \dfrac{0.881\,kq}{a}$

Chapter 26

1. $3kq^2/\ell$

3. 4.88 kJ

5. $v = 2q\sqrt{\dfrac{k}{m\ell}}$

7. $6kq^2/a$

9. (a) 2.0 MV/m; (b) 9.9 kV; (c) 5.5 mJ

11. (a) 0.74 μC; (b) 40 kV

13. $\frac{1}{2}kQ^2\left(\dfrac{1}{a} - \dfrac{1}{b}\right)$

15. (b) $dW = 2kq\,dq/a$; (c) $W = kQ^2/a$

17. 1 km^3

19. 9×10^{30} J/m^3

21. 24 μJ

25. $(kQ^2/R)(2^{2/3} - 1) = 0.60$ mJ

27. $U/\ell = \pi a^4\rho^2/16\varepsilon_0$

29. ± 14 C

31. 6.5 mF

33. 0.74 nF

35. 55 pF

39. 70 nF

41. 1 μF stores 15 times as much energy

43. (a) 30 μF; (b) 0.1 μF; (c) 0.01 μF

45. (a) 5.0 kW; (b) 250 μF; (c) 0.50 W

47. (a) Increases by factor of 2.5; (b) drops to 40% of its original value

51. Equal

53. (a) 6.0 μF; (b) 0.55 μF; (c) 0.83 μF, 1.3 μF, 1.5 μF, 2.2 μF, 2.8 μF, 3.7 μF

55. (a) 2 series pairs in parallel or two parallel pairs in series; (b) 4 in series

57. 0.86 μF

61. $\pm 1\%$

63. (a) 64 V; (b) drops from 16 mJ to 14 mJ

65. (a) 3.5 mm; (b) 87 kV

67. 126 pF

69. (a) 50 nC, 170 nC; (b) 23 μJ, 77 μJ

71. 1.4 mm

73. (a) 0.90 J; (b) 1.8 J; energy comes from work done by agent separating the plates

75. (a) 1.2 μF; (b) 24 μC

77. 13 min

79. $\dfrac{kq^2}{a}(2\sqrt{3} - \frac{15}{2}) \approx -4.04\dfrac{kq^2}{a}$

81. (a) $C = \frac{1}{2}(\kappa + 1)C_0$; (b) $U = \dfrac{C_0 V_0^2}{\kappa + 1}$; (c) $F = \dfrac{2C_0 V_0^2(\kappa - 1)}{L(\kappa + 1)^2}$, into capacitor

83. (a) 75 mF; (b) 1.4×10^{12} J

85. (a) $Q^2/2\varepsilon_0 a$; (b) $Q^2/\varepsilon_0 a$; (a) is right since (b) includes the fields of *both* plates, and a plate doesn't experience a force from its own field

87. $31d^2kp^2/1280\ell^5$

89. 7.2 pF/m

Chapter 27

1. 9.4×10^{18}

3. 2.9×10^5 C

5. 1.9×10^{11}

7. 7.65 MA/m^2

9. 1.23 cm/s

11. 0.31 mA

13. (a) 37 A/m^2; (b) 86%

15. 9.71 μC

17. 0.17 V/m

19. 2.2×10^{-6} $\Omega\cdot$m

21. (a) 5.95×10^7 $(\Omega\cdot$m$)^{-1}$; (b) 4.5 $(\Omega\cdot$m$)^{-1}$

23. 6.4×10^{-15} s

25. 253°C

27. 25 Ω

29. 2.34 mA

31. 25 mA

33. 1.5 kA

35. (a) 17 mΩ; (b) 86 A; (c) 18 MA/m^2; (d) 1.7 V/m

37. $d_{\text{Al}} = 1.26\,d_{\text{Cu}}$

39. (a) 2.07 cm; (b) 2.60 cm; (c) aluminum

41. 34 mΩ

43. 1.38 kW

45. 160 μA

47. 240 Ω

49. 48 W

51. 960 W·h = 3.5 MJ

53. Resistor with more power has $\sqrt{2}$ times greater diameter

55. (a) 150 A; (b) 3.4 km

57. 0.54 mA

59. 0.94 Ω

61. (a) 8.7 kA; (b) 15%

63. 2.9 A

65. 2.5 A

67. 120 A

69. 17 J/K

Chapter 28

5. 1.4 hours

7. 6.0 V

9. 229 kΩ

11. 1.5 A

13. 0.02 Ω

15. 45 Ω

17. 30 A

19. R_1 for each

21. 24

23. (a) 162 Ω; (b) 125 mW

25. (a) $\dfrac{R_1 \mathcal{E}}{R + 2R_1}$; (c) $\frac{1}{2}\mathcal{E}$

27. 2.45 W

29. $(\mathcal{E}_2 R_1 - \mathcal{E}_1 R_2)/(R_1 + R_2)$

31. $\frac{7}{5}R$

33. $I_1 = 2.79$ A, $I_2 = 2.36$ A,
$I_3 = 0.429$ A
35. $\mathcal{E}_2 > 5.49$ V
37. 8.5 nA, downward
39. 1.6% low
41. 1.2 kW41.24.99 kΩ
43. (a) 20 V; (b) 3.0 mA
49. (a) 9.0 V; (b) 1.5 ms; (c) 0.32 μF
51. (a) 0.35 s; (b) 0.17 s
53. 3.4 μF
55. (a) $I_1 = 25$ mA, $I_2 = 0$, $V_C = 0$;
(b) $I_1 = I_2 = 10$ mA, $V_C = 60$ V;
(c) $I_1 = 0$, $I_2 = 10$ mA,
$V_C = 60$ V; (d) $I_1 = I_2 = 0$,
$V_C = 0$
57. (a) $3\mathcal{E}/4R$; (b) $2\mathcal{E}/3R$
59. 3.4 kΩ
61. (a) 4.51 V; (b) 35.2 Ω
63. 1.07 A, left to right
65. (a) 13.0 V; (b) 2.23 mA
67. 15.9 ms
69. 83 μs
71. (a) 0; (b) 1.0 A; (c) 0.75 A; (d) 0;
(e) 1.0 A; (f) 3.0 A; (g) 3.0 A;
(h) 1.0 A
73. (b) 22 hours

Chapter 29

1. (a) 1.6 mT; (b) 2.3 mT
3. (a) 2.0×10^{-14} N; (b) 1.0×10^{-14} N;
(c) 0
5. (a) $-1.1\hat{\imath} +1.5\hat{\jmath} + 1.7\hat{k}$ mN
7. $\mathbf{B} = 0.13\hat{k}$ T; $\mathbf{v}_2 = -14\hat{\imath}$ km/s
9. $-24.9\hat{\imath} - 40.1\hat{\jmath} - 87.3\hat{k}$ fN
11. 40.1° or 140°
13. (a) $1.2\hat{\imath} + 0.45\hat{\jmath}$ fN;
(b) $-1.2\hat{\imath} + 35\hat{\jmath} - 15\hat{k}$ fN
15. 3.9 mm
17. 1.5 mT
19. $r_{\text{proton}} = 43\, r_{\text{electron}}$
21. (a) 86 mT; (b) 1.01 keV
23. 1.3 μs
25. (a) 15 MHz; (b) 19 MeV; (c) 6467
29. 0.43%
31. 1.1 mm, 2.6 mm
33. 0.38 N
35. (a) 49 mT; (b) 0.73 N/m
37. 43 kN
39. 0.12 T
41. 21 mN, diagonally toward the
upper right
45. 76 mT
47. (a) 1.1 mA·m²; (b) 1.0 mN·m

49. 0.15 A·m²
51. (a) 0.35 A·m²; (b) 4.2×10^{-2} N·m
53. 1.97×10^{-25} J = 1.23 μe V
55. $42\hat{\imath} + 88\hat{\jmath} - 25\hat{k}$ fN
57. 30 km
59. 0.27 N, to right
61. 0.010 T
63. 6.8 mm
65. (a) 12.8 N/m; (b) 24.9 cm
67. $I = Mg/2Bd$
69. 77 mT
73. $\mu = 9.25\times10^{-24}$ A·m²

Chapter 30

1. 12 cm
3. 1.23 mT
5. 3.8 GA
7. 0.875 cm²
9. 732
11. Between the wires, 2.0 cm from
center of 5.0-A wire
13. 23° west of magnetic north
15. $\mu_0 I/4a$, into page
17. $\dfrac{\mu_0 I}{4ab}(b - a)$, out of the page
19. 5 μN
21. 3.8 mm
23. 13.2 μN/m, at 71.6° below
right-pointing horizontal
25. 23.5 mN
27. 7.0 A
29. 24 A
31. 123 mA
33. (a) 0; (b) 0.36 mT; (c) 1.9 mT;
(d) 0.50 mT
35. (a) $\mu_0 J_0 r^2/3R$; (b) $\mu_0 J_0 R^2/3r$
37. (a) 5.3 mm; (b) maximum;
(c) 130 A
41. (a) 0; (b) $\dfrac{\mu_0 I(r^2 - a^2)}{2\pi r(b^2 - a^2)}$; (c) $\dfrac{\mu_0 I}{2\pi r}$
43. 17 T
45. (a) 38 mT; (b) 5.9 μT
47. 3.3 m
49. $1/2\pi nR$
51. $\chi_M = -1.6\times10^{-3}$; diamagnetic
53. 7.2×10^3
55. $I_{\text{outer}} = 2I_{\text{inner}}$, in opposite direction
57. Out of page
59. 1 km
61. (a) 8.0 μT; (b) 4.0 μT; (c) 0
63. (a) 0.40 mT; (b) 1.0 nT
65. $B = \mu_0 I/\ell$ inside, $B = 0$ outside
67. 55A

Chapter 31

3. 1.4×10^{-4} T·m²
5. 160 T/s
7. (a) 0.30 A; (b) 0.20 A
9. $B^2\ell^3 v/R$
11. 39 V
13. 0.32 V
15. 9.0 μA, counterclockwise in
Fig. 31-5
17. (a) $I = -25$ mA for $0 < t < 2$ s;
$I = 0$ for 2 s $< t < 3$ s;
$I = +25$ mA for 3 s $< t < 5$ s;
(b) $P = 3.1$ mW for $0 < t < 2$ s
and 3 s $< t < 5$ s; otherwise 0
19. (a) Left to right; (b) 140 μA;
(c) 28 μA
21. (a) $I_R = -I_{\text{peak}}\cos\omega t$, where
(b) $I_{\text{peak}} = 110$ mA; (c) 0
23. 0.16 s
25. 7.1 mV
27. (a) Downward; (b) $(B\ell v)^2/R$
29. $v_{\text{final}} = \mathcal{E}/B\ell$; R affects time to
reach final speed
31. (a), (b) Both 6.7 mA,
counterclockwise; (c) 0.44 mW in
both cases
33. (a) 25 mA; (b) 1.25 mN;
(c) 2.5 mW; (d) 2.5 mW
35. (a) 77 mV; (b) 94 mV
37. 1.57 μN
39. $dB/dt = 10$ T/s
41. $E = \frac{1}{2}bh$, to the left above the field
region and to the right below
43. $\frac{16}{3}B_0 x_0^2$
45. 42 mA, clockwise
47. $mgR/B^2\ell^2$
49. $\frac{1}{2}BR^2\omega$
51. 58 T/ms
53. $I = at^2$, with $a = 0.81$ A/s²
57. (a) 2.4 km; (b) 2.89 kW; (c) \$6.94;
(d) their generators get harder to
turn, so they use more fuel
59. (a) $J = rb/2\rho$; (b) $P = \pi b^2 a^4 h/8\rho$

Chapter 32

1. 120 V
3. 12 V
5. (a) $-2\pi fMI_p\cos2\pi ft$; (b) 133 mH
7. $\mu_0 n^2\pi R^2\ell$
9. $\dfrac{\mu_0\ell}{2\pi}\ln\!\left(\dfrac{a + w}{a}\right)$
11. 3.2 mH

13. 40 kV
15. 1350
17. (a) 2.1 A; (b) -1.5 A (minus indicates direction reversal)
19. 26 A/ms
21. 11 A
25. 130 Ω
27. 15 s
29. (a) 0.11 H; (b) 20 mA
31. (a) 76 mA; (b) 4.4 V (c) 7.6 V; (d) 2.2 A/s; (e) 0.58 W
33. 400 Ω
35. 50 Ω
37. (a) 2.0 A; (b) 6.0 A; (c) 60 V
39. 100 mA
41. (a) 52 J; (b) 1.8 s
43. (a) 2.5 kW; (b) no
45. 15 W
47. (a) 5.7 MJ; (b) 31 mΩ; (c) 39 s
49. 9.9×10^8 J/m^3
51. 10^{11} times that of gasoline; 2600 times that of U-235
53. Smaller by factor $1/4n^2R^2$
55. 10^{18} J
57. $|\mathcal{E}| = 2Mbt$
59. 48 H
61. (a) 18.4 V; (b) 0; (c) 70 V
63. $(\mu_0 I^2 \ln 100)/4\pi$
65. (a) $L = \dfrac{\mu_0 N^2 \ell}{2\pi} \ln\left(\dfrac{R + \ell}{R}\right)$
67. (a) $P = I_0^2 R e^{-2Rt/L}$
69. $E/B = 1/\sqrt{\mu_0 \varepsilon_0} = 3.0 \times 10^8$ m/s $= c$

Chapter 33

1. $V = 325 \sin(314t)$, with V in volts and t in seconds.
3. 9.9 V
5. (a) 350 mA; (b) 1.50 kHz
9. $V_{\text{rms}} = V_p/\sqrt{3}$
11. $I_1 = I_p \cos\phi$, $I_2 = I_p \sin\phi$
13. 45 mA
15. (a) 804 Ω; (b) 48.2 Ω; (c) 2.41 Ω
17. 1.47 μF
19. 15.9 kHz
21. (a) 10 mA; (b) 14 V; (c) 7.7 mA
23. 2.7 mC
25. 0.32 A
27. 8.23 kHz or 5.17×10^4 s^{-1}
29. 4.9 pF to 42 pF
31. 3.65 F
33. (a) 1.63 A; (b) 4.58 μs

35. (a) 63 V; (b) 89 V; (c) 764 mA; (d) 99 μJ
37. (a) $1/\sqrt{2}$; (b) 1/2; (c) $-1/\sqrt{2}$; (d) 1/2
39. Close switch B for 702 ms, then simultaneously close A and open B. After 351 ms, open A; (b) 400 V
41. 0.22 μF
43. 16.2 V
45. (a) 0.43 μH; (b) $R > 16$ Ω
47. (a) $V_{Rp} = 23.86$ V, $V_{Cp} = 28.19$ V, $V_{Lp} = -28.05$ V; (b) $V_{R\text{rms}} = 16.9$ V, $V_{C\text{rms}} = 256$ V, $V_{L\text{rms}} = 255$ V
49. (a) above; (b) current lags by approximately 49°
51. (a) I leads V by 63.6°; (b) I lags V by 81.7°
53. 500 W
55. (a) 80 Ω; (b) 97 Hz
57. (a) 5.5%; (b) 9.1%; (c) large
59. 5.0 mA
61. (a) 8.91 V; (b) 1.38 kΩ
63. $4f_1$
65. 13.2 V
67. 0.64 Ω
69. 8.25 V
71. 36.2 nF, 11.5 nF
73. $C = \dfrac{L[\ln(U_0/U_1)]^2}{4\pi^2 N^2 R^2}$
77. $R = 400$ Ω, $L = 67$ mH, $C = 0.094$ μF
79. 1.3 kN/m

Chapter 34

1. 1.3 nA
5. (a) 0; (b) 8.33×10^{-13} T; (c) 9.26×10^{-13} T
7. $-x$
9. (a) $\sqrt{2}E$; (b) $(\hat{\mathbf{j}} - \hat{\mathbf{i}})/\sqrt{2}$
13. 0.24 s
15. 1 ns
17. 600 m
19. 2.32
21. 5000 km
23. 27.3 MHz
25. 15 kV/m
27. 1.1 pT
29. 63°
31. 30°
33. $0.34S_0$
35. $0.304S_0$
37. $S = S_0 \cos^2 \omega t$, with $\omega = 20\pi$ s^{-1}
39. 12 GW/m^2

41. 2.7×10^{-10} W/m^2
43. (a) 157 W/m^2; (b) 344 V/m; (c) 1.15 μT
45. 1.1%
47. 3.9×10^{26} W
49. (a) 8.3×10^{-26} W/m^2; (b) 7.9×10^{-12} V/m
51. (a) 4.6 kW; (b) 52.5 mV/m
53. (a) as $1/r$; (b) as $1/r^2$
55. 6.0 mPa
57. 5.0 μN
59. 6.18×10^3 years
61. $E_p = 40$ V/m, $B_p = 0.13$ μT
63. 1/4
65. 4.2 μN
67. 17.7 μPa
71. (a) 1.0 MV/m; (b) 4.3 mm; (c) 64 mJ; (d) 2.1×10^{-10} kg·m/s; (e) 64 W
73. Long, with cylindrical symmetry
75. 0.3 μm

Part 4 Cumulative Problems

1. 6.0 MV
3. 15.7 mA, top to bottom
5. (b) $c/\sqrt{\kappa}$

Chapter 35

1. 15°
3. $\pm 0.5°$
5. (a) 2; (b) 210°
9. 126 nm
11. 1.57
13. Ethyl alcohol
15. 1.83
17. 5.1 m
19. (a) 3.20×10^{14} Hz; (b) 937 nm
21. (a) 49.8°; (b) 42.2°; (c) 22.4°
23. (a) 61.3°; (b) 80.9°; (c) there is none
27. $\sqrt{2}$
29. 2.62×10^8 m/s
31. 53.5°
35. 36.5° to 38.1°
37. About 3.4 cm
39. 67.5°
41. 36.9°
43. 1.96×10^8 m/s
45. 2.32 m
47. 28.8°
49. (a) base; (b) 63.2°
51. 35.2°
53. $n = 1.17$
59. (b) 42.1°

Chapter 36

1. Mirror surface 55° to horizontal
3. (a) 30 cm; (b) virtual, 60 cm behind mirror
5. (a) Image height is 1/4 object height; (b) inverted
7. (a) 12.4 cm in front of mirror; (b) 3.22 times
9. (a) 24.3 cm behind the mirror; (b) 29 mm; (c) virtual
11. 18 cm in front of mirror
13. 7.42 cm
15. 40 cm
17. (a) 20 cm; (b) reduced to 55% actual size
19. 12 cm
21. 47.7 mm
23. 2.3 mm
27. (a) Real, inverted, 7.7 cm high; (b) virtual, upright, 7.7 cm high
29. 29 cm or 41 cm from the candle
31. 40 cm
35. $\ell' = -67.9$ cm
37. 2
39. 7.56 mm
41. Virtual image, 81 cm from lens on same side as object
43. (a) 40 cm; (b) 160 cm; (c) -170 cm (the lens becomes a diverging lens)
45. (a) 15.3 cm; (b) 1.63
47. Real image, magnified 2.74 times
49. (a) 5.0 m; (b) 37 cm
51. (a) Enlarged 2.9 times at 110 mm
55. 1.85 cm
57. -17.7 cm
59. (a) 2.0 m; (b) 3.0 m in front of the mirror
61. 25 cm
63. 96 cm
65. ($\ell = 85.4$ cm, $m = -1.81$); ($\ell = 155$ cm, $m = -0.552$)
67. Real image, 109 cm on other side of lens
69. (a) 8.31 mm; (b) 92 cm from my eye
71. No, one is virtual, the other real
75. (a) 1.1 m from primary; (b) elliptical

Chapter 37

1. 484 nm
3. (a) 95 cm; (b) 3.8 mm
5. 1.25 mm
7. 17.7 cm, 44.7 cm
9. 0.034°
11. (a) 17.1 cm; (b) 20.0 cm
13. 4
15. (a) 4.8°, 9.7°; (b) 2.9°, 6.8°
17. (a) 8.97°; (b) 51.3°
19. (a) 2nd; (b) 1st
21. 6th order
23. 3200
25. 415 nm, 581 nm
27. Echelle grating has 60% greater resolving power
29. 2000
31. 103 nm
33. 424 nm, 594 nm
35. (a) 75.2 nm; (b) violet
37. 368 nm
39. 5
41. 236
43. 375 nm (i.e., $\frac{3}{4}\lambda$)
45. 545 nm
47. 1022
49. $a/\lambda = 1$
51. 26.6°
53. 0.0162
55. 1.3 m
57. 2.0 μm
59. 6.9 km
61. For diameters greater than 14 cm
63. 7645
65. 0.01 nm
67. 77.2 nm
69. 46 m
71. 484 nm
75. 5542
77. Every 2.8 s
79. 6.0 km/s
81. 3.0 μm

Part 5   Cumulative Problems

1. $m_0 = (n - 1)d(\sin\alpha)/\lambda_0$
3. 3.2 min
5. (b) $x = \dfrac{\sqrt{3}}{2a}\ln\left[2(1 - ay - \sqrt{\tfrac{1}{4} - 2ay + a^2y^2})\right]$

Chapter 38

1. (a) 4.50 h; (b) 4.56 h; (c) 4.62 h
3. (a) $v/c = \tan\theta$, with θ the amplitude of the sine curve. Here $\theta = 20''$ (20/3600 degree), giving $v = 29$ km/s; (b) the orbit is nearly circular
5. 41 cm
7. (a) 8.26 h; (b) 6.28 h
9. (a) 0.857c; (b) 9.69 min
11. 0.14c
13. $c/\sqrt{2}$
15. Twin A: 83 years; twin B: 40 years
17. 0.96c
19. 0.996c
21. (a) B first, by 5.74 min; (b) A first, by 13.1 min; (c) essentially simultaneous
23. A, by 6.4 My
27. (a) 21.7 m; (b) 12.4 m
29. 0.918c
31. 3.4
33. (a) 2.1 MeV; (b) 1.6 MeV
35. 0.36c
37. 5.3×10^{-8} kg·m/s, about the same as the insect
39. 5.9×10^{-30} kg
41. (a) 0.020c; (b) 0.55c; (c) 0.94c; (d) essentially c
47. (a) -0.75×10^{10} ly^2; (b) 99×10^{10} ly^2; events can be causally related only if $(\Delta s)^2 > 0$
49. 0.274c
51. (a) 16 ns; (b) 4.8 m
53. (a) 4.2 ly; (b) -2.4 years (i.e., B occurs earlier)
55. 0.395c
57. 0.9999953c
59. 598 m
61. 0.95c

Chapter 39

1. (a) 4.1 neV; (b) 2.1 eV; (c) 12.4 keV
3. (a) 1.6×10^{-24} J; (b) 3.9×10^{26} photons/s
5. (a) 1.7×10^{28} s^{-1}; (b) 3.2×10^{15} s^{-1}; (c) 1.3×10^{18} s^{-1}
7. β ($n_1 = 5$)
9. $n = 229$
11. 73 cm/s
13. 1.6 km/s
15. Electron: no; proton: yes
17. 12 pm
19. 0.0034°
21. 2.5 h
23. 20 minutes
25. 0.64 kg
27. 0
29. $\bar{u}\,\bar{u}\,\bar{d}$
31. $+e$
33. (a) 10.2 eV; (b) $n_1 = 2$, $n_2 = 1$
35. The proton
37. 1.16×10^6 m/s
39. 18 pm
41. (a) 1 eV; (b) 5 MeV
43. 10–20 billion years

Index

Page numbers in *italics* refer to illustrations; page numbers followed by t refer to tables.